The Touring Gui

ANTIQUE SHOPS

In England

Written & Compiled by
Carol Fisher

All touring maps in this book are based upon
Ordnance Survey Travelmaster Series of Great
Britain 1:250 000 with the permission of the
Controller of Her Majesty's Stationery Office.
© Crown Copyright

Published by Carol Fisher
PO Box 531, Melksham,
Wiltshire SN12 8SL

Distributed in the U.S.A. by
Seven Hills Book Distributors
49 Central Avenue
Cincinnati, OH45202

Printed by Staples Printers St. Albans Ltd, Great Britain

Cover Picture: *Evening over Westminster,* Charles E. Hannaford.
By courtesy of J. Morton-Lee, Hayling Island.

Contents

Penman Antiques Fairs

Chelsea Antiques Fair

Chelsea Old Town Hall, King's Road, SW3
1994: September 13-24
1995 (provisional): March 7-18 and September 12-23
Traditional and intimate, one of Britain's major antique events.

West London Antiques Fair

Kensington Town Hall, W8.
1994: August 18-21
1995: January 12-16, August 17-20
Busy, friendly, varied & colourful. 90 stands.

Westminster Antiques Fair

Royal Horticultural Hall, Vincent Square, SW1.
1994: December 1-4.
1995: April 27-30, November 30-December 3.
Quality fair with 50 traditional stands, plus a seasonal feature area.

Kensington Antiques Fair

Kensington Town Hall,W8.
1994: November 3-6.
1995: November 2-5.
Quality furniture 1600-1920,
plus accessories & collectors' items.

Armoury House Antiques Fair

Honourable Artillery Company Headquarters, City Road, EC1.
New in 1995: in the first half of July.
Under canvas in the 5 acre grounds of the H.A.C.
100+ stands. A special atmosphere.

Further details from Penman Antiques Fairs,
P.O. Box 114, Haywards Heath, Sussex. RH16 2YU.
Tel: 0444 482514. Fax: 483412

List of Maps

HERITAGE ANTIQUES FAIRS

We welcome you to our regular fairs in Central London in which professional dealers will display a wide range of reasonably priced antiques including jewellery, glass, silver, plate, enamels, porcelain, textiles, prints and objects.

KENSINGTON PALACE HOTEL
De Vere Gardens, Kensington High Street, London W8
Sundays 1994: 8th May, 4th Sept.,
16th Oct, 13th Nov.

LONDON MARRIOTT HOTEL
Grosvenor Square, London W1
Sundays 1994: 15th May, 19th June, 17th July, 18th Sept,
2nd Oct, 30th Oct, 20th Nov, 11th Dec.

LONDON HILTON ON PARK LANE
22 Park Lane, London W1
Sundays 1994: 22nd May, 26th June, 10th July,
11th Sept, 23rd Oct, 27th Nov.

ROYAL LANCASTER HOTEL
Bayswater Road, London W2
Sundays 1994: 5th June, 3rd July,
25th Sept, 4th Dec.

REMBRANDT HOTEL
11 Thurloe Place, London SW7
Sundays 1994: 12th June, 24th July,
9th Oct, 6th Nov, 18th Dec.

For further dates and information
Patricia & Ralph Harvey
PO Box 149, London W9 1QN.   Tel: 071-624 5173

Reigns of the Kings and Queens of England from 1066

William I	1066 - 1087	William & Mary	1689 - 1702
William II	1087 - 1100	Anne	1702 - 1714
Henry I	1100 - 1135	George I	1714 - 1727
Stephen	1135 - 1154	George II	1727 - 1760
Henry II	1154 - 1189	George III	1760 - 1820
Richard I	1189 - 1199	George IV	1820 - 1830
John	1199 - 1216	William IV	1830 - 1837
Henry III	1216 - 1272	Victoria	1837 - 1901
Edward I	1272 - 1307	Edward VII	1901 - 1910
Edward II	1307 - 1327	George V	1910 - 1936
Edward III	1327 - 1377	Edward VIII	1936 - 1936
Richard II	1377 - 1399	George VI	1936 - 1952
Henry IV	1399 - 1413	Elizabeth II	1952 -
Henry V	1413 - 1422		
Henry VI	1422 - 1461		
Edward IV	1461 - 1483	**Dates of Periods and Styles**	
Edward V	1483 - 1483		
Richard III	1483 - 1485	Elizabethan	1558 - 1603
Henry VII	1485 - 1509	Jacobean	1603 - 1648
Henry VIII	1509 - 1547	Cromwellian	1648 - 1659
Edward VI	1547 - 1553	William & Mary	1689 - 1702
Mary I	1553 - 1558	Queen Anne	1702 - 1714
Elizabeth I	1558 - 1603	Georgian	1714 - 1820
James I	1603 - 1625	Chippendale	1749 - 1779
Charles I	1625 - 1649	Adam	1762 - 1792
The Commonwealth	1649 - 1660	Hepplewhite	1775 - 1800
Charles II	1660 - 1685	Sheraton	1790 - 1805
James II	1685 - 1688	Empire	1804 - 1814
		Regency	1814 - 1830

FORTHCOMING FAIRS 1994

April 23/24
THE LANCASHIRE ANTIQUES FAIR
Rossall School, Fleetwood

May 7/8
LEICESTER COUNTY ANTIQUES FAIR
Prestwold Hall, Loughborough

May 21/22
STAFFORD COUNTY ANTIQUES FAIR
Sandon Hall, Nr. Stone

July 16/17
NORTH COTSWOLDS ANTIQUES FAIR
Stanway House, Nr. Winchcombe

August 19/20/21
SOUTH COTSWOLDS ANTIQUES FAIR
Westonbirt School, Nr. Tetbury

September 2/3/4
WEST SUSSEX ANTIQUES FAIR
Christ's Hospital, Horsham

September 9/10/11
THE BEARWOOD ANTIQUES FAIR
Bearwood, Nr. Wokingham, Berkshire

September 23/24/25
THE COTSWOLDS OAK & COUNTRY
ANTIQUES FAIR
Painswick House, Painswick

October 7/8/9
LITTLECOTE ANTIQUES FAIR
Littlecote House, Hungerford, Berkshire

October 14/15/16
CHESHIRE COUNTY ANTIQUES FAIR
Arley Hall, Nr. Knutsford

October 22/23
RUTLAND ANTIQUES FAIR
Uppingham School, Leicestershire

October 29/30
STAFFORD COUNTY ANTIQUES FAIR
Sandon Hall, Nr. Stone

November 26/27
LEICESTER COUNTY ANTIQUES FAIR
Prestwold Hall, Loughborough

December 17/18
THE SOUTH COTSWOLDS CHRISTMAS ANTIQUES FAIR
Westonbirt School, Tetbury

Enquiries: 0249 661111
COOPER ANTIQUES FAIRS

Trade Association Abbreviations

ABA	Antiquarian Booksellers Association
ATCC	Antique Tools Collectors Club
ATD	Art Teachers Diploma
BA	Booksellers Association
BABADA	Bath & Bradford-on-Avon Antique Dealers Association
BADA	British Antique Dealers Association
BAFRA	British Antique Furniture Restorers Association
BHI	British Horological Institute
BJA	British Jewellers Association
BNTA	British Numismatic Traders Association
BT	Book Trust
BWCMG	British Watch & Clock Makers Guild
CADA	Cotswold Antique Dealers Association
CADO	Cliffe Antique Dealers Organisation (Lewes)
CMJ	Company of Master Jewellers
CTS	China Trade Society
Cumbria ADA	Cumbria Antique Dealers Association
FATG	Fine Arts Trade Guild
DADA	Dorking Antique Dealers Association
FPPF	Federation of Professional Picture Framers
GA	Gemmological Association of Great Britain
IBD	Institute of British Designers
ILAB	International League of Antiquarian Booksellers
IMCOS	International Map Collectors Society
LAPADA	London & Provincial Antique Dealers Association
NADA	Nottingham Antique Dealers Association
NAG	National Association of Goldsmiths
NAWCCC	National Association of Watch & Clock Collectors (USA)
OMRS	Orders Medals Research Society
PAADA (PADA)	Petworth Antique Dealers Association
PBFA	Provincial Book Fairs Association
PCCGB	Print Collectors Club of Great Britain
PTS	Philatelic Trade Society
RSA	Royal Society of Arts
TATHS	Tools & Trade History Society
TVADA	Thames Valley Antique Dealers Association
WADA	Warwick Antique Dealers Association.

Note: Some abbreviations maybe be prefixed M or F denoting Member or Fellow.

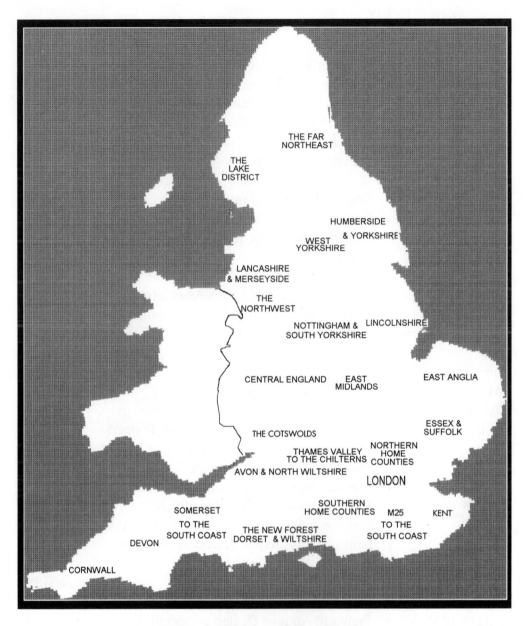

The 24 Tours of England

the Collector

骨董品名録

FEBRUARY/MARCH 94

HANNAH BARLOW

FEBRUARY & MARCH EVENTS

Touring in search of antiques can be hard work! 'the Collector' is especially designed for serious trade and private buyers of antiques and collectables who wish to save time and effort in their searches. Published bi-monthly it provides specialist dealer listings with maps showing their precise locations , a cross-referenced stock specialisation index, current fairs data plus feature articles – all contained in a handy, pocket-sized format

Subscriptions: UK £12, Europe £24, Elsewhere £30, USA (12 issues) $70
Payment in Yen, Dollars or Sterling. Visa/Mastercard/Eurocard accepted

For a free specimen copy please write to the address below

Barrington Publications, 54 Uxbridge Road, London W12 8LP   Tel/Fax. 081-740 7020

11

Introduction

This book, now in its second edition, was essentially born from my experience and interest in the whole English antiques trade. On entering antiques publishing in the late 70's, I found it very different from 'normal' business. The people appeared more independent and sometimes even downright eccentric. They seemed to operate for the love of the beautiful and interesting things they bought and sold rather than any expectation of growing rich. Fifteen years on, many of the characters are still larger than life and not many have grown wealthy. They continue to work from the crack of dawn, and often earlier, till late at night for the kind of return that city businessmen would not cross the road for. However, no matter how bad things get - and in the recession things have got very tough - almost nobody gives up the trade voluntarily. By and large they are a generous, humorous bunch of people always ready for a drink and a chat - in that order if possible.

My intention was to encourage buyers to visit dealers outside London, so in the first edition London was omitted deliberately. However, I have had so many requests to include the capital city as well as those areas not covered last time that this edition has more than doubled in size.

Designed for private customers and dealers wanting to visit antique shops outside their own area, *The Touring Guide to Antique Shops in England* gives planned routes aimed at getting the most from a straightforward buying trip or a more leisurely touring holiday. There are 24 tours each with its own map and generous information on the historic towns, cities and villages and other places of interest along the routes. In all, details are given on over 2,700 antique shops in over 750 locations ranging from city conurbations to picturesque, rural villages, from the majestic scenery of the Derbyshire peaks to the more subtle beauty of East Anglia.

The guide can be used to do one complete trip, a part of one or just day trips by car or train to one town. Estimated trip times are not given as this depends on as traffic, weather, length of stop, the number of shops and other places visited, etc. Also, in many areas, for example the Lake District, the countryside is so beautiful and there are so many things to see, I would be surprised if anybody stuck rigidly to the routes.

These tours are my selection and others might have chosen differently. The principle used is that each should provide an enjoyable holiday as well as the chance to buy antiques. I would recommend local Tourist Information Centres en route to provide far more local knowledge than space allows in a book like this which is specifically designed to be small, light and easily portable. Additionally, some dealers have made comments on their area and recommendations for hotels and restaurants and these I have included in their entries.

To make the shop listings as accurate as possible I distributed questionnaires. The selection was made from those who returned the form. Some only provided partial information and, in these cases, this is reflected in their entries. In spite of using this method of compiling the lists, inevitably between returning the forms and publication there have been changes. I would strongly advise anyone travelling to see a particular antique dealer to telephone first. You should also remember that many dealers work alone so if they are attending an antiques fair or auction their shops will occasionally be closed regardless of the regular opening hours.

Soon work will start on gathering information for an updated edition of this book with new and revised tours. Please, please, whether a tourist, a dealer, a library or a tourist officer do feel free to make criticisms, helpful comments, suggest improvements. Particularly I would love to know HOW exactly you used the guide and whether it fulfilled expectations. Write to: The Touring Guide to Antique Shops, P.O. Box 531, Melksham, Wiltshire SN12 8SL, England or fax to 0225 (international 44225) 790939

The best suggestions will receive a free copy of the next guide. In the mean time I hope that you find the book most useful and enjoyable. Good hunting!

THE
DECORATIVE ANTIQUES
& TEXTILES FAIRS

THE MARQUEE,
KING'S COLLEGE, CHELSEA

20th-25th September 1994
21st-26th March, 1995
19th - 24th September 1995

ENTRANCE FULHAM ROAD,
OPPOSITE ST. MARK'S GROVE

Organised by:
Harvey (Management Services) Ltd.,
P.O. Box 149, London W9 1QN. Tel: 071-624 5173

London

The first record of settlement in London was in AD43 when the Romans set up a stronghold called *Londinium* at what is now Cornhill. Then it was just a small hill by a narrow part of the Thames overlooking the surrounding flat land. This stronghold became the centre of the road network that the Romans built throughout England.

By the time that Boudicca (Boadicea) launched her rebellion against the Romans in AD60, *Londinium* was a thriving town. However, Boudicca attacked it and reduced it to ashes. The Romans rebuilt the town and it continued to flourish, becoming the administrative centre for the province. City walls were built, which may still be seen in places, and so was the largest basilica outside of Rome itself.

After the Romans left England in the fifth century, London declined for some years but its fortunes revived with the coming of the Saxons. It was ideally situated for trade with Europe and it continued to prosper until the Normans arrived. William the Conqueror confirmed its pre-eminence when he was crowned at Westminster Abbey and made London his capital.

The city had two centres of power. The City, which was a centre of wealth and trade, and Westminster, the seat of royal power. The earliest surviving map of London, showing the city in 1558, gives an idea of how small it was. There was only one bridge spanning the Thames and east of the Tower of London and north of Clerkenwell there were farms and orchards. West of what is now Aldwych the only buildings were alongside the river. At that time the population stood at about 90,000 people but by the end of the 16th century it had more than doubled to 200,000.

Over the following two centuries, in spite of the Great Fire and the plague, London grew outwards. Villages like Highgate and Islington also spread. Development started on a larger scale south of the Thames giving a need for more bridges. Both Westminster and Blackfriars Bridges were completed in the mid 18th century.

The coming of the railways started a massive expansion in the capital. As the hub of a great empire and an international financial centre, the demand for labour grew. Public transport allowed workers to travel into the City from their homes in the suburbs. Before this people had always had to live close to their place of employment.

London's last great disaster was the blitz during the Second World War. The bombing started on 7th September 1940 and between then and 11th May 1941, 18,800 tons of high explosive bombs were dropped. Many people spent their nights in shelters or tube stations. While many of the stations were safe because they were so deep underground, others were not. A direct hit was scored on Marble Arch tube station resulting in many casualties and at Balham, in South

London

London, a bomb fractured a water main, the station flooded and a number of people were drowned. By the end of the war, of the City's 677 acres, 164 had been laid waste, Throughout the whole of London, more than 15,000 people were killed and over three and a half million houses had been destroyed.

Barnes and Chiswick

Barnes still retains much of the character of a rural village. It has a village green with a pond and the Sun Inn, by the green, dates from the 18th century. Until the early 19th century the area was quite inaccessible as the only routes were either from the river or across Barnes Common which was marshland until it was drained in the mid 19th century. It was in 1827 that a road was constructed to give access from Hammersmith Bridge. The railway arrived in 1846, giving rise to wide-scale development of the area.

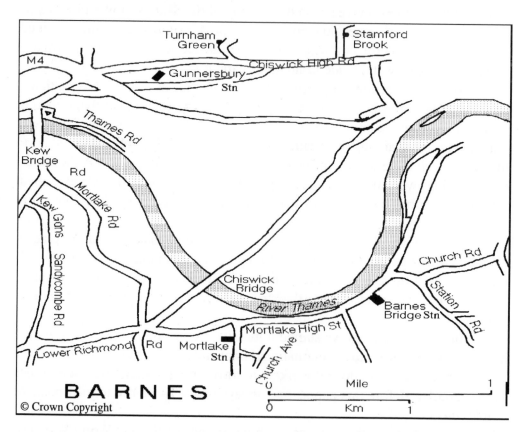

There are a number of historic houses in Barnes including Milbourne House originally built in the 15th century but with little of the original fabric remaining. Now much of it dates from the 16th century and it has an 18th century facade. One of its most famous inhabitants was the novelist Henry Fielding.

Across the river from Barnes, Chiswick was also a very rural area until the mid

19th century and the coming of the railways. From earliest times, however, there were a number of settlements mostly along the river, with the origins of Chiswick itself in Church Street and Chiswick Lane.

Chiswick House in Burlington Lane, half a mile from the station, was completed in 1729 by the third Earl of Burlington. Built in the Italian style, the house was used solely to display the Earl's library and art collection. He lived in a house nearby that has since been demolished.

Bermondsey

In 1082 the building of an abbey was started in this area by a branch of the Benedictines. Various grants of land were given to the abbey, first by William Rufus and then by Henry I. King Stephen exempted it from paying taxes, granted it the right to hold courts of law and gave it more land nearby. The abbey flourished until the time of the Dissolution of the Monasteries when the buildings were sold and demolished. Some of the stones were used in building Bermondsey House which once stood on the site of the present day Bermondsey Square.

By the 18th century the area was still very rural although leather tanneries had been set up in Long Lane and there was other development along the river bank. However by the mid 19th century parts of Bermondsey had degenerated into dismal slums.

Tower Bridge connects Tower Hill to Bermondsey. One of London's most distinctive landmarks, it was constructed between 1886 and 1894. Directly across the river from Bermondsey stands the Tower of London started by William the Conqueror and said to be the best example of a medieval fortress in Britain. The outer walls enclose an area of 18 acres and it is encircled by a deep moat. During its thousand year history it has served as a palace, prison, royal armoury, mint, treasury and library. However, the Tower is best known as a place of tragedy and suffering. The two princes were kept here by Richard III until they disappeared, thought murdered. Anne Boleyn and Catherine Howard, wives of Henry VIII,

BERMONDSEY

© Crown Copyright

were executed here as was Lady Jane Grey and the Earl of Essex. Many others were also imprisoned here and then executed either on Tower Hill or Tower Green.

Chelsea and Knightsbridge

The village of Chelsea was mentioned in the Domesday Book but it was not until the 16th century that it became fashionable. Sir Thomas More, later to be executed in the Tower of London, had a house here as did Henry VIII, the Duke of Norfolk and the Earl of Shrewsbury. In the 19th century, residents like Whistler and Rossetti gave the area a more Bohemian character and led to the founding of the Chelsea Arts Club, still going strong today.

The most well-known building in Chelsea is probably the Royal Hospital founded by Charles II, and designed by Sir Christopher Wren, to care for sick and aged soldiers. The building was finished in 1692 and it has had few alterations since. In May every year since 1913, except during the war, the Royal Horticultural Society has held their flower show in the grounds.

The main road through Chelsea, running from Sloane Square to Fulham, is the King's Road. Originally this was a private road used by Charles II to go to Hampton Court. It only became a public thoroughfare in 1830. One of the many businesses that occupied premises here was Thomas Crapper, makers of water closets, whose name introduced a new word into the English language.

Sloane Square, like many of the streets in the area, is named for Sir Hans Sloane who bought the manor of Chelsea in 1712. He had two daughters who each inherited half of his estate. One married Lord Cadogan and the other George Stanley who came from Paultons in Hampshire. These names are also reflected in the streets.

Belgravia, north of Sloane Square, takes its name from Belgrave in Leicestershire, where the Grosvenor family, owners of the land, had an estate. Right into the 18th century this was an area of fields and the haunt of footpads. The first houses were built in 1726 in what is now Grosvenor Place. Few other buildings were constructed, however, until the first half of the 19th century when Lord Grosvenor leased the

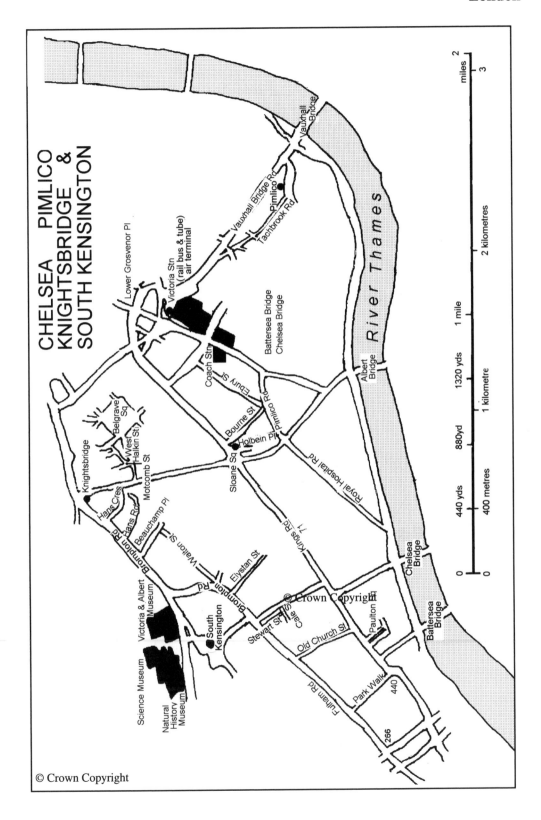

CHELSEA PIMLICO
KNIGHTSBRIDGE &
SOUTH KENSINGTON

River Thames

Vauxhall Bridge
Vauxhall Bridge Rd
Pimlico Rd
Tachbrook Rd
Lower Grosvenor Pl
Victoria Stn
(rail bus & tube)
air terminal
Battersea Bridge
Chelsea Bridge
Coach Stn
Ebury St
Belgrave Sq
West Halkin St
Knightsbridge
Motcomb St
Bourne St
Holbein Pl
Sloane Sq
Pimlico Rd
Albert Bridge
Royal Hospital Rd
Hans Cres
Hans Rd
Beauchamp Pl
Brompton Rd
Walton St
Kings Rd
Elystan St
Brompton Rd
Victoria & Albert Museum
South Kensington
Science Museum
Natural History Museum
Stewart St
Cale St
Old Church St
Paulton St
Fulham Rd
Park Walk
Chelsea Bridge
Battersea Bridge

71
440
266

© Crown Copyright

2
3 miles

2 kilometres

1 mile

1320 yds
1 kilometre

880yd

440 yds
400 metres

0
0

land to Thomas Cubitt for development. It quickly became fashionable and has remained so.

Knightsbridge was a village as early as the 11th century. Famous for its taverns in the 17th century, it was also a popular place for duels and highwaymen. The village green, commemorated in the name Knightsbridge Green, was situated where the Scotch House stands today. Harrods, another famous landmark, stands on the Brompton Road. In 1849 Henry Harrod took a small grocer's shop which his son, Charles, bought from him in 1861. He rapidly expanded the business in terms of staff numbers, premises and range of stock. Unfortunately, in December 1883, a fire totally destroyed the shop. Charles Harrod impressed his customers by still delivering all their orders in time for Christmas. The store was rebuilt in 1884 and five years later he sold it. Without him sales began to fall and so he was brought back for a further two years. The famous frontage, known throughout the world, was completed in 1905 and the remaining rebuilding and redesigning work was finished in 1939. It is now one of the world's largest stores.

Covent Garden to Bloomsbury

Covent Garden was owned by the Abbey of St Peter and consisted mainly of

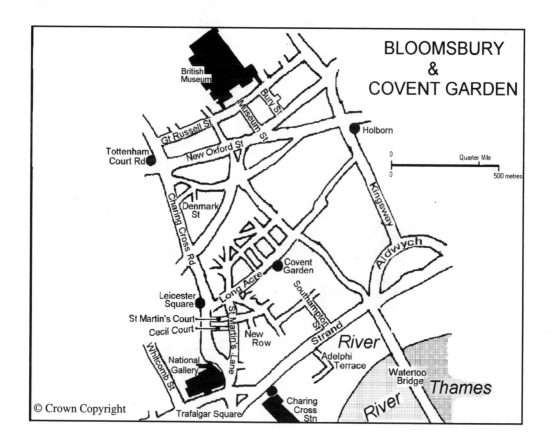

fields up until the Dissolution of the Monasteries. Then it was granted to the Earl of Bedford, John Russell, who built a house on the site of what was later Southampton Street. In the early 17th century Inigo Jones was commissioned to design fine houses to the north of Bedford House. These were constructed around a piazza and showed a strong Italian influence. Their foreign style militated against them and the area never became truly fashionable. In 1670 the Earl of Bedford was granted a licence to hold a flower and vegetable market there. This market continued for 300 years and it was only in 1974 that it moved to a new purpose built site at Nine Elms on the south side of the river.

One of the most notorious slums in London could be found in the area. Seven Dials, described by Dickens, was sited where Mercer, Monmouth and Earlham Streets now meet. Development of the area was completed in the early 18th century and was intended to be a fashionable address, however it became a place for the poorest of the poor as well as cut-throats and thieves. The area was largely cleared out when Shaftesbury Avenue and Charing Cross Road were built.

The Strand, in earlier centuries, ran by the river but by the Middle Ages land had been reclaimed and bishops' palaces ran alongside the Thames. After the Dissolution of the Monasteries these church estates went to the Crown and were given to court favourites who built their own magnificent mansions there. The present day street pattern between the Strand and the river owes much to these 16th century estates because roads ran up to or around estates, ending abruptly or turning corners in an apparently inexplicable way.

Nearby St Martin's Lane was constructed in the early 17th century and immediately became a fashionable address. Mozart, as a child, played in Cecil Court, a small lane now connecting St Martin's Lane to Charing Cross Road, although the latter was only built in the late 19th century.

New Oxford Street runs along the northern side of Covent Garden, at the top of Charing Cross Road. It was built in 1847 as an extension to Oxford Street which was originally a Roman road running from Hampshire to Suffolk. North of New Oxford Street is the area known as Bloomsbury. This was developed by the Dukes of Bedford, the Russell family, who played such a large part in the development of Covent Garden. In the early 20th century the area became associated with the Bloomsbury Group, people like E.M. Forster, Virginia and Leonard Woolf, Lytton Strachey and John Maynard Keynes.

Bloomsbury is also the home of the British Museum, founded in 1753. It started when Sir Hans Sloane left his collection of books and antiquities to the nation on the condition that £20,000 was paid into his estate. Since then the museum has expanded and now offers a superb collection of antiquities including the Elgin Marbles, the Rosetta Stone, the Sutton Hoo treasure and two of the four existing copies of Magna Carta.

London

Fulham

The Manor of Fulham was owned by the Bishops of London from the 8th century. The area supported a number of small settlements like Fulham Town and Parson's Green which were not united until the great development of London in the 19th century. The Bishop's official residence, until 1973, was Fulham Palace. The existing building dates from the 15th century and stands on the site of a Roman settlement and nowadays houses a museum.

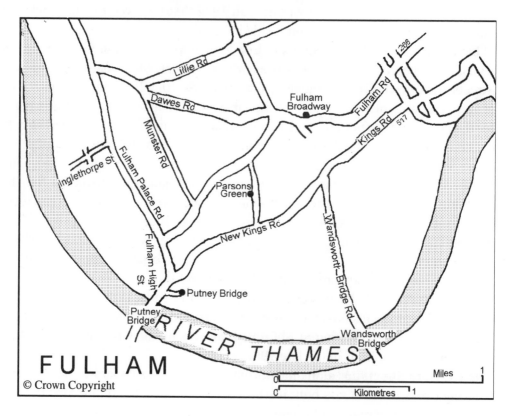

Fulham Road, which runs from the Brompton Road to Fulham Palace Road, dates from the 15th century and was a major coaching route to Portsmouth and the south west.

Hampstead

There is evidence of settlements in Hampstead in prehistoric times. Two barrows have been found in the area, one on Primrose Hill which has been flattened, and another on Parliament Hill. During medieval times the area belonged to the church and, still being forest, was used for hunting. The trees were mostly cut down for rebuilding London after the Great Fire in 1666. In the early 18th century Hampstead became a fashionable for its health giving spring water and people

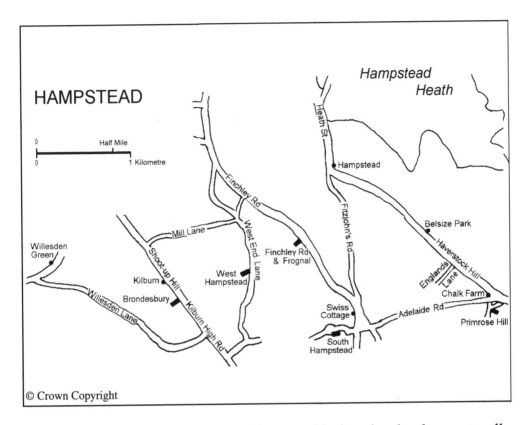

© Crown Copyright

flocked to the Heath to take the water. It was at this time that development really started.

During the 19th and 20th centuries Hampstead has rapidly expanded although it has retained much of its village character and it has remained a highly fashionable place to live.

Kenwood House, in Hampstead Lane, was originally built in 1616 although it was largely rebuilt just eighty years later. In the second half of the 18th century much of the house was remodelled by Robert Adam. Now the late 17th century building lies behind an 18th century facade. The house contains the Iveagh Bequest of Old Master and British Paintings which includes works by Rembrandt, Vermeer, Hals, Gainsborough, Turner and Reynolds. There is also a fine collection of neo-classical furniture.

Islington

Originally owned by the canons of St Paul's, Islington, by the 16th century, boasted some wonderful mansions two of which were owned by Henry VIII who came here to hunt. Queen Elizabeth I often visited Sir John Spenser at Canonbury House and Sir Walter Raleigh, who had a house in Upper Street. However, Islington continued as a rural village well into the 19th century. As with so many other places, the railways brought about a huge increase in population and terraces of

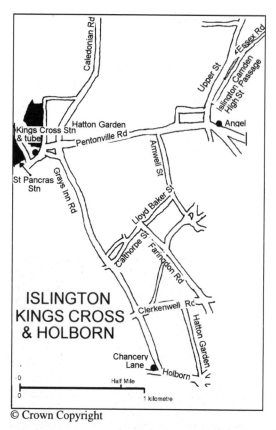

ISLINGTON
KINGS CROSS
& HOLBORN

© Crown Copyright

houses were built.

Upper Street was the start of the Great North Road and a major coaching route. The Angel, Islington, was a coaching inn and the nearest staging post to London. However, the Angel, Islington, is a misnomer because it stood just outside the Islington parish boundary. The original Jacobean inn was demolished in 1819 and rebuilt. Just eighty years later it was rebuilt again as Lyons Corner House. Near the Angel tube station and running parallel to Upper Street is Camden Passage, once called Pullens Row, and the major centre for antiques in this area.

Mayfair and St James's

Mayfair is the area bounded by Oxford Street, Regent Street, Park Lane and Piccadilly. It is so named because, from the late 17th century until the mid 18th century, there was a fair held here every year during the first two weeks of May. Development had started as early as the 1660s near the present day Piccadilly Circus and spread north and west until almost the whole the area was built up in less than a hundred years. The streets in the area reflect the names of the great estate holders who had owned the land. The Grosvenor Estate still owns the freehold of much the area. From the first, Mayfair was an extremely fashionable place to live and has remained so.

Grosvenor Square has probably always been the place with the greatest social *cachet* in Mayfair and the enormous rents have ensured that only the wealthiest people could afford to live there. Consequently the area has never suffered a decline. The American Embassy, completed in 1961, stands on the west side of the Square.

Building along Piccadilly, although an ancient route to the west, only began in the early 17th century. One of the first shops gave the street its name. Robert Baker sold picadils or ruffs hence Piccadilly. During the late 17th and early 18th centuries famous residents of the area included the Duke of Wellington, Lady Hamilton (Nelson's mistress) and her husband, and Lord Byron. The Ritz Hotel is sited on the south side of Piccadilly, next to Green Park. Synonymous with luxury, the hotel was completed in 1906 to the specifications of César Ritz, a Swiss hotelier.

Piccadilly Circus was constructed in 1819 and was intended to be as elegant as Regent Street but alterations in the late 19th century changed the original layout. The statue of Eros in the centre was erected in 1893 to commemorate the work done by Lord Shaftesbury and was meant to represent the Angel of Christian Charity not Eros.

Regent Street, designed by John Nash, was built to connect Regent's Park to Carlton House, home of the Prince Regent. It was also hoped that the new street would relieve traffic problems at Charing Cross and in the Strand. Quite quickly Regent Street became a most fashionable place and the shops catered for high society customers. By the beginning of the 20th century, however, the shops had started to cater more for the affluent middle classes. Regent Street has remained one of London's premier shopping areas.

St James's Palace was originally built by Henry VIII on the site of a hospital. It became the monarch's principal London residence after Whitehall Palace was destroyed by fire in 1698. In 1809 a large part of St James's Palace was also burnt down but rebuilding was completed by 1814. It was George IV who was the instigator of the move to Buckingham Palace. He had lived at Carlton House after a row with his father, then the king. After his accession to the throne he thought Carlton House not grand enough for a reigning monarch so he commissioned Nash to

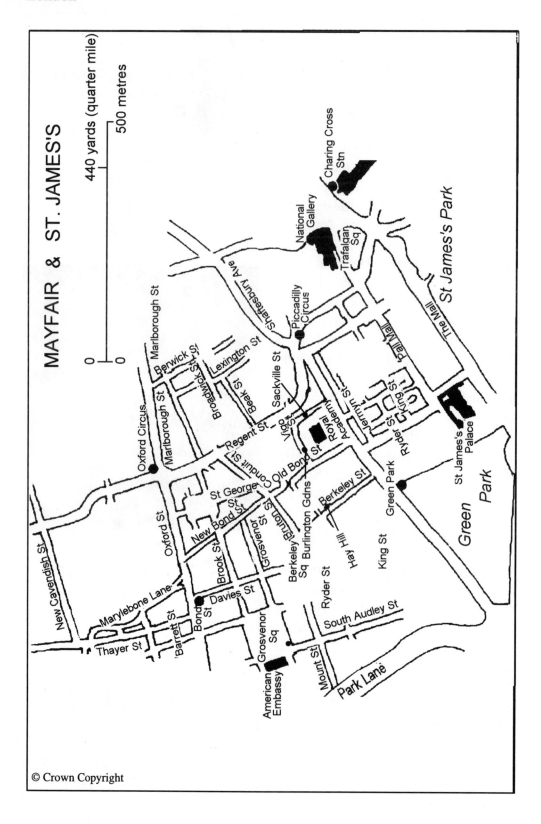

MAYFAIR & ST. JAMES'S

440 yards (quarter mile)

500 metres

© Crown Copyright

design a palace on the site of Buckingham House. Parliament, with great reluctance, authorised a budget of £200,000 to repair and improve Buckingham House. However, the King was determined to have a grand palace and, although the shell of the old house and some of the floorplan was retained, it was to be much bigger and more expensive to complete. King George IV died before it was finished as did his successor, William IV. Queen Victoria was the first monarch to live there. Its eventual cost was £700,000.

Portobello Road to Church Street NW8

Portobello Road is named for the farm to which it once led. The world famous market started in the 1870s and its traders were mostly gypsies dealing in horses

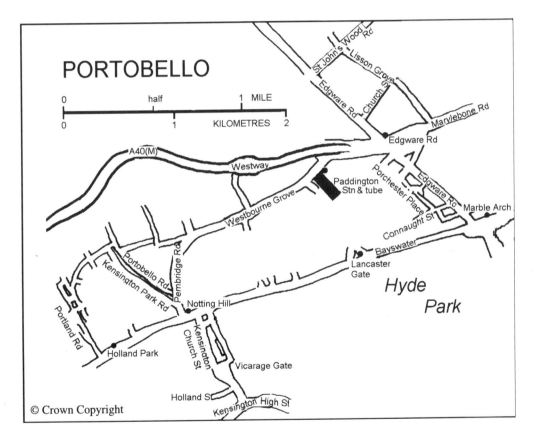

and herbs. Although the character of the market changed over the years, it only became a centre for antiques in 1948 when the Caledonian Road market closed. There are antique shops in the area open all week but the principal trading day is Saturday when antique dealers from all over the country come to buy and sell.

The area of Notting Hill Gate was a site of sand and gravel extraction from the 17th to 19th centuries and there was just a small settlement around this activity. Much of the surrounding land was countryside. Development started in the mid

19th century and the area was to prove one of contrasts between fine houses and terrible slums.

Edgware Road, lying to the east, follows the route of the Roman road of Watling Street. Starting at Marble Arch it runs north east to St John's Wood where it changes its name to Maida Vale. The area of St John's Wood got its name because, between the 14th and 16th centuries, it was owned by the Knights of St John of Jerusalem. As its name suggests, during that time it was mostly forested and it was only in the time of Cromwell that the trees were felled. During the next 300 years the area retained a rural charm, although there was some small scale development. As in so many other London villages, it was the railways that changed the character of St John's Wood. Many of the charming houses and squares that had been erected were demolished to make way for tracks and large scale development followed. However, it retains, in many places, a charming and gracious atmosphere.

ANTIQUE DEALERS
BARNES & CHISWICK
LONDON SW13 (081)

The Dining Room Shop, 62-64 White Hart Lane, SW13 0PZ TEL: 878 1020 FAX: 878 7404 PARKING: Easy OPEN: Mon-Fri 10-5.30, Sat 10.15-5.30 MIN: £1 MAX: £50,000 PERIOD: 18th-20th century SPECIALIST: Antique dining room furniture, china, glass, silver GENERAL: Antique wine & food prints, decorative table accessories OTHER INFO: Oxford & Cambridge boat race finish nearby. Riva or The Depot restaurants.

Joy Macdonald, 50 Station Road, Barnes, SW13 0LP TEL: 876 6184 PARKING: Easy OPEN: 10-5.30 (resident) MIN: £20+ PERIOD: 18th-20th century SPECIALIST: Large English & French gilt mirrors GENERAL: French fruitwood country tables, unusual decorative items inc chandeliers.

Wren Antiques, 49b Church Road, Barnes, SW13 9HH TEL: 741 7841 PARKING: Easy OPEN: 10-5 MIN: £50 MAX: £3,000 PERIOD: 18th-19th century SPECIALIST: Chandeliers GENERAL: General antiques OTHER INFO: Barnes is London's nearest village with a pond.

LONDON SW14 (081)

William Sheppee, 1a Church Avenue, SW14 8WW TEL: 392 2379 FAX: 878 9903 PARKING: Own carpark OPEN: Mon-Fri 8.30-5.30 MIN: £5 MAX: £5,000 PERIOD: 19th century GENERAL: Indian & colonial furniture, architectural items, treen OTHER INFO: Close M3 & M4 motorways.

LONDON SW15 (081)

R A Barnes Antiques, 26 Lower Richmond Road, Putney, SW15 1JP TEL: 789 3371 PARKING: Easy OPEN: 10-5.30 MIN: £20+ MAX: £3,000+ PERIOD: 18th-20th century SPECIALIST: Wedgwood, Chinese, Art Nouveau, brass, glass GENERAL: Furniture, paintings, copper, treen, English & Continental pottery & porcelain OTHER INFO: Good pubs etc overlooking River Thames.

The Clock Clinic Ltd, 85 Lower Richmond Road, Putney, SW15 1EU TEL: 788 1407 FAX:

780 2838 ASSNS: LAPADA PARKING: Medium OPEN: Tues-Fri 0-6, Sat 9-1 MIN: £350 MAX: £20,000 PERIOD: 17th-19th century SPECIALIST: English longcase clocks GENERAL: Antique clocks & barometers overhauled & guaranteed OTHER INFO: Look for our blue bollards, next to Half Moon, famous for jazz.

LONDON W4 (081)

J D Marshall, 38 Chiswick Lane, Chiswick, W4 2JQ TEL: 742 8089, 602 9809 PARKING: Easy OPEN: Mon-Wed 10-6, Thurs-Fri 10-7, Sat 10-5 MIN: £1 MAX: £10,000 PERIOD: 18th-19th century SPECIALIST: Decorative objects, lights, sculpture, neo-classical GENERAL: Large stock garden ornaments OTHER INFO: Just off M4, 20 mins Heathrow, Fouberts Hotel, plenty of restaurants.

Strand Antiques, 166 Thames Road, Chiswick TEL: 994 1912 PARKING: Easy OPEN: Seven days 12-5 MIN: £1 MAX: £500 PERIOD: 18th-19th century SPECIALIST: Glass GENERAL: General antiques OTHER INFO: Mini market of 8 dealers by the many Thames riverside pubs on Strand on the Green. Close to Chiswick House, Syon House, Kew Gardens.

BERMONDSEY

LONDON SE1 (071)

Bermondsey Antiques Market, Corner of Long Lane & Bermondsey Street TEL: 351 5353 FAX: 351 5350 OPEN: Fri 4am-2pm MIN: £5 MAX: £5,000 PERIOD: 17th-20th century GENERAL: 150+ dealers with extensive & varied selection of the unusual & collectable antique items OTHER INFO: 2 cafés serving very early breakfasts, bureau de change. Tubes: Borough, Tower Hill or London Bridge.

CHELSEA & BELGRAVIA

LONDON SW1 (071)

Anno Domini Antiques, 66 Pimlico Road TEL: 730 5496 ASNS: BADA PARKING: Medium OPEN: 10-1, 2.15-6 MIN: £20 MAX: £20,000 PERIOD: 18th-19th century SPECIALIST: Glass, pictures, celery vases GENERAL: Furniture, mirrors, screens, decorative items.

Andre de Canqueray, 227 Ebury Street, SW1W 8UT TEL: 730 5000 FAX: 730 7199 PARKING: Easy OPEN: 10-6 MIN: £100 MAX: £10,000 PERIOD: 18th-19th century GENERAL: French antiques OTHER INFO: Next to Boucherie Lamartine Roux-owned La Poule au Pot, French provincial food.

Chaucer Fine Arts Ltd, 45 Pimlico Road, SW1W 8NE TEL: 730 2972/5872 FAX: 730 5861 PARKING: Medium OPEN: Mon-Fri 10-6, Sat 10-1 PERIOD: 18th-19th century SPECIALIST: Old Master paintings & works of art.

The Delightful Muddle, 11 Upper Tachbrook Street, SW1V 1SN PARKING: Medium OPEN: Thurs, Fri 12-6 Sat 11-5 MIN: £1 MAX: £100 PERIOD: 19th-20th century GENERAL: Silver, glass, old lace, bric-a-brac.

Galerie Moderne Ltd, 10 Halkin Arcade, Motcomb Street, SW1X 8JJ TEL: 245 6907 FAX: 245 6341 PARKING: Medium OPEN: Mon-Fri 106 & by appt MIN: £500 PERIOD: 20th century SPECIALIST: Pre-war Rene Lalique glass including vases, scent, bottles, tableware, lighting fixtures, designs, car mascots, jewellery & statuettes. 20th century porcelain by Sevres OTHER INFO: Drones restaurant, Carlton Tower, Sheraton, Park Tower & Lowndes hotels.

Ross Hamilton Ltd, 95 Pimlico Road TEL: 730 3015 FAX: 730 3015 ASSNS: LAPADA PARKING: Easy OPEN: Mon-Fri 9.30-6, Sat 11-2 MIN: £200 MAX: £150,000 PERIOD: 17th-19th century SPECIALIST: Mostly English & Continental furniture GENERAL: Paintings, bronzes, porcelain, works of art & lacquer OTHER INFO: Several interior design & contemporary furniture designers' showrooms nearby

Heraz, 25 Motcomb Street, SW1X 8JU TEL: 245 9497 FAX: 235 7416 PARKING: Medium OPEN: Mon-Fri 10-6 MIN: £100+ PERIOD: 17th-19th century SPECIALIST: Textiles, cushions GENERAL: Antique Oriental, European, Aubusson & needlework carpets. Restoration & cleaning.

Christopher Hodsoll Ltd, 91 Pimlico Road, SW1W 8PH TEL: 730 3370 FAX: 730 1516 PARKING: Medium OPEN: Mon-Fri 9.30-6.30, Sat 10-4 MIN: £190 MAX: £150,000 PERIOD: 17th-19th century SPECIALIST: Own range of reproduction light fittings/furniture GENERAL: Furniture, works of art OTHER INFO: Business taken over from world famous Geoffrey

ADAMS
ANTIQUES
FAIRS

ROYAL
HORTICULTURAL HALLS

Vincent Square, Victoria, London SW1

Sundays 1994
**24th April, 22nd May, 19th June, 10th July,
28th August, 25th September, 23rd October,
13th November, 11th December**

Over 150 Exhibitors   9.30am–4.30pm.

THE DARTMOUTH HOUSE
ANTIQUES FAIR

37 Charles Street (Off Berkeley Square), Mayfair, London W1

Sundays 1994
**8th May, 5th June and monthly thereafter
– dates to be confirmed**

10.00am–5.00pm

**Adams Antiques Fairs
Tel: 071-254 4054**

Bennison who trained owner as interior decorator

The Horseman's Bookshop, 1 Lower Grosvenor Place, Buckingham Palace Road, SW1W 0EL TEL: 834 5606 FAX: 233 8001 ASSNS: ABA, Booksellers Assn of GB PARKING: Difficult OPEN: Mon-Fri 9-5.30, Sat 9-1 MIN: £2 MAX: £500 PERIOD: 17th-20th century SPECIALIST: Equine & equestrian world OTHER INFO: GB's only horse bookshop. Royal warrant holders to HM The Queen, HRH Prince Philip. Britsh Horse Society Award of Merit.

Christopher Howe, 36 Bourne Street, Belgravia, SW1W 8JA TEL: 730 7987 FAX: 730 0157 PARKING: Easy OPEN: Mon-Fri 9.30-6 MIN: £100 MAX: £100,000 PERIOD: 18th-19th century SPECIALIST: Enormous stock (1,500 sq ft separate warehouse) of English, Continental furniture & lighting

Christopher Hull Gallery, 17 Motcomb Street, SW1X 8LB TEL: 235 0500 PARKING: Easy OPEN: Mon-Fri 10-6, Sat 10-1 MIN: £500 MAX: £ 50,000 PERIOD: 20th century SPECIALIST: Modern British paintings & sculpture GENERAL: Artists of promise.

Sally Hunter Fine Art, 11 Halkin Arcade, Motcomb Street, SW1X 8JT TEL: 235 0934 PARKING: Medium OPEN: Mon-Fri 10-6 MIN: £200 MAX: £2,000 SPECIALIST: 20th century British art OTHER INFO: Knightsbridge shopping: Harrods, Harvey Nichols, and galleries. Hotels: Carlton Tower, Berkeley, Hyde Park etc.

David James, 3 Halkin Arcade, Motcomb Street, SW1X 8JT TEL: 235 5552 FAX: 235 5552 OPEN: Mon-Fri 11-6 & by appt MIN: £500 MAX: £20,000 PERIOD: 19th-20th century SPECIALIST: Fine Victorian watercolours & furniture GENERAL: Oils, Regency, Victorian, Edwardian furniture.

Keshishian, 73 Pimlico Road TEL: 730 8810 PARKING: 730 8803 ASSNS: BADA OPEN: Mon-Fri 9.30-6, Sat 10-5 PERIOD: 19th century SPECIALIST: Rare antique carpets, period tapestries, arts & crafts, carpets. Easter carpets OTHER INFO: 15th-18th century tapestries.

Dominic King Antique Glass, 85 Ebury Street, Belgravia, SW1W 4QY TEL: 824 8319/8310 ASSNS: Glass Assn, Glass Circle PARKING: Medium OPEN: Mon-Thurs 10-6 MIN: £20 MAX: £950 PERIOD: 18th-19th century SPECIALIST: 18th century drinking glasses & decanters GENERAL: Bristol & Stourbridge coloured glass, Victorian Hyacinth & Celery glasses. Wine related antiques, all glass pre 1900 especially dated & sealed wine bottles OTHER INFO: 5 mins from some of the world's greatest antiques. Queen's Gallery, Buckingham Palace, Victoria Station.

Kojis Antique Jewellery Ltd, Harrods, Fine Jewellery Room, Brompton Road TEL: 730 1234 extn 4072 FAX: 589 0655 PARKING: Difficult OPEN: Mon-Sat 10-6 MIN: £30 MAX: £50,000+ PERIOD: 17th-20th century SPECIALIST: Antiquities & ancient jewellery, collectable watches, antique, 20th century estate & designer jewellery. Valuation & repair.

Leuchars & Jefferson, 11 West Halkin Street, Belgrave Square, SW1X 8JL TEL: 235 2656 FAX: 823 1409 PARKING: Easy OPEN: 9.30-6 PERIOD: 18th century SPECIALIST: Fine furniture, Regency furniture & works of art OTHER INFO: Close to Mosiman's.

Lion Witch & Lampshade, 89 Ebury Street, SW1W 9QU TEL: 730 1774 PARKING: Easy OPEN: Mon-Tues, Thurs-Fri 10.30-5.30, Wed PM only MIN: £5 MAX: £1,500 PERIOD: 18th-20th century SPECIALIST: Lighting GENERAL: Unusual decorative objects OTHER INFO: Inexpensive hotels in Ebury Street.

Richard Miles, 8 Holbein Place, SW1W 8NL TEL: 730 1957 FAX: 824 8865 PARKING: Medium OPEN: Mon-Fri 10-5.30 MIN: £100 MAX: £50,000 PERIOD: 18th-19th century SPECIALIST: Anglo Indian & Chinese Colonial furniture, country house, Gothic & unusual woods.

Lennox Money (Antiques) Ltd, 93 Pimlico Road, SW1W 8PH TEL: 730 3070 FAX: 259 9563 PARKING: Medium OPEN: Mon-Fri 9.45-6, Sat 11-1 MIN: £250 MAX: £15,000 PERIOD: 18th-19th century SPECIALIST: Indian Colonial furniture, hanging lanterns GENERAL: Furniture & objects, lighting OTHER INFO: Nearest tube Sloane Square not Pimlico.

The O'Shea Gallery, 89 Lower Sloane Street, SW1W 8DA TEL: 730 0081 FAX: 730 1386 ASSNS: BADA, ABA, CINOA PARKING: Easy OPEN: Mon-Fri 9.30-6 Sat 9.30-1 MIN: £5

MAX: £5,000 PERIOD: 16th-19th century GENERAL: Worldwide maps & topographical prints, decorative prints, sporting, marine, botanical, natural history, architecture, caricature etc OTHER INFO: We exhibit at many US & UK antique fairs.

Parker Gallery, 28 Pimlico, SW1W 8LJ TEL: 730 6768 FAX: 259 9180 ASSNS: BADA, SLAD PARKING: Medium OPEN: Mon-Tues, Thurs-Fri 9.30-5.30, Wed 9.30-8 & by appt MIN: £38 MAX: £20,000 PERIOD: 18th-20th century SPECIALIST: Marine, military, topographical, sporting oils, watercolours & prints. Ship models, marine curios, maps, caricatures OTHER INFO: Army Museum.

Geoffrey Rose Ltd, 77 Pimlico Road, SW1W 8PH TEL: 730 3004 PARKING: Difficult OPEN: Mon-Fri 10.15-1, 2.15-6, most Sats 10.15-1 MIN: £500 MAX: £5,000 PERIOD: 18th-early 19th century GENERAL: English furniture OTHER INFO: Opposite modern furniture of Queen's nephew, Richard Linley.

Peta Smyth Antique Textiles, 42 Moreton Street, SW1V 2PB TEL: 630 9898 ASSNS: LAPADA, GMC PARKING: Medium OPEN: 10-5.30 MIN: £5 MAX: £5,000 PERIOD: 17th-19th century SPECIALIST: European early textiles GENERAL: Fabrics, needlework, tapestry, fragments & cushions.

Henry Sotheran, 80 Pimlico Road, SW1W 8PL TEL: 730 8756 FAX: 823 6090 OPEN: Mon-Fri 10-6, Sat 10-4 MIN: £5 MAX: £5,000+ PERIOD: 17th-19th century SPECIALIST: John Gould, David Roberts, Piranesi GENERAL: Architecture, travel & topography, natural history, antique prints OTHER INFO: Pimlico Road known as decorators alley, near Sloane Square tube.

Gerald Spyer & Son (Antiques) Ltd, 18 Motcomb Street, Belgrave Square, SW1X 8LB TEL: 235 3348 FAX: 823 2234 PARKING: Easy OPEN: Mon-Fri 10-6 MIN: £125 few ornaments MAX: £135,000 PERIOD: 18th-early 19th century SPECIALIST: Decorative English furniture GENERAL: English furniture, giltwood mirrors, ornaments & some decorative pictures OTHER INFO: Next to Knightsbridge & Sloane Square areas.

Trove, 71 Pimlico Road, SW1W 8NE TEL: 730

6514 PARKING: Medium OPEN: Mon-Fri 10-6, Sat 10-1 PERIOD: 17th-19th century SPECIALIST: Blue John GENERAL: Antique furniture, bronzes, decorative objects.

LONDON SW3 (071)

Number 12, Cale Street, Chelsea Green, SW3 3QU TEL: 581 5022 FAX: 581 3968 ASSNS: LAPADA PARKING: Easy OPEN: 10-5.30 MIN: £10 MAX: £20,000 PERIOD: 17th-18th century SPECIALIST: French provincial furniture.

Norman Adams Ltd, 8-10 Hans Road, SW3 1RX TEL: 589 5266 FAX: 589 1968 ASSNS: BADA, CINOA PARKING: Difficult OPEN: Mon-Fri 9-5.30 MIN: £400 MAX: £100,000+ PERIOD: 18th century SPECIALIST: Fine English furniture GENERAL: Furniture, mirrors, chandeliers, clocks, barometers OTHER INFO: Down west side of Harrods.

Antiquarius, 131-141 Kings Road, SW3 4PW TEL: 351 5353 FAX: 351 5350 PARKING: Medium OPEN: Mon-Sat 10-6 MIN: £5 MAX: £50,000 GENERAL: 120+ dealers offering jewellery, clocks, watches, silver, glass, antiquarian books, boxes, ceramics, porcelain, prints, paintings, collectables OTHER INFO: Centre is renowned for its diversity. Renovated antiques hall with café. Bureau de Change.

H C Baxter & Sons, 53 Stewarts Grove, SW3 6PU TEL: 352 9826 ASSNS: BADA, LAPADA PARKING: Medium OPEN: Wed, Thurs 9-5 & by appt MIN: £1,000 MAX: £50,000 SPECIALIST: English furniture 1730-1830 OTHER INFO: South Kensington near Victoria & Albert Museum etc.

Joanna Booth, 247 Kings Road, Chelsea, SW3

5EL TEL: 352 8998 FAX: 376 7350 ASSNS: BADA PARKING: Medium OPEN: Mon-Sat 10-6 MAX: £30,000 PERIOD: 17th-18th century SPECIALIST: Tapestry, textiles, Old Master drawings GENERAL: Furniture, sculpture, drawings, French books.

Chelsea Clocks & Antiques, Stand 113-4, Antiquarius, 135-143 Kings Road, Chelsea, SW3 4PW TEL: 352 8646 FAX: 376 4591 PARKING: Medium OPEN: 10-5.30 MIN: £10 MAX: £5,000 PERIOD: 19th-20th century SPECIALIST: Mantel & wall clocks GENERAL: Brass, wood, decorative & functional antiques.

Chenil Galleries, 181-183 Kings Road, Chelsea TEL: 351 5353 FAX: 351 5350 PARKING: Easy OPEN: Mon-Sat 10-6 MIN: £20 MAX: £100,000 PERIOD: 17th-20th century SPECIALIST: 30+ dealers offering Art Nouveau, Art Deco, & fine art GENERAL: 18th-19th century paintings, antique clothing, textiles & tapestries. Furniture, porcelain, silver, books, prints, toys, original carpets & jewellery OTHER INFO: Café & bureau de change. Nearest tube Sloane Square.

Michael Foster, 118 Fulham Road, Chelsea, SW3 6HU TEL: 373 3636 FAX: 373 4042 ASSNS: BADA PARKING: Medium OPEN: 9.30-6 PERIOD: 18th-early 19th century SPECIALIST: Dining tables, sofa tables GENERAL: English furniture & works of art.

Green & Stone, 259 Kings Road, SW3 5EL TEL: 352 6521 FAX: 351 1098 ASSNS: FATG PARKING: Medium OPEN: 9-5.30 MIN: £1,000 MAX: £20,000 PERIOD: 19th century SPECIALIST: Antique artist & writing implements GENERAL: Antique glass, lustre china, decorative French brocante, English watercolours.

E. Hollander Ltd, 84 Fulham Road, Chelsea, SW3 6HR TEL: 589 7239 FAX: 584 8479 ASSNS: BADA BHI MIN: £250 MAX: £75,000 PERIOD: 17th-19th century SPECIALIST: Clocks & Barometers GENERAL: Scientific instruments, sundials with the accent on English 18th century OTHER INFO: Full restoration service.

Stephanie Hoppen Ltd, 17 Walton Street TEL: 589 3678 FAX: 584 3731 PARKING: Medim OPEN: Mon-Fri 10-6, Sat 11-4 MIN: £200X: £5,000 PERIOD: 18th-20th century SPECIALIST: Exciting living artists, painters from times past GENERAL: Oils & watercolours, some prints OTHER INFO: Street is fascinating shopping area.

Anthony James & Son Ltd, 88 Fulham Road, Chelsea, SW3 6HR TEL: 584 1120 FAX: 823 7618 ASSNS: BADA CINOA PARKING: Easy OPEN: Mon-Fri 9.30-5.45 & by appt MIN: £300 MAX: £100,000 PERIOD: 18th-19th century SPECIALIST: Furniture.

Stanley Leslie, 15 Beauchamp Place, SW3 1NQ TEL: 589 2333 FAX: 589 3530 PARKING: Easy OPEN: 9-6 PERIOD: 18th-20th century GENERAL: Antique & modern silver & silverplate, cutlery, crystal etc.

The Map House, 54 Beauchamp Place, SW3 1NY TEL: 589 4325 FAX: 589 1041 ASSNS: ABA PARKING: Difficult OPEN: Mon-Fri 9.45-5.45, Sat 10.30-5 MIN: £5 MAX: £75,000 PERIOD: 16th-19th century SPECIALIST: Antique maps, prints, atlases OTHER INFO: Harrods 5 mins from.

Jacqueline Oosthuizen, 23 Cale Street, SW3

3QR TEL: 352 6071 FAX: 376 3852 ASSNS: LAPADA PARKING: Own carpark OPEN: Mon-Fri 10-6 & by appt MIN: £28 MAX: £9,000 PERIOD: 18th-19th century SPECIALIST: Staffordshire figures 1760-1890, cottages, animals, toby jugs. Antique & estate jewellery OTHER INFO: Many small hotels, museums etc. Kings Road.

Prides of London, 15 Paulton House, Paulton Square, SW3 5DU TEL: 586 1227 PARKING: Easy OPEN: By appt MIN: £1,000 MAX: £25,000+ PERIOD: 18th-19th century SPECIALIST: Regency brass inlaid furniture GENERAL: English furniture, objets d'art.

The Purple Shop, Antiquarius, 15 Flood Street, Chelsea, SW3 5ST TEL: 352 1127 FAX: 351 5350 PARKING: Medium OPEN: 10.30-5.30 MIN: £20 MAX: £20,000 PERIOD: 19th-20th century SPECIALIST: Art Nouveau, Art Deco, gentlemen's jewellery GENERAL: Antique & period jewellery OTHER INFO: Café on site, good antiques area.

Rogers de Rin, 76 Royal Hospital Road, Chelsea, SW3 4HN TEL: 352 9007 FAX: 351 9407 ASSNS: LAPADA PARKING: Easy OPEN: Mon-Fri 10-5.30, Sat 10-1 MIN: £100 MAX: £5,000+ PERIOD: 18th-19th century SPECIALIST: Wemyss ware, objets de vitrine, curiosities, Regency taste, tortoiseshell, tea caddies, Russian boxes, Staffordshire animals OTHER INFO: Ideally situated between 5 star Tante Claire & Foxtrot Oscar restaurants.

Julian Simon Fine Art Ltd, 70 Pimlico Road, SW1W 8LS TEL: 730 8673 FAX: 823 6116 ASSNS: BADA, LAPADA PARKING: Medium OPEN: Mon-Fri 10-6, Sat 10-4 MIN: £1,000 MAX: £150,000 PERIOD: 18th-early 20th century SPECIALIST: English & Continental paintings.

Robert Stephenson Oriental Carpets, 1 Elystan Street, Chelsea Green, SW3 3NT TEL: 225 2343 PARKING: Medium OPEN: on-Fri 10.30-5.30, Sat 10-1 MIN: £100 MAX: £25,000 PERIOD: 19th-20th century SPECIALIST: Room sized carpets, East European flatweaves GENERAL: Carpets, rugs & runners from Persia, India, Turkey. Kilims. Cleaning & repairs. Advice on problems OTHER INFO: Relaxing village atmosphere, ideal shopping area.

O F Wilson Ltd, Queens Elm Parade, Old Church Street, Chelsea, SW3 6EJ TEL: 352 9554 FAX: 351 0765 PARKING: Easy OPEN: Mon-Fri 9.30-5.50, Sat 10.30-1 MIN: £250 MAX: £50,000 PERIOD: 18th-19th century SPECIALIST: Marble & stone mantels GENERAL: Continental furniture, painted & gilt furniture & mirrors, chandeliers.

Clifford Wright Antiques Ltd, 104-106 Fulham Road, SW3 6HS TEL: 589 0986 FAX: 589 3565 ASSNS: BADA, Master Carvers Assn PARKING: Easy OPEN: 9-5.30 MIN: £1,000 MAX: £185,000 SPECIALIST: 18th century carved giltwood mirrors & consoles GENERAL: 18th & 19th century furniture & works of art.

COVENT GARDEN & BLOOMSBURY LONDON WC1 (071)

Abbott & Holder, 30 Museum Street, WC1A 1LH TEL: 637 3981 PARKING: Medium OPEN: Mon-Sat 9.30-6 MIN: £10 MAX: £10,000 PERIOD: 18th-20th century SPECIALIST: British watercolours & drawings GENERAL: Pictures OTHER INFO: The Coffee Gallery.

Classic Collection, 2 Pied Bull Yard, Bury Place, WC1A 2JR TEL: 831 6000 FAX: 831 5424 PARKING: Medium OPEN: 9-5.30 PERIOD: 19th-20th century GENERAL: Collectable cameras & optical toys.

George & Peter Cohn, Unit 21, 21 Wren Street, WC1X 0HF TEL: 278 3749 PARKING: Own carpark OPEN: Mon-Fri 9.30-4 PERIOD: 19th century SPECIALIST: Chandeliers & antique lights. Restoration & cleaning.

J A L Franks, 7 New Oxford Street, WC1A 1BA TEL: 405 0274 FAX: 430 1259 PARKING: Difficult OPEN: Mon-Fri 10.30-5.30 MIN: £2 MAX: £1,000 PERIOD: 17th-20th century SPECIALIST: Postcards, cigarette cards, antique maps.

Jessop Classic, 67 Great Russell Street, WC1 TEL: 831 3640 FAX: 831 3956 PARKING: Difficult OPEN: Mon-Sat 9-5.30 MIN: £10 MAX: £10,000+ PERIOD: 19th-20th century SPECIALIST: Antique & classic cameras, optical toys, magic lanterns, second-hand camera

books & lenses OTHER INFO: British Museum close.

The Print Room, 37 Museum Street, WC1A 1LP TEL: 430 0159 PARKING: Easy-underground carpark OPEN: Mon-Fri 10-6, Sat 10-4 MIN: £2 MAX: £10,000 PERIOD: 17th-19th century SPECIALIST: Caricatures, botanicals, Hogarth, topography GENERAL: Original antique prints & maps OTHER INFO: Opposite British Museum, Museum Tavern pub.

S J Shrubsole Ltd, 43 Museum Street, WC1A 1LY TEL: 405 2712 PARKING: Medium OPEN: Mon-Fri 9-5.30 MIN: £50 MAX: £50,000 PERIOD: 17th-18th century SPECIALIST: Fine early silver GENERAL: Georgian silver & old Sheffield plate.

LONDON WC2

Apple Market, 41 The Market, Covent Garden, WC2E 8RF TEL: 836 9136 FAX: via 240 5770 ASSNS: Antiques & Collectables Committee PARKING: Difficult OPEN: Mon & alternate Sun 9-7 GENERAL: 40 dealers with wide variety of stock.

A H Baldwin & Sons Ltd, 11 Adelphi Terrace, WC2N 6BJ TEL: 930 6879 FAX: 930 9450 PARKING: ASSNS: BADA, BNTA, Intl Assn of Professional Numismatists OPEN: Mon-Fri 9-5 MIN: £1 MAX: £50,000 PERIOD: 17-20th century SPECIALIST: Classical, medieval & later coins, medals & accessories. No ultra-modern OTHER INFO: Fifth generation family business.

Ann Creed Books Ltd, 22 Cecil Court, WC2N 4HE TEL: 836 7757 FAX: 240 1439 PARKING: Difficult OPEN: Mon-Sat 10.30-18.30 MIN: £5 MAX: £3,000+ PERIOD: 19th-20th century SPECIALIST: Only out-of-print & rare books on fine & applied art including 20th century design and avante-garde OTHER INFO: Cecil Court is a quaint byway of old fashioned bookshops unique to London.

Stanley Gibbons Ltd, 399 Strand, WC2R 0LX TEL: 836 8444 FAX: 836 7342 ASSNS: Philatelic Traders Society PARKING: Difficult OPEN: Mon-Fri 8.30-6, Sat 10-4 MIN: 30p MAX: £50,000+ PERIOD: 19th-20th century SPECIALIST: Rare stamps, postal history from UK & British Commonwealth GENERAL: 3 million+ stamps from Abu Dhabi to Zimbabwe, widest range of albums, catalogues, accessories, books OTHER INFO: In centre of Theatreland, Covent Garden, Savoy Hotel.

Grosvenor Prints, 28 Shelton Street, Covent Garden, WC2H 9HP TEL: 836 1979 FAX: 379 6695 PARKING: Medium OPEN: Mon-Fri 10-6, Sat 11-4 MIN: £10 MAX: £2,000 PERIOD: 18th-19th century SPECIALIST: Portraits, UK & foreign topography, sporting, dogs, decorative, most trades, natural history etc OTHER INFO: Covent Garden Market, best Italian restaurant in London, Neal St.

Arthur Middleton, 12 New Row, Covent Garden, WC2N 4LF TEL: 836 7042/7062 FAX: 497 2486 PARKING: Medium OPEN: Mon-Fri 10-6.30 MIN: £150 MAX: £70,000+ PERIOD: 18th-20th century SPECIALIST: Early globes & scientific instruments OTHER INFO: Customer comment: The only shop like it east of the Mississipi. Advice given on exciting Covent Garden etc.

Avril Noble, 2 Southampton Street, WC2E 7HA TEL: 240 1970 ASSNS: PBFA, IMCOS, AMPF OPEN: 10-6 MIN: £2 MAX: £3,000 PERIOD: 17th-19th century SPECIALIST: Antique maps & views GENERAL: Worldwide maps, Englsh countries, London, Ireland, Scotland, Wales. Botanical.

Pearl Cross Ltd, 35 St Martin's Court, St Martin's Lane, WC2N 4AL TEL: 836 2814 FAX: 240 2733 PARKING: Medium OPEN: 9.30-4.45 MIN: £50 MAX: £5,000ish PERIOD: 19th-20th century SPECIALIST: Jewellery, silver GENERAL: Some good clocks & objets d'art.

Henry Pordes Books Ltd, 58-60 Charing Cross Road, WC2H 0BB TEL: 836 9031 FAX: 886 2201 PARKING: Difficult OPEN: Mon-Sat 10-7 MIN: £1 MAX: £1200+ PERIOD: 17th-20th century SPECIALIST: Judaica, art, literature GENERAL: Daily changing stock on every conceivable subject, antiquarian & new remainders OTHER INFO: Chinatown nearby for best Chinese food, Soho, Covent Garden.

Stage Door Prints, 1 Cecil Court, St Martin's Lane, WC2N 4EZ TEL: 240 1683 PARKING: Difficult OPEN: Mon-Fri 11-6, Sat 11.30-6 MIN: £1 MAX: £1,250 PERIOD: 18th-20th century SPECIALIST: Opera, ballet, music & theatre prints & signed photos. Victorian Valentine cards, greetings cards & scraps GENERAL: Prints & maps on most subjects, small antiques, performing arts book room

Trafalgar Square Collectors Centre, 7 Whitcomb Street, Trafalgar Square, WC2H 7HA TEL: 930 1979 PARKING: Easy OPEN: 10.30-5 MIN: £1 MAX: £5,000 PERIOD: 19th-20th century SPECIALIST: Military medals & coins GENERAL: Militaria, banknotes, badges, bonds, miniature medals.

Zeno, The Greek Bookshop, 6 Denmark Street, WC2H 8LP TEL: 836 2522 FAX: 836 2522 ASSNS: ABA PARKING: Difficult OPEN: Mon-Fri 9.30-6, Sat 9.30-5 MIN: £1 MAX: £2,000+ PERIOD: 18th-20th century SPECIALIST: Antiquarian & modern books GENERAL: Cyprus, Greece, Middle East, Balkans, Byzantium history & travel etc.

FULHAM
LONDON SW3

Tony Bunzl, 344 Kings Road TEL: 352 3697 PARKING: Easy OPEN: Mon-Fri 10-5.30 MIN: £100 MAX: £20,000 SPECIALIST: European vernacular furniture 1600-1900.

Old Church Galleries, 320 Kings Road, Chelsea, SW3 5UH TEL: 351 4649 FAX: 351 4449 ASSNS: FATG PARKING: Easy OPEN: 10-6 MIN: £5 MAX: £5,000 PERIOD: 17th-19th century SPECIALIST: Antique maps & engravings, London GENERAL: Botanical, natural history, topography, architectural, sporting prints, framing OTHER INFO: Near Kings Road antique markets.

LONDON SW6 (071)

Alasdair Brown Antiques, 560 Kings Road, SW6 2DZ TEL: 736 8077 FAX: 736 3625 PARKING: Medium OPEN: Mon-Fri 10-6, Sat 10-5 MIN: £250 MAX: £20,000 PERIOD: 18th-19th century SPECIALIST: Furniture, Regency arts & crafts GENERAL: Lighting, decorative items.

Barclay-Samson Ltd, 39 Inglethorpe Street, SW6 6NS TEL: 381 4341 FAX: 610 0434 PARKING: Easy OPEN: By appt MIN: £100 MAX: £10,000 SPECIALIST: 19th & 20th century lithographic posters.

Robert Barley Antiques, 48 Fulham High Street, SW6 3LQ TEL: 736 4429 PARKING: Easy OPEN: Mon-Fri 9.30-5.30, Sat 10-1 MIN: £20 MAX: £20,000 SPECIALIST: Unusual & beautiful objects & pictures 500 BC-1940.

Benchmark, 287 Lillie Road, Fulham TEL: 610 2050 FAX: 610 2050 PARKING: Easy OPEN: 10-5 & by appt MIN: £100 MAX: £20,000 PERIOD: 19th-20th century SPECIALIST: Architect designed furniture GENERAL: Gothic revival, aesthetic, Art & Crafts, signed & designed furniture OTHER INFO: In established antiques area.

Big Ben Clocks, 5 Broxholme House, New Kings Road, SW6 4AA TEL: 731 0072 FAX: 384 1957 PARKING: Medium OPEN: By appt MIN: £150 MAX: £8,000 PERIOD: 18th-19th century SPECIALIST: Longcase clocks from country 30 hours to fine London walnut & mahogany clocks OTHER INFO: Long established business in prime antiques area.

Nicholas Harris Gallery, 564 Kings Road, SW6 2DY TEL: 371 9711 FAX: 371 9537 ASSNS: BADA, LAPADA PARKING: Medium OPEN: Mon-Fri 10-6, Sat 10.30-6 MIN: £250+ PERIOD: 19th-20th century SPECIALIST: Aes-

thetic, arts & crafts, Art Deco silver GENERAL: English, American & Oriental silver. Ceramics & decorative art 1860-1960 OTHER INFO: Close to Chelsea Harbour in main area for antiques & decorators items.

Simon Horn Furniture Ltd, 117-121 Wandsworth Bridge Road TEL: 736 3522 FAX: 736 3522 ASSNS: IDDA (corporate member) PARKING: Easy OPEN: 9.30-5.30 MIN: £120 MAX: £6,000 PERIOD: 18th-20th century SPECIALIST: French classical & antique wooden beds of any size. English traditional or French provincial OTHER INFO: Good shopping & excellent brassierie opposite.

Fairfax Fireplaces & Antiques, 568 Kings Road, SW6 2DY TEL: (0249) 652030 FAX: Same PARKING: Easy OPEN: 10-5 MIN: £20 MAX: £2,000 PERIOD: 18th-20th century SPECIALIST: Fireplaces & architectural GENERAL: Antique fixtures for restoring houses and advice on listed buildings.

P L James, 681 Fulham road, SW6 5PZ TEL: 736 0183 PARKING: Medium OPEN: 8-5 SPECIALIST: 18th & 19th century furniture of lacquer & painted furniture, mirrors etc Restoration of same.

Kings's Court Galleries, 951-953 Fulham Road TEL: 610 6939 PARKING: Medium OPEN: 9.30-5.30 MIN: £8 MAX: £2,500 PERIOD: 17th-19th century SPECIALIST: Antique prints & maps GENERAL: Decorative & sporting prints, limited editions.

Lunn Antiques Ltd, 86 New Kings Road, Parsons green, SW6 4LU TEL: 736 4638 FAX: 371 7113 PARKING: Medium OPEN: Mon-Sat 10-6 PERIOD: 17th-20th century SPECIALIST: London's largest stock of antique lace GENERAL: Linen sheets & pillowcases, table linen, nightdresses etc.

Magpies, 152 Wandsworth Bridge Road. Fulham, SW6 2UH TEL: 736 3738 PARKING: Easy OPEN: Mon-Sat 10-5.30 MIN: £1 MAX: £200 PERIOD: 19th-20th century GENERAL: antiques & bric-a-brac, kitchenalia, cutlery, boxes, china, glass, lighting, small furniture, fire tools, decoratives.

Michael Marriot, 588 Fulham Road, SW6 5NT TEL: 736 3110 PARKING: Easy OPEN: 10-5.30 MIN: £50 MAX: £20,000 PERIOD: 18th-19th century SPECIALIST: English furniture, wide selection of prints.

David Martin-Taylor Antiques, 558 King's Road, SW6 2DZ TEL: 731 4135 FAX: 371 0029 ASSNS: LAPADA PARKING: Easy (at rear) OPEN: Mon-Fri 9.30-5.30 & by appt MIN: £20 MAX: £7,000 PERIOD: 18th-19th century GENERAL: Mainly 19th century English & Continental furniture, screens, mirrors, decorative objects & wicker furniture.

Sylvia Napier, 554 Kings Road, SW6 2DZ TEL: 371 5881 PARKING: Own carpark OPEN: 10-6 MIN: £50 MAX: £18,000 PERIOD: 17th-20th century SPECIALIST: Chandeliers GENERAL: Decorative.

Old Pine & Painted Furniture, 594 Kings Road, SW6 2DX TEL: 736 5999 PARKING: Medium OPEN: Mon-Sat 10-5.30 MIN: £75 MAX: £3,500 PERIOD: 19th century SPECIALIST: Pine & painted furniture.

Paul Orssich, 117 Munster Road, SW6 6DH TEL: 736 3869, 371 9886 ASSNS: PBFA PARKING: Easy OPEN: Mon-Fri 9.30-6 & by appt MIN: £10 MAX: £5,000 PERIOD: 17th-20th century SPECIALIST: Old & rare books, Spain & Hispanic studies GENERAL: Old maps worldwide, Art Deco illustrations 1915-1935.

M Pauw, 606 Kings Road, SW6 2DX TEL: 731 4072 FAX: 731 7356 PARKING: Medium OPEN: Mon-Sat 9-6 MIN: £200 MAX: £10,000 PERIOD: 18th-19th century SPECIALIST: Good Continental & English furniture, objects & light fixtures.

John Spink, 14 Darlan Road, Fulham, SW6 5BT TEL: 731 8292 FAX: 731 6955 PARKING: Easy OPEN: By appt please MIN: £500 MAX: £50,000 SPECIALIST: Fine quality British watercolours 1720-1920 all in top condition.

Trowbridge Gallery, 555 Kings Road, SW6 2EB TEL: 371 8733 FAX: 371 8138 ASSNS: LAPADA PARKING: Easy OPEN: 9.30-5.30 MIN: £55 MAX: £1,000 PERIOD: 17th-18th century SPECIALIST: Decorative antique prints & handmade frames GENERAL: Botanical, natural history, architecture & reproduction range.

Tulissio de Beaumont, 277 Lillie Road TEL: 385 0156 ASSNS: LAPADA PARKING: Easy OPEN: Mon-Sat 10-6 MIN: £20 MAX: £5,000

PERIOD: 17th-20th century SPECIALIST: Period lighting GENERAL: Furniture, scupture, pictures & decorative antiques OTHER INFO: 12 dealers (6 new this year) in fast-growing antiques street

LONDON SW10 (071)

Chalow UK Ltd, The Plaza, 535 Kings Road TEL: 351 0008 FAX: 351 0003 ASSNS: LAPADA PARKING: Easy OPEN: Mon-Sat 9-5 MIN: £100 MAX: £7,500 PERIOD: 18th-19th century GENERAL: European country & decorative, handmade furniture.

Jonathan Cooper, Park Wall Gallery, 20 Park Walk, SW10 0AQ TEL: 351 0410 PARKING: Medium OPEN: Mon-Fri 10-6.30 MIN: £250 MAX: £250,000 PERIOD: 20th century GENERAL: Modern British & European OTHER INFO: Good restaurants in Park Walk.

Hares Antiques, 498 Kings Road, SW10 0LE TEL: 351 1442 (0285) 653513 ASSNS: Costwold ADA PARKING: Medium OPEN: Mon-Sat 10-5.30 MIN: £100 MAX: £30,000 PERIOD: 18th-19th century SPECIALIST: Period dining tables & chairs, upholstery GENERAL: Wide selection. Restoration & re-upholstery.

Stephen Long, Albion House, 348 Fulham Road, SW10 9UH TEL: 352 8226 PARKING: Easy OPEN: Mon-Fri 9-1, 2.15-5.30, most Sats AM only MIN: £10 MAX: £1,000 PERIOD: 18th-19th century GENERAL: English pottery, glass & smalls, fabrics, painted furniture.

McVeigh & Charpentier, 498 Kings Road TEL: 351 1442 PARKING: Easy OPEN: 10-5.30 MIN: £300 MAX: £5,000 PERIOD: 18th-19th century SPECIALIST: Continental furniture GENERAL: Objets d'art, mirrors, beds, garden statuary & ironwork.

H W Poulter & Son, 279 Fulham Road, SW10 9PZ TEL: 352 7268 FAX: 351 0984 PARKING: Easy OPEN: Mon-Fri 9-5, Sat 10-1 MIN: £250 MAX: £50,000 PERIOD: 18th-19th century SPECIALIST: Marble, stone, wood chimney pieces GENERAL: Fenders, firegrates, fire irons, chandeliers OTHER INFO: Marble restoration on chimney pieces, figures, tops. Bespoke marble tops made.

Harriet Wynter Ltd, 50 Redcliffe Road, SW10 9NJ TEL: 352 6494 FAX: 252 9312 ASSNS:

BADA PARKING: Medium OPEN: By appt only MIN: £15 MAX: £50,000 PERIOD: 17th-early 19th century SPECIALIST: Early scientific instruments GENERAL: Antique decorative items, early furniture, paintings & sculpture OTHER INFO: In short Victorian terrace just off Fulham Road full of attractive shops & restaurants.

HAMPSTEAD & KILBURN
LONDON NW3 (071)

Dolphin Coins, 2c Englands Lane, Hampstead, NW3 4TG TEL: 722 4116 FAX: 483 2000 ASSNS: BNTA PARKING: Easy OPEN: 9-5, Sat by appt MIN: £5 MAX: £7,500 PERIOD: 25 AD-1937 SPECIALIST: World coins GENERAL: British coins.

John Denham Gallery, 50 Mill Lane, Hampstead, NW6 1NJ TEL: 794 2635 PARKING: Easy OPEN: 10-5, Sun 11-5, Sat, Mon PM only MIN: £20 MAX: £5,000 PERIOD: 17th-20th century SPECIALIST: Paintings, watercolours, drawings, etc. Restoration & framings service.

S Farrelly, 152 Fleet Road, Hampstead, NW3 2QX TEL: 485 2089 PARKING: Medium OPEN: 10-5 MIN: £2 MAX: £4,000 PERIOD: 18th-20th century GENERAL: General antiques OTHER INFO: Hampstead Heath, Kenwood House near, John Keats' House.

LONDON NW6 (071)

Gallery Kaleidoscope, 66 Willesden Lane, Kilburn, NW6 7SX TEL: 328 5833 PARKING: Easy OPEN: Mon-Sat 10-6 MIN: £20 MAX: £2,000 PERIOD: 19th-20th century GENERAL: Paintings, sculpture, ceramics OTHER INFO: Lots of local junk shops.

Scope Antiques, 64 Willesden Lane, Kilburn, NW6 7SX TEL: 328 5833 PARKING: Easy OPEN: 10-6 MIN: £20 MAX: £2,000 PERIOD: 19th century GENERAL: Furniture, glass, pottery, decorative items etc OTHER INFO: Good bargain-finding area.

ISLINGTON
LONDON N1 (071)

At The Sign of the Chest of Drawers, 281 Upper Street, N1 2TZ TEL: 359 5909 FAX: 359 5909 PARKING: Medium OPEN: Seven days 10-6 MIN: £1 MAX: £1,500 PERIOD: 19th-20th century SPECIALIST: Antique pine & country furniture. Reproduction.

William Bedford plc, 46 Essex Road, N1 8LN TEL: 226 9648 FAX: 226 6225 ASSNS: LAPADA, CPTA PARKING: Own carpark OPEN: Tues-Sat 9.30-5.30 MIN: £500 MAX: £120,000 PERIOD: 17th-19th century SPECIALIST: Dining room & library furniture GENERAL: Period English, Irish, Continetal furniture & works of art. Bespoke reproductions.

Bushwood Antiques, 317 Upper Street, N1 TEL: 359 2095 FAX: 704 9578 ASSNS: LAPADA PARKING: Medium OPEN: 9.30-5.30 MIN: £250 MAX: £10,000 PERIOD: 18th-19th century SPECIALIST: Antique furniture GENERAL: Clocks, lighting, objets d'art in 14,000+ sq ft showroom.

Cassandra Keen, 18 Georgian Village, Camden Passage, NI 8EA TEL: 359 6534 ASSNS: LAPADA PARKING: Medium OPEN: Wed 7-3, Sat 8-4 MIN: £100 MAX: £1,500 PERIOD: 18th-early 20th century SPECIALIST: French mirrors & fin de siècle lighting GENERAL: Across the board.

Peter Chapman Antiques, 10 Theberton Street, N1 0QX TEL: 226 5565 FAX: 348 4846 ASSNS: LAPADA PARKING: Easy OPEN: Mon-Sat 9.30-6 MIN: £50 MAX: £15,000 PERIOD: 18th-19th century SPECIALIST: Furniture, paintings, objets d'art, lanterns, mirrors, decoratives. Restoration service. No reproductions.

Commemoratives, 3 Pierrepoint Arcade, Camden Passage, N1 8EF ASSNS: Torquayware Collectors' Society PARKING: Medium OPEN: Wed, Sat 10-5 & by appt MIN: £5 MAX: £200 PERIOD: 19th-20th century SPECIALIST: Eggcups, royal & political commemoratives, mottoware, glassware, decorative pottery, collectables.

Dog & Cat Box Antiques & Collectables, Shop 3 (upstairs), Georgian Village, Camden Passage, N1 8EA TEL: 223 6272 FAX: 892 4387 PARKING: Medium OPEN: Wed, Sat 8-3.30 & by appt MIN: £10 MAX: £500 PERIOD: 19th century to 1960's SPECIALIST: Cat & dog related items GENERAL: Victorian & contemporary pictures, prints, ceramics, metal, jewellery, books OTHER INFO: Frederick's rerstaurant.

Dome Antiques (Exports) Ltd, 75 Upper Street, N1 0NU TEL: 226 7227 FAX 704 2960 PARK-

ING: Medium OPEN: 9-5 MIN: £100 MAX: £5,000 PERIOD: 18th-19th century GENERAL: Desks, dining tables & chairs, bookcases, occasional tables, etc OTHER INFO: Opposite Camden Passage.

Vincent Freeman Antiques, Camden Passage, N1 2UD TEL: 226 6178 FAX: 226 7231 PARKING: Medium OPEN: Tues-Wed, Fri-Sat 10-5 MIN: £50+ MAX: £20,000+ PERIOD: 19th century SPECIALIST: Antique cylinder & disc music boxes GENERAL: Furniture & objects.

Get Stuffed, 105 Essex Road, N1 5SL TEL: 226 1364 FAX: 359 8253 PARKING: Medium OPEN: Mon 12-4.30, Tues, Wed, Fri 10.30-4.30, Thurs 10.30-1, Sat 12-3 MIN: £25 MAX: £25,000 PERIOD: 19th-20th century SPECIALIST: Glass domes GENERAL: All aspects of taxidermy.

Graham Gallery, 104 Islington High Street, Camden Passage, N1 8EG TEL: 354 2112 FAX: 704 0728 ASSNS: LAPADA PARKING: Medium OPEN: Tues-Sat 10-5 MIN: £ 25 MAX: £50,000 PERIOD: 19th-early 20th century SPECIALIST: Unique fine English marquetry furniture, stylish silver, romantic Victorian oils OTHER INFO: Next to Frederick famous restaurant.

Gordon Gridley Antiques, 28 & 41 Camden Passage, Islington, N1 8EA TEL: 226 0643 ASSNS: CPTA PARKING: Medium OPEN: Tues-Sat 10-4.30 MIN: £50 MAX: £20,000 PERIOD: 17th-19th century SPECIALIST: Folk art & naïve paintings, English ironstone GENERAL: English & Continental furniture, paintings, sculpture, metalware, decorative objects OTHER INFO: 1,000 sq ft warehouse at rear. 2 internationally famed restaurants.

Hart & Rosenberg, 2-3 Gateway Arcade, 355 Upper Street, Camden Passage, N1 0PD TEL: 359 6839 FAX (081) 676 8984 ASSNS: CPTA PARKING: Easy OPEN: Tues, Fri 10.30-5, Wed 9-5, Sat 10-5 & by appt MIN: £50 MAX: £4,000 PERIOD: 17th-20th century SPECIALIST: Oriental ceramics GENERAL: English & Continental ceramics, works of art & decoratives OTHER INFO: Opposite Business Design Centre, close to Angel tube station.

Heritage Antiques, 112 Islington High Street, N1 8EG TEL: 226 7789 ASSNS: LAPADA

PARKING: Easy OPEN: Wed & Sat & by appt MIN: £20 MAX: £5,000 PERIOD: 17th-19th century SPECIALIST: Metalware, some oak GENERAL: Domestic & decorative metalware.

House of Steel, 400 Caledonian Road, N1 1DN TEL: 607 5889 FAX: 607 5889 PARKING: Own carpark OPEN: Mon-Fri 9-5 & by appt MIN: £5+ MAX: £3,000 PERIOD: 19th-20th century SPECIALIST: Metal antiques, ornamental & architectural metalware, fireplaces, railings, gates, garden furniture, lighting, steel tables & chairs OTHER INFO: Reproductions in cast steel, brass.

Diana Huntley, 8 Camden Passage, N1 3ED TEL: 226 4605 FAX: 359 0240 ASSNS: LAPADA PARKING: Medium OPEN: Tues, Fri 10-4, Wed 7.30-4, Sat 9-4 MIN: £100 MAX: £10,000 PERIOD: 19th century SPECIALIST: European porcelain GENERAL: Meissen, Minton, Coalport, Wedgwood, Derby services.

Inheritance, 8-9 Gateway Arcade, Camden Passage, N1 0PD TEL: 226 8305 FAX: 226 8305 ASSNS: CPTA PARKING: Easy OPEN: 10-4 PERIOD: 19th century SPECIALIST: Japanese porcelain GENERAL: Paintings, furniture, silver OTHER INFO: Mistress Plum homemade pastries, King's Head pub/theatre.

Intercol London, Upper Gallery, 11 Camden Passage, N1 8DY TEL: 349 2207 FAX: 346 9539 ASSNS: CPTA PARKING: Easy OPEN: Wed, Sat 9-5 MIN: £5+ MAX: £5,000 PERIOD: 18th-20th century SPECIALIST: Playing cards, maps, money & related books.

Islington Antiques, 14 Essex Road, N1 8LN TEL: via 226 6867 PARKING: Easy OPEN: Seven days 9-6 MIN: £15 MAX: £2,000 PERIOD: 19th century SPECIALIST: Original antique pine furniture.

Jane House Antiques, 15 Camden Passage, N1 8EH TEL: 359 1343 PARKING: Easy OPEN: Tues-Sat 10-4.30 MIN: £400 MAX: £7,000 SPECIALIST: Georgian & Victorian furniture.

Japanese Gallery, 23 Camden Passage, N1 8EA TEL: 226 3347 PARKING: Easy OPEN: 10-6 MIN: £5 MAX: £10,000 PERIOD: 19th-20th century SPECIALIST: Japanese woodcut prints GENERAL: Japanese arts, screens & furniture OTHER INFO: Good B&B's help through Camden Traders Assn.

Jubilee Photographica, 10 Pierrepoint Row, Camden Passage, N1 TEL: 607 5462(home) FAX: Yes PARKING: Medium ASSNS: CPTA OPEN: Wed, Sat 10.30-3.30 & by appt MIN: 5p snaps MAX: £1,500 PERIOD: 18th century-1939 SPECIALIST: Daguerrotypes, Ambrotypes, Tirotypes, all types of paper prints, stereocards, viewers, categorised cartes de visite, cabinet-sized prints, albums, topographical & family photographs. Photoframes, graphoscopes, magic lanterns & slides OTHER INFO: Family photo dating service. Great Italian restaurant upstairs.

Thomas Keen Antiques, 11 Theberton Street, N1 0QY TEL: 226 0626 FAX: 354 5625 ASSNS: LAPADA PARKING: Easy OPEN: 10-5.30 MIN: £10 MAX: £20,000 PERIOD: 17th-18th century GENERAL: English furniture.

Carol Ketley, 9 Georgian Village, 30-31 Islington Green, Camden Passage, N1 8EA TEL: 359 5529, (0831) 827284 FAX: 226 4589 ASSNS: LAPADA PARKING: Medium OPEN: Wed 8-3, Sat 10-4 MIN: £5+ MAX: £100 mostly but up to £800 PERIOD: 19th century SPECIALIST: Decanters, glassware, English pottery OTHER INFO: 300 dealers in Camden Passage.

Sara Lemkow & Rookery Farm Antiques, 12 Camden Passage, N1 8ED TEL: 359 0190 FAX: 704 2095 ASSNS: CPTA PARKING: Medium OPEN: 10-5 MIN: £15 MAX: £1,000 PERIOD: 18th-19th century SPECIALIST: Pine furniture, oil lamps, GENERAL: Kitchenalia, scales, copper & brass.

Michael Lewis, 16 Essex Road, N1 8LN TEL: 359 7733 ASSNS: LAPADA, CPTA PARKING: Easy OPEN: Sat 8-6, Sun 8-5 & by appt MIN: £5 MAX: £10,000 PERIOD: 18th-19th century SPECIALIST: British & Irish period pine & country furniture.

Finbar Macdonnell, 17 Camden Passage, NI TEL: 226 0537 PARKING: Medium OPEN: 10-6 MIN: £5 MAX: £1,000 PERIOD: 17th-20th century GENERAL: Decorative prints, carica-tures, Vanity Fair, Japanese OTHER INFO: Big market Wed & Sat AM.

The Mall Antiques Arcade, Camden Passage, N1 TEL: 351 5353 FAX: 351 5350 PARKING: Medium OPEN: Tues, Thurs, Fri 10-5, Wed 7.30-5, Sat 9-6 GENERAL: 35 shop units with specialists in antique furniture, porcelain, silver, glass, jewellery, decoratives, prints, lighting & Oriental art OTHER INFO: 1st floor restaurant. Prime trading is on Weds being Camden Passage market day.

London Militaria Market, Angel Arcade, Camden Passage, N1 TEL: (0628) 822503 FAX: (0628) 822503 PARKING: Medium OPEN: 8-2 MIN: £ 1MAX: £2,000+ PERIOD: 19th century SPECIALIST: Military helmets, badges, uniforms, regimental brooches, medals, swords, aviation items OTHER INFO: 35 dealers from all over England.

Laurence Mitchell Antiques Ltd, 13 & 27 Camden Passage, N1 8EA TEL: 359 7599 PARKING: Medium OPEN: 10-5, Wed 8-5 MIN: £100 MAX: £20,000 PERIOD: 18th-19th century SPECIALIST: Probably largest UK stock of Meissen GENERAL: General, porcelain, works of art, decorative furniture.

Jacqueline Oosthuizen Antiques, 1st Floor (upstairs), Georgian Village, Camden Passage, N1 8EA TEL: 352 6071, 226 5393 FAX: 376 3852 PARKING: Easy OPEN: Wed & Sat 8-4 MIN: £28 MAX: £3,000 PERIOD: 18th-19th century SPECIALIST: Staffordshire figures 1760-1890, cottages, animals, toby jugs GENERAL: Antique & estate jewellery.

Marcus Ross Antiques, 14 & 16 Pierrepoint Row, Camden Passage, N1 8EF TEL: 359 8494 FAX: 359 0240 ASSNS: CPTA PARKING: Medium OPEN: Tues-Wed, Fri-Sat 10-5 MIN: £20 MAX: £8,000 PERIOD: 17th-19th century SPECIALIST: Japanese Imari, Chinese Blue & White Chen Lung porcelain.

Style Galleries, 1 Georgian Village, Camden Passage, N1 TEL: 359 7867, (0831) 229640 PARKING: Easy OPEN: Wed 9-4, Sat 9.30-4.30 MIN: £150 MAX: £15,000 PERIOD: 19th-20th century SPECIALIST: Art Nouveau/Deco GENERAL: Pewter, WMF Liberty, bronze, ivories, Lalique Loetz lighting OTHER INFO: We are the gallery which published reprint of WMF

1906 catalogue.

Tadema Gallery, 10 Charlton Place, Camden Passage, N1 8AJ TEL: 359 1055 FAX: 704 9335 ASSNS: LAPADA PARKING: Medium OPEN: Wed, Fri, Sat 10-5 MIN: £150 MAX: £20,000 PERIOD: 20th century SPECIALIST: Abstract art & jewellery from Art Nouveau to artist designed pieces circa 1980.

Turn On Lighting, 116-118 Islington High Street, Camden Passage, N1 8EG TEL: 359 7616 ASSNS: Decorative Arts Society, Historic Lighting Club, Lighting Assn PARKING: Easy OPEN: Tues-Sat 10.30-5 PERIOD: 18th-20th century SPECIALIST: Lighting c.1840-1940 OTHER INFO: Almeida Theatre, Granitas French/Italian restaurant.

De Verzamelaar, 1st Floor (upstairs), Georgian Village, Camden Passage, NI 8EA TEL: 359 3322 FAX: 376 3852 PARKING: Easy OPEN: Wed, Sat 8-4 MIN: £10 MAX: £2,000 PERIOD: Late 19th-early 20th century SPECIALIST: Dutch Art Nouveau ceramics & Boer War memorabilia.

Yesterday Child, Angel Arcade, 118 Islington High Street, N1 8EG TEL & FAX: (0908) 583403 PARKING: Medium OPEN: Wed, Sat 9-3 MIN: £100 PERIOD: 20th century SPECIALIST: Enormous stock of antique dolls & miniatures.

LONDON NW1 (071)

Victorian Fireplace Co, 53 West Yard, Camden Lock, NW1 8AF TEL: 482 2543 FAX: 417 9946 PARKING: Medium OPEN: Wed-Sun 10.30-5 MIN: £95 MAX: £600 PERIOD: 19th-20th century SPECIALIST: Original Victorian, Edwardian fireplaces & accessories OTHER INFO: Camden Lock Market Sat, Sun- marvellous.

MAYFAIR & ST JAMES'S
LONDON SW1 (071)

Verner Amell Ltd, 4 Ryder Street, St James's, SW1Y 6QB TEL: 925 2759 FAX: 321 0210 ASSNS: SLAD PARKING: Difficult OPEN: Weekdays 10-5.30 MIN: £10,000 MAX: £1.5 million SPECIALIST: 17th century Dutch, Flemish, Italian paintings GENERAL: 19th century Scandinavian paintings.

J H Bourdon-Smith Ltd, 24 Mason's Yard, Duke Street, St James's, SW1Y 6BU TEL: 839 4714 FAX: 839 3951 ASSNS: BADA PARKING: Medium/difficult OPEN: Mon-Fri 9.30-6 MIN: £20 MAX: £50,000 SPECIALIST: Early Georgian to Victorian silver OTHER INFO: Excellent shopping area, Fortnum & Mason's, Christie's auction house etc.

The Armoury of St James's, 17 Piccadilly Arcade, SW1Y 6NH TEL: 493 5082 FAX: 499 4422 ASSNS: OMRS PARKING: Medium OPEN: Mon-Fri 9.30-5.30, Sat 11-4.30 MIN: £5 PERIOD: 18th-20th century SPECIALIST: Military & civil medals of the world GENERAL: Militaria, handpainted military figurines & toy soldiers OTHER INFO: At the centre of everything.

Thomas Heneage Art Books, 42 Duke Street, St James's, SW1Y 6DJ TEL: 930 9223 FAX: 930 9223 PARKING: Medium OPEN: Mon-Fri 10-6 MIN: £5 SPECIALIST: Art reference books GENERAL: Reference books for fine & decorative arts worldwide in or out of print OTHER INFO: Between Fortnum & Mason's & Christie's.

Longmire, 12 Bury Street, St James's SW1 TEL: 930 8720 PARKING: Medium OPEN: Mon-Fri 10-5, Sats in Nov/Dec MIN: £190 MAX: £50,000 PERIOD: 19th-20th century SPECIALIST: World's largest collection of cufflinks, old & new GENERAL: Custom made individual Victorian ladies jewellery OTHER INFO 3 Royal Warrants. New York Times quote: The rarest relic of a civilized age-Longmire's personal service.

MacConnal-Mason Gallery, 14 Duke Street, St James's SW1Y 6DB TEL: 839 7693 FAX: 839 6797 PARKING: Easy OPEN: 9-6 MIN: £2,000 PERIOD: 18th-20th century.

Mall Galleries/Federation of British Artists, The Mall TEL: 930 6844 FAX: 839 7830 PARKING: Easy but expensive! OPEN: Mon-Sat 10-5 MIN: £100 MAX: £5,000 PERIOD: 20th century SPECIALIST: Contemporary art (mainly traditional styles), paintings, sculpture etc OTHER INFO: Housed in a Nash house, close to Trafalgar Sq & Buckingham Palace.

Polak Gallery Ltd, 21 King Street, St James's, SW1Y 6QY TEL: 839 2371 ASSNS: BADA PARKING: Difficult OPEN: Mon-Fri 9.30-5.30 MIN: £1,000 MAX: £60,000 PERIOD: 19th-20th century GENERAL: English, European &

contemporary artists OTHER INFO: Opposite Christie's.

St George's Gallery/Zwemmer, 8 Duke Street, St James's, SW1Y 6BN TEL: 930 0935/4930 FAX: 930 3534 PARKING: Difficult OPEN: 10-6 MIN: £5 MAX: £25,000 PERIOD: 20th century SPECIALIST: Fine & decorative art books GENERAL: New & out-of print books OTHER INFO: Worldwide mail order available. 100 yds from Royal Academy of Art. In heart of central London's antique world.

Johnny Van Haeften Ltd, 13 Duke Street, St James's, SW1Y 6DB TEL: 930 3062 FAX: 839 6303 ASSNS: BADA, SLAD, TEFAF PARKING: Medium OPEN: Mon-Fri 10-6 & by appt MIN: £5,000 MAX: £2 million PERIOD: 17th century SPECIALIST: Dutch & Old Master paintings only.

Robert Wace Ancient Art Ltd, 107 Jermyn Street, SW1Y 6EE TEL: 495 1623 FAX: 930 7310 ASSNS: ASA IADAA PARKING: Difficult OPEN: 10-5 MIN: £100 MAX: £15,000+ PERIOD: Up to 1000 AD SPECIALIST: Antiquuities: Greek, Roman, Egyptian, Near Eastern & Celtic. Anglo Saxon.

LONDON W1A (071)

Astarte Gallery, Britannia Hotel, Grosvenor Square, W1A 3AN TEL: 409 1875 FAX: 409 1875 ASSNS: ADA PARKING: Own carpark OPEN: Mon-Fri 10-5 & by appt MIN: £5 MAX: £10,000 PERIOD: BC to 6th century AD SPECIALIST: Ancient Egypt, Rome, Greece items GENERAL: Coins ancient & modern OTHER INFO: Comfortable hotel premises, all facilities, heart of West End.

LONDON W1M (071)

Blunderbuss Antiques, 29 Thayer Street, W1M 5LJ TEL: 486 2444 PARKING: Medium OPEN: 9.30-4.30 MIN: £1 PERIOD: 17th-20th century SPECIALIST: Antique arms, armour & militaria.

The Button Queen, 19 Marylebone Lane, W1M 5FF TEL: 935 1505 ASSNS: British Button Society PARKING: Medium OPEN: Mon-Fri 10-6, Sat 10-1.30 PERIOD: Some 18th, 19th-20th century SPECIALIST: Buttons, old & antique GENERAL: Modern buttons OTHER INFO: Wheelchair access.

Brian Fielden, 3 New Cavendish Street, W1M 7RP TEL: 935 6912 PARKING: Medium OPEN:

Mon-Fri 9.30-1, 2-5.30, Sat 9.30-1 MIN: £500 MAX: £20,000 PERIOD: 18th-19th century SPECIALIST: English period furniture OTHER INFO: 200 yds to Wallace Collection.

E Joseph Booksellers, 1 Vere Street, W1M 9HQ TEL: 493 8353 PARKING: 629 2759 ASSNS: ABA, BADA OPEN: Mon-Fri 9.30-5.30 MIN: £50 MAX: £40,000 PERIOD: 17th-20th century GENERAL: Antiquarian books, fine bindings, library sets, childrens illustrated.

David Richards & Sons, 12 New Cavendish Street TEL: 935 3206/0322 FAX: 224 4423 ASSNS: LAPADA PARKING: Medium OPEN: 9.30-5.30 & by appt MIN: £25 MAX: £5,000 PERIOD: 18th-20th century SPECIALIST: Old Sheffield plate, Victorian plate.

Venners Antiques, 7 New Cavendish Street, W1M 7RP TEL: 935 0184 PARKING: Meters OPEN: Tues-Fri 10.15-4.15, Sat 10-1 MIN: £10 MAX: £10,000 PERIOD: 18th-19th century SPECIALIST: English pottery & porcelain.

Wilkins & Wilkins, 1 Barrett Street, W1M 6DN TEL: 935 9613 FAX: 935 5720 PARKING: Medium OPEN: 10-5 MIN: £500 MAX: £10,000 PERIOD: 17th-18th century SPECIALIST: British decorative paintings & portraits.

LONDON W1R (071)

Bernheimer Fine Arts Ltd, 32 St George Street, W1R 9FA TEL: 499 0293 FAX: 409 1814 ASSNS: BADA, CINOA, SLAD PARKING: Medium OPEN: 10-5.30 PERIOD: 17th-18th century SPECIALIST: Continental furniture, Old Master paintings, Oriental ceramics, Han & Tang dynasties.

Andrew Edmunds, 44 Lexington Street, W1R 3LH TEL: 437 8594 FAX: 439 2551 PARKING: Difficult OPEN: Mon-Fri 10-6 MIN: £85 MAX: £2,000 PERIOD: 18th-19th century SPECIALIST: English caricatures GENERAL: Prints OTHER INFO: Excellent restaurant next door.

Liberty plc, Antiques & Fine Art Dept, Regent Street, W1R 6AH TEL: 734 1234, FAX: 734 8323 PARKING: Medium OPEN: Mon-Sat 9.30-6, Thurs till 7.30 MIN: £30 MAX: £10,000 PERIOD: 19th-20th century SPECIALIST: Furniture & metalware 1860-1920 including Arts & Crafts movement, with pieces by Liberty & Co, Heal's etc OTHER INFO: World famous department store. Restaurant & 2 cafés in store.

Sheppard & Cooper Ltd, 11 St George Street, W1R 9DF TEL: 629 6489 FAX: 495 2905 PARKING: Difficult OPEN: Weekdays 10-6 MIN: £70+ SPECIALIST: Ancient & antique glass.

Stephen Somerville Ltd, 32 St George Street, W1R 9FA TEL: 493 8363 PARKING: Difficult OPEN: Mon-Fri 10-5 PERIOD: 18th-20th century SPECIALIST: English paintings, drawings, watercolours, prints, Old Master works.

LONDON W1V (071)

J & A Beare Ltd, 7 Broadwick Street, W1V 1FJ TEL: 437 1449 FAX: 439 4520 ASSNS: Intl Society of Violin & Bow Makers, BADA PARKING: Difficult OPEN: Mon-Fri 9-12.15, 1.30-5 PERIOD: 17th-20th century SPECIALIST: Musical instruments of the violin family & their accessories only.

MacConnal-Mason Gallery, 15 Burlington Arcade, Piccadilly, W1V 9AB TEL: 839 7693 FAX: 839 6797 PARKING: Easy OPEN: 9-6 MIN: £2,000 PERIOD: 18th-20th century.

Michael Rose, 3 Burlington Arcade, Piccadilly, W1V 9AB TEL: 493 0714 FAX: 491 1051 NAG PARKING Medium OPEN: 9.30-5.45 MIN: £50 PERIOD: 19th-20th century SPECIALIST: Period & antique jewellery.

W Sitch & Co Ltd, 48 Berwick Street, W1V 4JD TEL: 437 3776 PARKING: Medium OPEN: Mon-Fri 9-5.30, Sat 9-1 PERIOD: 19th-20th century GENERAL: Late Victorian & Edwardian lighting, chandeliers, wall brackets, floor standards etc.

LONDON W1X (071)

Asprey, 165-169 New Bond Street, W1Y 0AR TEL: 493 6767 FAX: 491 0384 ASSNS: BADA PARKING: Medium OPEN: Mon-Fri 9-5.30, Sat 9-1 MIN: £60 MAX: £60,000 PERIOD: 17th-18th century SPECIALIST: Furniture, silver, clocks, glass, fabergé.

Raymond Bernadout, 18 Grosvenor Street, Mayfair, 355 4531 ASSNS: BADA TEL: 355 4531 PARKING: Easy OPEN: 9-5 MIN: £2,000 MAX: £100,000 PERIOD: 17th-20th century SPECIALIST: Quality not quantity, antique decorative carpets, rugs, tapestries, textiles OTHER INFO: Restoration, cleaning, valuations.

Burlington Gallery Ltd, 10 Burlington Gardens,

W1X 1LG TEL: 734 9228 FAX: 494 3770 PARKING: Difficult OPEN: Mon-Fri 9.30-5.3-, Sat 10-5 MIN: £30 MAX: £12,000 PERIOD: 18th-19th century SPECIALIST: Sporting prints, Cecil Aldin & other antique prints, Some watercolours especially Hugh Cushing OTHER INFO: Museum of Mankind next door, celebrated Columbian café.

Burlington Paintings Ltd, 12 Burlington Gardens, W1X 1LG TEL: 734 9984 FAX: 494 3770 ASSNS: BADA PARKING: Difficult OPEN: Mon-Fri 9.30-5.30, Sat 10-5 not bank holiday weekends MIN: £500 MAX: £50,000 PERIOD: 19th-20th century GENERAL: British & European oils.

Ermitage Ltd, 14 Hay Hill, W1X 7LJ TEL: 499 5459 FAX: 499 5459 PARKING: Medium OPEN: Mon-Fri 10-5 & by appt MIN: £100 MAX: £100,000 PERIOD: 17th-20th century SPECIALIST: Fabergé, Russian works of art, European silver.

Frost & Reed Fine Art, 16 Old Bond Street, W1X 3DB TEL: 629 2457 FAX: 499 0299 ASSNS: BADA, SLAD PARKING: Medium OPEN: Mon-Fri 9-5.30 MIN: £500 MAX: £350,000 SPECIALIST: 20th century artists: Dawson, Dyf, Penny, Sir A.J.Munnings, St Clair Davis, P. Smith GENERAL: 19th & 20th century British & European, especially sporting paintings & impressionists/post impressionist watercolours & drawings.

Deborah Gage (Works of Art) Ltd, 38 Old Bond Street, W1X 3AE TEL: 493 3249 FAX: 495 1352 ASSNS: Bond Street Assn PARKING: Difficult OPEN: Mon-Fri 9.30-5.30 MIN: £2,000 MAX: £100,000 SPECIALIST: 17th-18th century European decorative arts & paintings, 19th century & modern British paintings.

Hancocks & Co, 1 Burlington Gardens W1X 2HP TEL: 493 8904 FAX: 493 8905 ASSNS: BADA PARKING: Easy OPEN: 9.30-5.30 MIN: £50 MAX: £250,000 PERIOD: 17th-20th century SPECIALIST: Jewellery & silver OTHER INFO: Opposite Burlington Arcade.

Harvey & Gore, 4 Burlington Gardens, Old Bond Street, W1X 1LH TEL: 493 2714 FAX: 493 0324 ASSNS: BADA PARKING: Medium OPEN: 9.30-5 MIN: £250 MAX: £50,000 PERIOD: 18th-20th century SPECIALIST: Fine antique jewellery & silver.

W R Harvey & Co (Antiques) Ltd, 5 Old Bond Street, W1X 3TH TEL: 499 8385 495 0209 ASSNS: BADA PARKING: Medium OPEN: Mon-Sat 10-5.30 MIN: £250 MAX: £250,000 SPECIALIST: Fine English furniture 1675-1830 GENERAL: Furniture, clocks, barometers, engravings, pictures, mirrors, objet d'art OTHER INFO: Ideally set in centre of Mayfair between Sotheby's & Christie's.

John Jaffa (Antiques) Ltd, 13 Royal Arcade, 28 Old Bond Street, W1X 3HD TEL: 499 4228 FAX: 499 4228 PARKING: Medium OPEN: Mon-Fri 10-5.30 MIN: £50 MAX: £20,000 PERIOD: 18th-19th century SPECIALIST: English & Continental enamels, gold snuff boxes GENERAL: Objets de vertu, fine silver OTHER INFO: Opposite Brown's Hotel on Albermarle Street running through to Old Bond Street.

Kennedy Carpets, 9a Vigo Street, W1X 1AL TEL: 439 8873 FAX: 437 1201 ASSNS: LAPADA PARKING: Medium OPEN: Mon-Sat 9.30-6 MIN: £250 MAX: £150,000 PERIOD: 19th-20th century SPECIALIST: Decorative carpets GENERAL: Antique & collectable carpets, kilims & rugs OTHER INFO: Les Madeleines Brasserie opposite.

Meltons, 27 Bruton Place, W1X 7AB TEL: 629 3612 FAX: 495 3196 PARKING: Easy OPEN: 9-5.30 by appt MIN: £100 MAX: £15,000 PERIOD: 19th century SPECIALIST: Unusual, decorative GENERAL: Smalls, porcelain, terracotta, upholstered OTHER INFO: Opposite excellent Guinea Grill.

Portal Gallery, 16a Grafton Street/Bond Street, W1X 3LF TEL: 493 0706 FAX: 629 3506 PARKING: Medium OPEN: Mon-Fri 10-5.30, Sat 10-1 MIN: £50 MAX: £2,000 PERIOD: 17th-19th century SPECIALIST: Idiosynchratic objects GENERAL: Victorian fly catchers & optical testing instruments to biscuit tins, assortment of Vestas, money boxes, treen OTHER INFO: Selection of objet tatzkas.

Henry Sotheran Ltd, 2-5 Sackville Street, Piccadilly, W1X 2DP TEL: 439 6151 ASSNS: ABA, ILAB, PBFA PARKING: Medium OPEN: Mon-Fri 9.30-6, Sat 10-4 MIN: £5 MAX: £25,000 PERIOD: 17th-20th century SPECIALIST: Antiquarian books, prints, library furniture OTHER INFO: In heart of Mayfair's prestigious shopping area, close all Bond Street's fine antique dealers.

LONDON W1Y (071)

Gregg Baker Oriental Art, 34 Brook Street, W1Y 1YA TEL: 629 7926 FAX: 495 3872 ASSNS: BADA, LAPADA PARKING: Medium OPEN: Mon-Fri 10-6 & by appt MIN: £500 MAX: £100.000 PERIOD: 17th-19th century SPECIALIST: Japanese & Chinese works of art GENERAL: Paper screens, bronzes & carvings in many materials.

Bond Street Antiques Centre, 124 New Bond Street TEL: 351 5353 FAX: 351 5350 PARKING: Medium OPEN: Mon-Fri 10-5.45 MIN: £100 MAX: £250,000 PERIOD: 19th-20th century SPECIALIST: Antique jewellery & silver GENERAL: Watches, porcelain, glass, Oriental antiques, portrait miniatures & paintings OTHER INFO: Tubes: Bond Street/Green Park.

Charles Ede Ltd, 20 Brook Street, W1Y 1AD TEL: 493 4944 FAX: 491 2548 ASSNS: IADAA, CINOA PARKING: Medium OPEN: Tues-Fri 12.30-4.30 & by appt MIN: £50 MAX: £100,000 GENERAL: Greek, Roman, Egyptian & Near Eastern antiquities 5000 BC-600 AD OTHER INFO: Claridges 50 yds.

Grays Antique Market, 58 Davies Street, W1Y 1LB TEL: 629 7034 FAX: 493 9344 PARKING: Difficult OPEN: Mon-Fri 10-6 MIN: £1 MAX: £30,000 PERIOD: 17th-20th century SPECIALIST: Antique jewellery, medical instruments, commemorative china, prints, silver, Oriental GENERAL: Clocks, watches, furniture, glass, lace, majolica, militaria, sporting collectables OTHER INFO: Basement café. Heart of West

End shopping area & close to Philips, Sotheby's.

Grays in the Mews, 1-7 Davies Mews, W1Y 1AR TEL: 629 7034 FAX: 493 9344 PARKING: Difficult OPEN: Mon-Fri 10-6 MIN: £1 MAX: £30,000 PERIOD: 17th-20th century SPECIALIST: Toys, ancient art, antiquities, jewellery, chess books, medical instruments, clocks & watches, coins, glass, golfiana, militaria, Oriental ceramics, Persian art, toys OTHER INFO: Basement café & bureau de change.

Hadji Baba Ancient Art, 34a Davies Street, W1Y 1LD TEL: 499 9363 FAX: 493 5504 ASSNS: ADA, IADA PARKING: Difficult OPEN: 10-5 MIN: £200 MAX: thousands PERIOD: 2nd millenium BC-19th century AD SPECIALIST: Antiquities-Egyptian, pre-Islamic, Persia, Islamic, Near Eastern OTHER INFO: Parallel to Bond Street & close to Claridges Hotel.

Howard Antiques, 8 Davies Street, Berkeley Square TEL: 629 2628 PARKING: Easy OPEN: 10-6 MIN: £250 PERIOD: 18th-19th century SPECIALIST: English & Continental furniture GENERAL: Period ornaments, vases, candlesticks, chandeliers, objets d'art etc OTHER INFO: Between Claridges and Connaught hotels.

Mayfair Carpets Gallery Ltd, 41 New Bond Street, W1Y 0HB TEL: 493 0126 FAX: 408 2496 PARKING: Easy OPEN: 9.30-6 MIN: £59 MAX: £250,000 PERIOD: 19th-20th century SPECIALIST: Very rare antique Persian & Turkish silk & wool carpets & rugs.

Mayfair Carpets Gallery Ltd, 47 Conduit Street, TEL: 493 0126 FAX: 408 2496 PARKING: Easy OPEN: 9.30-6 MIN: £59 MAX: £250,000 PERIOD: 19th-20th century SPECIALIST: Very rare antique Persian & Turkish silk & wool carpets & rugs.

Mayfair Gallery, 36 Davies Street, W1Y 1LG TEL: 491 3435 FAX: 491 3437 PARKING: Medium OPEN: 10-6 MIN: £500 MAX: £10,000 PERIOD: 19th-20th century SPECIALIST: French porcelain & furniture GENERAL: Antiques & decorative arts.

Mayfair Gallery, 37 South Audley Street, W1Y 5DH TEL: 491 3436 FAX: 491 3437 PARKING: Medium OPEN: 10-6 MIN: £500 MAX: £10,000 PERIOD: 19th-20th century SPECIALIST:

French porcelain & furniture GENERAL: Antiques & decorative arts.

Nicholas S Pitcher Oriental Art, 1st Floor, 29 New Bond Street, W1Y 9HD TEL: 499 6621 FAX: 491 1662 PARKING: Medium OPEN: 10-5 & by appt (advisable to ring anyway) MIN: £100 MAX: £10,000 PERIOD: 17th-18th century and much earlier SPECIALIST: Early Chinese pottery & porcelain GENERAL: Chinese & Japanese works of art OTHER INFO: Buys at auction & in Far East.

Robin Kennedy, 29 New Bond Street, W1Y 9HD TEL: 4081238 FAX: 491 1662 PARKING: Medium OPEN: Mon-Fri 10-6 MIN: £50 MAX: £5,000 PERIOD: 18th-20th century SPECIALIST: Fine Japanese prints OTHER INFO: 30 yds from Sotheby's.

Jonathan Potter Ltd, 125 New Bond Street, W1Y 9AF TEL: 491 3520 FAX: 491 9754 ASSNS: ABA, BADA, LAPADA PARKING: Medium OPEN: Weekdays 10-6 & by appt MIN: £50 MAX: £10,000 PERIOD: 15th-19th century SPECIALIST: Original antique British & worldwide maps.

Jonathan Robinson, 1st Floor, 29 New Bond Street, W1Y 9HD TEL: 493 0592 FAX: 491 1662 PARKING: Medium OPEN: 10-5 MIN: £40 MAX: £10,000 PERIOD: 17th-20th century and much earlier SPECIALIST: Chinese porcelain GENERAL: Oriental works of art OTHER INFO: 4 doors from Sotheby's. On 1st floor so ring bell.

Toynbee-Clarke Interiors Ltd, 95 Mount Street, W1Y 5HG TEL: 499 4472/3 FAX: 495 1204 PARKING: Meters OPEN: Mon-Fri 9.30-5.30 MIN: £1,000 MAX: £100,000 PERIOD:

18th-early 19th century SPECIALIST: Chinese export wallpaper GENERAL: Decorative Continental furniture, works of art & paintings OTHER INFO: Between Grosvenor & Connaught hotels, opposite Scotts restaurant.

PORTOBELLO RD TO CHURCH ST NW8 LONDON W2 (071)

John Bonham, Murray Feely Fine Art, 46 Porchester Road, W2 6ET TEL: 221 7208 FAX: 589 0655 PARKING: Easy OPEN: 10.30-5.30 or by appt MIN: £100+ MAX: £50,000 PERIOD: 18th-20th century SPECIALIST: British & Continental surrealism.

Ruby Buckle Antique Fireplaces, 18 Chepstow Corner, Pembridge Villas, W2 4XE TEL: 229 8843 PARKING: Medium OPEN: 10-6 PERIOD: 19th century GENERAL: Pine, marble & stone fireplaces.

Hosain's Books & Antiques, 25 Connaught Street, W2 2AJ TEL: 262 7900 FAX: 402 2119 PARKING: Medium OPEN: Tues-Fri 11-5 MIN: £25 MAX: £3,000 PERIOD: 17th-20th century SPECIALIST: Rare books, pictures & manuscripts on India, Central Asia, Islamic World OTHER INFO: Manuscript pre 17th century. Near several picture galleries.

Mark Gallery, 9 Porchester Place, Marble Arch, W2 2BS TEL: 262 4906 FAX: 224 9416 ASSNS: BADA, CINOA PARKING: Easy OPEN: Mon-Fri 10-1, 2-6, Sat 11-1 SPECIALIST: 16th-19th century Russian icons GENERAL: Modern prints from the French school, contemporary.

LONDON W8 (071)

Valerie Arieta, 97b Kensington Church Street, W8 7LN TEL: 243 1074 PARKING: Medium OPEN: 10.30-5.30 MIN: £20 MAX: £8,000 PERIOD: 19th century SPECIALIST: North American Indian & Eskimo art GENERAL: Paintings, folk art, curiosities.

Garry Atkins, 107 Kensington Church Street, W8 7LN TEL: 727 8737 PARKING: Medium OPEN: 10-5.30 MIN: £100 MAX: £5,000 PERIOD: 17th-18th century SPECIALIST: English & continental pottery.

Eddy Bardawil Antiques, 106 Kensington Church Street, W8 7LN TEL: 221 3967 FAX: 221 5124 ASSNS: BADA PARKING: Easy OPEN: Mon-Fri 9.30-5.30, Sat 10-1 MIN: £500 MAX: £25,000 PERIOD: 18th-early 19th century GENERAL: Furniture & works of art.

Baumkotter Gallery, 63a Kensington Church Street, W8 4BA TEL: 937 5171 FAX: 938 2312 ASSNS: LAPADA PARKING: Easy OPEN: Mon-Fri 9.30-6 MIN: £300 MAX: £60,000 PERIOD: half 17th, 10% 18th & 40% 19th century SPECIALIST: Oil paintings.

David Brower Antiques, 113 Kensington Church Street, W8 7LN TEL: 221 4155 FAX: 221 6211 PARKING: Medium OPEN: Mon-Fri 10-6 MIN: £200 MAX: £10,000 PERIOD: 19th century SPECIALIST: Continental, Oriental, English porcelain & bronzes.

H W Deutsch, 111 Kensington Church Street, W8 7LN TEL: 727 5984 ASSNS: LAPADA PARKING: Medium OPEN: Mon, Thurs, Fri PERIOD: 18th-19th century SPECIALIST: Silver GENERAL: Porcelain, objets d'art.

Geoffrey Godden Chinaman, 1st Floor, (access through Klaber & Klaber shop), 2a Bedford Gardens, Kensington Church Street, W8 7EH TEL: 727 4573 ASSNS: BADA PARKING: Medium OPEN: Mon-Fri 10-1, 2-5, Sat 10.30-4 MIN: £50 MAX: £500 PERIOD: 19th century SPECIALIST: English Ceramics OTHER INFO: World authority on English ceramics (many reference books).

Graham & Oxley (Antiques) Ltd, 101 Kensington Church Street, W8 7LN TEL: 229 1850 FAX: 792 3348 ASSNS: BADA PARKING: Medium OPEN: 10-5.30 MIN: £100 MAX: £25,000 PERIOD: 18th-19th century SPECIALIST: English porcelain & engravings GENERAL: Decorative accessories.

Robert Hales Antiques Ltd, 131 Kensington Church Street, W8 7LP TEL: 229 3887 PARKING: Medium OPEN: Tues-Fri 9.30-5.30 MIN: £100 MAX: £50,000+ PERIOD: 17-19th century and earlier SPECIALIST: Oriental, Islamic, tribal arms & armour.

Jeanette Hayhurst Fine Glass, 32a Kensington Church Street, W8 4HQ TEL: 938 1539 PARKING: Medium OPEN: Mon-Fri 10-5, Sats 12-5 MIN: £10 MAX: £5,000 SPECIALIST: 18th-20th century glass, contemporary art glass.

Hope & Glory, 131a Kensington Church Street, W8 7LP TEL: 727 8424 PARKING: Medium OPEN: Tues-Fri 10-5, Sat 10-2 MIN: £5 MAX: £500 PERIOD: 19th-20th century SPECIALIST:

Commemorative items mainly ceramics.

Iona Antiques, P.O. Box 285, W8 6HZ TEL: 602 1193 FAX: 371 2843 ASSNS: BADA PARKING: Medium OPEN: Anytime by appt MIN: £1,000 MAX: £20,000 SPECIALIST: 19th century paintings of animals.

Jonathan Horne Antiques Ltd, 66c Kensington Church Street, W8 4BY TEL: 221 5658 FAX: 792 3092 ASSNS: BADA PARKING: Medium OPEN: 9.30-5.30 MIN: £45 MAX: £30,000 PERIOD: 13th-19th century SPECIALIST: Fine English pottery.

Japanese Gallery, 66d Kensington Church Street, W8 4BY TEL: 229 2934 PARKING: Medium OPEN: 10-6 MIN: £5 MAX: £10,000 PERIOD: 19th-20th century SPECIALIST: Japanese woodcut prints GENERAL: Japanese arts, screens & furniture.

John Jesse, (estd 1963), 160 Kensington Church Street, W8 4BN TEL: 229 0312 FAX: 229 4732 PARKING: Easy OPEN: 10-6 MIN: £50+ PERIOD: 1880-1980 SPECIALIST: Art Nouveau, Deco objets, furniture GENERAL: Silver, glass, jewellery, lamps, paintings, ceramics & posters OTHER INFO: Near one of London's best restaurants, Kensington Place.

Peter Kemp Antiques, 170 Kensington Church Street, W8 4BN TEL: 229 2988 FAX: 229 2988 PARKING: Difficult OPEN: 10-5 MIN: £200 MAX: £250,000 PERIOD: 17th-18th century SPECIALIST: Oriental & Continental ceramics.

Kensington Fine Arts, 46 Kensington Church Street, W8 4BY TEL: 937 5317 PARKING: Medium OPEN: 10-5.30 MIN: £600 MAX: unlimited SPECIALIST: 17th century to Victorian. Restoration.

Klaber & Klaber Antique Porcelain, 2a Bedford Gardens, Kensington Church Street, W8 7EH TEL: 727 4573 PARKING: Easy OPEN: 10-1, 2-5 MIN: £50 MAX: £25,000 SECIALIST: 18th century English & Continental porcelain & enamels.

Lev Antiques, 97a Kensington Church Street, W8 7LN TEL: 727 9248 PARKING: Medium OPEN: 10.30-5.30 MIN: £5 MAX: £500 PERIOD: 18th-20th century SPECIALIST: Jewellery, silver GENERAL: Paintings, curios.

Little Winchester Gallery, 36a Kensington Church Street, W8 4BX TEL: 937 8444 PARK-

ING: Easy OPEN: 11-6 MIN: £500 MAX: £35,000 SPECIALIST: French 19th-20th GENERAL: Dutch 19th century, English primitives.

London Gallery, 66 Kensington Church Street, W8 4BY TEL: 792 2166 FAX: 938 3056 PARKING: Easy OPEN: 10-6 MIN: £2 MAX: £2,000 PERIOD: 19th-20th century SPECIALIST: London Oriental arts GENERAL: Ceramics, pottery, prints, glass OTHER INFO: Excellent B&B around corner, Vicarage Gardens. Close to Kensington Palace.

E & H Manners, 66a Kensington Church Street, W8 4BY TEL: 229 5516 FAX: 229 5516 PARKING: Medium OPEN: Mon-Fri 10-5.30 MIN: £100 MAX: £20,000 PERIOD: 18th century SPECIALIST: European porcelain.

Michael Coins, 6 Hillgate Street, W8 7SR TEL: 727 1518 PARKING: Medium OPEN: Mon-Fri 10-5 PERIOD: 17th-20th century GENERAL: Coins, banknotes, stamps etc.

Roderick Antiques - Clocks, 23 Vicarage Gate (junction Kensington Church Street), W8 4AA TEL: 937 8517 FAX: 937 8517 ASSNS: LAPADA PARKING: Medium OPEN: 10-5 MIN: £200 MAX: £5,000 PERIOD: 18th-19th century SPECIALIST: 200+ longcase, carriage, bracket, skeleton & decorative clocks OTHER INFO: All stock fully restored & guaranteed. Export arranged.

Constance Stobo, 31 Holland Street, W8 4NA TEL: 937 6282 PARKING: Medium open; Mon-Fri 11-5, Sat 10-2 MIN: £80 MAX: £3,500 PERIOD: 18th-19th century SPECIALIST: English Lustreware, Staffordshire animals.

RODERICK ANTIQUES
CLOCKS

23 VICARAGE GATE, LONDON W8 4AA
(Junction Kensington Church Street) Tel: 071 937 8517

OVER 200 ANTIQUE CLOCKS IN STOCK
INCLUDING: LONGCASE, CARRIAGE,
BRACKET, SKELETON AND
DECORATIVE FRENCH CLOCKS
ON TWO FLOORS

Stockspring Antiques, 114 Kensington Church Street, W8 4BH TEL: 727 7995 FAX: 727 7995 ASSNS: LAPADA PARKING: Medium OPEN: Mon-Fri 10-5.30, Sat 10-1 MIN: £5 MAX: £5,000 PERIOD: 18th century SPECIALIST: English porcelain figures, Liverpool porcelain, pre 1830 English porcelain, Oriental porcelain GENERAL: World's main antique porcelain street.

Pamela Teignmouth & Son, 108 Kensington Church Street, W8 4BH TEL: 229 1602 FAX: 229 1602 PARKING: Medium-meters OPEN: 10-6 MIN: £30 MAX: £7,500 PERIOD: 18th-19th century SPECIALIST: Decorative furniture GENERAL: English & Continental furniture & decorative objects.

Mary Wise & Grosvenor Antiques Ltd, 27 Holland Street TEL: 937 8649 PARKING: Medium OPEN: Mon-Fri 9.30-5.30 MIN: £100 MAX: £5,000 PERIOD: 18th-19th century SPECIALIST: Chinese watercolours GENERAL: Bronzes, porcelain, works of art.

LONDON W11 (071)

Arbras Gallery, 292 Westbourne Grove, W11 2PS TEL: 226 5221 FAX: 226 5221 ASSNS: PADA PARKING: Difficult OPEN: Fri 10-4, Sat 7-4.30 & by appt MIN: £20 MAX: £5,000 PERIOD: 19th-20th century SPECIALIST: Silver, decorative arts GENERAL: Fine antique boxes, objects, pictures, prints, antique linens, books OTHER INFO: On site Britain's largest wholesaler of modern silver photograph frames.

P R Barham Antiques, 111 Portobello Road, W11 2QB TEL: 727 3397 FAX: 243 1719 ASSNS: LAPADA PARKING: Easy OPEN: Mon-Sat 9-5 MIN: £50+ MAX: £15,000 PERIOD: 18th-20th century SPECIALIST: Fine Victorian furniture & clocks GENERAL: Good Continental furniture, French, Dutch, paintings & decorative items.

Barham Antiques, 83 Portobello Road, W11 2QB TEL: 727 3845 FAX: 727 3845 PARKING: Easy OPEN: 10-5 MIN: £10 MAX: £6,000 PERIOD: 19th century SPECIALIST: Boxes, inkwells, glass, tea caddies, Victoriana.

Books & Things, at Arbras Gallery, 292 Westbourne Grove, W11 2PS TEL: 370 5593 FAX: 370 5593 ASSNS: ABA, PBFA PARKING: Difficult OPEN: Sat only 7-4 MIN: £5

MAX: £2,000 PERIOD: 19th-20th century SPECIALIST: Posters & photography GENERAL: Books: childrens illustrated, decorative art, modern 1st editions OTHER INFO: Good bistro next door.

F E A Briggs/Wellington Antiques, 73 Ledbury Road, W11 2AG TEL: 727 0909 PARKING: Medium OPEN: 8.30-5.30 MIN: £150+ MAX: £6,000 PERIOD: 19th century SPECIALIST: Mainly Victorian but some 18th and Edwardian furniture OTHER INFO: Warehouse & 2 shops. Interesting new pub, Beach Blanket Babylon.

Butchoff Antiques, 229 & 233 Westbourne Grove, W11 2SE TEL: 221 8174 FAX: 792 8923 ASSNS: LAPADA PARKING: Easy OPEN: Mon-Fri 10-6, Sat 10-4 MIN: £1,000 MAX: £30,000 PERIOD: 17th-19th century SPECIALIST: Dutch marquetry, satinwood furniture GENERAL: Quality English & Continental furniture.

Jack Casimir Ltd, 23 Pembridge Road, W11 3HG TEL: 727 8643 ASSNS: BADA, LAPADA PARKING: Medium OPEN: Mon-Sat 9.30-5.30 & by appt SPECIALIST: 16th-19th century brass, copper & pewter OTHER INFO: Fourth generation family business.

Sheila Cook Textiles, 184 Westbourne Grove, W11 2RH TEL: 792 8001 PARKING: Medium OPEN: Tues-Sat 10-6 MIN: £1 MAX: £5,000 PERIOD: 18th-20th century SPECIALIST: Textiles GENERAL: Decorative antiques.

John Dale Antiques, 87 Portobello Road, W11 2QB TEL: 727 1304 ASSNS: PADA PARKING: Difficult on Sats OPEN: Mon-Fri 10-4, Sat 7-5 MIN: £5 MAX: £1,500 PERIOD: 17th-19th century SPECIALIST: Stained glass, antiquities, toys, cameras, golf collectables GENERAL: Furniture, paintings & prints.

Peter Delehar & His Three Sisters, 146 Portobello Road, W11 2DZ TEL: (081) 866 8659 PARKING: Difficult OPEN: Sat 9-4 MIN: £50 MAX: £5,000 PERIOD: 15th-20th century SPECIALIST: Scientific & medical instruments GENERAL: Fine bijouterie, textiles, objects, ephemera, costume jewellery OTHER INFO: Organizer of world's largest scientific & instrument (& related books etc) fair.

The Facade, 196 Westbourne Grove, W11 2RH TEL: 727 2159 PARKING: Medium OPEN:

Tues-Sat 10.30-5 MIN: £1 MAX: £5,000 PERIOD: 19th-20th century SPECIALIST: French lighting & decorative furniture.

Fleur de Lys Gallery, 227a Westbourne Grove, W11 2SE TEL: 727 8595 PARKING: Easy OPEN: Mon-Sat 10.30-5 MIN: £1,000 MAX: £5,000 PERIOD: 19th century SPECIALIST: All decorative oil paintings of Dutch, English, European schools.

J Freeman, 85a Portobello Road, W11 2QB TEL: 221 5076 FAX: 221 5329 PARKING: Medium OPEN: 9-5 MIN: £5 MAX: £3,000 PERIOD: 19th-20th century SPECIALIST: Silver + plate, canteens of cutlery.

Garrick Coleman Antiques, Stand II, Van's Arcade, 105 Portobello Road, W11 2QR TEL: 937 5524 PARKING: Difficult OPEN: Sat 8-2 & by appt MIN: £50 MAX: £5,000 PERIOD: 17th-19th century SPECIALIST: Fine chess sets & boards, glass paperweights, works of art & decorative arts.

Patricia Harbottle, Stand 16, Geoffrey Van's Arcade, 107 Portobello Road, W11 2QR TEL: 731 1972 ASSNS: PADA PARKING: Difficult OPEN: Sat 6.45-3 MIN: £5 MAX: £1,500 PERIOD: 18th-19th century SPECIALIST: Wine-related antiques.

Hirst Antiques, 59 Pembridge Road, W11 3HN TEL: 727 9364 PARKING: Difficult OPEN: 10-6 MIN: £2 MAX: £10,000 PERIOD: 17th-20th century SPECIALIST: Fourposter & half tester beds GENERAL: Sculpture, bronzes, decorative items.

Jones Antique Lighting, 194 Westbourne Grove, W11 2RS TEL: 229 6866 FAX: 229 6866 PARKING: Medium OPEN: 6 days 9.30-6 MIN: £15 MAX: £5,000 SPECIALIST: All forms of antique lighting GENERAL: 5,000 original lamps 1860-1960.

Peter Kennedy, 1st Floor, 305 Westbourne Grove, W11 2QA TEL: 243 1416 FAX: 243 2271 ASSNS: ABA PARKING: Easy OPEN: By appt MIN: £10 MAX: £2,000 PERIOD: 17th-19th century SPECIALIST: Prints & books (illustrated only).

Kleanthus Antiques Ltd, Stouts Antiques Market, 144 Portobello Road, W11 2DZ TEL: 727 3649 FAX: (081) 980 1199 , (0923) 897618 ASSNS: LAPADA, PADA PARKING: Difficult

OPEN: Sat 6.30-4 PERIOD: 18th-20th century SPECIALIST: Vintage wrist & pocket watches (Rolex, Cartier etc), Georgian, Victorian, Art Nouveau/Deco jewellery, silver, clocks, objets de vertu OTHER INFO: Guarantees with all purchases.

Magus Antiques, 187 Westbourne Grove, W11 2RS TEL: 229 0267 ASSNS: LAPADA PARKING: Easy OPEN: Mon-Sat 10-5.30 MIN: £25 MAX: £7,500 PERIOD: 18th-19th century GENERAL: Decorative items & collectables, works of art.

Daniel Mankowitz, 208a Westbourne Grove, W11 2RH TEL: 229 9270 FAX: 229 4687 PARKING: Easy OPEN: 10-6 MIN: £50+ MAX: £15,000 PERIOD: 17th-18th century SPECIALIST: Early & unusual furniture, sculptures, paintings, textiles, & decoratives.

Robin Martin Antiques, 44 Ledbury Road TEL: 727 1301 PARKING: Easy OPEN: 10-5.30 MIN: £200 MAX: £15,000 PERIOD: 17th-19th century GENERAL: English & Continental furniture, works of art.

Mercury Antiques, 1 Ladbroke Road, W11 3PA TEL: 727 5106 ASSNS: BADA PARKING: Medium OPEN: Mon-Sat 10-5.30 PERIOD: 18th-19th century SPECIALIST: English porcelain & pottery, Delft, glass.

Myriad Antiques, 131 Portland Road, Holland Park Avenue TEL: 229 1709 Parking Easy OPEN: Mon-Sat 11-6 MIN: £5 MAX: £1,500 PERIOD: 18th-20th century SPECIALIST: Decorative unusual items including garden furniture, kitchen, bathrooms, beds OTHER INFO: 2 amusing & delectable restaurants.

Peter Petrou, 195 Westbourne Grove, W11 2SB TEL: 229 9575 FAX: 229 9575 PARKING: Medium OPEN: 10-6 MIN: £100 MAX: £50,000 PERIOD: 17th-20th century SPECIALIST: Vienna bronzes, Blue John, sculpture GENERAL: Works of art, Oriental & European bronzes, antiquities, ethnographica, good decorative items OTHER INFO: Palio restaurant.

Rogers Antiques Gallery, 65 Portobello Road TEL: 351 5353 FAX: 351 5350 PARKING: Medium OPEN: Sat 7-4 MIN: £5 MAX: £5,000 PERIOD: 18th-20th century GENERAL: Good jewellery & silver OTHER INFO: Since 1974 first & longest Portobello Road gallery with own café serving quality homemade food.

Louis Stanton, 299-301 Westbourne Grove, W11 2QA TEL: 727 9336 FAX: 727 5424 ASSNS: BADA, CINOA PARKING: Easy OPEN: 6 days 10-5.30 MIN: £100 MAX: £20,000 SPECIALIST: Early oak furniture 1550-1700 GENERAL: Objects pre1840 OTHER INFO: Wonderful ethnic restaurants.

Stern Art Dealers, 46 Ledbury Road, W11 2HB TEL: 229 6187 FAX: 229 6187 ASSNS: LAPADA PARKING: Easy OPEN: 10-6 MIN: £300 MAX: £7,000 SPECIALIST: Paintings by Pissaro family GENERAL: 19th century & early 20th century British post-impressionist.

Themes & Variations, 231 Westbourne Grove, W11 2SE TEL: 727 5531 FAX: 221 6378 OPEN: 10-1, 2-6 SPECIALIST: Exclusive Fornasetti furniture, 1940-70's furniture, Murano glass & Italian ceramics 1950-60's, contemporary designers.

Wynard Wilkinson Antique Silver, 165-169 Portobello Road TEL: 229 0539 FAX:L 229 3506 PARKING: Medium OPEN: Sat 7-3.30 MIN: £5 MAX: £50,000 PERIOD: 17th-20th century SPECIALIST: Collectors silver, colonial & provincial GENERAL: Table silver + plate OTHER INFO: Green painted stall, T.F. Wilkinson always wears green baize apron.

LONDON NW8 (071)

Alfies Antique Market, 13-25 Church Street, NW8 8DT TEL: 723 6066 FAX: 724 0999 PARKING: Easy OPEN: 10-6 MIN: £5 MAX: £5,000 PERIOD: 18th-20th century GENERAL: Whole spectrum of antiques & collectables

OTHER INFO: 200 dealers with 370 stands, England's largest covered antique market with rooftop restaurant.

Beverley, 30 Church Street, Marylebone, NW8 TEL: 262 1546 PARKING: Medium OPEN: Mon-thurs 11-7, Fri-Sat 9.30-7 MIN: £5 MAX:£7,000 PERIOD: 19th-20th century SPECIALIST: Clarice Cliff, Suzie Cooper, Art Deco GENERAL: 1850-1950 ceramics, metals, glass OTHER INFO: Seashell restaurant (London's famous fish & chips).

J. Nicholas Drummond, 6 St Johns Wood Road, NW8 8RG TEL: 286 6452 FAX: 286 6452 PARKING: Medium OPEN: By appt MIN: £200 MAX: £40,000 PERIOD: 19th-20th century SPECIALIST: Continental, American, British oils GENERAL: 19th century paintings supplied to the trade, decorators, hotels etc OTHER INFO: Lords Cricket Ground.

Patricia Harvey Antiques, 42 Church Street, NW8 8EP TEL:262 8989 FAX: 262 9090 PARKING: Easy OPEN: Mon-Fri 10-6, Sat 12-5 MIN: £50 MAX: £5,000 PERIOD: 17th-20th century SPECIALIST: Decorator's accessories, textiles, beautiful and unusual items GENERAL: Primitive watercolours, paintings, decorative furniture OTHER INFO: Established antiques area, plenty of trade, 3 cafés.

Lenson-Smith, 11 Church Road, Lisson Grove, NW8 8EE TEL: 724 7763 PARKING: Medium OPEN: 10-5 MIN: £50 MAX: £5,000 PERIOD: 19th-20th century SPECIALIST: Animalia GENERAL: Decorative, interesting items.

Kent and South East Sussex

This tour starts and finishes in the south east outer suburbs of Greater London, passes through the industrial landscape of North Kent and the Thames Estuary, continues on to Canterbury, takes in three of the historic Cinque Ports, Rye, Sandwich and Hythe, and finally goes through the beautiful gentle countryside of western Kent.

After first stopping in the pleasant town of Beckenham the route continues to Chislehurst which, in spite of being on the edge of the metropolis, still retains the appearance of a rural village. It is famous for its underground chalk galleries, the Chislehurst Caves, and for its association with Napoleon III and the Empress Eugenie who lived at Camden House. There is a memorial on the large wooded common to their son who died in in the British war against the Zulus.

Proceeding onwards via Orpington and Northfleet to Rochester, the route eventually takes the A2 which was once the Roman road of Watling Street. Rochester was a Roman town, situated where Watling Street crosses the River Medway. It has a medieval castle following the lines of the earlier Roman fortress which, because of the extreme strategic importance of the site, was one of the first to be consructed. Rochester's cathedral attracted enough pilgrims for present day visitors to see the steps worn down by their feet. Henry VIII first met Anne of Cleves, The Flanders Mare, at the Old Hall in the town. She was one of his luckier wives - she was only divorced. Lovers of Charles Dickens will find interest in Rochester as it was a setting in *Great Expectations* and he lived at Gads Hill from 1857 to 1870. At Eastgate House, in the High Street, there is the Charles Dickens Centre which recreates Victorian life for the visitor.

After first stopping in Cuxton we next arrive in Chatham, the famous naval shipyard town. The Medway Heritage Centre there is well worth a visit. It tells the story of the Medway from earliest times to the present day. In 1765 the Victory, Nelson's ship at Trafalgar, was launched at Chatham. In the Chatham Historic Dockyard there are 47 Scheduled Ancient Monuments, mainly from the 18th century. This is said to form the most complete surviving early to mid 18th century dockyard in the country. There are eight museum galleries covering 400 years of shipbuilding history. The award winning "Wooden Walls" display recreates the building of a wooden warship in the mid 18th century. The Royal Engineers Museum displays examples of military engineering starting with an assault bridge built by Julius Caesar. General Gordon of Khartoum, the most renowned Royal Engineer, is commemorated here.

From Chatham the route detours across the M2 to the small town of Hollingbourne with its many fine historic buildings. Close by is the spectacular Leeds Castle which was for centuries a royal castle and given to the wives of the kings of England. We also visit the village of Harrietsham with its 18th century

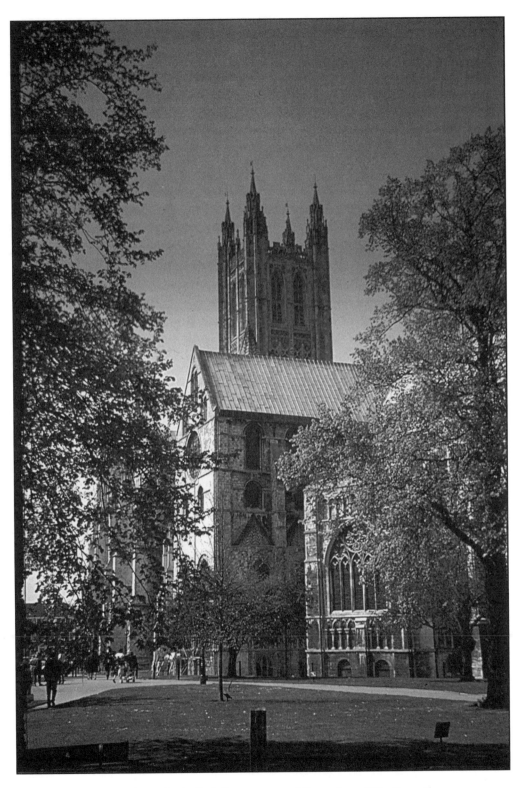

Canterbury Cathedral. By courtesy of Canterbury City Council

Kent and South East Sussex

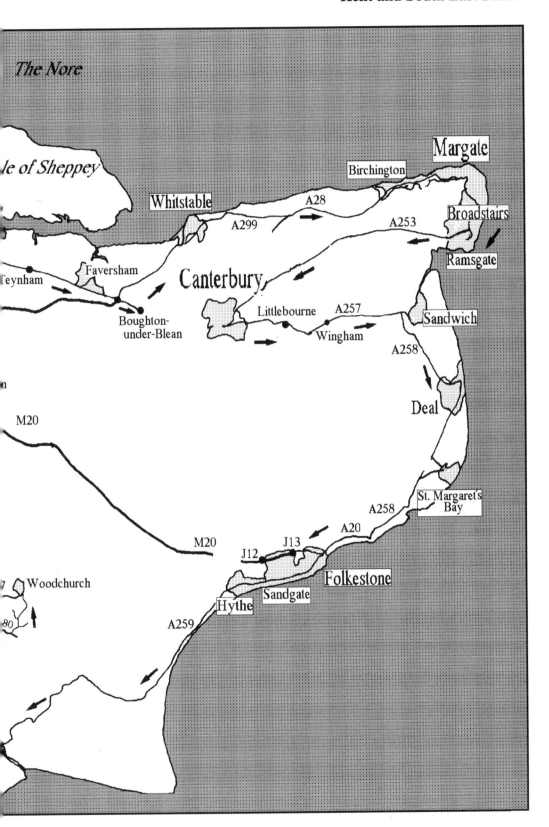

The Nore

le of Sheppey

Whitstable

Birchington

A28

A299

A253

Margate

Broadstairs

Teynham

Faversham

Canterbury

Ramsgate

Boughton-under-Blean

Littlebourne

A257

Wingham

Sandwich

A258

M20

Deal

St. Margaret's Bay

A258

A20

M20

J12

J13

Woodchurch

80

Folkestone

Sandgate

Hythe

A259

almshouses before returning to the A2.

The tour now passes through the picturesque village of Teynham, a fruit growing centre since the days of Henry VIII, before reaching the market town of
Faversham. Once a flourishing port the town contains many buildings of note. At
the Fleur de Lys Heritage Centre in Preston Street there are audio-visual displays
covering a 1000 years of the town's history and giving information on the town's
400 listed buildings. It is housed in an old inn where, in 1540, an infamous murder was plotted. Thomas Arden was murdered by his wife and this later became
the subject of the play *Arden of Faversham.*

Now we turn towards the Thames estuary and the resort of Whitstable, famous
for its oysters. The Whitstable to Canterbury railway line was the first passenger
line in the country and the town has one of the oldest railway bridges, built in
1834.

Continuing along the A299 the route passes through Birchington, a quiet seaside resort where the grave of Dante Gabriel Rossetti may be seen in the churchyard. Quex House, a Georgian mansion in the town, is also well worth a visit.
Altered during Victorian times, the house is very much a tribute to Major Percy
Powell-Cotton who was born in 1866 and died in 1940. During his numerous
visits to Africa, Major Powell-Cotton assembled one of the finest collections of
African ethnography in the world. He also created great dioramas using some
500 African and Asian animals. Additionally, the Major gathered a unique collection of Chinese Imperial porcelain as well as a good collection of English and
Continental porcelain now housed in the adjoining purpose-built museum.

Margate, once an important port, is the next stop on this route. Nowadays it is
principally known as a seaside resort and has all the attractions expected. Continuing along the coast we arrive in Broadstairs where Dickens wrote *David
Copperfield* in a house he rented for the summer and which was the original
Bleak House. Part of the building is now a Dickens Museum and in Victoria
Place stands the Dickens House Museum with rooms furnished in Dickensian
style.

Now the route turns inland to Canterbury which was a Roman administrative
centre although there had been a settlement here since prehistoric times. The
present city walls follow those originally built by the Romans, even the gates
correspond to the Roman ones. In AD597 St Augustine landed in Kent and built
a priory on the site of the present cathedral precincts. He also built an abbey
outside the city walls where he was buried as were other early archbishops. This
abbey was torn down in the reign of Henry VIII during the Dissolution of the
Monasteries and now only the ruins can be seen.

The Cathedral is the city's major attraction. There has been a cathedral on the
site since Saxon times and it has long been the main church of English Christians.
The Archbishops of Canterbury were usually extremely powerful and often coun-

Weavers, Canterbury. By courtesy of Canterbury City Council

sellors to kings. The stories attached to it are many. Amongst the most famous is the murder in December 1170 of Thomas à Becket, Archbishop of Canterbury. Becket had long been a favourite of Henry II but then they quarrelled over the legal privileges of the clergy. Four of Henry's knights, thinking the King wanted Becket dead, came to the Cathedral and murdered him there. It could be said that the final victory belonged to Thomas à Becket though, because he was made a saint in 1173 and his tomb became a principal place of pilgrimage. King Henry II himself visited it and, as a penance, was scourged by the monks in front of the tomb.

The beauty of the Cathedral is well-known and its points of interest too numerous to mention. A visit to the Tourist Information Centre and possibly the Cathedral bookshop is essential to appreciate it.

The city itself is very attractive with its crooked streets and timber framed houses projecting over the pavements. One notable feature is King's School which has a unique exterior Norman staircase. There are also long stretches of the city walls left standing.

Numerous museums exist, amongst the most interesting are the Canterbury Centre, St. Alphege Lane, which is in a converted medieval church, Canterbury Heritage Museum, Stour Street, again housed in a medieval building, the Roman Mosaic in Butchery Lane, and The West Gate, a museum of arms and armour housed in a 14th century gatehouse.

From Canterbury we go through the pretty villages of Littlebourne and then to Wingham which has a 15th century inn, the Red Lion, typical of many of the half-timbered houses in the village. Also notable is the 600 year old church with its green copper spire and timbered arcade.

Next stop is Sandwich, one of the Cinque Ports and a truly delightful place with many medieval buildings. Some of the more notable being the Customs House, a medieval timber building with a later brick skin, St. Clement's Church whose tower dates back to 1100 and the Guildhall dating from 1579. The finest of Sandwich's timbered houses can be found in Strand Street constructed on reclaimed land. One of the most memorable features is the Barbican, built in 1539 as a defensive work but later used as a toll house for the bridge and still in use as late as 1978.

The Roman ruin of Richborough Castle, to the west of Sandwich, has walls up to 25 feet high still standing on three sides and dates from the last days of Roman occupation of Britain. The castle was built as a defence against Saxon marauders. In the centre of the area lies the foundation of a triumphal arch built in AD85 to celebrate the Roman invasion of Britain.

From Sandwich we move along the coast to Deal with its many Georgian houses and pebble beach. Ships may be seen passing relatively close to the shore here because the treacherous Goodwin Sands lie only 5 miles offshore. Deal Castle was built by Henry VIII as part of his defences against invasion. The tour now passes on to St Margaret's-at-Cliffe, situated on cliffs that rise to 400 feet above the sea. The village has a notable late Norman church where early ship carvings may be seen in the nave.

Next is Folkestone which was heavily bombed during the Second World War. It has a wide grassy promenade, The Leas, along the clifftop and many attractive wooded walks down to the beach. Rosemary bushes are planted along the road running from The Leas to the harbour in remembrance of the many soldiers who marched down this road to embark on troopships but who never returned. The adjoining seaside town of Sandgate has a good bathing beach albeit with pebbles rather than sand and also a reconstructed 16th century castle. The neighbouring Cinque Port, Hythe, is also well known as a holiday resort and is the terminus for the narrow gauge Romney, Hythe and Dymchurch Railway.

Following the A259 the tour now arrives in the charming and pretty Cinque Port of Rye, full of half-timbered and Georgian buildings. Even in the time of Henry James, the American novelist, it was a tourist attraction. He lived in Lamb House from 1897 to 1914 where he wrote *The Ambassadors* and *The Golden Bowl*. The Mayor of Rye between the First and Second World Wars was another novelist, E.F. Benson, famous for his Mapp and Lucia novels, and he lived in the very same house which now belongs to the National Trust.

It is difficult to pick out individual places to visit in Rye. Any visitor is going to be happy just to walk around the streets. The town is very well-endowed with pubs, reputedly seventeen in all, quite a lot for a small town. Also worth mentioning is the museum in the Ypres Tower.

Then, via the villages of Wittersham and Woodchurch, we move on to Tenterden which once held Cinque Port rights. For theatre lovers, there is Smallhythe Place which houses the Ellen Terry Memorial Museum with momentoes of Dame Ellen Terry and Mrs Siddons amongst others. In nearby Sissinghurst there is a literary connection at Sissinghurst Castle, once the home of writers, Harold Nicolson and his wife Vita Sackville-West. When they took it over in 1930 it was virtually derelict. Over the next ten years they restored the Tudor buildings and made a beautiful garden from the former wilderness.

Rolvenden and Sandhurst are next on the route followed by Lamberhurst, famous for its vineyards and wine-making. Another interesting place in Lamberhurst is Owl House Gardens, 13 acres of beautiful gardens with lawns, oaks, elm, birch, rhododendrums, azaleas and camellias. It also has an informal sunken water garden. These surround a 16th century smuggler's cottage. From there we pass Scotney Castle, once a moated 14th century castle now with only the curtain wall and one of the towers remaining but set in lovely, romantic gardens. The next village of Goudhurst is notable for its Culpepper monuments and brasses and for Finchcocks, a fine 18th century house in beautiful gardens and parkland. Finchcocks also has a wonderful collection of historical keyboard instruments most of which are restored to concert condition.

Our next stop, Cranbrook, is sited on a hill above the Kentish Weald and has many interesting features. The Elizabethan Old Cloth Hall is one of the many fine, historic buildings in the town. The church is also of interest with a porch dating from 1291.

Moving into mid-Kent we pass through Headcorn, once closely associated with weaving as shown by its 15th century Cloth Hall, and Sutton Valence where the grave of John Willes, who introduced round arm bowling into cricket, may be seen. We then arrive in West Malling, a market town with the remains of a Norman castle and abbey. From there we detour through West Peckham and Hadlow before rejoining the main route to go though East Peckham and Five Oak Green to arrive at the ancient town of Tonbridge. The Saxons had a fortress here and later a castle was built on the same mound. Only the 13th century gatehouse remains and in the 18th century a mansion was built alongside.

From Tonbridge the tour goes to Sevenoaks whose most notable place of interest is Knole, a 15th century mansion set in a most beautiful park of 1000 acres. The house was built by Thomas Bourchier, Archbishop of Canterbury, and it remained the property of the Archbishops until Thomas Cranmer was forced to give it to Henry VIII. It was given to Thomas Sackville by Elizabeth I and that family, first the Earls then the Dukes of Dorset, have lived there ever since.

Knole's wonderful treasure house of furnishings can be attributed to the sixth Earl who was Lord Chamberlain to William III and as such was entitled to take any discarded furnishings from the royal palaces. This is definitely a house that should be visited.

Four and a half miles east of Sevenoaks, off the A25, stands Ightham Mote, one of the most complete medieval moated manor houses in the country. A National Trust property, this 14th century house standing in a wooded valley, has half-timbered upper storeys and steeply pitched gables. Alterations made through the centuries do not detract from its appearance as local stone was used and the changes were in keeping with the style of the house.

From Sevenoaks there is slight detour on the route to the village of Shoreham and then we turn west again through Sundridge, on the edge of Sevenoaks, to Brasted and Westerham.

Westerham has famous associations. General Wolfe was born in 1727 in Quebec House and lived there for his first eleven years. Wolfe was famous for his defeat of the French in Canada but was killed on the Heights of Abraham at the very moment of his victory. Quebec House is now owned by the National Trust and has been restored to its 17th century appearance.

Chartwell, two miles south of Westerham, was the home of Sir Winston Churchill, Britain's greatest wartime prime minister. Owned by the National Trust, the views from the house across the Kentish countryside are lovely. There are six doors from the house into the garden, perhaps indicating its importance to the residents of Chartwell. There are many reminders of Sir Winston. His paintings hang on the walls, the stand-up desk where he wrote his books is still here as are his medals, uniforms and the family photographs. A most poignant reminder of one of his favourite spots is the garden chair standing where he used to sit by the pond to feed his fish.

Our last stop on this tour is Biggin Hill, closely associated with aviation particularly during the Second World War when it was used as a Battle of Britain airfield. From there we follow the A223 back into London.

ANTIQUE DEALERS

BECKENHAM (081)

Norman Witham, 2 High Street TEL: 650 9096 PARKING: Medium OPEN: Fri-Sat or by appt MIN: £5 MAX: £500 PERIOD: 18th-20th century SPECIALIST: English small china & glass GENERAL: Good old English china teaware OTHER INFO: 20 mins from London's Victoria.

FARNBOROUGH (0689)

Farnborough (Kent) Antiques, 10 Church Road, BR6 7DB TEL: 851834, ASSNS: BADA PARKING: Easy OPEN: Sats 9.30-5.30 & by appt MIN: £250 MAX: £5,000 PERIOD: 16th-18th century SPECIALIST: Oak furniture & wood carvings GENERAL: OTHER INFO: Close to Kent countryside: Knole, Chartwell, Westerham & Brasted

ORPINGTON (0689)

James Higinton TEL: 261418 FAX: 261600 OPEN: By appt GENERAL: Arms & armour, old fishing tackle.

CHISLEHURST (081)

Michael Sim, 1 Royal Parade, BR7 5PG TEL: 467 7040 FAX: 467 8944 ASSNS: LAPADA PARKING: Own carpark OPEN: Seven days 9-6 MIN: £250 MAX: £50,000 PERIOD: 18th-19th century SPECIALIST: Clocks, barometers, miniatures GENERAL: Georgian & Regency furniture OTHER INFO: Historic village in a NT conservation area, the place of exile & death of Napoleon III.

NORTHFLEET (0474)

Northfleet Hill Antiques, 36 The Hill, DA11 9EX TEL: 321521 PARKING: Easy OPEN: Tues, Fri, Sat 9.30-5 MIN: £1 MAX: £800 PERIOD: 19th-20th century GENERAL: Furniture & collectables OTHER INFO: Coach & Horses, Queen's Head & Ye Olde Leather Bottle pubs.

ROCHESTER (0634)

Francis Iles, Rutland House, La Providence TEL: 843081 PARKING: Medium OPEN: Mon-Sat 9.30-5.30 MIN: £120 MAX: £10,000 PERIOD: Contemporary SPECIALIST: Pictures - Rowland Hilde, Clive, Madgwick, Kenneth Denton etc GENERAL: All mediums, traditional style OTHER INFO: Dickens interest, 10th century castle & cathedral.

Memories Antique Centre, 128 High Street, ME1 1JT TEL: 811044 PARKING: Medium OPEN: Mon-Sat 9-5 MIN: £2 MAX: £400 PERIOD: 19th-20th century GENERAL: General antiques OTHER INFO: 14 dealers on 4 floors. Dickens Centre, Gordon Hotel.

CUXTON (0634)

Country Pine Antiques Co, Upper Bush Farm, Upper Bush, ME2 1HQ TEL: 296929, 844090 FAX: 296393 PARKING: Own carpark OPEN: Mon-Sat 8.30-7 & by appt MIN: £100 MAX: £1,500 PERIOD: 18th-20th century SPECIALIST: Antique pine furniture.

CHATHAM (0634)

Antiquities, 5 Ordnance Mews, The Historic Dockyard, ME4 4TE TEL: 818866 FAX: 818877 ASSNS: GMC PARKING: Easy OPEN: Mon-Fri 10-3, also weekends but best by appt MIN: £100 MAX: £15,000 PERIOD: 15th-17th century (engravings & etchings) otherwise 19th-20th century GENERAL: Chandeliers, wall lights, etchings & engravings inc Old Masters OTHER INFO: Sited in a living museum.

HARRIETSHAM (0622)

Judith Peppitt, Chegworth Manor Farm, Chegworth Road, ME17 1DD TEL: 859313 PARKING: Own carpark OPEN: Anytime by appt MIN: £20 MAX: £2,000 PERIOD: 18th-20th century SPECIALIST: British watercolours OTHER INFO: Superb Leeds Castle. Great Danes Hotel.

TEYNHAM (0795)

Jackson-Grant Antiques, The Old Chapel, 133 London Road, ME9 9QJ TEL: 522027 FAX: (0634) 727064 PARKING: Easy OPEN: Mon-Sat 10-5, Sun 1-5 (resident) MIN £1 MAX: £5,000+ PERIOD: 17th-early 20th century SPECIALIST: Early coffers when available GENERAL: 3,500 sq ft of antiques (no repro), porcelain, jewellery, silver etc, good trade call OTHER INFO: First place in England to grow cherries. Tearooms opposite.

FAVERSHAM (0795)

Squires Antiques, 3 Jacob Yard, Preston Street, ME13 TEL: 531503 FAX: 59160 PARKING: Easy OPEN: Mon-Tues, Fri-Sat 10-5 MIN: £1 MAX: £3,000 PERIOD: 17th-20th century GENERAL: Wide variety of everything OTHER INFO: Ancient buildings in historic town, local museum, sailing barges on The Creek.

BOUGHTON-UNDER-BLEAN (0227)
Jean Collyer, 194 The Street, ME13 9AL TEL: 751454 PARKING: Own carpark OPEN: 10-5 Tue, Fri & Sat, or by appt MIN: £2 MAX: £1,000 PERIOD: 18th-19th century SPECIALIST: Porcelain & glass GENERAL: Some silver, lace & furniture OTHER INFO: Near to Canterbury & cathedral, plenty of old buildings, pubs, and excellent Garden House restaurant opposite.

WHITSTABLE (0227)
Tankerton Antiques, 136 Tankerton Road, CT5 2AN TEL: 266490 PARKING: Medium OPEN: Tues 10-4, Wed 10-1, Thurs-Sat 10-5 MIN: £1 MAX: £2,000 PERIOD: 18th-20th century SPECIALIST: 10,000+ postcards GENERAL: English china, glass, furniture & collectables OTHER INFO: Excellent for birdwatching (Swale Estuary) and watersports

BIRCHINGTON (0843)
John Chawner Antiques, 36 Station Approach, CT7 9RD TEL: 843309 PARKING: Own carpark OPEN: 10.30-12.30, 1.30-5, closed Tues MIN: £5 MAX: £5,000 PERIOD: 18th-20th century SPECIALIST: Clocks & barometers GENERAL: Repairs, restorations, valuations.

MARGATE (0843)
R.G. Scott Furniture Mart, Bath Place, Grotto Hill, CT9 2BU TEL: 220653 ASSNS: FSB PARKING: Medium OPEN: 9.30-1, 2-5 MIN: £1 MAX: £2,000 SPECIALIST: Refinishing goods GENERAL: Large quantity on 3 floors all types antiques & s/h furniture OTHER INFO: Upholstery, French polishing, cabinet-making, restorations on site.

BROADSTAIRS (0843)
Broadstairs Antiques & Collectables, 49 Belvedere Road, CT10 1PF TEL: 861965 PARKING: Easy OPEN: Summer 10-5, Winter 10-4.30 MIN: £1 MAX: £1,000 PERIOD: 19th-20th century SPECIALIST: Victorian teaplates, lace & linen GENERAL: Small furniture, pretty china, cutlery-all pre 1940 OTHER INFO: Pretty harbour & safe sandy beaches. Charles Dickens Museum & Bleak House (both open) where Dickens stayed & wrote part of "Pickwick Papers" and "The Old Curiosity Shop". Dickens Festival in June - we all dress in Dickensian dress and parade in Town. Events throughout week, all welcome. Folk Week every August, Admiral

Dundonald Hotel 4 doors away, coffee & light snacks in The Coffee House, Charlotte Street.

RAMSGATE (0843)
De Tavener Antiques, 24 Addington Street TEL: 582213 ASSNS: GMC, Horological Assn PARKING: Easy OPEN: Mon-Sat 9.30-5.30, Wed AM only SPECIALIST: Clocks, barometers GENERAL: Bric-a-brac.

CANTERBURY (0227)
Antique & Design, Unit 14, Graham Bell House, Roper Close, CT1 2RD TEL: 762871 FAX: 762871 PARKING: Own carpark OPEN: Mon-Fri 9-5, Sat 10-2 or by appt MIN: £5 MAX: £2,500 PERIOD: 18th-20th century SPECIALIST: Antique pine furniture GENERAL: Shipping furniture, some reproduction, i.e. shelves & tables OTHER INFO: Stock of 1,300+ pieces in 10,000 sq ft, free container loading, credit facilities.

Burgate Antiques, 10c Burgate, CT1 2HG TEL: 456500 PARKING: Easy OPEN: Mon-Sat 10-5 MIN: £2 MAX: £2,000 PERIOD: 18th-20th century SPECIALIST: Period furniture, porcelain, silver GENERAL: Jewellery, clocks, Art Deco, militaria, lead soldiers, old prints, books, watercolours. Egyptian antiquities OTHER INFO: Antiques Centre with 12 dealers on 2 floors backing onto Cathedral grounds.

The Chaucer Bookshop, 6 Beer Cart Lane, CT1 2NY TEL: 453912 ASSNS: ABA, PFBA PARKING: Medium OPEN: Mon-Sat 10-5 MIN: £1 MAX: £500 PERIOD: 17th-20th century GENERAL: Good general stock, books and prints OTHER INFO: 4 mins walk S.W. of Cathedral, inside City walls.

Nan Leith's "Brocanterbury", Curios, 68 Stour Street, CT1 2NZ TEL: 454519 PARKING: Easy 5 mins walk OPEN: 12-6pm & anytime by appt (resident) MIN: £2 MAX: £75 PERIOD: late 19th-20th century SPECIALIST: Pressed glass & art glass GENERAL: A veritable hoard of collectables & books, prints OTHER INFO: Cathedral, antiquarian bookshops. "Brocante" North European word for such stock.

Parker-Williams Antiques, 22 Palace Street TEL: 768341 ASSNS: LAPADA PARKING: Good OPEN: Mon-Sat 10-1, 2-6 MIN: £10 MAX: £10,000 PERIOD: 17-19th century SPECIALIST: Good quality furniture, clocks, porcelain GENERAL: Silver, bronzes, copper, brass, watercolours & oils, OTHER INFO: Historic city with many places of interest with good selection of antique shops.

Michael Pearson Antiques, 2 The Borough, CT1 2DR TEL: 459939 PARKING: Good OPEN: Mon-Sat 10-6, Thurs AM only PERIOD: 17th-early 19th century SPECIALIST: Woodcarvings GENERAL: Early oak & walnut country furniture OTHER INFO: UK's second most visited city after London.

Pine & Things Ltd, Oast Interiors, Wincheap Road TEL: 470283 FAX: 470283 PARKING: Own carpark OPEN: Mon-Sat 9-5.30, Sun 10-4 MIN: £5 MAX: £1,000 PERIOD: 19th-20th century SPECIALIST: Repro & antique pine furniture OTHER INFO: Hop Poles pub next door.

Saracen's Lantern, 8-9 The Borough, CT1 2DR TEL: 451968 PARKING: Easy OPEN: 9-4 MIN: £1 MAX: £2,500 PERIOD: 18th-20th century GENERAL: Pottery, porcelain, silver, plate, furniture, paintings, prints, postcards, books OTHER INFO: So full of attractions city needs 3-4 days to do it justice.

Stablegate Antiques, 19 The Borough, CT1 2DR TEL: 764086 PARKING: Easy OPEN: 10-5.30 closed Mon MIN: £10 MAX: £2,500 PERIOD: 19th-20th century SPECIALIST: Small furniture GENERAL: Jewellery, dolls, pictures, glass, furniture (some larger pieces) OTHER INFO: Good food & specialist shops in street.

LITTLEBOURNE (0227)

Jimmy Warren Antiques & Garden Ornaments, Cedar Lodge, 28 the Hill, CT3 1TA TEL: 721510 FAX: 722431 PARKING: Own carpark OPEN: Seven days 9-6 MIN: £10 MAX: £6,000 PERIOD: 18th-20th century SPECIALIST: Edwardian, Victorian, Georgian furniture & large stocks of fine garden statuary, urns, etc all set in landscaped gardens.

WINGHAM (0227)

Bridge Antiques, High Street, CT3 1DE TEL: 720445 PARKING: Own carpark OPEN: Mon-Sat 9-5, closed Weds MAX: £10,000 PERIOD: 18-20th century SPECIALIST: Fine period furniture, porcelain, paintings, dolls GENERAL: Shipping goods OTHER INFO: Excellent restaurant opposite. Good golf locally.

Lloyd's Bookshop, 27 High Street, CT3 1AW

TEL: 720774 ASSNS: ABA PARKING: Easy OPEN: Mon-Sat 9.30-1, 2.15-5 MIN: £1 MAX: £600 PERIOD: 17th-20th century SPECIALIST: Early children's books GENERAL: All subjects including prints, watercolours & music OTHER INFO: Beautiful Kentish village dating from 13th century. Several restaurants and antique shops.

Old College Antiques, 31 High Street, CT3 1AB TEL: 720783 PARKING: Medium OPEN: 10-5 MIN: £1 MAX: £1,000 PERIOD: 17th-20th century GENERAL: Furniture & unusual antiques, some French decorative OTHER INFO: Shop sited in 13th, part 16th, century building, site of Wingham Ecclesiastical College.

Silvesters Antiques, 33 High Street, CT3 1AB TEL: 720278, (0843) 41524 ASSNS: LAPADA PARKING: Own small carpark MIN: £20 MAX: £1,000 PERIOD: 18th-20th century GENERAL: Period and decorative furniture & objects OTHER INFO: Wingham dates from 1200, close to Canterbury & Sandwich, an ancient town Julius Caesar landed nearby (Roman fort at Richborough).

SANDWICH (0304)

Noah's Ark Antique Centre, 5 King Street, CT13 9BT TEL: 611144 PARKING: Medium OPEN: Mon, Tues, Thurs-Sat 10-4.30 MIN: £2 MAX: £400 PERIOD: 18th-19th century SPECIALIST: Staffordshire figures, fairings GENERAL: Porcelain, pottery, silver + plate, glass, oils, watercolours and prints OTHER INFO: Most interesting old town, still retaining its medieval street plan. Principal Cinque Port with plethora of buildings dating from 13th-18th century.

James Porter Antiques, 5 Potter Street TEL: 612218 PARKING: Medium OPEN: Mon-Sat 10-5 but early closing Weds (ring bell if closed) MIN: £30 MAX: £850 PERIOD: 19th century OTHER INFO: Bell Hotel (parking on riverbank). Fleur-de-Lys Hotel, Cherubs coffee shop in Potter Street.

DEAL (0304)

Quill Antiques, 12 Alfred Square TEL: 375958 PARKING: Easy OPEN: Varies MIN: £1 MAX: £500 PERIOD: 18th-20th century GENERAL: Ceramics, bric-a-brac, small furniture, silver.

ST MARGARET'S BAY (0304)

Alexandra's Antiques, 1-3 The Droveway TEL:

Kent and South East Sussex

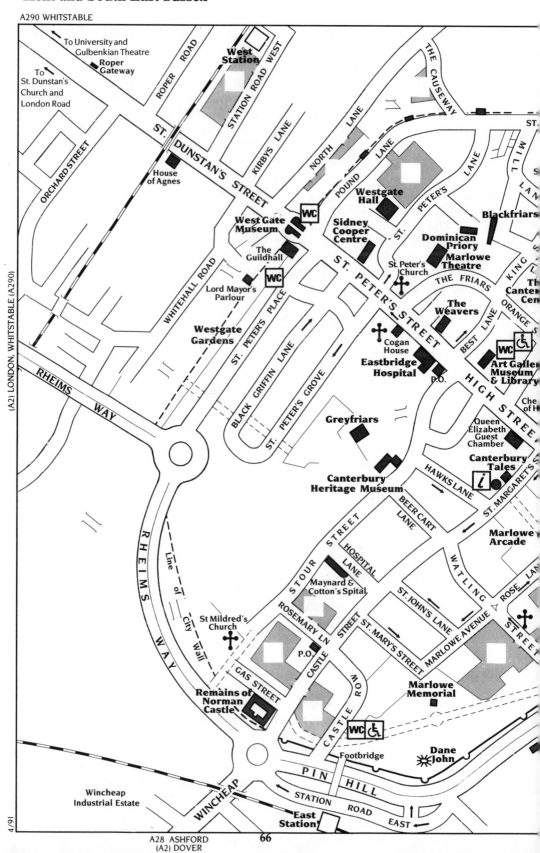

A290 WHITSTABLE

To University and
Gulbenkian Theatre

Roper
Gateway

To
St. Dunstan's
Church and
London Road

ROPER ROAD

West
Station

STATION ROAD WEST

THE CAUSEWAY

ST.

ST. DUNSTAN'S STREET

KIRBYS LANE

House
of Agnes

ORCHARD STREET

NORTH LANE

POUND LANE

Westgate
Hall

ST. PETER'S LANE

MILL LANE

Blackfriars

West Gate
Museum

WC

Sidney
Cooper
Centre

Dominican
Priory

Marlowe
Theatre

KING

The
Canter
Cen

The
Guildhall

WC

St. Peter's
Church

ST. PETER'S STREET

THE FRIARS

ORANGE

WHITEHALL ROAD

Lord Mayor's
Parlour

Westgate
Gardens

ST. PETER'S PLACE

BLACK GRIFFIN LANE

ST. PETER'S GROVE

Cogan
House

The
Weavers

Eastbridge
Hospital

P.O.

BEST LANE

WC

Art Gall
Museum
& Library

Che
of H

RHEIMS WAY

Greyfriars

HIGH STREET

Queen
Elizabeth
Guest
Chamber

Canterbury
Tales

i

Canterbury
Heritage Museum

HAWKS LANE

ST. MARGARET'S

Marlowe
Arcade

(A2) LONDON, WHITSTABLE (A290)

RHEIMS WAY

Line of City Wall

STOUR STREET

BEER CART LANE

HOSPITAL LANE

WATLING

ROSE LAN

STREET

Maynard &
Cotton's Spital

ST. JOHN'S LANE

MARLOWE AVENUE

St Mildred's
Church

ROSEMARY LN

CASTLE STREET

ST. MARY'S STREET

GAS STREET

P.O.

CASTLE ROW

Marlowe
Memorial

Remains of
Norman
Castle

WC

Dane
John

Footbridge

PIN HILL

Wincheap
Industrial Estate

WINCHEAP

STATION ROAD EAST

East
Station

4/91

66

A28 ASHFORD
(A2) DOVER

Street Map of Canterbury
By courtesy of Canterbury
City Council

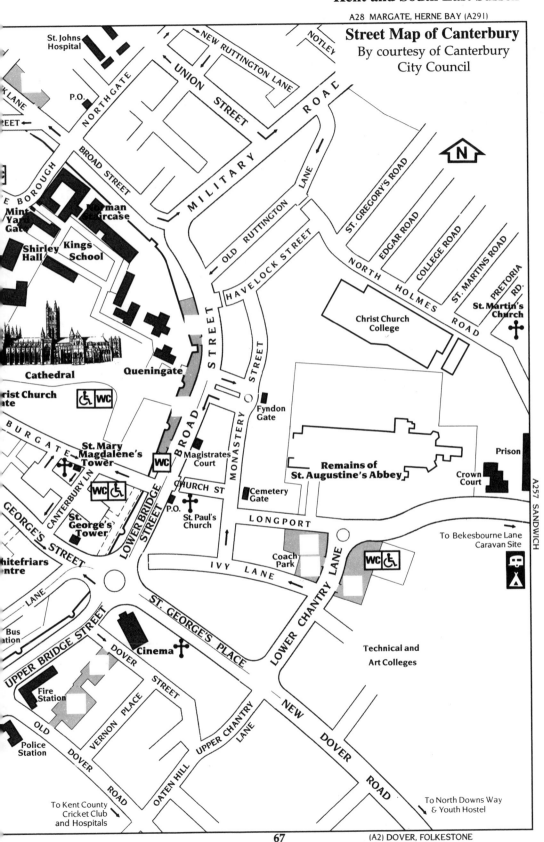

853102 FAX: 853306 PARKING: Own carpark OPEN: 10-4 MIN: £5 MAX: £1,500 PERIOD: 19th-20th century GENERAL: Victorian watercolours, silver + plate, furniture, jewellery, bric-a-brac, lace.

FOLKESTONE (0303)

Alan Lord Antiques, 71 Tontine Street, CT20 1JR TEL: 253674 (24 hr) PARKING: Easy OPEN: Mon, Tues, Thurs & Fri 9-1 & 2-4.30, Weds 9-1, Sat 10-1 MIN: £5 MAX: £5,000 PERIOD: 18th-19th century SPECIALIST: Furniture GENERAL: China, some shipping goods OTHER INFO: Harbour ferry to France. Shop is up from harbour.

SANDGATE (0303)

Antiques Etcetera, 93 High Street, CT20 3BY TEL: 249389 PARKING: Own carpark OPEN: Mon-Sat 10-5.30 PERIOD: 20th century GENERAL STOCK: Mainly books & a little furniture. OTHER INFO: Imperial Hotel, Hythe.

Beaubush House Antiques, 95 High Street, CT20 3BY TEL: 249099 ASSNS: LAPADA PARKING: Medium OPEN: Mon-Sat 9.30-5.30 MIN: £150 MAX: £4,000 PERIOD: 18th-19th century SPECIALIST: Pottery & porcelain GENERAL: Furniture, jewellery, collectables & textiles OTHER INFO: Sandgate Hotel.

Christopher Buck Antiques, 56-60 High Street, CT20 3AP TEL: 221229 FAX 249339 ASSNS: LAPADA PARKING: Easy OPEN: Mon-Tues, Thurs-Fri 10-5.30 MIN: £200 MAX: £20,000 PERIOD: 18th-early 19th century SPECIALIST: Quality English furniture OTHER INFO: 20+ shops with wide antiques range.

Churchill Galleries Antiques Centre, 13-15 Sandgate High Street, CT20 3BD TEL: 249574 PARKING: Easy OPEN: Mon-Sat 10-6, Suns 11-6 MIN: £5 MAX: £5,000 PERIOD: 18th-20th century GENERAL: 12 dealers with wide varied stock OTHER INFO: Seaside village, 16th century castle. 35 dealers in one street.

Dench Antiques, Cromwell House, 32 High Street, CT20 3AP TEL: 240824 PARKING: Medium OPEN: 10-4 MIN: £600 MAX: £8,000 PERIOD: 17th-19th century SPECIALIST: Period furniture-oak, walnut OTHER INFO: 5 star Imperial Hotel, Hythe.

Michael W Fitch Antiques, 99 Sandgate High Street, CT20 3BY TEL: 249600 FAX: 249600 ASSNS: LAPADA PARKING: Own carpark OPEN: Mon-Sat 10-5.30 MIN: £150 MAX: £10,000 PERIOD: 18th-19th century SPECIALIST: Dining & library furniture GENERAL: Furniture, clocks OTHER INFO: Warehouse with antiques for trade buyers, Channel Tunnel/M20 5 mins.

Freeman & Lloyd, 44 High Street, CT20 3AP TEL: 248986 ASSNS: BADA, LAPADA PARKING: Easy OPEN: Mon, Tues, Thurs-Sat 9.30-5.30 MIN: £150 MAX: £50,000 PERIOD: 18th-early 19th century SPECIALIST: English period furniture GENERAL: Tea caddies, clocks, bronzes, pictures OTHER INFO: Dover Castle, Channel Tunnel Exhibition, day trips to France. 2 country house hotels within 20 mins - Chilston Park & Eastwell Manor

Robin Homewood Antiques, 59a High Street, CT20 3AH TEL: 249466 PARKING: Medium OPEN: Mon-Sat 9.30-5.30 PERIOD: 18th-20th century GENERAL: General antiques OTHER INFO: Romney, Hythe and Dymchurch Railway, Dover Castle.

Hyron Antiques, 86 High Street, CT20 3BY TEL: 240698 PARKING: Medium OPEN: Mon-Sat 9.30-5.30 MIN: £1 MAX: £750 PERIOD: 19th-20th century GENERAL: Victorian, Edwardian furniture, bric-a-brac OTHER INFO: Sandgate Castle, Euro Tunnel Exhibition & entrance. Seafront B&B's.

Jonathan Greenwood Antiques, Sandgate Antiques Centre, 61-63 High Street, CT20 3AH TEL: 248987 ASSNS: LAPADA PARKING: Easy OPEN: Seven days 9.30-5.30 MIN: £5 MAX: £10,000 PERIOD: 18th-20th century SPECIALIST: Furniture, jewellery, pictures GENERAL: General antiques OTHER INFO: Port Lympne Zoo, 2 golf courses, large seaside funfair, huge Sunday market.

G. & D.I. Marrin & Sons, 149 Sandgate Road, CT20 2DA TEL: 253016 FAX: 850956 ASSNS: ABA, PFBA PARKING: Easy OPEN: Mon-Sat 9.30-5.30 (winter closed lunchtime) MIN: £1 MAX: £5,000 PERIOD: 18th-20th century SPECIALIST: Books on First World War GENERAL: Kentish topography and general fine books.

J T Rutherford & Son, 55 High Street TEL 249315 PARKING: Easy OPEN: 8.30-6 MIN:

£3 MAX: £8,000 PERIOD: 17th-19th century
SPECIALIST: Weapons, furniture.

HYTHE (0303)

Den of Antiquity, 35 Dymchurch Road, CT21
6JE TEL: 267162 PARKING: Easy OPEN: 9-5
PERIOD: 19th-20th century SPECIALIST:
Jewellery & Staffordshire GENERAL: Wide
range of interesting stock OTHER INFO: We
have largest piece of Staffordshire known to
exist, and a live macaw.

Samovar Antiques, 158 High Street, CT21 5JR
TEL: 264239 PARKING: Own carpark OPEN:
Mon-Sat 9.30-5 MIN: £5 MAX: £1000+
PERIOD: 18th-20th century SPECIALIST: Ori-
ental carpet & rugs GENERAL: Antiques, fur-
niture, silver etc

RYE (0797)

Herbert Gasson, The Lion Galleries, Lion
Street, TN31 7LB TEL: 222208 PARKING:
Medium OPEN: 9-5.30 MIN: £60 MAX: £5,000
PERIOD: 17th-19th century SPECIALIST:
Early oak & country furniture GENERAL: Pre
1850 furniture, copper & brass OTHER INFO:
Jeake's House Hotel, The Bistro, Landgate, the
church & Rye's cobbled streets.

Landgate Antiques, 22 Landgate, TN31 7LP
TEL: 224746 FAX: 225143 ASSNS: LAPADA
PARKING: Medium OPEN: Usually seven days
9-5.30 MIN: £20 MAX: £6,500 PERIOD: 19th
century GENERAL: Decorative items

Ann Lingard, 18-22 Rope Walk, TN31 7NA
TEL: 223486 FAX: 224700 ASSNS: LAPADA
PARKING: Own carpark OPEN: Mon-Sat 9-5.30
& by appt MIN: £1 MAX: £2,000 PERIOD:
19th-20th century SPECIALIST: Antique pine
furniture. Kitchen shop GENERAL: Complementary antique accessories, china, glass, copper, brass box & wooden objects, etc (no reproductions). Trade warehouse nearby, shippers
welcome OTHER INFO: Ancient Cinque Port
town. Small population 4,000.

The Mint Arcade, 71 The Mint, TN31 7EN
TEL: 225952 PARKING: Medium OPEN: Seven
days 10-5 PERIOD: 19th-20th century
SPECIALIST: Original cigarette cards, handmade wooden picture frames, old dolls & teddys,
handpainted soldiers, dried flowers & old
jewellery.

Rye Antiques, 93 High Street, TN31 7JN TEL:

222257 PARKING: Easy OPEN: 9.30-5.30 MIN:
£5 MAX: £500 PERIOD: 18th-20th century
SPECIALIST: Cameo jewellery GENERAL:
Silver, copper, brassware, small oak, pewter,
jewellery, some glassware & porcelain OTHER
INFO: Whole town is an antique gem with
wealth of antique shops & all facilities.

WITTERSHAM (0797)

Old Corner House, 6 Poplar Road, TN30 7PG
TEL: 270236 PARKING: Easy OPEN: 10-5,
closed Friday MIN: £20 MAX: £5,000 PERIOD:
17th-19th century SPECIALIST: Early English
ceramics especially Blue & White, samplers,
carvings, English watercolours GENERAL:
Country furniture OTHER INFO: Always an interesting visit with several good pubs nearby
for lunch or, Rye teashops, if should Auntie be
with you.

WOODCHURCH (0233)

Treasures, 1-3 The Green, TN26 3PE TEL:
860249 PARKING: Easy OPEN: 10-5.30, closed
Thurs MIN: £1 MAX: £700 PERIOD: 19th-20th
century SPECIALIST: Stripped antique pine

GENERAL: Pine & other furniture, china, linen & collectables OTHER INFO: Situated by the delightful village green, cricket etc in summer.

TENTERDEN (0580)

John McMaster, 5 Sayers Square, Sayers Lane, TN30 6BW TEL: 762941 ASSNS: BADA PARKING: Easy OPEN: Mon-Sat 9-5.30 MIN: £10 MAX: £10,000 PERIOD: 18th-19th century SPECIALIST: Georgian furniture, engravings GENERAL: Large stock quality silver + plate, porcelain, glass OTHER INFO: Cinque Port of Rye. Sissinghurst, Bodiam, steam railway.

Weald Antiques Gallery, 106 High Street, TN30 6HT TEL: 762939 FAX: 241960 PARKING: Easy OPEN: Mon-Sat 10-5 MIN: £5 MAX: £4,000+ PERIOD: 17th-19th century SPECIALIST: Silver, oak, dolls, teddies GENERAL: Mahogany furniture, ceramics, jewellery, objets d'art, collectables OTHER INFO: Bustling little town with Peggoty's Teashop in tree-lined walk.

ROLVENDEN (0580)

Falstaff Antiques, 63-67 High Street, TN17 4LP TEL: 241234 PARKING: Easy OPEN: Mon-Sat 9-6 MIN: £1 MAX: £500 PERIOD: 19th-20th century GENERAL: Antiques & reproductions OTHER INFO: Motor Museum also at this site.

Kent Cottage Antiques, 39 High Street, TN17 4LP TEL: 241719 PARKING: Easy OPEN: 9.30-4 by appt MIN: £50 MAX: £1,500 PERIOD: 18th-20th century SPECIALIST: Scent bottles GENERAL: Porcelain, silver, small furniture OTHER INFO: Motor Museum, Hole Park Gardens, Great Maytham Hall.

J.D. & R.M. Walters, 10 Regent Street, TN17 4PE TEL: 241563 ASSNS: GMC PARKING: Easy OPEN: 8-6 PERIOD: 18th-19th century SPECIALIST: Antique furniture restorers & makers of period copies up to circa 1830. OTHER INFO: Close to Tenterden, Kent's most picturesque town.

SANDHURST (0580)

Forge Antiques & Restorations, Rye Road, TN18 5JG TEL: 850665, 850308 PARKING: Own carpark OPEN: Variable, phone first MIN: £1 MAX: £3,000 PERIOD: 19th-20th century SPECIALIST: Tunbridgeware, rosewood tables, work tables, bookcases, chairs, porcelain, tea services, glass OTHER INFO: Also furniture re-pair workshops.

LAMBERHURST (0892)

The China Locker, Bedwyn Cottage, The Slade, TN3 8HV TEL: 890555 PARKING: Own carpark OPEN: Anytime (resident on premises) MIN: £5 MAX: £45 PERIOD: Mainly 19th century GENERAL: 18th-19th century prints & watercolours OTHER INFO: Scotney Castle, Bewl Reservoir.

GOUDHURST (0580)

Old Saddlers Antiques, Church Road, TN17 1BH TEL: 211458 PARKING: Easy OPEN: Mon, Wed-Sat 9.30-12, 2.30-5.30 MIN: £5 MAX: £500+ PERIOD: 18th-20th century SPECIALIST: Heavy horse brasses & decorations GENERAL: Blue & White transferware, brass, copper, wrought iron. Victorian & Georgian jewellery, pewter OTHER INFO: One of the prettiest villages with wonderful views over the High Weald of Kent, 12th century church, lovely old inns.

CRANBROOK (0580)

Cranbrook Antiques (6 dealers), 15 High Street TEL: 712173 PARKING: Easy OPEN: Mon-Sat 10-5 MIN: £1 MAX: £1,000 PERIOD: 18th-early 20th century SPECIALIST: Postcards, cigarette cards, sporting antiques, textiles, silver GENERAL: Jewellery, pine furniture, small furniture & domestic antiques OTHER INFO: 5 other shops. The George Hotel where Queen Elizabeth I stayed. One of the last working windmills in country.

Cranbrook Gallery, 21b Stone Street, TN17 3HE TEL: 713021 ASSNS: FATG PARKING: Easy OPEN: Tues-Fri 9-5, Sat 9-4 MIN: £8 MAX: £1,000 SPECIALIST: Prints, maps, watercolours OTHER INFO: Near Sissinghurst Castle. Town museum with working windmill.

The Old Bakery, St David's Bridge, TN17 3HN TEL: 713103 FAX: 712407 ASSN: BADA, LAPADA PARKING: Easy OPEN: Mon-Sat 9.30-5 Weds AM only MIN: £50 MAX: £15,000 PERIOD: 17th-18th century SPECIALIST Oak & walnut furniture, some metalware OTHER INFO: Pretty Wealdon town dominated by large windmill.

Swan Antiques, Stone Street, TN17 3HP TEL: 712720 PARKING: Own carpark OPEN: Mon, Tues, Thurs-Sat 9.30-5.30 MIN: £10 MAX:

Derek Roberts Antiques

25 Shipbourne Road, Tonbridge, Kent TN10 3DN
Tel: 0732 358986   Fax: 0732 770637
FINE ANTIQUE CLOCKS

We have one of the more extensive stocks of fine fully restored antique clocks and music boxes in the country and if we have not got what you want we will try and find it and, if you wish, send you details and photographs. We are only 30 miles south of London and within easy reach of the airports.

£5,000 PERIOD: 18th-19th century SPECIALIST: Country furniture, folk art GENERAL: Early painted & primitive furniture.

HEADCORN (0622)
Penny Lampard, 31-33 High Street, M£17 9NG TEL: 890682 PARKING: Easy OPEN: 10-5.30 MIN: £25 MAX: £2,000 PERIOD: 18th-20th century SPECIALIST: Clocks, barometers GENERAL: Stripped pine & dark wood OTHER INFO: Coffee shop on premises.

SUTTON VALENCE (0622)
Sutton Valence Antiques, ME17 3AP TEL/FAX: Shop 843333, Warehouse 675332 PARKING: Own carpark OPEN: Mon-Sat 10-5.30 shop, 9-5.30 warehouse, Sun 10-5 MIN: £1 MAX: £10,000 PERIOD: 19th-20th century GENERAL: Georgian to 1940's furniture, china, glass, metalware, paintings etc OTHER INFO: 5,000 sqft warehouse full of furniture.

WEST MALLING (0732)
Andrew Smith Antiques, 89 High Street, ME19 6NA TEL: 843087 National Pawnbrokers Assn PARKING: Easy OPEN: 9.30-5.30 MIN: £20 MAX: £3,000 PERIOD: 20th century SPECIALIST: Secondhand gold jewellery GENERAL: Silver items, diamond & gem sets, pearls, some antique jewellery.

WEST PECKHAM (0732)
Persian Rug Gallery, Vines Farm, Matthews Lane, ME18 5JS TEL: 850228 PARKING: Own carpark OPEN: 9-6 MIN: £20 MAX: £10,000 PERIOD: 19th-20th century SPECIALIST: 200+ rugs & carpets etc. Repairs & hand cleaning.

FIVE OAK GREEN (0892)
Lafayette Antiques, The Barn, Mill House, Badsell Road, TN12 6QU TEL: 832802 PARK-ING: Own carpark OPEN: Mon, Wed, Fri, Sat 11-5 MIN: £10+ MAX: £1,000+ PERIOD: 19th-20th century GENERAL: General antiques OTHER INFO: Whitbread Hop Farm.

EAST PECKHAM (0622)
Desmond & Amanda North, The Orchard, Hale Street, TN12 5JB TEL: 871353 PARKING: Easy OPEN: Anytime by appt MIN: £80 MAX: £3,500 PERIOD: 19th-20th century SPECIALIST: Cushions, tablemats, coasters made from old rugs GENERAL: Old & antique persian & other Oriental rugs, carpets, runners, hangings, cushions OTHER INFO: Nothing new or contemporary. People come here to buy things that don't look bought. Suggestions made.

TONBRIDGE (0732)
Barden House Antiques, 1-3 Priory Street, TN9 2AP TEL: 350142 PARKING: Easy OPEN: Mon-Sat 10-5, Sun by appt MIN: £1 MAX: £500 usually PERIOD: 19th-20th century SPECIALIST: Watercolours GENERAL: 6 dealers with furniture, china, glass, prints, oil paintings, jewellery, linen & lace, postcards, silver, copper & brass. OTHER INFO: Small market town with castle & large recreation ground surrounded by River Medway, pleasant stop between historic Sevenoaks & Tunbridge Wells.

Derek Roberts Antiques, 25 Shipbourne Road, TN10 3DN TEL: 358986 FAX: 770637 ASSNS: BADA, CINOA PARKING: Easy OPEN: Mon-Sat 9.30-5.30 or by appt MIN: £1,000 clocks & £200 Tunbridgeware MAX: £100,000 (clocks) PERIOD: 17th-19th century SPECIALIST: Probably UK's widest range of fully restored antique clocks, music boxes etc OTHER INFO: Penshurst Place, Hever & Leeds castles,

Kent and South East Sussex

Chartwell (Churchill's home) & Knowle.

HADLOW (0732)

The Pedlars Pack, The Square, TN11 0DA TEL: 851296 ASSNS : LAPADA PARKING: Easy OPEN: Tues, Thurs-Sat 10-5.30 MIN: £3 MAX: £800 PERIOD: 17th-20th century SPECIALIST: Old oak, copper, brass, pewter GENERAL: Mahogany, china, glass, silver plate, jewellery, pottery, walnut, prints OTHER INFO: Hadlow Folly, St Mary's Church (1000 years old). Cremaillère restaurant.

SEVENOAKS (0732)

Amherst Antiques, 23 London Road, Riverhead TN13 2BU TEL: 455047 PARKING: Difficult OPEN: Mon, Tues, Thurs-Sat 9.30-5 MIN: £10 MAX: £4,000 PERIOD: 18th-20th century SPECIALIST: Tunbridgeware, 19th century European ceramics GENERAL: Small furniture, silver, coloured glass, prints OTHER INFO: Shop on main A25. Good buying route through Brasted & Westerham. Chartwell, Hever Castle, Penshurst Place, Ightham Mote & Knole House all nearby.

The Antiques Centre, 120 London Road, Tubs Hill, TN13 1BA TEL: 452104 PARKING: Easy OPEN: 10-1, 2-4.30, but Weds & Sat 10-1 & by appt (ring doorbell-resident) MIN: £5 MAX: £5,000 PERIOD: 17th-19th century GENERAL: Large & small furniture in mahogany, oak, etc plus all interesting & decorative items, silver, porcelain, brass, copper. Reference books on antiques. OTHER INFO: Close to Knowle House, Hever Castle, Igtham Mote. Close to station, London 25 mins.

Bradbourne Gallery, 4 St John's Hill, TN13 3NP TEL: 460756 FAX: 460756 PARKING: Easy OPEN: Mon-Fri 9.30-5, Sats 9-1 MIN: £1 MAX: £1,000+ PERIOD: 18th-20th century GENERAL: Furniture, silver, copper, brass, jewellery, glass, china, kicthenalia, bygones OTHER INFO: Interior design service.

Chandlers Antiques & Upholstery, 4b St John's Hill TEL: 743680 PARKING: Easy OPEN: Mon-Fri 9.30-5, Sat 9.30-1 MIN: £20 MAX: £3,000 PERIOD: 18th-20th century SPECIALIST: Furniture GENERAL: Ceramics, glass, pictures.

Mandarin Gallery, 32 London Road, Riverhead, TN13 2DE TEL: 457399 PARKING: Easy OPEN: Mon, Tues, Thurs-Sat 9.30-5 MIN: £150 MAX: £3,500 PERIOD: 18th-20th century SPECIALIST: Chinese hardwood furniture GENERAL: Porcelain, paintings, ivories OTHER INFO: Donnington Manor Hotel.

Sheldon Ward Antiques, 57 St Johns Hill, TN13 3NY TEL: 455311 PARKING: Medium OPEN: Tues, Thurs 10-5, Fri 2-5, Sat 10-1 MIN: £10 MAX: £1,200 PERIOD: 19th-20th century GENERAL STOCK: Furniture & mixed bric-a-brac OTHER INFO: Penshurst Place, Knole House, Hever Castle & 6 others within 10 miles and all 12th-15th century.

SHOREHAM (0959)

The Porcelain Collector, High Street, TN14 7TD TEL: 23416 PARKING: Easy OPEN: By appt MIN: £50 MAX: £2,000 PERIOD: 19th-20th century SPECIALIST: Worcester porcelain from founding of original companies to present day, Lambeth wares GENERAL: English & Continental porcelain figures up to Art Deco period, modern porcelain & bronze limited editions, particularly military subjects OTHER INFO: Specialist in porcelain restoration. In unspoilt River Darenth valley.

SUNDRIDGE (0959)

Sundridge Gallery, 9 Church Road TEL: 564104 PARKING: Own carpark OPEN: 10-5.30 & by appt MIN: £80 MAX: £15,000 PERIOD: 19th-20th century SPECIALIST: Quality British watercolours, some oils GENERAL: Some period rugs OTHER INFO: Close to Brasted village, Ide Hill (NT) & Emmetts.

Colin Wilson Antiques, 103 Main Road, TN14 6EQ TEL: 562043 PARKING: Medium OPEN: 10-5 MIN: £200 MAX: £2,000 PERIOD: 19th century SPECIALIST: Mahogany furniture GENERAL: Chests, tables, bookcases, sets of chairs, single armchairs OTHER INFO: Chartwell, Ightham Mote (NT) etc

BRASTED (0959)

The Attic (Sevenoaks) Ltd., The Village House, TN16 1HU TEL: 63507 ASSNS: ABA PARKING: Own carpark STOCK: 18th-20th century.

Courtyard Antiques, High Street TEL: 64483 PARKING: Own carpark OPEN: Mon-Sat 10-5.30 MIN: £20 MAX: £3,000 PERIOD: 19th-20th century SPECIALIST: Large Victorian wind-out tables, jewellery, silver GENERAL: Furniture, porcelain OTHER INFO: Near

Chartwell, Knole Park & Sevenoaks.

Peter Dyke, Kentish House, High Street, TN16 1RJ TEL: 9.30-5 PARKING: Easy OPEN: 9.30-5 MIN: £250 MAX: £10,000 PERIOD: 18th-19th century SPECIALIST: Library & dining room furniture GENERAL: Georgian, some Victorian furniture, mainly early 19th century items, some paintings OTHER INFO: In centre of village next to popular tearooms

Roy Massingham Antiques, The Old Coach House, High Street TEL: 62408 ASSNS: LAPADA PARKING: Good OPEN: Mon-Sat 9.30-5.30 MIN: £150 MAX: £15,000 PERIOD: 18th-19th century SPECIALIST: Furniture GENERAL: Pictures and decorative furniture.

Old Bakery Antiques, High Street, TN16 1JA TEL: 562994 PARKING: Easy OPEN: 9.30-5.30 MIN: £200 MAX: £2,500 PERIOD: 18th-19th century SPECIALIST: Antique pine & country furniture OTHER INFO: Kent's premier antique village, 18+ shops.

The Old Manor House, The Green, TN16 1JL TEL: 562536 PARKING: Easy OPEN: 10-5.30 MIN: £1 MAX: £4,000 PERIOD: 18th-20th century SPECIALIST: Mantel/regulators/longcase clocks GENERAL: Barometers, small furniture, mirrors, lights, copperware, boxes OTHER INFO: Chartwell, Emmetts Gardens, Quebec House, Biggin Hill aerodrome, Squerryes Court, Knole Park.

Southdown House Antiques, High Street, TN16 1JE Tel: 563522 PARKING: Own carpark OPEN: Mon-Sat 9.30-5.30 not Bank Hols MAX: £5,000 PERIOD: 18th-early 20th century SPECIALIST: Derby porcelain, watercolours GENERAL: Furniture, pictures, porcelain, metalware, glass, textiles.

Dinah Stoodley, High Street, TN16 1JE TEL: 563616 PARKING: Own carpark OPEN: Mon-Sat 9.30-5.30 PERIOD: 17th-18th century MIN: £50 MAX: £10,000 SPECIALIST: Period oak & country furniture, English ceramics.

Tilings Antiques, High Street TEL: 564735 PARKING: Easy OPEN: Mon-Sat 10-5 MIN: £10 MAX: £2,000 PERIOD: 17th-19th century GENERAL: Furniture, porcelain, decorative items, needlework.

WESTERHAM (0959)

Apollo Galleries, 19-21 Market Square, TN16 1AN TEL: 562200 ASSNS: LAPADA PARKING: Medium OPEN: Mon-Sat 9.30-5.30 MIN: £20 MAX: £12,500 PERIOD: 18th-early 20th century (mainly 19th) SPECIALIST: Victorian oils & bronzes GENERAL: Clocks, watercolours, furniture, porcelain, silver, pottery, glass boxes, objets d'art OTHER INFO: King's Arm Hotel, Chartwell (NT), Honours Mill restaurant in centre Edenbridge (expensive but superb!).

Castle Antiques Centre, 1 London Road, TEL: 562492 PARKING: Medium OPEN: Mon-Sat10-5 MIN: £1 MAX: £500 PERIOD: 19th-20th century SPECIALIST: Linen GENERAL: Silver plate, books, postcards, small furniture, country bygones, carpets (8 dealers) OTHER INFO: Centre of tourist area, Penshurst Place, Hever Castle, Knole House, Quebec House, Chartwell. Good hotels, 50 local antique shops, 6 antiques centres.

Anthony Hook Antiques, 3 The Green, TN16 1AT TEL: 562161 PARKING: Medium OPEN: 9-5.30 MIN: £100 MAX: £10,000 PERIOD: 18th-20th century GENERAL: Furniture.

Hugh McNair Antiques, Fullers Hill TEL: 562970 PARKING: Medium OPEN: Mon-Sat 10-5 MIN: £5 MAX: £1,000 PERIOD: 18th-19th century SPECIALIST: Small silverware GENERAL: Furniture, music boxes OTHER INFO: Centre of very popular, busy tourist & antiques area but well worth stopping. 2 large carparks on outskirts of town.

Mistral Galleries, 12 Market Square, TN16 1AW TEL: 564477 FAX: 61417 PARKING: Easy OPEN: Mon-Sat 9.30-5.30 MIN: £500 MAX: £50,000 PERIOD: 18th-19th century SPECIALIST: Victorian oil paintings & watercolours GENERAL: Fine quality period English & continental furniture, porcelain, silver, bronzes OTHER INFO: Historic Westerham and its neighbouring village, Brasted, boast an enormous selection of antiques shops. Also some great pubs. Squerry's Court, Quebec House, Emmett's Gardens

Old Hall Antiques, 24 Market Square, TN16 1AR TEL: 563114 ASSNS: LAPADA PARKING: Easy MIN: £30 MAX: £10,000+ PERIOD: 17th-19th century SPECIALIST: Early oak furniture GENERAL: Brass, copper, pewter, Delft carvings

Taylor-Smith Antiques & Books, 4 The Grange, High Street, TN16 1AH TEL: 563100 PARKING: Own carpark OPEN: Mon-Sat 10-5 MIN: £50 MAX: £15,000 PERIOD: 18th-19th century SPECIALIST: Items relating to Sir Winston Churchill, furniture, Lalique, Gallé and Art Deco OTHER INFO: Westerham has 14 antique shops.

BIGGIN HILL (0959)

Antiques & Country Pine International, Leaves Green Trading Company, Unit 4, Concorde Business Centre, The Airport, TN16 3YN TEL: 540449 FAX: 540448 PARKING: Own carpark OPEN: Mon-Sat 10-5 MIN: £5 MAX: £500 PERIOD: 18th-20th century SPECIALIST: Full range of pieces made from antique timbers GENERAL: Antique & reproduction country pine furniture from all over UK & Europe, wholesale/retail. Containers packed for overseas OTHER INFO: World famous WWII Battle of Britain airfield, 4 miles from Winston Churchill's home at Chartwell.

M25 to the East Sussex Coast

Royal Pavilion, Brighton. By courtesy of Brighton Borough Council.

This tour starts and ends on the southern fringes of Greater London. Most of the route passes through the lovely Surrey and Sussex countryside with historic market towns and including some of the most famous and, once upon a time, most fashionable of English seaside resorts.

We start in the small town of Carshalton before moving on to Croydon. Seeing modern Croydon, it is almost impossible for the visitor to guess at its ancient origins. Situated on the Roman road between London and Portsmouth, from Norman times the area was owned by the Archbishops of Canterbury. The Archbishops' 14th century manor house still exists and is now used as a school. With the coming of the railways the population increased rapidly throughout the 19th century. Croydon Airport was built in 1915 and it was from here that Amy Johnson left for her record breaking flight to Australia. During the Second World War the town was heavily bombed which led to extensive rebuilding and the construction of the modern town centre seen today.

Sanderstead and Kenley are the next towns on the tour before we arrive in the linked towns of Reigate and Redhill, the latter having an unusual museum: the

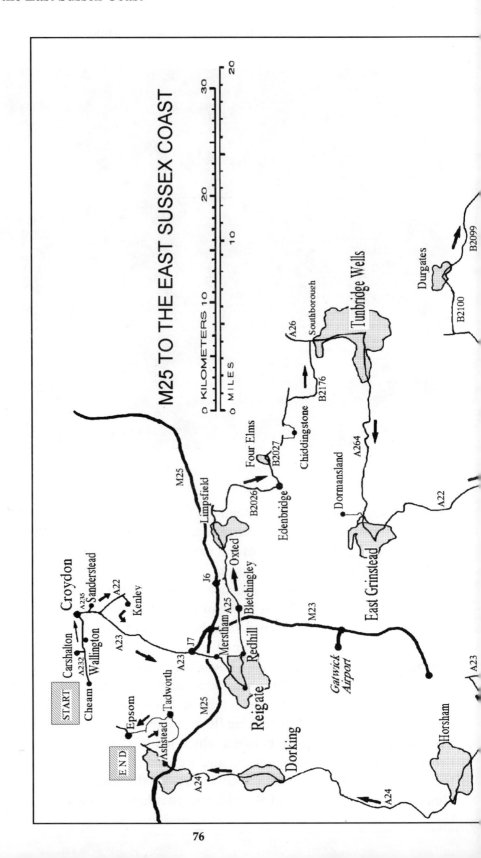

M25 TO THE EAST SUSSEX COAST

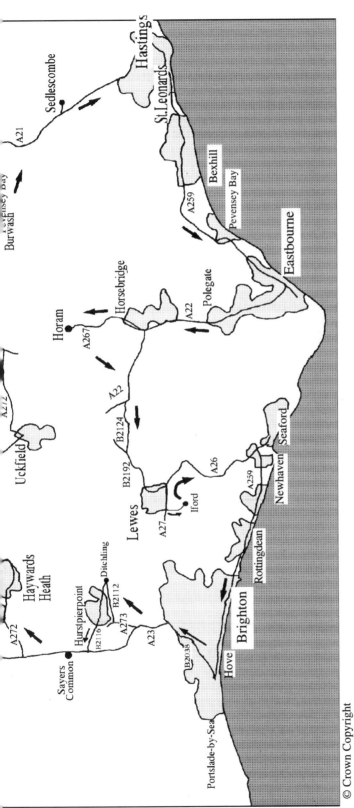

Royal Earlswood Hospital Museum dealing, unsurprisingly, with medical history. Following the A25 the route reaches Bletchingley, Oxted and Limpsfield.

Nearby Edenbridge is close to the 13th century, double-moated Hever Castle, the childhood home of Henry VIII's tragic Queen, Anne Boleyn. This magnificent castle is set in 40 acres of garden featuring a maze, topiary, a wonderful Italian garden and a 35 acre lake. It was in these gardens that Henry VIII is said to have courted Anne Boleyn. At the beginning of this century the American millionaire, William Waldorf Astor, bought the castle and spent three years restoring it and filling it with wonderful things. Now there are exhibitions on the Astors and Anne Boleyn as well as a regimental museum.

Now on to the village of Chiddingstone with its castle. This is mostly an 18th and 19th century building although it does incorporate part of a late 17th century manor house. It contains some fascinating things: Egyptian antiquities, Japanese swords and armour, lacquerware, Stuart and Jacobite memorabilia as well as fine furniture and paintings.

Southborough and Tunbridge Wells are our next stops. Tunbridge Wells, perhaps seen now as the epitome of suburban gentility, began life in the 17th century as a fashionable spa. The area of the Pantiles takes its name from the large roofing tiles that were laid as a pavement.

After detouring slightly to Dormansland the next town is East Grinstead. The town appears as a typical commuter sprawl but in the High Street it still retains the layout and many of the buildings of a medieval market town. Still standing are 16th century half-timbered houses and some even date from the 14th and 15th centuries. Another landmark, the Sackville College (not an educational college but rather almhouses), was built by the the Earl of Dorset, Thomas Sackville, and was completed in 1619. One of the wardens was the Rev. John Mason Neale who ran the college from 1846 until his death twenty years later. He wrote the hymns Good King Wenceslas and Jerusalem the Golden.

The Sackville family also had a less charitable claim to fame in the town. Before the 1832 Reform Act, East Grinstead was a rotten borough with only 48 plots having the right to vote attached to them. The Sackvilles bought enough of the plots to control the seat.

East Grinstead is renowned in the field of medicine for the revolutionary plastic surgery work done at the Queen Victoria Hospital by Sir Archibald McIndoe. He started in the hospital at the beginning of the Second World War and continued there until his death in 1960. He is particularly famous for his work on severely burned airmen whose special club, The Guinea Pigs, is still centred on the Queen Victoria.

From East Grinstead we continue to Uckfield which has the Sheffield Park Garden on the A275. This is a beautiful garden with a series of lakes joined by cascades and with a great variety of lovely and unusual plants. It is also close to the famous Bluebell Railway at Sheffield Park. This operates vintage steam trains between here and Horsted Keynes in Sussex.

Turning east our next stop is Mayfield with some buildings dating from the 16th century, then we continue on to Durgates before taking the B2099 to the village of Hurst Green and then the A265 to the charming village of Burwash. Iron smelting was an important industry here in past centuries and the oldest iron gravestone in Sussex may be found in the churchyard. Rudyard Kipling lived in the 17th century house, Batemans, from 1902 to 1936 and also used the area as a setting in *Puck of Pook's Hill.*

Going via Sedlescombe the tour reaches Hastings, a Cinque Port. In Saxon times this was an important harbour. When William the Conquerer arrived to start his conquest of England he landed a few miles away at Pevensey Bay and went to Hastings where he built a fortress. He then marched to Battle and defeated King Harold. The ruins of the later Hastings Castle can still be seen on the site of that Norman fortress.

The Hastings Embroidery, an interesting modern feature displayed in the Town Hall, is nearly 250 feet long and was made in 1966 to commemorate the 900th anniversary of the Battle of Hastings. It consists of over eighty events from British history including the murder of Becket right up to the 1953 conquest of Everest. Also on display are items of maritime history. Another fascinating museum is the award winning Shipwreck Heritage Centre in Rock-a-Nore Road. The major exhibits here are from three local wrecks, a warship from 1690, a Dutch ship dated 1749 and a Danish ship of 1861. This is the only museum in Britain licensed and equipped with radar to monitor shipping in the English Channel. It also has a direct link to satellites for weather forecasting.

Now turning west along the coast we pass through St Leonards and Bexhill to arrive in Pevensey, where William the Conqueror landed. The castle here dates from the 4th century AD. It was one of the forts built all along the coast from Hampshire to Norfolk as defences against the Saxons. Unlike some other forts of the period, Pevensey did not fall into disuse after the departure of the Romans and in fact the Normans built a castle on the site. During the Middle Ages Pevensey Castle saw considerable action. It was held by the rebel Bishop of Bayeaux, Odo, against the king in 1088 and had to be retaken by siege. Some 15 years later it was used by another rebel, the Count of Mortain, in a revolt against Henry I which resulted in that family losing Pevensey. Its troubled history continued until the 15th century in spite of the fact that by then it was in a sad state of disrepair with contemporary reports of walls falling down and the keep being in a ruinous condition. It was only in 1587 when England was threatened by the Spanish Armada that the castle was repaired as part of the coastal defences but after this it was once again left to decay. The castle's last service was during the Second World War when once again invasion threatened. The castle had 'pill-boxes' (gun emplacements) built on some of the Roman walls and bastions and the medieval towers were adapted for the accommodation of troops. These alterations were all camouflaged to blend into the rest of the castle.

Our next stop is Eastbourne, seen by many as the epitome of the genteel 19th century seaside resort with its elegant parades and gardens. For those interested in seeing how the town looked in Victorian times the Towner Art Gallery & Local History Museum have a display of watercolours of Eastbourne in the 1850s. The Museum covers the area from prehistoric to Edwardian times and is housed in a Georgian manor house.

We now turn north to reach Polegate, Horsebridge and, detouring a little, Horam, before again heading westwards for the town of Lewes, situated on a gap in the South Downs through which flows the River Ouse. The town has a history going back at least to Saxon times. King Alfred established a fort here and later the Norman, William de Warenne, Earl of Surrey and Sussex and son-in-law of William the Conqueror, built a castle on two artificial mounds made of large lumps of quarried chalk. This castle saw little action until 1264 when Simon de Montfort fought and defeated Henry III just outside Lewes. Soon after this two towers were added to the keep and in the 14th century a barbican was built. However, it was then ignored as being of little military significance. By the early 17th century it was gradually being demolished for building material. It was only when a local merchant leased it and converted the keep into a summer house that the rest was saved. Now remains of the walls and barbican can still be seen.

There is a connection with one of Henry VIII's wives in the town. When Henry divorced his fourth wife he gave her a house in Lewes, now called Anne of Cleves house. Built at the beginning of the 16th century with additions made later in the century, it is now used as a folk museum and houses the Every Collection of ironwork, including spits, ladles, stewpans, embossed firebacks, and chimney-cranes. The museum also displays furniture, local crafts and prisoner-of-war art made by Russian prisoners from the Crimea.

The twisting High Street contains many buildings of interest: houses that are flint-faced, Georgian, timber-framed, stucco, tile-clad. At the top of the High Street stands the Norman church of St Anne's, the oldest church in Lewes. Immediately to the south is Southover High Street where St John's Church now houses the remains of William de Warenne and his wife, Gundrada. This church was originally the guesthouse of the Priory of St Pancras, founded by William and Gundrada. Apart from the guesthouse, the priory was destroyed in the Dissolution of the Monasteries and only a few walls and foundations can be seen.

Two notable houses stand a mile apart on the Eastbourne to Lewes road: Firle Place and Glynde Place. The first was originally a Tudor mansion but much altered in the 18th century. It now has an important collection of European and British paintings. The house has been the home of the Gage family since the 15th

The Lanes, Brighton. By courtesy of Brighton Borough Council

century and contains items relating to General Gage, Commander of the British Forces in the American War of Independence. Glynde Place is a lovely 16th century house built around a courtyard. It has an interesting collection of pictures, bronzes and historical documents.

After first visiting Iford we again head for the coast and the towns of Seaford, Newhaven and Rottingdean before arriving in Brighton. Originally called Brighthelmstone, it is the most famous of the Sussex seaside resorts. It owes it pre-eminence to the Prince Regent who first visited the small fishing village in 1783. Here he built the Royal Pavilion which was originally constructed to a much more conventional design. Later alterations gave it the flamboyance and startling Oriental flavour which has made it such an enduring landmark and symbol of the town. However unthinkable Brighton without the Royal Pavilion might seem this almost happened. During the reign of Queen Victoria the Pavilion was left to decay and was nearly demolished in 1850. It was only saved by the residents of Brighton raising £50,000 to buy it. Over the years it has been restored to its former splendour and its original contents returned.

The Lanes are another quaint, much visited feature of the town, particularly for the antiques enthusiast. This is an area of narrow alleys and tiny squares, some of which are the remains of old Brighthelmstone rebuilt in the 17th century after part of the original village had been washed away by the sea.

The adjoining town of Hove has an interesting museum: The British Engineerium in Nevill Road. This is a working steam museum in the restored Goldstone Pumping Station. It has an Eastons and Anderson beam engine from 1876 and many other full size engines and hundreds of models. The museum recounts the story of the development of the many different uses of steam power. It also undertakes restoration projects from all over the world and the work done on these can be viewed in their workshops.

After first visiting Portslade the route turns north to Ditchling, Hurstpierpoint, Sayers Common and Cuckfield before reaching Haywards Heath and Lindfield. The next town, Horsham is well worth a visit. It has been a borough and market town since the 13th century. Its most notable feature is the Causeway which is a quiet street lined with timber-framed and Georgian houses leading down to the 13th century church. At the top of the Causeway stands the 16th century Causeway House which is now a museum with exhibits ranging from prehistory to bicycles. Five miles from Horsham on the junction of the A279 and A281 stands Leonardslee Gardens. This is a most beautiful place set in a valley with six lakes. It has wonderful displays of camellias, magnolias, rhododendrons and azaleas. It also has an exhibition of Bonsai. We now go on to Dorking, a pleasant town surroundedby beautiful Green Belt countryside preventing urban expansion. The town boasts fine 17th century, Georgian and Victorian buildings

The Bluebell Railway. By courtesy of Brighton Borough Council

in its High Street.

Box Hill, one mile north of Dorking on the A24, is a striking landmark rising 400 feet above the River Mole. It is a beautiful area with the gentle rounded features of a chalk escarpment and crowned with beechwoods. The summit gives breath-taking views over the surrounding countryside and it is a popular place for day trips from London.

Ashtead, Tadworth and Epsom are the last stops on this tour. The latter is famous for its racecourse on Epsom Downs, a mile and a half from the town. The Derby has been run here since 1780 and it is also the scene of another great classic race, the Oaks. The town was well-known in the 18th century for its medicinal springs from which we get the name Epsom Salts. Back on the edges of the capital city, we finish the tour.

ANTIQUE DEALERS

CHEAM VILLAGE (081)

Rogers Antique Interiors, 22 Ewell Road, SM3 8BU TEL: 643 8466 FAX: 715 9898 ASSNS: LAPADA PARKING: Easy OPEN: 10-5.30, closed Wed MIN: £50 MAX: £2,000 PERIOD: 18th-20th century SPECIALIST: Furniture GENERAL: Decorative items, pictures, upholstered furniture, smalls. Fabrics, wallpaper, full Sesksner ranges. Interior design service OTHER INFO: Nonsuch Palace (Henry VIII's outer London residence), Yeoman's House (open), World champion's Ballroom Dance Centre.

CARSHALTON (081)

McDonald Antiques, 376 Carshalton Road, TEL: 669 7402 ASSNS: BAFRA PARKING: Medium OPEN: Mon-Sat 10.30-6 MIN: £2 MAX: £500 PERIOD: 19th-20th century GENERAL: Antique & shipping furniture, general smalls, collectors junk OTHER INFO: Next to Windsor Castle pub

WALLINGTON (081)

Manor Antiques, 75a Manor Road TEL: 669 5970 PARKING: Easy OPEN: Mon, Tues, Thurs-Sat 10.30-5 MIN: £1 MAX: £500 PERIOD: 19th-20th century GENERAL: General antiques.

CROYDON (081)

G.E. Griffin, (estd 1890), 43a Brighton Road, South Croydon, CR2 6EB TEL: 688 3130 PARKING: Easy OPEN: 8-5 MIN: £10 MAX: £10,000 PERIOD: 19th-20th century SPECIALIST: Furniture GENERAL: Antiques.

Collectors Corner, 43 Brighton Road, South Croydon, CR0 6EB TEL: 680 7511 PARKING: Medium OPEN: Tues, Thurs-Sat 9.30-4.30 MIN: £5 MAX: £10,000 PERIOD: 19th-20th century SPECIALIST: Dinky, die cast toys, old dolls, teddies GENERAL: Cigarette cards, postcards, furniture, bric-a-brac & any collectable items OTHER INFO: Ashcroft Theatre.

Trengrove, 46 South End, CR0 1DP TEL: 688 2155 PARKING: Medium OPEN: 9.30-4, closed Wed MIN: £5 MAX: £5,000 PERIOD: 19th-20th century GENERAL: Wide range, bit of everything.

KENLEY (081)

Michael Addison Antiques, 28-30 Godstone Road, CR8 5JE TEL: 668 6714 PARKING: Easy OPEN: 10-5 MIN: £100 MAX: £2,000 PERIOD: 18th-20th century GENERAL: Victorian, Georgian & Edwardian furniture OTHER INFO Selsdon Park Hotel.

MERSTHAM (0737)

The Old Smithy, 7 High Street TEL: 642306 FAX: 660 8633 PARKING: Own carpark OPEN: 10-5 & by appt MIN: £1 MAX: £2,500 PERIOD: 18th-20th century SPECIALIST: Lighting, glassware GENERAL: Furniture, collectables, pictures, prints OTHER INFO: 2 more shops here, 14th century church.

REIGATE (0737)

Bourne Gallery, 31-33 Lesbourne Road, RH2 7JS TEL: 241614 ASSNS: LAPADA PARKING: Easy OPEN: Mon, Tues, Thurs-Sat 10-1 & 2-5.30, Weds 10-1 MIN: £150 MAX: £10,000 PERIOD: 19th-20th century SPECIALIST: Pictures, oil paintings, British and European watercolours OTHER INFO: La Barbe, fine French cuisine.

Heath Antiques, 15 Flanchford Road, RH2 8AB TEL: 244230 PARKING: Easy OPEN: Mon-Fri 10-6, Sats & Suns 2-5, prefer prior appt MIN: £2 MAX: £1,500 PERIOD: 18th-20th century SPECIALIST: Small furniture, porcelain GENERAL: Silver, porcelain, country artefacts, furniture OTHER INFO: Shop is on Reigate Heath, just off A25 Dorking Rd.

Bertram Noller (Reigate), 14A London Road, RH2 9HY TEL: 242548 PARKING: Easy OPEN: Mon, Thurs & Sat 9.30-1 & 2-5.30 MIN: £1 MAX: £500 PERIOD: 19th-20th century SPECIALIST: Fireplace equipment, including brass fenders & fire grates GENERAL: Brass, copper, silver, lamps, small furniture & curios OTHER INFO: Shop backs onto castle moat, mound & caves under castle.

REDHILL (0737)

F.G. Lawrence & Sons, 89 Brighton Road, RH1 6PS TEL: 764196 PARKING: Own carpark OPEN: Mon, Tues, Thurs, Fri 9-1 & 2-5, Wed 9-1 & Sats 10-1 MIN: £50 MAX: £5,000 PERIOD: 17th-20th century SPECIALIST: Georgian, Victorian, Edwardian furniture OTHER INFO: Bridge House Motel, Reigate Hill Hotel.

BLETCHINGLEY (0883)

The Cider House Galleries Ltd., Norfolk House, 80 High Street, RH1 4AA TEL: 742198 FAX: 744014 PARKING: Own carpark OPEN:

Mon-Fri 9.30-5.30. Sats 10-1 MIN: £250 MAX: £40,000 PERIOD: 17th-20th century SPECIALIST : 19th century Victorian GENERAL: 600+ oils in stock OTHER INFO: Village has 9 antique shops. Close to Nutfield Priory Hotel.

Post House Antiques, High Street, RH1 4PE TEL: 743317 PARKING: Easy OPEN: Mon-Fri 10-5, Sats 9.30-4 or by appt MIN: £10 MAX: £1,500 PERIOD: 18th-20th century SPECIALIST: Antique restored lighting GENERAL: Wood, metal, decorative etc in 6 showrooms.

OXTED (0883)

Antiques & Interiors, 64 Station Road East TEL: 712806 PARKING: Easy OPEN: Mon-Sat 9.30-5.30 MIN: £5 MAX: £2,000 PERIOD: 19th-20th century GENERAL: Wide range of antiques, interior design OTHER INFO: Coffee shop on site, good lunches.

Treasures, 151 Station Road East TEL: 713301 PARKING: Medium OPEN: Mon-Sat 10-5 MIN: £1 MAX: £500 PERIOD: 19th century GENERAL: Antique Centre with 12 dealers offering porcelain, clocks, silver, jewellery, small furniture, pictures, collectables etc.

LIMPSFIELD (0883)

Limpsfield Watercolours, High Street TEL: 717010 PARKING: Easy OPEN: Tues 11-3, Thurs, Fri 10-2, Sat 10-3 MIN: £7 MAX: £5,000 PERIOD: 19th-20th century SPECIALIST: Victorian, Edwardian watercolours GENERAL: Contemporary artists, antiquarian prints OTHER INFO: Old Lodge restaurant opposite, Chartwell, Hever Castle.

EDENBRIDGE (0892)

Chevertons of Edenbridge Ltd, 67-71 High Street, TN8 5AL TEL: 863196, 863358 FAX: 864298 ASSNS: LAPADA PARKING: Own carpark OPEN: Mon-Sat 9-5.30 MIN: £250 MAX: £25,000 PERIOD: 17th-19th century SPECIALIST: English & Continental furniture in 20 showrooms.

FOUR ELMS (0732)

Treasures, The Crossroads TEL: 700363 PARKING: Easy OPEN: Mon-Sat 10-5 MIN: £1 MAX: £285 PERIOD: 19th-20th century GENERAL: 9 dealers with quality silver, jewellery, porcelain, linen, small furniture.

CHIDDINGSTONE (0892)

Barbara Lane Antiques, Tudor Cottages, TN8 7AH TEL: 870577 PARKING: Own carpark OPEN: Daily (as much as possible) 12 noon-5 PERIOD: 17th-19th century GENERAL: Furniture, glass, ceramics, brass, bric-a-brac OTHER INFO: National Trust houses in village, many famous buildings in the area.

SOUTHBOROUGH (0892)

Henry Baines, 14 Church Road, TN4 0RX TEL: 532099 ASSNS: LAPADA PARKING: Easy OPEN: Mon-Fri 9.30-5, Sat 10-4.30 MIN: £50 MAX: £15,000 PERIOD: 17th-19th century SPECIALIST: Early English & Continental oak & country furniture especially sets of country chairs GENERAL: We import French farm tables.

TUNBRIDGE WELLS (0892)

Amadeus Antiques, 32 Mount Ephraim TEL: 544406 PARKING: Own carpark OPEN: 9.30-5 MIN: £10 MAX: £5,000 PERIOD: 19th-20th century SPECIALIST: Unusual interesting furniture GENERAL: China, bric-a-brac, lighting OTHER INFO: Town centre a short walk.

Annexe Antiques, 33 The Pantiles, TN2 5TE TEL: 547213 PARKING: Medium OPEN: Mon, Tues, Thurs-Sat 9.30-5 MIN: £5 MAX: £2,000 PERIOD: 17th-20th century SPECIALIST: Antique weapons, books, prints, games, Staffordshire china, silver & porcelain.

Nicholas Bowlby, 9 Castle Street, TN1 1XJ TEL: 510880 PARKING: Medium OPEN: Tues, Thurs-Sat 10-5.30 MIN: £50 MAX: £20,000 century SPECIALIST: Early 19th-early 20th century watercolours GENERAL: Paintings OTHER INFO: In town's prettiest street close to Pantiles.

Chapel Place Antiques, 9 Chapel Place, TN1 1YP TEL: 546561 PARKING: Easy OPEN: Mon-Sat 9-6 MIN: £1 MAX: £3,000+ PERIOD: 19th-20th century SPECIALIST: New, hallmarked silver, picture frames, candlesticks etc GENERAL: Antique & new jewellery, glass, brass, copper, silver plate etc OTHER INFO: Pantiles area & Chapel Place is old & quite charming.

Clare Gallery, 21 High Street TEL: 38717 PARKING: Medium OPEN: Mon-Sat 9-5.30 MIN: £3 MAX: £20,000 PERIOD: 19th-20th century SPECIALIST: Paintings GENERAL: Ceramic & glass giftware.

PANTILES SPA ANTIQUES

4/5/6 Union House, The Pantiles,
Royal Tunbridge Wells,
Kent TN4 8HE
Telephone: 0892 541377

*Visit our spacious showroom
and select treasures from our large
collection of antiques.*

County Antiques, 94 High Street TEL: 530767 PARKING: Medium OPEN: Mon-Sat 10-5 MIN: £10 MAX: £1,000 PERIOD: 18th-20th century GENERAL: Oak, mahogany, chairs, treen, silver plate.

Cowden Antiques, 24 Mount Ephraim Road TEL: 520752 ASSNS: LAPADA PARKING: Medium OPEN: 10-5 MIN: £50 MAX: £5,000 PERIOD: 17th-19th century GENERAL: Period oak, mahogany & decorative items OTHER INFO: Listed Thackery's restaurant & bistro.

Franca Antiques, 2-4 Castle Street TEL: 525779 PARKING: Medium OPEN: 10.30-5.30 MIN: £5 MAX: £1,500 PERIOD: 19th-20th century GENERAL: Prints, postal history, furniture, china, glass, jewellery, silver.

Graham Gallery, 1 Castle Street, TN1 1XJ TEL: 526695 PARKING: Medium OPEN: Tues, Thurs-Sat 10.30-5 MIN: £100 MAX: £4,500 PERIOD: 19th-20th century SPECIALIST: Watercolours & modern British paintings OTHER INFO: Castle Street (off High Street), is village area & centre for specialist shopping.

Hadlow Antiques, No.1 The Pantiles TEL: 529858 PARKING: Medium OPEN: Mon, Tues, Thurs, Fri 10-1 & 2-5. Wed, Sat 10-1 PERIOD: 17th-20th century SPECIALIST: Clocks, watches, instruments, dolls, automata, mechanical music.

Linden Park Antiques, 7 Union Square, The Pantiles, TN4 8HE TEL: 538615 PARKING: Easy OPEN: Mon-Sat 10-5.30 MIN: £10+ MAX: £5,000 PERIOD: 19th-20th century SPECIALIST: Extending tables, Victorian dining room furniture GENERAL: Furniture, porcelain, prints, brass, copper OTHER INFO: In the historic colonnaded shopping area, The Pantiles, which grew around the Chalybeate Spa Spring in 18th century.

Pantiles Spa Antiques, 4-6 Union House, The Pantiles, TN4 8HE TEL: 541377 FAX: (0435) 862748 PARKING: Easy OPEN: Mon-Sat 9.30-5 MIN: £30 MAX: £20,000 PERIOD: 17th-19th century SPECIALIST: Dolls GENERAL: Wide variety furniture includes dining tables, silver, porcelain, jewellery all in spacious showroom in room settings.

Rare Chairs, 37 Quarry Road TEL: 521783 PARKING: Easy OPEN: 10-5.30 MIN: £150 MAX: £2,500 PERIOD: 18th-19th century SPECIALIST: Bottom back chairs GENERAL: Furniture.

Patricia Russell Antiques, 43 Mount Ephraim, TN4 8AA TEL: 523719 PARKING: Medium OPEN: 10-5.30 MIN: £20 MAX: £800 PERIOD: 18th-19th century GENERAL: Jewellery, silver, paintings, small furniture, china OTHER INFO: Spa, Royal Wells hotels, Thackerays's restaurant.

Strawson Antiques, 39-41 The Pantiles, TN2 5TE TEL: 530607 PARKING: Easy OPEN: Mon, Tues Thurs-Sat 9.30-5.30. Wed AM only MIN: £20 MAX: £5,000 PERIOD: 18th-19th century SPECIALIST: Tunbridgeware GENERAL: Furniture OTHER INFO: The Pantiles, Eridge, Hever, Tonbridge, Penshurst castles all close.

John Thompson, 27 The Pantiles TEL: 547215 PARKING: Medium OPEN: 9.30-1, 2-5.30 MIN: £100 MAX: £5,000 PERIOD: 18th-20th century GENERAL: Quality furniture & paintings, decorative items.

Tunbridge Wells Antique Centre, 12 Union Square, The Pantiles TEL: (0474) 834120 PARKING: Easy OPEN: Mon-Sat 9.30-5 MIN: £1 MAX: £5,000 PERIOD: 18th-20th century SPECIALIST: Staffordshire figures, linen & lace, jewellery GENERAL: 24 dealers in 2,500 sq ft showing furniture, silver, pottery, pine, pictures etc OTHER INFO: Pantiles has all facilities, 3 antique centres and 6 antique shops.

Up Country, The Old Corn Stores, 68 St.Johns Road, TN4 9PE TEL: 523341 FAX: 530382 PARKING: Own carpark OPEN: Mon-Sat 9-5.30 MIN: £20 MAX: £5,000 PERIOD: 19th-20th century SPECIALIST: Period, pine & fruitwood furniture GENERAL: Country furniture & decorative artefacts OTHER INFO: 4,000 sq ft in 5 showrooms in world's first pedestrian shopping area. Courier service. Shipping services with parent company. Packing & restorations.

DORMANSLAND (0342)

Keith Atkinson Antiques, Moorhawes Farm,Sandhawes Hill, RH19 3NR TEL: 87765 Mobile: 0860 323387, 0836 640041 FAX: 87767 PARKING: Own carpark OPEN: Seven day customer service MIN: £20 MAX: £10,000 PERIOD: 19th-20th century GENERAL: Georgian, Victorian, Edwardian & shipping furniture. OTHER INFO: Gravetye Manor, Hever Castle, other dealers.

EAST GRINSTEAD (0342)

The Antique Print Shop, 11 Middle Row, High Street, RH19 3AX TEL: 410501 FAX: 410795 PARKING: Easy OPEN: Mon-Sat 9.30-6 MIN: £10 MAX: £5,000 PERIOD: 15th-19th century SPECIALIST: Rare 15th, 16th century maps GENERAL: Wide selection of antique maps & prints covering many subjects. Decorative prints OTHER INFO: Gravetye Manor, Alexander House. Excellent hotels etc.

UCKFIELD (0825)

Barnes Gallery, 8 Church Street, TN22 1BJ TEL: 762066 PARKING: Easy OPEN: Tues-Sat 10-1, 2-5 MIN: £100 MAX: £5,000 PERIOD: 19th century SPECIALIST: Watercolour scenes of rural England GENERAL: Watercolours, oil paintings & drawings OTHER INFO: Horsted Place Hotel associated with East Sussex National Golf club, caters particularly for overseas clients.

I.R. Deverall, Duval House, The Glen, Cambridge Way, TN22 2AB TEL: 762474 PARKING: Own carpark OPEN: By appt PERIOD: 17th century SPECIALIST: Antique Maps GENERAL: Colourme service.

Georgian House Antiques, 222 High Street, TN22 1RE TEL: 765074 FAX: 765074 PARKING: Easy OPEN: Mon-Sat 10-6 PERIOD: 17th-19th century SPECIALIST: English domestic oak & country furniture & related decorative objects GENERAL: Furniture & decorative items.

Ringles Cross Antiques, Ringles Cross, TN22 1HF TEL: 762909 PARKING: Own carpark OPEN: Mon-Sat 9-6. Resident MIN: £50 MAX: £5,000 PERIOD: 17th-18th century SPECIALIST: English furniture made from indigenous woods, walnut, oak, fruitwoods, accessories. Some Oriental furniture OTHER INFO: Many historic houses & gardens near, Bluebell Railway 10 miles

MAYFIELD (0435)

Gravener Antiques, High Street, TN20 6AA TEL: 873389 PARKING: Easy OPEN: Mon-Fri 9-5.30, Sat 9-1 MIN: £100 MAX: £5,000

PERIOD: 18th-19th century SPECIALIST: Furniture OTHER INFO: Picturesque village steeped in history. 16th century hotel.

DURGATES (0892)
Park View Antiques, The High Street, TN5 6DE TEL: 783630 PARKING: Easy OPEN: 10-5 MIN: £5 MAX: £1,000 PERIOD: 18th-20th century SPECIALIST: Country furniture & artifacts GENERAL: Native wood furniture, pine, oak etc, cast iron, kitchenalia, lighting OTHER INFO: Scotney Castle, Bewl Water, Bartley Mill, Lamberhurst vineyards.

HURST GREEN (0580)
Pigeon House Antiques, 52 London Road, TN19 7PN TEL: 860474 ASSNS: LAPADA PARKING: Easy OPEN: 9am-10pm & by appt MIN: £50 MAX: £15,000 PERIOD: 18th-19th century SPECIALIST: Furniture & decorative items. Mirrors, chandeliers etc.

BURWASH (0435)
Michael Walsh, Chaunt House, High Street TEL: 882221 PARKING: Easy OPEN: 10-5.30, closed Mon MAX: £1,000 PERIOD: 19th-20th century SPECIALIST: Clocks, watches, barometers OTHER INFO: 1993 Best Kept Village award, tearooms etc.

SEDLESCOMBE (0424)
Claire Kinloch, Bulmer House, The Green, TN33 0QA TEL: 870364 PARKING: Easy OPEN: Wed-Sat 10-5 MIN: £1 MAX: £1,000 PERIOD: 19th-20th century SPECIALIST: Antique dolls, original dolls clothing, teddies, toys GENERAL: Antique children's & baby clothes, quilts.

HASTINGS (0424)
Nakota Curios, 12 Courthouse Street, Old Town, TN35 5PB TEL: 438900 PARKING: Medium OPEN: Mon, Tues, Thurs-Sat 10.30-1, 2.30-5 MIN: £1 MAX: £300 PERIOD: 19th-20th century GENERAL: Occasional ethnographical items, jewellery, paintings, glass, small furniture, textiles, country items, china OTHER INFO: The old town of Hastings with its fishing quarter, 16th-18th century buildings & streets, is unique and worth visiting in its own right.

ST LEONARDS-ON-SEA (0424)
Aarquebus Antiques, 46 Norman Road, TN38 0EJ TEL: 433267 ASSNS: LAPADA PARKING: Easy OPEN: 9-1, 2-5.30 MIN: £50 MAX: £5,000 PERIOD: 17th-19th century SPECIALIST: Period furniture GENERAL: Furniture, porcelain, glass, oils, watercolours, bric-a-brac.

Banner Antiques, 56 Norman Road, TN40 1BN TEL: 420050 PARKING: Medium OPEN:10-5, closed Weds MIN: £10 MAX: £1,500 PERIOD: 19th-20th century SPECIALIST: Royal Worcester porcelain, Blue & White transfer ware. GENERAL: Furniture, porcelain, treen & watercolours OTHER INFO: Cinque Port hotel & Cooden Resort Hotel, site of Battle of Hastings in 1066.

The Book Jungle, 24 North Street, TN38 0EX TEL: 421187 PARKING: Medium OPEN: 10-5, closed Weds MIN: £1 MAX: £100 PERIOD: 19th-20th century GENERAL: Secondhand books.

Hastings Antique Centre, 59-61 Norman Road, TN38 0EG TEL: 428561 PARKING: Easy OPEN: Mon-Sat 9-5.30 MIN: £5 MAX: £3,000 PERIOD: 19th-20th century SPECIALIST: Sporting goods, clocks, jewellery GENERAL: Furniture, pine, paintings, porcelain, gold, silver, watches, textiles, Victoriana, architectural items OTHER INFO: Historic, excellent tourist centre, museums, numerous antique shops.

Helgato Antiques, 121 Bohemia Road (A21), TN37 6RL TEL: 423049 PARKING: Medium OPEN: 10-5 MIN: £3 MAX: £500 PERIOD: 18th-19th century GENERAL: Porcelain, glass, objets d'art & vertu, prints, maps pre 1890, books.

John Lang Antiques, 65 Norman Road, TN38 0EG TEL: 714848 PARKING: Medium OPEN: Mon-Fri 10-5, Sat 10-1 MIN: £2 MAX: £1,500 PERIOD: 18th-19th century GENERAL: Georgian, Victorian & shipping furniture, smalls, house clearance items OTHER INFO: Historical area with caves and castle. 21 other antique shops + 1 antique centre close.

Monarch Antiques, 6 Grand Parade TEL: 445841 FAX: 434338 PARKING: Medium OPEN: Mon-Fri 9-5, or by appt MIN: £10 MAX: £3,000 PERIOD: 19th-20th century GENERAL: Victoriana & shipping goods.

BEXHILL-ON-SEA (0424)
Bexhill Antique Centre, TEL: 830554 OPEN: By appt OTHER INFO: Not run as an antiques centre but houses 3 floors of furniture

Bexhill Antique Exporters, 56 Turkey Road TEL: 225103, 210182 FAX: 731430 PARKING: Own carpark OPEN: Mon-Fri 8-5.30 MIN: £50 MAX: £5,000 PERIOD: 18th-20th century OTHER INFO: One of the largest exporters in the southeast.

PEVENSEY BAY (0323)
The Old Mint House Antiques, High Street, BN24 5LF TEL: 762337 FAX: 762337 ASNS: LAPADA PARKING: Own carpark OPEN: Mon-Sat 9-5.30 MIN: £5 MAX: £20,000 PERIOD: 18th-20th century SPECIALIST: Furniture GENERAL: Clocks, china, metalware. Shipping goods export OTHER INFO: 40,000 sq ft. Opposite Pevensey Castle

EASTBOURNE (0323)
Bell Antiques, 47 South Street TEL: 641339 PARKING: Medium OPEN: 9.30-4.40 MIN: £5 MAX: £500 PERIOD: 18th-20th century GENERAL: Pottery, porcelain, small furniture, lace, dolls, glass, watercolours & prints.

Bygones, 24 Willingdon Road, Old Town TEL: 737537 PARKING: Medium OPEN: Mon, Tues, Thurs & Sat 10.30-5 MIN: £1 MAX: £200 PERIOD: 19th-20th century SPECIALIST: Vintage clothing 1920's to early 1950's GENERAL: Accessories, jewellery, linen OTHER INFO: Lovely seafront leading up to famous Beachy Head surrounded by the South Downs, 2 museums, Old Town has many antique shops.

Camilla's Bookshop, 57 Grove Road, BN21 4TX TEL: 736001 PARKING: Medium OPEN: Mon-Sat 10-6 MIN: £1 MAX: £1,000 PERIOD: 17th-20th century SPECIALIST: 500,000 books, aviation, crafts, miitary, transport GENERAL: Many old novels, good history, religious section. 250 Churchill books OTHER INFO: Beachy Head, Seven Sisters Country Park, Pevensey Castle (1066 & all that), superb walking country, Art Gallery (Towner), Museum of shops, New Marina.

John Cowderoy Antiques, 42 South Street TEL: 720058 ASNS: LAPADA, GMC PARKING: Medium OPEN: Mon, Tues, Thurs, Fri 9.30-1, 2.30-5 PERIOD: 18th-20th century SPECIALIST: Antique musical boxes, clocks GENERAL: General antiques.

John Day of Eastbourne Fine Art, 9 Meads Street, BN20 7QY TEL: 725634 PARKING:

Easy OPEN: 10-4 MIN: £100 MAX: £10,000 SPECIALIST: Victorian oils & watercolours, East Anglian paintings. Restoration on site GENERAL: 1800-1930's English & Continental paintings.

Eastbourne Antique Market, 80 Seaside TEL: 720128 PARKING: Easy OPEN: Mon-Fri 10-5.30, Sat 10-5 PERIOD: 18th-20th century GENERAL: 40 stalls antiques & collectables.

Timothy Partridge Antiques, 46 Ocklynge Road, BN21 1PP TEL: 638731 PARKING: Easy OPEN: Mon-Fri 10-5, Sat 10-1 MIN: £10 MAX: £300 PERIOD: 19-20th century SPECIALIST: Furniture GENERAL: General antiques.

Pharaohs Antique Centre, 28 South Street TEL: 738655 PARKING: Medium OPEN: Mon-Sat 10-5 MIN: £1 MAX: £1,200 PERIOD: 19th-20th century GENERAL: Pine furniture, kitchenalia, light fittings, postcards, prints, some medical items, drawing instruments, lace, linen, brassware OTHER INFO: 6 other shops & Edgar Horns auctioneers in same street.Famous resort with theatres, museum, Butterfly House,

THE BRITISH MARKET

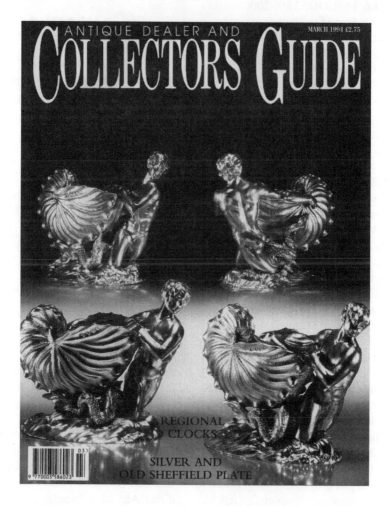

**Collectors' Guide is Britain's best-selling monthly magazine
devoted to the world of antiques and the fine and decorative arts.**

Every issue contains wide-ranging and informative feature articles on antique funiture,
ceramics, silver, pictures and collectables, together with comprehensive coverage of price
movements in the salerooms, recent discoveries and items coming up for sale.

Complete trade, auction, antiques fair and dealer news is provided
and restoration and questions of authenticity are regularly examined.

*Special subscription offer to Readers of The Touring Guide to Antique Shops in England
– £24 for 12 issues (normally £33) or USA $60 for 12 issues (normally $70).*

For details Tel: 071-318 5868.

**Antique Dealer & Collectors Guide
PO Box 805, Greenwich, London SE10 8AS.**

Museum of Shops.

Raymond Smith, 30 South Street TEL: 734128 ASSNS: ABA PARKING: Medium OPEN: Mon. Tues, Thurs-Sat 9-5.30 MIN: £1 MAX: £1,000 PERIOD: 17th-20th century SPECIALIST: Theology GENERAL: Most subjects.

Stewart Gallery, 25 Grove Road TEL: 729588 PARKING: Medium OPEN: Mon-Sat 9-5.30 MIN: £10 MAX: £15,000 PERIOD: 19th-20th century OTHER INFO: 100+ restaurants, all nationalities.

Lloyd Williams Antiques, Anglo-American Warehouse, 2A Beach Road, BN22 7EX TEL: 648661 FAX: 648658 PARKING: Easy OPEN: Mon-Sat 9.30-5 or by appt MIN: £30 MAX: £3,000 PERIOD: 19th-20th century SPECIALIST: Good quality oak GENERAL: 2,000+ pieces shipping furniture.

POLEGATE (0323)

Graham Price Antiques Ltd, Unit 4, Chaucer Industrial Estate, BN26 6JD TEL: 487167 FAX: 483904 PARKING: Own carpark OPEN: Mon-Fri 9-6 & by appt MIN: £10 MAX: £5,000 PERIOD: 18th-20th century SPECIALIST: Larger items of furniture suitable for commercial use GENERAL: English, Continental furniture & decorative items with a country base.

HORSEBRIDGE (0323)

Horsebridge Antiques, 1 North Street, BN27 4DJ TEL: 844414 PARKING: Own carpark OPEN: Mon-Sat 10-5 MIN: £10 MAX: £1,000 PERIOD: 18th-20th century GENERAL: Country items, collectables etc OTHER INFO: good food opposite.

HORAM (0435)

John Botting Antiques, Winstan House, High Street, TN21 0ER TEL: 33553, 33626, (0860) 333038 FAX: 33553 PARKING: Own carpark OPEN: Mon, Tues, Sat 9-5.30, by appt & by chance MIN: £5 MAX: £1,000 PERIOD: 19th-20th century SPECIALIST: French direct imports GENERAL: Georgian, Victorian Edwardian, 1920's furniture & effects. French furniture assorted items mainly purchased privately OTHER INFO: Merrydown Cider factory.

LEWES (0273)

Charleston Antiques, 14 Lansdown Place TEL: 477916 PARKING: Medium OPEN: Tues-Sat 10-5 MIN: £150 MAX: £1,500 PERIOD: Late 18th-20th century SPECIALIST: Arts & Crafts furniture/inlaid mahogany GENERAL: English furniture 1780-1920.

Cliffe Antiques Centre, 47 Cliffe High Street, BN7 2AN TEL: 473266 PARKING: Own carpark OPEN: Mon-Sat 9.30-5 GENERAL Collectables, Victoriana, paintings, prints, furniture, china, jewellery etc OTHER INFO: Interesting castle, Anne of Cleves Museum. Ancient county town situated on river.

Cliffe Gallery Antiques, 39 Cliffe High Street, BN7 2AN TEL: 471877 ASSNS: CADO PARKING: Easy OPEN: 9-5 MIN: £3 MAX: £2,700 PERIOD: 18th-20th century GENERAL: Pine, mahogany, oak, bric a brac, kitchenalia, luggage, fishing, pictures.

Coombe House Antiques, 121 Malling Street, BN7 2RJ TEL: 473862 FAX: 479645 ASSNS: BADA CINOA LAPADA PARKING: Own carpark OPEN: Mon-Fri 9.30-6 & by appt PERIOD: 18th-19th century SPECIALIST: English furniture & decorative items GENERAL: Works of art, clocks, paintings, garden items OTHER INFO: On A26 south of Horsted Place. County House Hotel & Glyndebourne Opera House. London 1 hr, Brighton 15 mins.

A.J. Cumming, 84 High Street, BN7 1XN TEL: 472319 ASSNS: ABA PARKING: Medium OPEN: Mon-Fri 10-5, Sat 10-5.30 PERIOD: 19th-20th century SPECIALIST: Antiquarian books OTHER INFO: Shelleys & White Hart Hotel. 3 bookshops.

H.P. Dennison & Son, 22 High Street, BN7 2LN TEL: 480655 PARKING: Medium OPEN: Mon-Tues, Thurs-Sat 9-4.30 MIN: £120 MAX: £2,500 PERIOD: 19th-20th century GENERAL: Furniture.

Felix Gallery, 2 Sun Street, BN7 2QB TEL: 472668 PARKING: Medium OPEN: Mon-Sat 10-6 MIN: £10 MAX: £2,000 PERIOD: 18th-20th century SPECIALIST: "Cats in Art" & collectables only GENERAL: Paintings, prints, pottery, bronzes, pewter, porcelain, bronze, silver, objets d'art OTHER INFO: 11th century castle, Norman & Roman ruins. Prize-winning Tourist Information Centre.

The Fifteenth Century Bookshop, 99-100 High Street, BN7 1XH TEL: 474160 FAX: 477488 PARKING: Easy OPEN: Mon-Sat 10-5.30 MIN:

BOB HOARE ANTIQUES

PINE AND COUNTRY ANTIQUES

❄

Specialists in antique pine furniture to the trade and retail market.

❄

Unit Q, Phoenix Place,
North Street, Lewes, E. Sussex
Telephone: 0273 480557

£1 MAX: £1,000 PERIOD: 17th-20th century SPECIALIST: Collectable childrens/illustrated books GENERAL: Secondhand & antiquarian books on all subjects. Our shop is an original 15th century building, (oldest in town).

Foundry Lane Antiques Centre, 15 Cliffe High Street, BN7 2AH TEL: 475361 PARKING: Easy OPEN: Tues-Sat 10-5 MIN: £2 MAX: £1,000 PERIOD: 19th-20th century SPECIALIST: Arts & Crafts, Nouveau, Deco, Victorian GENERAL: General antiques OTHER INFO: 6 centres & 20+ antiques shops.

Bob Hoare Pine Antiques, Unit Q, Phoenix Place, North Street TEL: 480557 FAX: 471298 PARKING: Own carpark OPEN: Mon-Fri 8-6, Sat 9-1 MIN: £50 MAX: £3,000 PERIOD: 18th-19th century SPECIALIST: Line presses, tables GENERAL: Furniture.

Lewes Antiques Centre, 20 Cliffe High Street, BN7 1AH TEL: 476148 PARKING: Medium OPEN: Mon-Sat 9.30-5, Sun 12-4 MIN: £1 MAX: £950 PERIOD: 19th century GENERAL: General Antiques.

Pastorale Antiques, 15 Malling Street TEL: 473259 FAX: 473259 PARKING: Easy OPEN: Mon-Sat 10-5.30 & by appt PERIOD: 18th-19th century SPECIALIST: 8,000 sq ft warehouse of pine & European country furniture, mahogany & decoratives.

Pine Furniture, 6 Station Street TEL: 474842 PARKING: Own carpark OPEN: 9-5, Wed & Sat 9-1 MIN: £100 MAX: £2,500 PERIOD: 19th century SPECIALIST: Pine, longcase pine clocks GENERAL: Furniture.

Trevor Antiques and Works of Art, Trevor House, 110 High Street, BN7 1XY TEL: 471975 ASSNS: BADA PARKING: Own carpark OPEN: Mon-Sat 9-6 but appt advisable MIN: £5,000 MAX: £250,000 PERIOD: Late 17th-early 19th century SPECIALIST: Furniture & works of art OTHER INFO: Glyndebourne, 11th century castle.

IFORD (0273)

John Bird Antiques, Norton House, BN7 3EJ TEL: 483366 PARKING: Own carpark OPEN: 24 hrs by appt MIN: £10 MAX: £5,000 PERIOD: 17th-20th century SPECIALIST: Lacquer & painted furniture GENERAL: English furniture in oak, pine, fruitwood & mahogany. Accessories & garden antiques OTHER INFO: Why not visit Virginia Woolf's Monks House at Rodmell & Charleston Farmhouse, country retreat of the Bloomsbury set.

NEWHAVEN (0273)

Newhaven Flea Market, 28 Southway, BN9 LA TEL: 517207, 516065 PARKING: Own arpark OPEN: Seven days 10-5.30 MIN: £1 AX: £500 PERIOD: 19th-20th century GENERAL INFO: Bric-a-brac & furniture.

Leonard Russell, 21 Kings Avenue, Denton, N9 0NB TEL: 515153 ASSNS: BADA PARKING: Easy OPEN: By appt only MIN: £350 MAX: £2,500 PERIOD: 18th-early 19th century SPECIALIST: Early English pottery figures 1700-1835 GENERAL: Animals, toby jugs, busts, plaques, from factories of Whieldon, Ralph Wood, Enoch Wood, Sherratt, Marked Walton, Salt.

SEAFORD (0323)

Steyne House Antiques, Steyne House, 35 Steyne Road, BN25 1HT TEL: 895088 PARKING: Easy OPEN: Tues-Fri 10.30-5, Sat 10.30-

4 MIN: £20 MAX: £800+ PERIOD: Some 18th, mostly 19th century SPECIALIST: Victorian, Staffordshire figures GENERAL: English pottery & porcelain, also Continental & Oriental.

ROTTINGDEAN (0273)

Trade Wind, Little Crescent, BN2 7GE TEL: 301177 PARKING: Own carpark OPEN: By appt only MIN: £60+ MAX: £900+ PERIOD: 17th-19th century SPECIALIST: Wide selection wine labels GENERAL: Small furniture, English porcelain, coloured glass, other choice items all pre-1920 OTHER INFO: Rottingdean noted for Rudyard Kipling.

BRIGHTON (0273)

Art Deco Etc, 73 Upper Gloucester Road, BN1 3LQ TEL: 329268 ASSNS: ATA PARKING: Easy MIN: £1 MAX: £2,000 PERIOD: 19th-20th century SPECIALIST: Art Deco, Art Nouveau, Arts & Crafts, 1950's, pottery, glass, furniture, lighting, mirrors, pictures, collectables.

Ashton's, 1-3 Clyde Road, Preston Circus, BN1 4NN TEL: 605253 PARKING: Medium OPEN: Mon-Fri 9.30-5.30, Wed AM only, Sat 10-4 MIN: £1 MAX: £1,500 PERIOD: 19th-20th century GENERAL: 4 showrooms of varied stock ranging from modern repro to Victorian & antique & shipping furniture.

Attic Antiques, 23 Ship Street TEL: 326378 PARKING: Medium OPEN: Mon-Sat 10.45-1, 2.15-5 MIN: £25 MAX: £2,000+ PERIOD: 18th-19th century SPECIALIST: Oriental antiques, glass, clocks, tantulus GENERAL: General antiques.

H. Balchin, 17-19 Castle Street (off Preston Street), BN1 2HD PARKING: Difficult unless loading OPEN: 9.30-1, 2,30-5.30, Thurs/Sat AM only PERIOD: 18th-19th century SPECIALIST: Furniture GENERAL: China, glass.

Bears & Friends, 41 Meeting House Lane, BN1 1HB TEL: 208940 FAX: 202736 PARKING: Medium OPEN: Mon-Fri 9-5.30, Sat 9-6, Sun 10-6 MIN: £1 MAX: £5,000 PERIOD: 20th century SPECIALIST: Old & new teddy bears GENERAL: Old dolls & bear-related items, furniture & pictures.

Brighton Antique Wholesalers, 39 Upper Gardner Street, BN1 4AN TEL: 695457 PARKING: Easy OPEN: Mon-Sat 9-5.30 MIN: £5 MAX: £10,000 PERIOD: 17th-20th century

GENERAL: Basic shipping to fine period & Victorian.

Brighton Flea Market, 31a Upper St James's Street, BN1 2JN TEL: 624006 PARKING: Medium OPEN: Seven days 9.30-5.30 MIN: £1 MAX: £1,000 PERIOD: 19th-20th century GENERAL: Bric-a-brac & furniture.

Sheila Cashin, 40 Upper North Street, BN1 3FH TEL: 326619 PARKING: Medium OPEN: Mon-Sat 10-5 MIN: £5 MAX: £2,000 PERIOD: 19th century SPECIALIST: Lacquer & Victorian bamboo well restored GENERAL: Decorative & painted furniture, papier maché, china, furniture.

Classic Automobilia & Regalia Specialists, (C.A.R.S.), 4-4a Chapel Terrace, Kemp Town, BN2 1HU TEL: 601960 FAX: 623846 ASSNS: Pedal Car Collectors Club PARKING: Own carpark OPEN: 10-6 MIN: £50+ MAX: £5,000 PERIOD: 20th century SPECIALIST: Automobilia, car mascots, car badges, memorabilia, motoring nostalgia. Restoration of old pedal cars from pre/post war periods OTHER INFO: Featured on TV with subject *Does size matter* comparing us in child/s Ferrari P.40 with UK's tallest man alongside! Had lots of film/TV work.

D.H. Edmunds Ltd, 28 Meeting House Lane, The Lanes, BN1 1HB TEL: 328871, 327713 FAX: 326627 ASSNS: JIS PARKING: Medium OPEN: 10-5.30 MIN: £50 MAX: £ 50,000+ PERIOD: 19th-20th century SPECIALIST: Antique & precious jewellery OTHER INFO: Royal Pavilion 5 mins.

Alan Fitchett Antiques, 5-5a Upper Gardner Street, BN1 4AN TEL: 600894 FAX: 600894 PARKING: Easy OPEN: Mon-Fri 9-5.30 MIN: £50 MAX: £10,000 PERIOD: 17th-20th century SPECIALIST: Victorian walnut, marquetry & Continental GENERAL: Furniture.

Paul Goble Jewellers, 44 Meeting House Lane, The Lanes, BN1 1HB TEL: 202801 FAX: 202736 ASSNS: NAG, N.A.Pawnbrokers PARKING: Medium OPEN: Mon-Sat 9-5.30, Sun 10-5.30 MIN: £5 MAX: £25,000 PERIOD: 17th-20th century SPECIALIST: Antique & period jewellery, silver GENERAL: Wide range of jewellery all secondhand, 15th century-1950's, pictues & prints, old dolls & bears OTHER INFO: In heart of The Lanes, Grand Hotel, Hospitality Inn.

Hallmarks, 4 Union Street, BN1 1HA TEL: 725477 PARKING: Medium OPEN: Mon-Sat 9-5 MIN: £15 MAX: £3,000 PERIOD: 19th-20th century SPECIALIST: Collectable items, scent bottles, vinaigrettes GENERAL: A wide range of solid silver & plate. Many useful table items, new silver photo frames (the largest selection in Sussex) & old jewellery.

Simon Hatchwell Antiques, 94 Gloucester Road, BN1 4AP TEL: 691164 FAX: 691164 PARKING: Own carpark OPEN: 9-1, 2-5 & by appt MIN: £2 PERIOD: 19th-20th century SPECIALIST: French, Continental, Biedermeier furniture GENERAL: Mahogany, birch, Victorian antiques, furniture for the home.

M & D Hawkins, 27 Meeting House Lane, The Lanes TEL: 321357 ASSNS: LAPADA PARKING: Medium OPEN: Mon-Sat 9-5.30 MIN: £2 MAX: £4,500 PERIOD 17th-20th century SPECIALIST: Antique weapons, militaria, armour, cannon GENERAL: All antiques , silver, bronzes etc with strong emphasis on military & maritime armour. Swords from 1300AD

OTHER INFO: Hospitality Inn, Grand, Metropole, London 50 mins by train.

House of Antiques, 17 Prince Albert Street, BN1 1HF TEL: 327680 ASSNS: LAPADA PARKING: Difficult OPEN: Mon-Sat 10-5 MIN: £150 MAX: £15,000 PERIOD: 18th-20th century GENERAL: Jewellery & silver.

Hynford Antiques, 143 Edward Street, BN2 2JG TEL: 679936 PARKING: Medium OPEN: Tues, Thurs, Sat 10.30-4, Wed AM only or by appt MIN: £1 MAX: £250 PERIOD: 19th-20th century SPECIALIST: Brighton prints & ephemera. Far Eastern prints, Oriental collectables GENERAL: Prints, postcards, collectors items, bygones & small furniture.

J.H. Jewellery, Hallmarks, 4 Union Street, The Lanes, BN1 1HA TEL: 725477 PARKING: Medium OPEN: Mon-Sat 9-5 MIN: £70 MAX: £3,500 PERIOD: 19th-20th century SPECIALIST: Engagement gem-set rings GENERAL: Antique jewellery, wedding bands.

Kingsbury Antiques, 4 Union Street, The Lanes, BN1 1HA TEL: 725477 PARKING: Medium OPEN: 725477 MIN: £10 MAX: £3,000 PERIOD: 19th-20th century SPECIALIST: Vinaigrettes, nutmeg graters.

Leoframes, 70 North Road, BN1 1YD TEL: 695862 PARKING: Medium OPEN: Mon-Sat 9-5.30 MIN: £3 MAX: £600 PERIOD: 18th-19th century GENERAL: Prints of sport, topography, botanical, hunting, fashion, maps, all pre 1920.

Michael Norman Antiques Ltd, 15 Ship Street, BN1 1AD TEL: 326712, 329253, 329264 FAX: 206556 ASSNS: BADA PARKING: Medium OPEN: Mon-Sat 9-1, 2-5.30, & by appt MIN: £1,000 MAX: £70,000 PERIOD: 18th-19th century SPECIALIST: English furniture in showroom setting (5 showrooms) GENERAL: Georgian & Regency furniture OTHER INFO: Royal Pavilion, Hotels: Grand, Metropole etc Seafood restaurants: English's or Wheeler's.

Oasis Antiques, 39 Kensington Gardens, BN1 4AL TEL: 683885 PARKING: Easy (opposite) OPEN: Mon-Sat 10-5.30 MIN: £1 MAX: £5,000 PERIOD: 17th-20th century SPECIALIST: Period lighting, decorative arts GENERAL: Art Nouveau, Art Deco, Arts & Crafts, furniture & objects, glass, bronze, European & Oriental period clothes OTHER INFO: Constantly changing stock. Good trade discount (21 yrs in trade).

Brian & Colin Page, 18 Regent Arcade, East Street, BN1 1HR TEL: 609310 FAX: 609310 ASSNS: ABA PARKING: Medium OPEN: Mon-Sat 10-5.30 MIN: £2 MAX: £5,000 PERIOD: 17th-20th century & earlier SPECIALIST: Japanese & Chinese works of art, antiquarian & rare books GENERAL: British & European decorative arts, historic cameras & scientific instruments OTHER INFO: Oriental porcelain from 10th century. Next to Town Hall, close to Lanes.

Colin Page Antiquarian Books, 36 Duke Street, BN1 1AG TEL: 325954 FAX: 746246 ASSNS: ABA PARKING: Difficult OPEN: Mon-Sat 10-5.30 MIN: £1 MAX: £10,000 PERIOD: 17th-20th century SPECIALIST: Colour plate books, leather bindings GENERAL: 10,000+ quality books.

Dermot & Jill Palmer Antiques, 7-8 Union Street, The Lanes, BN1 1HA TEL: 328669 FAX: 777641 PARKING: Medium OPEN: Mon-Sat 9-6 & by appt MIN: £5 MAX: £5,000 PERIOD: 18th-20th century GENERAL: Mainly 19th century English & French furniture & objects. OTHER INFO: One of earliest genuine antique shops in The Lanes.

B. Ponting Antiques, 53 Upper North Street TEL: 329409 PARKING: Medium OPEN: Mon-Sat 9.30-5.30 MIN: £100 MAX: £6,000 PERIOD: 18th-20th century SPECIALIST: English furniture.

Prinnys Antique Gallery, 3 Meeting House Lane, BN1 1HB TEL: 204554 PARKING: Medium OPEN: Mon-Sat 9.30-5 MIN: £5 MAX: £5,000 PERIOD: 18th-20th century SPECIALIST: Art Deco & Nouveau GENERAL: Maps, silver, jewellery, clocks, watches, ivory, prints, porcelain, paintings, rare amber etc OTHER INFO: Cafe on site in this 18th century building, reputedly with ghost.

Pyramid, 9a Kensington Gardens, BN2 5JS TEL: 607991 PARKING: Medium OPEN: Mon-Fri 10-5.30, Sat 9-6 MIN: £1 MAX: £1,500 PERIOD: 20th century SPECIALIST: Art Deco GENERAL: Period lighting, old telephones, furniture, mirrors, radios, collectables.

Recollections, 1a Sydney Street, BN1 4EN TEL: 681517 PARKING: Medium OPEN: Mon-Sat 10.30-5 MIN: £3 MAX: £650 PERIOD: 19th-20th century SPECIALIST: Fireplace accessories including 100+ fenders GENERAL: Small brass, copper, small arch salvage items, oil lamps, studio pottery, boxes. Shop crammed with cornucopia of small easily affordable items.

Tapsell Antiques, 159 Middle Street, BN1 1AL TEL: 328341 ASSNS: LAPADA PARKING: Own small carpark OPEN: Mon-Sat 9-5.30 MIN: £5 MAX: £40,000 PERIOD: 18th-19th century SPECIALIST: Chinese Blue & White and Japanese porcelains GENERAL: Clocks, European furniture and porcelain OTHER INFO: We have 3 shops together. Large stock. Trade calls out of hours and collection from station etc.

Timewarp, 6 Sydney Street, BN1 4EN TEL: 607527 PARKING: Medium OPEN: 10.30-6 MIN: £2 MAX: £800 PERIOD: 20th century SPECIALIST: 100+ working oil lamps GENERAL: Art Deco, lighting to present day, associated bric-a-brac.

Graham Webb, 59 Ship Street, BN1 1AE TEL: 321803 FAX: 321803 PARKING: Difficult OPEN: Tues-Fri 10-5, Sat 10-1.30 MIN: £650 MAX: £19,000 (now) PERIOD: 19th century SPECIALIST: Musical boxes & mechanical music

The Witch Ball, 48 Meeting House Lane, BN1 1HB TEL: 326618 FAX: 329127 PARKING: Medium OPEN: 10.30-6 MIN: £1 MAX: £2,000 PERIOD: 17th-19th century SPECIALIST: Antiquarian maps & prints.

E & B White, 43-47 Upper North Street, BN1 3FH TEL: 328706 PARKING: Difficult OPEN: Mon-Fri 9.30-4.30, Sat 9.30-1 MIN: £50 MAX: £3,000 PERIOD: 18th-19th century SPECIALIST: Country oak GENERAL: Oak furniture.

HOVE (0273)

Michael Norman Antiques Ltd, Palmeira House, 82 Western Road, BN3 1JB TEL: 326712, 329253 FAX: 206556 ASSNS: BADA PARKING: Own carpark OPEN: Mon-Sat 9.30-1, 2-5.30 MIN: £500 MAX: £50,000 PERIOD: 17th-19th century SPECIALIST: English furniture GENERAL: General antiques.

Sussex Commemorative Ware Centre, 88 Western Road, BN3 1JB TEL: 773911 FAX: 747866 PARKING: Easy OPEN: Mon-Fri 9-12, Sat 9-12 & 2-3.30 & by appt MIN: £1 MAX:

£1,500 PERIOD: 19th-20th century SPECIAL-IST: Commemoratives, British & foreign royalty, military, political, also royalty postcards OTHER INFO: Royal Pavilion, Brighton which has the Willett Collection of early commemoratives.

Yellow Lantern Antiques Ltd, 34a & 34b Holland Road, BN3 1JL TEL: 771572, 455476 ASSNS: LAPADA PARKING: Easy OPEN: Mon-Sat 9-1, 2.15-5.30 MIN: £50 MAX: £7,500 PERIOD: 18th-19th century SPECIALIST: Regency furniture, French clocks, ormolu & bronzes GENERAL: Georgian to William IV furniture, paintings, chandeliers, fine art & porcelain OTHER INFO: All stock in pristine condition. Dudley Hotel, Richards restaurant.

PORTSLADE (0273)
Peter Semus Crafting Antiques, The Warehouse, Gladstone Road, BN41 1LJ TEL: 420154 FAX: 430355 PARKING: Own carpark OPEN: 8-5 MIN: £1 MAX: £2,000 PERIOD: 19th-20th century GENERAL: 1920's furniture, conversions from old wood, restoration OTHER INFO: Container packing own stock/nationwide service.

J. Powell (Hove) Ltd, 120 Wellington Road, BN41 1DN TEL: 411599 FAX: 421591 ASSNS: LAPADA PARKING: Medium OPEN: Mon-Sat 7.30-5.30 MIN: £50 MAX: £3,000 PERIOD: 18th-20th century SPECIALIST: English furniture & clocks. OTHER INFO: Topps Hotel.

DITCHLING (0273)
Dycheling Antiques, 34 High Street (shop) & 12 Lewes Road (showroom), BN6 8TA TEL: 842929 PARKING: Easy OPEN: 10.30-5.30 MIN: £50 MAX: £5,000 PERIOD: 18th-19th century SPECIALIST: Dining chairs & finder service GENERAL: Furniture OTHER INFO: Olde Worlde historic village with many famous artists, past & present. Craft & picture galleries, museum, country park, 13th century church.

Nona Shaw Antiques, 4, 8 West Street, BN6 8TS TEL: 843290, 327398 PARKING: Easy OPEN: Mon-Tues, Fri-Sat 11-5 MIN: £5 MAX: £500 PERIOD: 18th-19th century GENERAL: General antiques, cottage furniture.

HURSTPIERPOINT (0273)
Julian Antiques, 124 High Street TEL: 832145 ASSNS: LAPADA PARKING: Own carpark

OPEN: Mon-Fri 9-6 MIN: £100 MAX: £3,000 PERIOD: 19th century SPECIALIST: French mirrors & fireplaces & other French items.

Samuel Orr Clocks, 36 High Street, BN6 9RS TEL: 832081 PARKING: Own carpark OPEN: Tues-Sat 10-5.30 MIN: £200 MAX: £15,000 PERIOD: 18th-19th century SPECIALIST: Longcase, bracket Vienna wall & carriage clocks.

SAYERS COMMON (0273)
Recollect Studios, The Old School, London Road, BN6 9HX TEL: 833314 ASSNS: UKIC PARKING: Own carpark OPEN: Tues-Fri 10-5, Sat 10-2 MIN: £1 MAX: £200 PERIOD: 19th-20th century SPECIALIST: Dolls, dolls houses, miniatures, dolls hospital supplies-wigs, eyes. Antique-style replacement heads, bodies etc. Repairs GENERAL: Porcelain & wax dolls mainly repro, OTHER INFO: Mail order catalogue £2 (overseas £4.50)

CUCKFIELD (0444)
David Foord-Brown Antiques, High Street TEL: 414418 ASSNS: LAPADA PARKING: Own carpark OPEN: Mon-Sat 10-5.30 PERIOD: 18-19th century SPECIALIST: Furniture, porcelain.

Richard Usher Antiques, 23 South Street, RH17 5LB TEL: 451699 PARKING: Medium OPEN: 10-5.30, Wed & Sat AM only MIN: £5 MAX: £2,000 PERIOD: 17th-19th century GENERAL: Furniture, decorative items OTHER INFO: Attractive village, Ockenden Manor Hotel in walking distance.

HAYWARDS HEATH (0444)
David Burkinshaw, Sugworth Farmhouse, Borde Hill Lane, RH16 1XP TEL: 459747 PARKING: Own carpark OPEN: 9-5 MIN: £2,000 MAX: £45.000 PERIOD: 18th-19th century SPECIALIST: Antique pedestal & partner's desks (restored).

LINDFIELD (0444)
Hinsdale Antiques, 75 High Street, RH16 TEL: 483200 FAX: 484736 PARKING: Medium OPEN: 10-5 MIN: £5 MAX: £5,000 PERIOD: 18th-20th century SPECIALIST: Dolls GENERAL: General antiques.

HORSHAM (0403)
L.E. Lampard & Sons, 23-31 Springfield Road, RH12 2PW TEL: 64332, 54012 PARKING: Medium OPEN: Mon-Sat 8-1, 2-5.30 MIN: £5

MAX: £5,000 PERIOD: 18th-19th century GENERAL: Period oak & mahogany furniture OTHER INFO: Kings Head Hotel.

DORKING (0306)

Tom Burton & Rod Johnston, Dorking Antiques Centre, 17-18 West Street, RH4 1BS TEL: 740915 PARKING: Easy OPEN: Mon-Sat 10-5.30 MIN: £50 MAX: £500 PERIOD: 19th century SPECIALIST: Ceramics, mainly British Ironstone and Blue & White GENERAL: Victoriana including desk sets, small Victorian & Edwardian furniture.

Dorking Antique Centre, 17-18 West Street TEL: 740915 PARKING: Easy OPEN: Mon-Sat 10-5.30 MIN: £50 MAX: £45,000 PERIOD: 18th-19th century SPECIALIST: Furniture GENERAL: 25 dealers offering a complete range OTHER INFO: Wide selection of paintings & porcelain. Two 18th century pubs in street.

Dorking Desk Shop, 41 West Street, RH4 1BU. TEL: 883327 FAX: 875363 ASSNS: LAPADA, DADA PARKING: Medium OPEN: Mon-Fri 8-5.30, Sat 10.30-1, 2-5 MIN: £10 MAX: £10,000 PERIOD: 18th-19th century SPECIALIST: All types of desks including 30 partners GENERAL: Antique writing furniture, bureaux bookcases rolltypes, chairs, tables, secretaires.

The Dorking Emporium, 1a West Street TEL: 876646 PARKING: Easy OPEN: Mon-Fri 10-5, Sat 10-5.30 MIN: £1 MAX: £4,000 PERIOD: 18th-20th century SPECIALIST: Georgian & Edwardian mahogany furniture GENERAL: Antique Centre, good variety of antiques, collectables, pictures, books, Art Deco OTHER INFO: Coffee shop providing homemade light lunches. Dorking is a centre for antiques having 3 antique centres & innumerable antique shops.

Hampshires of Dorking, 51-52 West Street, RH5 4LB TEL: 887076 FAX: 881029 PARKING: Own carpark OPEN: Mon-Sat 9.30-5.30 MIN: £300 MAX: £50,000 PERIOD: Late 17th-19th century SPECIALIST: Fine Georgian, 16th-early 19th century satinwood, mahogany, walnut, some oak, rosewood OTHER INFO: Burford Bridge Hotel, Fountain Garden, Chinese restaurant, Box Hill etc.

Hebeco, 47 West Street, RH4 1BU TEL: 875396 PARKING: Easy OPEN: 10.30-5 MIN: £5+ MAX: £3,000+ PERIOD: 18th-20th century

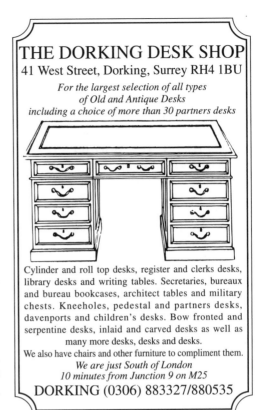
SPECIALIST: Silver, glass, pewter.

John Lang Antiques, Kings Head Court, 11 High Street, RH14 1AR TEL: 882203 PARKING: Easy OPEN: Mon, Tues, Thurs-Sat 9-5 MIN: £25 MAX: £1,500 PERIOD: 18th century SPECIALIST: Country furniture, oak GENERAL: Coffers, chess, brass, copper, decorators items OTHER INFO: 32 antiques shops and 5 antiques centres.

King's Court Galleries, 54 West Street TEL: 9.30-5.30 PARKING: Easy OPEN: 9.30-5.30 MIN: £8 MAX: £2,500 PERIOD: 17th-19th century SPECIALIST: Antique prints & maps GENERAL: Decorative & sporting prints limited editions.

Norfolk House Galleries, 48 West Street, RH4 1BU TEL: 881028 PARKING: Easy OPEN: 10-5 MIN: £100 MAX: £10,000 PERIOD: 17th-19th century SPECIALIST: Dining tables & sets of chairs GENERAL: Quality Georgian & Regency furniture OTHER INFO: Excellent B&B at Fairdene Guest House.

Ockley Antiques, 43 West Street TEL: 885007

PARKING: Easy OPEN: Mon-Sat 9.30-5 MIN: £50 MAX: £1,800 PERIOD: 19th-20th century SPECIALIST: Bespoke kitchens in antique pine GENERAL: Antique pine (not repro) OTHER INFO: Workshops are 5 miles away where we have another shop: Ockley Antiques, The Green, Ockley, Surrey, TEL: 712266.

Oriental Carpets & Decorative Arts, 37 West Street, RH4 1BU TEL: 876370 FAX: (0483) 202983 PARKING: Medium OPEN: 10-5, closed Wed MIN: £150 PERIOD: 19th-20th century SPECIALIST: Oriental carpets & rugs, antique & semi-antique OTHER INFO: Valuation, repair & cleaning. Beautiful countryside, good hotels & an orgy of restaurants.

Elaine Saunderson Antiques, 18-18a Church Street TEL: 881231 PARKING: Easy OPEN: 9.30-5.30 & by appt (resident) MIN: £50 MAX: £10,000 PERIOD: 18th-early 19th century SPECIALIST: Furniture.

Thorpe & Foster Ltd, 50 West Street, RH4 1BU TEL: 881029 FAX: 881029 PARKING: Own carpark OPEN: 9.30-5.30 MIN: £3 MAX: £50,000 PERIOD: Late 17th-19th century SPECIALIST: Fine Georgian furniture.

Victoria & Edward Antiques Centre, 61 West Street TEL: 889645 PARKING: Easy OPEN: Mon-Sat 9.30-5.30 MIN: £2 MAX: £4,000 PERIOD: 18th-20th century GENERAL: Wide range of scintillating antiques.

Pauline Watson Antique Jewellery, Old King's Head Court (by pump corner), RH14 1AR TEL: 885452 ASSNS: NAG registered valuer, Fellow of Gemmological Assn of GB PARKING: Easy OPEN: Mon-Sat 9.30-5. MIN: £25 MAX: £5,000 PERIOD: 18th-19th & some 20th century SPECIALIST: Seals, Victorian jewellery GENERAL: Antique jewellery & some silver

West Street Antiques, 63 West Street, RH4 1BS TEL: 883487 PARKING: Easy OPEN: 9.30-5.30 MIN: £20 MAX: £10,000 PERIOD: 18th-19th century SPECIALIST: Arms & armour, fishing tackle GENERAL: Furniture.

Patrick Worth, 11 West Street TEL: 884484 ASSNS: BADA PARKING: Easy MIN: £850 MAX: £15,000 PERIOD: 18th-19th century SPECIALIST: 18th century & Regency, also decorative items OTHER INFO: Fine old market town with Tudor & Georgian buildings, West Street is given over to antique shops.

ASHTEAD (0372)

Bumbles, 90 The Street, KT21 1AW TEL: 276219 PARKING: Easy OPEN: Mon-Sat 9.30-5.30 MIN: £1 MAX: £2,500 PERIOD: 19th-20th century SPECIALIST: Clocks, barometers, oil lamps, furniture GENERAL: Local prints, porcelain, glass, metalware, silver, plate etc. Broad restoration services.

Memory Lane Antiques, 102 The Street, KT21 1AW TEL: 273436 PARKING: Easy OPEN: Mon-Tues, Thurs-Sat 10-4 MIN: £5 MAX: £3,000 GENERAL: General antiques.

TADWORTH (0737)

Ian Caldwell, 9a The Green, Dorking Road, KT20 5SQ TEL: 813969 ASSNS: LAPADA PARKING: Easy OPEN: 10-5 MIN: £1 MAX: £10,000 PERIOD: 17th-19th century SPECIALIST: Georgian town furniture GENERAL: Furniture, prints, watercolours, oils, porcelain, etc OTHER INFO: Boxhill, Epsom Racecourse, & Walton-on-the-Hill.

EPSOM (0372)

Fogg Antiques, 75 South Street, KT18 7P TEL: 726931 PARKING: Medium OPEN: Mon-Fri 9-5.30, Sat 10-6 MIN: £10 MAX: £900 PERIOD: 19th-20th century SPECIALIST: Antique & old pine GENERAL: Old pine, newly made up pieces from reclaimed timber. Reproduction items.

Southern Home Counties

The Pagoda, Kew Gardens

Starting in Greater London, this tour passes through the market towns and pretty villages of Surrey, Sussex and Hampshire and then continues to the cities of Chichester and Portsmouth. The return to London snakes back through Sussex and Surrey.

The first stop is in the London suburb of Wimbledon, known throughout the world as the home of tennis. At the time of the Domesday Book, Wimbledon was part of the manor of Mortlake but it was in the Middle Ages that the village started to grow. The Rose and Crown, in the High Street, dates from the mid 17th century and Eagle House from 1613. In 1838 Wimbledon was one of the first south London villages to get a railway station although the great residential expansion took place in the last quarter of the 19th century. One of the great attractions of the area is Wimbledon Common, covering about 1100 acres and completely unenclosed. A restored windmill stands on the common. The original was built in the 17th century but the present one was constructed in 1817.

Kew, our next stop, is world famous for the Royal Botanic Gardens begun in 1759. Continuing on, Richmond, now a part of Greater London still retains a character of its own. Situated on the River Thames it contains many Georgian and Queen Anne buildings. One of the town's most notable features is Richmond Park which covers approximately 2000 acres. Herds of deer still roam the park at will.

Nearby Twickenham, now largely a residential suburb of London, has some Georgian houses in Syon Row and Montpelier Row. The modern church of All Hallows, built in 1940, incorporates a Wren tower which once stood in the City of London and was re-erected here.

The next stops are Hampton and Hampton Hill. The major attraction in this area is the world-famous palace of Hampton Court. This magnificent building, set in beautiful and

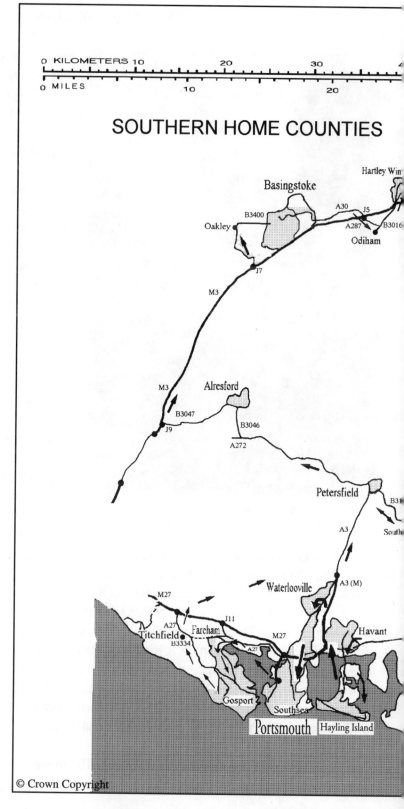

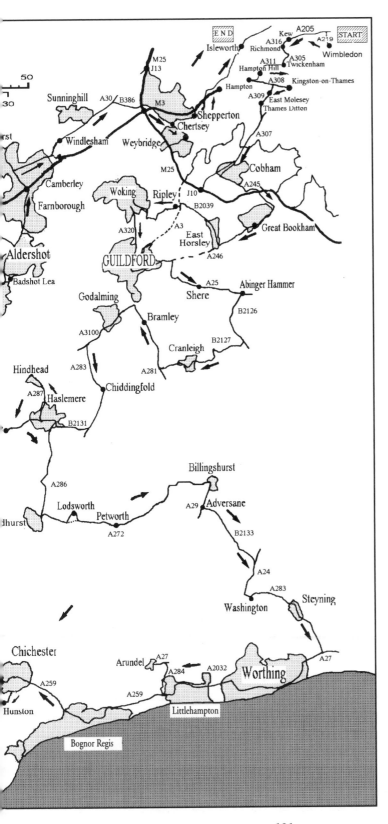

extensive gardens, was built by Cardinal Wolsey who was compelled to make a gift of it to Henry VIII. Five of Henry's wives lived here and it continued as a royal residence until 1760.

Kingston-upon-Thames, our next call, has a Coronation Stone said to have been used for crowning Saxon kings. From Kingston we carry on to Thames Ditton and East Molesey before arriving in Cobham where the remains of Bronze Age settlement and Roman pottery have been found. From there we continue to Great Bookham where the church is of particular interest. Built in the 11th century, remains of contemporary frescoes may be seen on the north wall.

The tour continues, via East Horsley and Ripley, to the town of Woking, situated on the disused Basingstoke Canal. Old Woking, once a market town, has several interesting houses in the high street including the 17th century manor house.

Our next stop is the busy town of Guildford. Standing on an ancient route crossing the River Wey, Guildford has been important since early times. The town prospered in the 16th century because of the local weaving industry. The High Street has a variety of architecture, gabled overhung, timber-framed, Georgian and Victorian. Abbot's Hospital, an almshouse founded in 1619, has a brick entrance tower with corner turrets in the Tudor tradition, leading to a courtyard. Especially memorable is the Guildhall with its clock on a beam projecting over the pavement.

The next village is Shere where there is a story that King John watched a girl bathing in the Silent Pool, to the west of the town, and as a result the girl drowned herself. From there we continue onwards to Abinger Hammer, Cranleigh, Bramley and then Godalming. A market town set in a valley formed by River Wey, Godalming grew mainly along the route through the valley. In the early Middle Ages it was important as the centre of a large manor and parish with the town receiving a charter for a market in 1300. During the 16th century weaving became an important industry in the area and Godalming became the chief textile town in Surrey. A local attraction is the Pepperpot, a former town hall, built in 1814 and which now houses a local museum.

There is an unusual National Trust property in this area: the River Wey and Godalming Navigation which extends for nearly 20 miles from Godalming to the River Thames. From 1635 to 1653 Sir Richard Weston, the builder and original owner of the nearby mansion of Sutton Place, supervised the canalisation of the River Wey. He constructed 15 miles of navigation consisting of building 12 locks and digging ten miles of canal. In 1760 it was extended upstream by four miles to Godalming. The navigation was used principally to transport timber and other agricultural produce. The opening of the railways brought about its decline and it is now used for recreation.

Moving on, we pass through Chiddingfold, Hindhead, Haslemere and Bramshott Chase until we reach Midhurst, a picturesque small town with many Georgian and half-timbered buildings. The Spread Eagle is particularly interesting. It is a large coaching inn whose sign is reputed to date from 1430. The main attraction in Midhurst is Cowdray Park. Cowdray was a mansion started in the late 15th century by Sir

David Owen, said to be the son of Owen Glendower. He had financial difficulties so he sold the house to Sir William Fitzwilliam in 1529 who completed it. The mansion passed to his half-brother, Sir Anthony Browne, who had a curse put on him by a monk that his line would end by fire and by water because he was granted Battle Abbey at the Dissolution of the Monasteries. In 1793 his descendent drowned in the Laufenburg Falls on the Rhine and in the same year Cowdray caught fire and was reduced to ruins. Today, most of the gatehouse still stands as does enough of the shell of the building to give a good idea of its former splendour.

The route continues, via Lodsworth, to Petworth, a charming town with many 16th and 17th century buildings. With its boundary walls extending into the town, the great

Arundel Castle.
By courtesy of Brighton Borough Council

house dominates Petworth. The lords of the manor, the Percys, first came here in the 12th century. In 1682 Elizabeth Percy married the Earl of Somerset who built Petworth House, demolishing houses and diverting streets in the process. The house and grounds are now owned by the National Trust. Some of the house is used as an art gallery with pictures and sculptures ranging from Van Dyck to Turner. Portraits of the former owners, the Percys can be seen here. There is a portrait of the seventh Earl of Northumberland, Thomas Percy, who was beheaded for his support of Mary, Queen of Scots. Another unfortunate Percy was the ninth Earl who was implicated in the Gunpowder Plot and was imprisoned in the Tower of London for sixteen years. He was only released after payment of £11,000, an enormous amount then.

We continue onwards through Billingshurst, Washington, Adversane and Steyning until we come to the Worthing, on the south coast. Royalty made the town fashionable and changed it from small fishing village to stylish resort. The Prince Regent's sister, Princess Amelia, visited the village in 1798 and the differences in character between the Prince and Princess are reflected in the differences between the dashing atmosphere of Brighton and the altogether quieter and more refined Worthing. In

1894 Oscar Wilde wrote *The Importance of Being Earnest* here and the town itself has a small part in the play. As a baby, the hero was found in a handbag and was given the surname Worthing because the man who found him had a first class ticket to Worthing in his pocket at the time.

Unfortunately in the 1850s there was an outbreak of cholera and in the 1890s a typhoid epidemic which, not unnaturally, started a decline in the town's popularity. It was only between the two World Wars that the underlying public health problems were finally solved and this brought about an expansion of the town.

Worthing possesses an interesting museum which has a section devoted to Victorian dolls, toys and games and a costume gallery with clothes from the 18th century to modern times.

The prehistoric site of Cissbury Ring, three miles north of Worthing on the A24, has been the site of human of activity since Neolithic times. It was a flint mine with shafts descending to a depth of 40 feet and galleries extending along the seams of flint. An Iron Age fort was constructed there in about 250BC, covering an area of about 65 acres. This was abandoned before the arrival of the Romans although it was again fortified towards the end of Roman occupation, probably against the Saxons.

The next destination, Littlehampton, is now a seaside resort with pleasant sandy beaches but it was once an important port and royal dockyard for King Henry VIII. From here we move on to the small town of Arundel. The town pre-dates the Norman Conquest although it is the Norman castle, built by Roger de Montgomery, which dominates Arundel. The inner gateway dates from the 11th century, the keep from the 12th century and the outer barbican was built in the 13th century by the Fitzalan family. The Fitzalans retained the castle until the mid-16th century when it went to Thomas Howard, Duke of Norfolk. Dukes of Norfolk have lived there since apart from during the Civil War. In 1643 the castle was besieged by Roundheads who captured and occupied it until 1649. The damage caused then was not fully repaired until the 1890s.

Our next call is the pleasant seaside town of Bognor Regis whose name commemorates the visit by George V in 1929. Moving inland now, Chichester has been the social and administrative centre for western Sussex since Roman times. The street pattern, four main streets within a walled enclosure, remains that of a typical Roman town although now, of course, it has been much amplified. The cathedral was started in the late 11th century and completed in 1123 although it has been altered and enlarged considerably since then. The spire collapsed in 1861 but was rebuilt between 1865-67. The cathedral has long been a patron of the arts and there are many modern features in the cathedral testifying to the continuation of this tradition, e.g. the tapestry behind the high altar from 1966, the pulpit of concrete and cast aluminium, a Graham Sutherland painting in the St. Mary Magdalene Chapel and a window by Chagall in the retrochoir. The city contains many fine buildings and consists of a harmonious mixture of Georgian brick and medieval stone. The city is also home to the

HMS Victory, Portsmouth. By courtesy of Portsmouth City Council

Chichester Festival which runs from May to September each year.

The tour now moves off the mainland on to Hayling Island, a holiday resort covering only four square miles. It is connected to the mainland by a bridge and the island has good sandy beaches, fishing and sailing.

The route continues to Havant which, as the junction of numerous trackways and Roman roads, has had a settlement here since earliest times. Portsmouth, the next stop, was built around a natural harbour in the 12th century by John de Gisors, lord of the manor of Titchfield. After he rebelled against Richard I Portsmouth was taken over by the king who made it a royal borough. Although it was not as important as Southampton as a port, it was used for the embarkation of troops fighting France and consequently the French sacked the town several times.

Henry VIII built a dry dock here and also a castle at Southsea as part of the coastal defences. Parliamentary troops captured it during the Civil War and in the reign of Charles II it was used as a prison. Much of the castle was destroyed by an accidental explosion in 1760. Reconstructed in the 19th century, today it serves as a museum of Portsmouth's defensive history.

Portsmouth started to become important as a naval dockyard in the reign of Charles I and continued to expand in the 18th century. During the Napoleonic Wars, however, Portsmouth dockyard became prominent. Nelson's ship, HMS Victory, is berthed in a dock dating from that time with contemporary buildings nearby. The remains of the Mary Rose, the Tudor ship which was raised from Portsmouth harbour, are also on display here. The oldest of these buildings, the Royal Naval Academy, dates from 1732.

One of Portsmouth famous sons was Isambard Kingdom Brunel, born here in 1806. He worked with Sir Samuel Bentham (brother of the philosopher, Jeremy Bentham) and another engineer, Henry Maudslay in Portsmouth Dockyard. They designed machinery for making pulley blocks. These took the strain of ropes in rigging and were extremely important. The machinery they designed was steam-driven and is said to have been the first mass-produced components of this type in the world.

Some of the old town of Portsmouth still survives in spite of being heavily bombed during the Second World War. These bombsites have been rebuilt but the old street pattern still persists. John de Gisors started building the first church in 1180. Part of this was damaged during the Civil War but was rebuilt later. The church was made into a cathedral in 1927 and enlarged. Some of the earliest surviving Gothic architecture in the country can be seen in this church.

Moving on through the area we come to Gosport, Titchfield and then Fareham, with its Georgian houses. Once a major port, it was also the fashionable place for naval officers to live.

The tour now doubles back along the M27 and then turns north along the A3 to the quiet residential town of Waterlooville, once a hamlet called Waitland End, before reaching Petersfield with its country park of Buster Hill. It is well worth exploring the smaller country roads in this area because the town is surrounded by extremely beautiful countryside and pretty villages. An example is our next stop, South Harting, where the writer, Anthony Trollope, lived for a while.

Moving onwards we reach Alresford on the River Alre. Divided by the river into Old and New Alresford, this was a medieval wool town. It still has some attractive Georgian houses in Broad Street and graves of French prisoners-of war from the Napoleonic War may be seen in the churchyard.

The route moves westward to join the M3 for the village of Oakley and then Basingstoke. The overwhelming impression of this town is of a modern commercial and industrial city. However, it is a very old settlement and still has remnants from earlier times. The Church of St. Michael and All Angels has parts that date from the 12th, 15th and 16th centuries. Its 16th century stained glass came from the 13th century Chapel of the Holy Ghost, the remains of which may be seen near the railway station.

Taking the A30 the tour reaches the town of Odiham which is predominantly Georgian but has buildings surviving from earlier times. The George Inn dates from 1540 and the priory is 15th to 17th century. In the churchyard of the 14th century church stands a pest house, a reminder of the great plague of 1665. Odiham Castle is sited about a mile west of the town. Now little remains of this early 13th century castle that was besieged by the French in 1216.

From here we move on to Hartley Wintney and then Aldershot. Nowadays the town is synonymous with the British Army but until the mid 19th century it was just a quiet hamlet surrounded by heathland. Our next stop is the pleasant town of Farnham which has retained its mainly Georgian character. Some of its buildings are excellent examples of the period particularly in Castle Street and West Street. The town also has a Norman castle built by Henry of Blois. Formerly the seat of the Bishops of Winchester, this castle has Tudor and Jacobean additions.

Doubling back, we call at Farnborough in Hampshire, the home of the Royal Aircraft Establishment since 1906 and the internationally known Farnborough Air Festival, and then Camberley. This town also has strong associations with the armed forces as Sandhurst, the world famous army Royal Staff College, lies to the west.

Back on the A30, we continue through Windlesham and Sunninghill to the Thames-side town of Chertsey. A number of old building still exist amonst which is the 18th century Curfew House. It is said a man destined to be executed when curfew was sounded was saved because his lover hung on the clapper of the bell to prevent it being rung.

Moving onwards via Weybridge and Shepperton we reach our final destination, Isleworth on the Thames. There is evidence of settlement here from earliest times and the area is mentioned in the Domesday Book under the name of the Manor of Gristlesworde. The magnificent Syon House stands on the site of an earlier monastery. The present house was started in the late 16th century by Edward Seymour, Duke of Somerset. He was executed and the estate was given to John Dudley, Duke of Northumberland and father of Lady Jane Grey. He was also executed after his daugher's nine day reign as queen. Queen Elizabeth I gave the estate to Henry Percy, Earl of Northumberland and it has stayed in that family ever since. In the 17th century Inigo Jones was brought in to improve and alter the property but it is the work on the interior a century later by Robert Adams that nowadays sets the house apart. The striking Great Conservatory, said to have been the model for the Crystal Palace, was built in the 19th century.

ANTIQUE DEALERS

WIMBLEDON, LONDON SW19 (081)

Adams Room Antiques & Interiors, 18-20 Ridgeway, Wimbledon Village TEL: 946 4733, 946 7047 FAX: 946 4858 ASSNS: LAPADA GMC PARKING: Own carpark OPEN: Mon-Sat 9-5 MIN: £100 MAX: £15,000 PERIOD: 17th-19th century SPECIALIST: Fine English walnut, rosewood, mahogany GENERAL: French & decorative furniture & objects OTHER INFO: Large separate showrooms. Canazaro Park Hotel, French coffee shop, museums etc.

Allegras Lighthouse Antiques, 75-77 Ridgeway, Wimbledon Village, SW19 4ST TEL: 946 2050 FAX: 944 6338 ASSNS: LAPADA, Antique & Decorative Lighting Assn PARKING: Easy OPEN: Mon-Sat 12-5.30 MIN: £100 MAX: £3,000 PERIOD: 19th-20th century SPECIALIST: Antique lights, period mirrors GENERAL: Furniture, jewellery, gifts.

Clunes Antiques, 9 West Place, Wimbledon Common, SW19 4UH TEL: 946 1643 PARKING: Easy OPEN: Tues-Sat 10-4.30 MIN: £1 MAX: £150 PERIOD: 19th-20th century SPECIALIST: Staffordshire figures GENERAL: Country, some theatrical ephemera.

Mark J West, 39b High Street, Wimbledon Village TEL: 946 2811 FAX: 946 2811 ASSNS: BADA PARKING: Easy OPEN: Mon-Sat 10-5.30 MIN: £5 MAX: £5,000 PERIOD: 18th-19th century SPECIALIST: English & Continental glass GENERAL: London's largest stock of antique glass.

KEW (081)

Lloyds of Kew, 9 Mortlake Terrace, Kew TW9 3DT TEL: 940 2512 PARKING: Easy OPEN: Mon-Tues, Thurs-Fri 10-4, Sat 10-5.30 MIN: £1 MAX: £2,500 PERIOD: 20th century SPECIALIST: Large stock gardening/ botanical books- world's most comprehensive (annual catalogue) GENERAL: Small stock on most subjects with emphasis on natural history, travel & history OTHER INFO: Mainly out-of-print and old. 5 mins from Royal Botanic Gardens, Kew & Maids of Honour teashop.

Dennis Woodman Oriental Carpets, 105 North Road, TW9 4HJ TEL: 878 8182 PARKING: Easy OPEN: Tues-Sat 10-6 & by appt MAX: £5,000 PERIOD: 19th-20th century GENERAL: Oriental kilims & textiles.

RICHMOND (081)

Antiques Arcade, 22 Richmond Hill, TW10 6QX TEL: 940 2035 PARKING: Medium OPEN: Thurs, Sat 10-5 & by appt MIN: £120 MAX: £4,000 PERIOD: 18th-20th century SPECIALIST: Fine porcelain, Staffordshire figures, fine smallish furniture, childrens' furniture, objets d'arts, samplers, gift pieces, some copper, brass & glass OTHER INFO: Delightful historic town on River Thames, close to Heathrow. Richmond Hill & Petersham hotels.

Antique Mart, 72-77 Hill Rise, TW10 6UB TEL: 940 6942 PARKING: Medium OPEN: 10-1, 3-6 PERIOD: 18th-20th century SPECIALIST: English & French furniture.

Mollie Evans Antiques, 82 Hill Rise, TW10 6UB TEL: 948 0182 PARKING: Medium OPEN: Thurs, Sat 10-5.30, Sun 2.30-5.30 & by appt MIN: £25 MAX: £4,000 PERIOD: 17th-20th century SPECIALIST: 18th-19th century sculptures, paintings, drawings GENERAL:

Adams Room Antiques and Interiors

Specialists in 18th and 19th century English and French furniture & decorative objects, period homes refurbishment with our own restoration workshop

Grace & Camilla Seymour-Cole
18-20 The Ridgeway, Wimbledon Village, London SW19
Telephone: 081-946 7047 and 4733 Fax: 081-946 4858
Monday - Saturday 9.00am - 5.00pm.
Trade and Export

Country & decorative furniture, unusual objets d'art from all periods.

Peter & Debbie Gooday, 20 Richmond Hill, TW10 6QX TEL: 940 8652 PARKING: Easy OPEN: Tues, Thurs-Sat 11-5.30, Sun 2.30-5.30 & by appt MIN: £20 MAX: £6,000 PERIOD: 19th-20th century SPECIALIST: Art Nouveau/ Deco with tribal art.

Hill Rise Antiques, 26 Hill Rise, TW10 6UA TEL: 332 2941 (24 hrs) ASSNS: LAPADA PARKING: Own carpark OPEN: Mon, Tues, Thurs-Sat 10.30-5.30 or by appt MIN: £30 MAX: £10,000 PERIOD: 18th-19th century SPECIALIST: English mahogany furniture GENERAL: Period accessories, glassware, silver + plate, clocks, mirrors etc.

Hortons, 2 Paved Court, The Green, TW9 1LZ, TEL: 332 1775 ASSNS: LAPADA, Gemmological Assn of GB PARKING: Medium OPEN: Mon-Tues, Thurs-Sat 10-5 MIN: £50 MAX: £5,000+ PERIOD: 19th-20th century SPECIALIST: Jewellery GENERAL: Silver + plate.

F & T Lawson Antiques, 13 Hill Rise, TW10 6UQ TEL: 940 0461 PARKING: Medium OPEN: Mon-Sat 10.30-5.30 MIN: £5 MAX: £2,000 PERIOD: 18th-20th century SPECIALIST: Victorian & late Georgian furniture GENERAL: General antiques OTHER INFO: Good restaurants.

Marryat, 88 Sheen Road, TW9 1UF TEL: 332 0262 FAX: 332 0256 PARKING: Medium OPEN: Mon-Sat 10-5.30 MIN: £1 MAX: £3,000 PERIOD: 18th-20th century SPECIALIST: Early English ceramics GENERAL: Victorian oils, watercolours, quality furniture, silver, glass, decorative objects. Conservation & restoration service. Contemporary Art exhibitions.

Piano Nobile Fine Paintings, 26 Richmond Hill, TW10 6QX TEL: 940 2435 FAX: 940 2435 PARKING: Medium OPEN: Tues-Sat 10-6, Sun 11-6 during exhibitions MIN: £350 MAX: £100,000 PERIOD: 19th-20th century GENERAL: Museum quality paintings & sculpture for the private & corporate collector OTHER INFO: View of famous bend in the Thames beloved by all great painters.

Richmond Antiques, 28-32 Hill Rise, TW10 6UA TEL: 948 4638 PARKING: Medium OPEN: 11-5.30, closed Wed MIN: £1 MAX:

£2,000 PERIOD: 19th-20th century GENERAL: 20+ dealers trading in Georgian, Victoran, Edwardian mahogany, walnut & pine furniture, pictures. Wide variety of smalls & bric-a-brac.

Roderic Antiques, 84 Hill Rise, TW10 6UB TEL: 332 6766 FAX: 332 6766 PARKING: Medium OPEN: Mon-Tues, Thurs-Sat 10-5.30, Sun 2-5.30 MIN: £100 MAX: £10,000 PERIOD: 18th-19th century SPECIALIST: Satinwood & ebony colonial furniture GENERAL: Furniture.

TWICKENHAM (081)

Golden Oldies, 113 London Road, TW1 1EE TEL: 891 3067 PARKING: Medium OPEN: Tues-Fri 10-6, Sat 10-4 MIN: £2 MAX: £2,000 PERIOD: 19th-20th century SPECIALIST: Worlds largest stock of original cigarette card sets GENERAL: Film memorabilia, lead figures, comics, emphemera etc OTHER INFO: Publishers of *The Guide to Cigarette Card Collecting.*

Anthony C. Hall (Bookseller), 30 Staines Road, TW2 5AH TEL: 898 2638 ASSNS: ABA, PBFA PARKING: Easy OPEN: Mon-Tues, Thurs-Sat 9-5.30, Weds 9-1 MIN: £1 MAX: £2,000

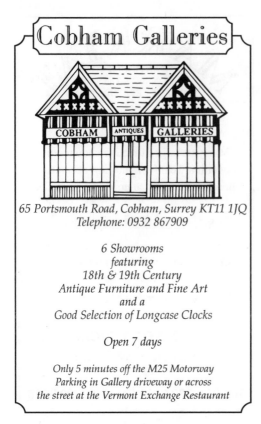

Cobham Galleries

65 Portsmouth Road, Cobham, Surrey KT11 1JQ
Telephone: 0932 867909

6 Showrooms
featuring
18th & 19th Century
Antique Furniture and Fine Art
and a
Good Selection of Longcase Clocks

Open 7 days

Only 5 minutes off the M25 Motorway
Parking in Gallery driveway or across
the street at the Vermont Exchange Restaurant

PERIOD: 17th-20th century SPECIALIST: Russian & East European studies, Middle East, Asia, Africa social & industrial history GENERAL: Also medium general stock.

Phelps Ltd, 133-135 St Margarets Road, East Twickenham, TW1 1RG TEL: 892 1778 FAX: 892 3661 ASSNS: LAPADA PARKING: Easy OPEN: Mon-Sat 9-5.30 MIN: £150 MAX: £6,000 PERIOD: 18th-20th century GENERAL: 6,000 sq ft mostly furniture & mirrors OTHER INFO: Excellent coffee & sandwiches opposite.

KINGSTON-UPON-THAMES (081)

Classic Automobilia & Regalia Specialists, (C.A.R.S.), 2 Applemarket, Eden Street, KT1 1JE TEL: (0273) 601960 FAX: (0273) 623846 ASSNS: Pedal Car Collectors Club PARKING: Own carpark OPEN: 10-6 MIN: £50+ MAX: £5,000 PERIOD: 20th century SPECIALIST: Automobilia, car mascots, car badges, memorabilia, motoring nostalgia. Restoration of old pedal cars from pre/post war periods OTHER INFO: Featured on TV with subject *Does size matter* comparing us in child's Ferrari P.40 with UK's

tallest man alongside. Had lots of film/TV work.

Cockrell Antiques, 278 Ewell Road, Surbiton, KT6 7AG TEL: 390 8290 PARKING: Easy OPEN: Thurs-Sat 9-6 & by appt (resident) MIN: £20 MAX: £5,000 PERIOD: 18th-20th century SPECIALIST: Furniture GENERAL: Silver plate, porcelain, pictures.

EAST MOLESEY (081)

Abbott Antiques, 75 Bridge Road, KT8 9HH TEL: 941 6398 PARKING: Easy OPEN: Mon-Sat 10-5 MIN: £50 MAX: £6,000 PERIOD: 18th-20th century SPECIALIST: Clocks.

B.S. Antiques, 39 Bridge Road TEL: 941 1812 PARKING: Easy OPEN: Mon-Sat 10-5, closed Wed MIN: £100 MAX: £3,000 PERIOD: 18th-19th century SPECIALIST: Old clocks, barometers, horological books. Repairs of clocks & barometers.

Court Gallery, 16 Bridge Road, KT8 2HA TEL: 941 2212 PARKING: Medium OPEN: Tues-Sat 8.30-4.30 MIN: £20 MAX: £2,000 PERIOD: 18th-20th century SPECIALIST: Oils GENERAL: Watercolours, engravings. Restoration & framing.

Hampton Court Antiques, 75 Bridge Road, KT8 9HH TEL: 941 6398 PARKING: Easy OPEN: Mon-Sat 10-5 MIN: £5 MAX: £1.500 PERIOD: 19th-20th century GENERAL: General antiques.

Hampton Court Emporium, 52-54 Bridge Road, KT8 9HA TEL: 941 9032 PARKING: Easy OPEN: Mon-Sat 9.30-5.30, Sun 10-5 PERIOD: 19th-20th century GENERAL: General antiques OTHER INFO: Delightful tea room on site.

Howard Hope - Gramophones & Phonographs, 21 Bridge Road, KT8 9EU TEL: 941 2472 FAX: 398 7630 PARKING: Easy OPEN: By appt MIN: £80+ MAX: £10,000 PERIOD: 19th-20th century SPECIALIST: Gramophones, phonographs, paper-vole, musical boxes, organs, typewriters, sewing machines & other Victorian and later mechanical & musical items OTHER INFO: Street is conservation area.

Nicholas Antiques, 31 Bridge Road, KT8 9ER TEL: 979 0354 PARKING: Easy OPEN: Mon-Sat 9.30-5.30 MIN: £5 MAX: £5,000 PERIOD: 18th-20th century SPECIALIST: Furniture & decorative items & gilt mirrors.

Sovereign Antiques Centre, 53 Bridge Road

TEL: 783 0595 PARKING: Medium OPEN: Mon-Sat 10-5 MIN: £1 MAX: £1,000 PERIOD: 19th-20th century GENERAL: General antiques.

THAMES DITTON (081)

David Curzon Gallery, 1 High Street, KT7 0SD TEL: 398 7860 PARKING: Easy OPEN: Wed-Sat 10-6 MIN: £30 MAX: £5,000 PERIOD: 19th-20th century GENERAL: Landscape, marine, figurative, architectural subjects.

Clifford & Roger Dade, Boldre House, Weston Green, KT7 0JP TEL: 398 6293 ASSNS: LAPADA PARKING: Own carpark OPEN: Mon-Sat 9-6 (resident) MIN: £300 MAX: £6,000 PERIOD: 18th-19th century SPECIALIST: Georgian mahogany furniture GENERAL: Period furniture & objects OTHER INFO: 3 excellent pubs on Green.

Fern Cottage Antiques, 28-30 High Street, KT7 0RY. TEL: 398 2281 PARKING: Medium OPEN: Mon-Sat 10-5.30 MAX: £2,000 PERIOD: 19th-20th century SPECIALIST: Charlotte Rhead, Clarice Cliff GENERAL: General antiques OTHER INFO: 1st floor craft shop.

COBHAM (0932)

Cobham Galleries, 65 Portsmouth Road, KT11 1JQ TEL: 867909, (0860) 544578 ASSNS: LAPADA PARKING: Own carpark OPEN: Mon-Sat 10-5, Sun 11-5 MIN: £20 MAX: £10,000 PERIOD: 18th-19th century SPECIALIST: Dining tables & chairs, Victorian oils & watercolours GENERAL: 6 showrooms of Georgian to Victorian period furniture OTHER INFO: Dining table finder service. Our showrooms extensively renovated in cottage dating from 18th century.

GREAT BOOKHAM (0372)

Roger A. Davis, 19 Dorking Road, KT23 4PU TEL: 457655, 453167 ASSNS: BHI AHI BWCG PARKING: Easy OPEN: Tues, Thurs, Sat 9.30-5.30 MIN: £30 MAX: £5,000 PERIOD: 18th-19th century SPECIALIST: Clocks, barometers, telescopes, Ironstone ware OTHER INFO: Polesden Lacy (NT) 400 yards.

EAST HORSLEY (0483)

A.E. Gould & Sons (Antiques) Ltd, Old Rectory Cottage, Ockham Road South, KT24 6QJ TEL: 283747 PARKING: Own carpark OPEN: Mon-Fri 9.30-5 MIN: £50 MAX: £5,000 PERIOD: 18th-20th century SPECIALIST: Ba-

rometers GENERAL: Large stock of English furniture in mahogany & walnut.

The Old Curiosity Shop, 9 Bishopshead Parade, KT24 6RT TEL: 284994 PARKING: Easy OPEN: Mon-Tues, Thurs-Fri 10-5, Sat 10-1 MIN: £150 MAX: £895 PERIOD: 19th century GENERAL: General antiques.

RIPLEY (0483)

Cedar House Gallery, GU23 6AE TEL: 211221 PARKING: Easy OPEN: 7 days ring bell (resident) MIN: £50 MAX: £20,000 PERIOD: 19th (mainly) & 20th century SPECIALIST: Decorative oils GENERAL: Oils & watercolours OTHER INFO: Surrey's best restaurant opposite, village green & cricket pitch.

J. Hartley Antiques Ltd, 186 High Street, GU23 6BB TEL: 224318 ASSNS: LAPADA PARKING: Easy OPEN: Mon-Fri 8.45-5.45, Sat 9.45-4.45 MIN: £100 MAX: £3,500 PERIOD: 18th-19th century GENERAL: English mahogany furniture, some walnut, oak etc OTHER INFO: Possibly England's largest remaining unenclosed village green. Lord Nelson & Lady Hamilton frequented the nearby Talbot Hotel. Pastimes was a watering stop for long distance stage coaches.

Manor House Antiques, High Street, GU23 6AF TEL: 225350 PARKING: Easy OPEN: Mon, Tues, Thurs-Sat 10-5.30, Weds 10-1 MIN: £2 MAX: £10,000 PERIOD: 17th-19th century SPECIALIST: Early oak, brass, copper GENERAL: Oak, walnut, mahogany, rosewood, British and Continental metalware, clocks.

Ripley Antiques, 67 High Street TEL: 224981 FAX: 225196 ASSNS: LAPADA PARKING: Easy OPEN: 9.30-5.30 MIN: £50 MAX: £10,000 PERIOD: 18th-20th century SPECIALIST: English & Continental furniture GENERAL: Decorative items, chandeliers, mirrors etc.

Sage Antiques & Interiors, High Street, GU23 6BB TEL: 224396 FAX: 211996 PARKING: Easy OPEN: Mon-Sat 9.30-5.30 MIN: £100 MAX: £10,000 PERIOD: 17th-19th century GENERAL: Period furniture pre-1830, mahogany, walnut, oak, country furniture, oil paintings, silver + plate, china OTHER INFO: 5 other quality antique shops with large showrooms.

Anthony Welling Antiques, Broadway Barn, High Street, GU23 6AQ TEL: 225384 ASSNS: BADA PARKING: Easy OPEN: Mon-Sat 9.30-

1, 2-5.30 MIN: £500 MAX: £6,000 SPECIAL-IST: Period oak & country furniture 1600-1830, Metals pre 1830 OTHER INFO 5 village pubs & 3 Egon Ronay recommended restaurants.

WOKING (0483)

Chattels Antiques, 156 High Street, Old Woking TEL: 771310 PARKING: Own carpark OPEN: Mon-Fri 9-5 MIN: £10 MAX: £10,000 PERIOD: 18th-19th century SPECIALIST: Longcase clocks, barometers GENERAL: 19th century furniture OTHER INFO: 30 years experience in the restoration of the 17th century clock case.

Knaphill Antiques, 38 High Street, Knaphill TEL: 473179 PARKING: Medium OPEN: Tues-Sat 9-6 MIN: £2 MAX: £1,500 PERIOD: 19th-20th century GENERAL: Furniture, china, barometers, clocks.

Manor Antiques & Restorations, 2 New Shops, High Street, GU22 9JW. TEL: 724666 FAX: 750366 ASSNS: GMC PARKING: Medium OPEN: Mon-Sat 10-5, by appt outside shop hours MIN: £200 MAX: £5,000 PERIOD: 18th-20th century SPECIALIST: Furniture GENERAL: Longcase clocks, china, glass, brass, prints, Edwardian/Georgian furniture, antique pine OTHER INFO: Good restoration service on furniture & clocks, rush & cane work undertaken, pine stripping.

Wych House Antiques, Wych Hill, GU22 0EV TEL: 764636 PARKING: Easy OPEN: 9-6 MIN: £5 MAX: £5,000 PERIOD: 18th-20th century SPECIALIST: Georgian & Victorian furniture.

GUILDFORD (0483)

The Antique Centre, 22 Haydon Place TEL: 67817 PARKING: Easy OPEN: Tues, Thurs, Fri 10-4, Sat 10-4.30 MIN: £1 PERIOD: 17th-20th century SPECIALIST: 7 separate shops dealing in silver, jewellery, glass, pottery, lace, oriental Devonware & collectables OTHER INFO: Cathedral, historic High Street, castle & gardens.

Denning Antiques, 1 Chapel Street, GU4 8AD TEL: 39595 PARKING: Easy OPEN: 10-5 MIN: £5 MAX: £1,000 PERIOD: 19th-20th century SPECIALIST: Silver, jewellery GENERAL: Lace, linen, collectables OTHER INFO: Close to High Street in fascinating side street.

Michael Stewart Galleries, 61 Quarry Street, GU1 3UA TEL: 504359 FAX: 575109 ASSNS: FATG PARKING: Medium OPEN: Tues-Sat 9.30-5.30 MIN: £25 MAX: £60,000 PERIOD: 20th century SPECIALIST: Sir William Flint originals GENERAL: Contemporary artists in watercolours, pastels, oils, limited editions, prints & sculpture OTHER INFO: Guildford Museum, haunted pub (King's Head).

Charles W. Traylen, Castle House, 49-50 Quarry Street, GU1 3UA TEL: 572424 FAX: 450048 ASSNS: ABA PARKING: Difficult OPEN: Tues-Sat 9-1 & 2-5 MIN: £1 MAX: £10,000 PERIOD: 17th-20th century SPECIAL-IST: Fine books & bound sets.

SHERE (0483)

Shere Antique Centre, Middle Street, GU5 9HF TEL: 202846 PARKING: Easy OPEN: Mon-Sat 10-5 MIN: £15 PERIOD: 18th-19th century GENERAL: Showrooms on 2 floor, 16 dealers in china, silver, furniture. Dateline 1930s.

Yesterday's Pine, Gomshall Lane, GU5 9HE TEL: 203198 PARKING: Easy MIN: £35 MAX: £1,500 PERIOD: 19th century SPECIALIST: Original Victorian pine OTHER INFO: Famous beauty spot with its Tillingborne River and views of North Downs.

ABINGER HAMMER (0306)

Abinger Bazaar (Junk Antiques), Guildford Road TEL: 730756 PARKING: Own carpark OPEN: Thurs, Sat, sun 11.30-5.30 MIN: £1 MAX: £300 PERIOD: 19th-20th century SPECIALIST: Fireplaces & grates plus accessories GENERAL: China, glass, brass, silver + plate, bric-a-brac OTHER INFO: Next to Frog Island vegetarian restaurant.

CRANLEIGH (0483)

Barbara Rubenstein Fine Art, Smithwood House, Smithwood Common, GU6 8QY TEL: 267969 FAX: 267575 PARKING: Own carpark OPEN: By appt MIN: £250 MAX: £5,000 PERIOD: 19th-20th century GENERAL: Watercolours & oils OTHER INFO: Stock housed in a Georgian house amid beautiful countryside.

BRAMLEY (0483)

Drummonds of Bramley Architectural Antiques Ltd, Birtley Farm, GU5 0LA TEL: 898766 Fax: 894393 PARKING: Own carpark OPEN: Mon-Fri 9-6, Sat 9.30-5, Sun 10-5 MIN: £10 MAX: £50,000 PERIOD: 17th-19th century

SPECIALIST : Architectural antiques, antique garden statuary & furniture GENERAL: Fully restored period bathrooms & many materials for restoration.

Memories Antiques, High Street, GU5 0HB TEL: 892205 PARKING: Easy OPEN: Mon-Sat 10-5 MIN: £1+ PERIOD: 18th-20th century GENERAL: 6 dealers with furniture, silver, brass, copper, glass, china, lace, old pine, kitchenalia, bygones, collectables OTHER INFO: Good trade call.

GODALMING (0483)

Cry For The Moon, 31 High Street, GU7 1AU TEL: 426201 FAX: 860117 PARKING: Easy OPEN: Mon-Sat 9.30-5.30 MIN: £50 MAX: £10,000 PERIOD: 19th-20th century SPECIALIST: Jewellery & silver GENERAL: Objets d'art, paintings, watches.

Heath-Bullock, 8 Meadrow, GU7 3HN TEL: 422562 FAX: 426077 ASSNS: BADA PARKING: Own carpark OPEN: Mon-Sat 10-1 & 2-4 MIN: £100 MAX: £10,000 PERIOD: 18th-19th century SPECIALIST: Upholstered furniture, especially leather chesterfields GENERAL: English & Continental furniture OTHER INFO: Godalming Museum, Inn-on-the-Lake Hotel, General Oglethorpe (founder of the State of Georgia) lived here.

Ivelet Books Ltd, Church Street Bookshop, 26 Church Street, GU7 1EW TEL: 418878 FAX: 418656 PARKING: Medium OPEN: Mon-Sat 10.30-5.30 MIN: £1 MAX: £3,000 PERIOD: 19th-20th century SPECIALIST: Books on architecture & interiors, gardening, natural history, topography, applied arts etc OTHER INFO: Gertrude Jekyll's home at Munstead Wood.

The Olde Curiosity Shoppe, 99 High Street GU6 1AQ TEL: 415889 PARKING: Easy OPEN: Mon-Sat 10-5 MIN: £1 MAX: £300 PERIOD: 19th-20th century GENERAL: Antiques, china, glass, silver, plate, jewellery, gifts.

David White Antiques, 34 Headrow GU7 3HT TEL: 427957 PARKING: Medium OPEN: Mon-Sat 9.30-5.30 MIN: £50 MAX: 10,000 PERIOD: 17th-19th century SPECIALIST: Country furniture GENERAL: Walnut, oak, elm, fruitwood, yew, period pine, Blue & White transfer-ware.

CHIDDINGFOLD (0428)

Manor House Interiors, 1 Chiddingfold Galleries, Petworth Road, GU8 4UF TEL: 682727 Fax: 682727 PARKING: Easy OPEN: Tues-Fri 9.30-1 & 2-5, Sat 9.30-1 MIN: £5 MAX: £300 PERIOD: 19th-20th century GENERAL: General antiques. Also interior design accessories OTHER INFO: Centre of Surrey/Sussex touring country. Lovely village on route to Petworth, Brighton etc, Crown Inn.

HASLEMERE (0428)

Bow Antiques Ltd, 6 Petworth Road TEL: 652886 PARKING: Easy OPEN: Mon-Tues, Thurs-Sat 9.30-5 MIN: £5 MAX: £3,500 PERIOD: 18th-20th century GENERAL: Georgian, Victorian, Edwardian furniture & early 20th century prints.

Surrey Clocks Centre, 3 Lower Street, GU27 2NY TEL: 651313 FAX: 651313 ASSNS: Antique Clock & Barometer Restoration PARKING: Easy OPEN: 9-5, Wed & Sat 9-1 MIN: £300 MAX: £6,000 PERIOD: 18th-19th century SPECIALIST: 200 clocks & barometers.

Woods Wharf Antiques Market, 56 High Street, GU27 2LA TEL: 642125 FAX: 725045 PARKING: Easy OPEN: 9.30-5.30 MIN: £5 MAX: £900 PERIOD: 19th-20th century GENERAL: General antiques OTHER INFO: Georgian Hotel opposite.

HINDHEAD (0428)

Albany Antiques, 8-10 London Road, GU26 6AF TEL: 605528 PARKING: Medium OPEN: Mon-Sat 9.30-6 MIN: £10 MAX: £3,000 PERIOD: 18th-19th century SPECIALIST: Georgian to Edwardian furniture GENERAL: Brass, china & bric-a-brac etc.

M.J. Bowdery, 12 London Road, GU26 6AF TEL: 606376 ASSNS: BADA PARKING: Own carpark OPEN: Mon-Sat 9-1 PERIOD: 18th-early 19th century GENERAL: English & Continental furniture OTHER INFO: Area of oustanding natural beauty, mostly NT.

Second Hand Rose, Bramshott Chase, GU26 6DB TEL: 604880 PARKING: Easy OPEN: Mon-Sat 10-5.30 MIN: £10 MAX: £1,000 PERIOD: 19th-20th century GENERAL: Georgian, Victorian, Edwardian, 20th century & modern furniture. Some brass, copper, pictures & mirrors OTHER INFO: Excellent meals & ale at country pub, Prince of Wales & Hammer Hotel alongside The Devil's Punchbowl.

MIDHURST (0798)

Foord Antiques, P.O. Box 14, GU29 0BS TEL: 6351 ASSNS: LAPADA PARKING: Own carpark OPEN: By appt MIN: £25 MAX: £10,000 PERIOD: 18th-early 19th century SPECIALIST: Furniture & boxes GENERAL: Treen, metal & decorative items.

LODSWORTH (0798)

Richard Garner Antiques, The Stores, GU28 9BZ TEL: 5513 PARKING: Easy OPEN: Mon-Sat 10-5 MIN: £30 MAX: £4,000 PERIOD: 19th century SPECIALIST: Staffordshire figures, pot-lids, Baxter prints GENERAL: General antiques, many unusual items.

PETWORTH (0798)

The Bacchus Gallery, Lombard Street, GU28 0AG TEL: 42844 FAX: 42634 OPEN: Mon-Sat 10-1, 2.30-5 MIN: £10 MAX: £5,000 PERIOD: 18th-20th century SPECIALIST: Wine related artefacts GENERAL: Glass, books, silver, prints, corkscrews, bin labels, etc (drink related only) OTHER INFO: Petworth House (National Trust), Goodwood House & Goodwood Races. Welldiggers pub for good food known locally as Testicle Ted's.

Baskerville Antiques, Saddlers house, Saddlers Row, GU28 0AN TEL: 42067 FAX: 43956 ASSNS: BADA PARKING: Own carpark OPEN: Mon-Sat 9.30-6 PERIOD: 18th-19th century SPECIALIST: Clocks & barometers GENERAL: Furniture OTHER INFO: Major antique centre.

Nigel Bassett, Swan House, Saddlers Row, GU28 0AN TEL: 44121 ASSNS: PAADA PARKING: Easy OPEN: Mon, Tues, Thurs-Sat 10-5.30 MIN: £50 MAX: £25,000 PERIOD: 18th-19th century SPECIALIST: Dining room furniture & accessories. GENERAL: Furniture, glass, silver, porcelain etc.

Lesley Bragge, Fairfield House, High Street, GU28 0AU TEL: 42324 ASSNS: LAPADA, PAADA PARKING: Easy OPEN: Mon-Sat 10-5 MIN: £50 MAX: £5,000 PERIOD: 18th-19th century SPECIALIST: Furniture, lighting GENERAL: Silver, prints, porcelain, mainly decorative OTHER INFO: Petworth House.

Nigel Cracknell (Antiques) Ltd., Clock House, Church St, Lombard Street, GU28 0AG Tel: 44188 ASSNS: BADA PARKING: Medium Open: 9.30-5 MIN: £500 MAX: £30,000 PERIOD: 17th-19th century SPECIALIST: Quality furniture.

Frith Antiques, New Street, GU28 0AS TEL: 831606, 43155 PARKING: Easy OPEN: 10.30-5 MIN: £5 MAX: £4,000 PERIOD: 18th-19th century SPECIALIST: Antique fishing tackle, games, pastimes GENERAL: Country furniture & related items.

Granville Antiques, High Street, GU28 0AU TEL: 43250 ASSNS: BADA CINOA PARKING: Easy OPEN: Normally Mon-Sat 10-5 but appt advisable MIN: £100 MAX: £10,000 PERIOD: 18th-19th century GENERAL: English & Continental furniture (mainly pre 1840) & selected accessories.

Grove House Antiques, Middle Street, GU28 0BD, TEL: 42563 PARKING: Easy OPEN: Mon-Sat 10-5 MIN: £100 MAX: £10,000 PERIOD: 18th-19th century GENERAL: Country furniture & decorative objects.

Griffin Antiques, Church Street, GU28 0AD TEL: 43306 FAX: 44136 ASSNS: PAADA PARKING: Medium OPEN: Mon-Sat 10-1, 2-5.30 MIN: £50 MAX: £5,000 PERIOD: 17th-19th century SPECIALIST: Oak furniture, metalware, Blue & White china.

John G. Morris Ltd, Market Square, GU28 0AH TEL: 42305 ASSNS: BADA, CINOA PARKING: Easy OPEN: Mon, Tues, Thurs-Sat 9.45-5.30. Weds 9.45-1 MIN: £7 MAX: £25,000 PERIOD: 18th-19th century SPECIALIST: English furniture & associated items.

Petworth Antique Market, East Street, GU28 0AB TEL: 42073 PARKING: Own carpark OPEN: Mon-Sat 10-5.30 PERIOD: 17th-20th century SPECIALIST: Antique market with wide range of stock & prices.

Red Lion Antiques, New Street, GU28 0AS TEL: 44485 FAX: 42367 ASSNS: PAADA PARKING: Medium OPEN: 10-5.30 MIN: £50 MAX: £10,000 PERIOD: 17th-19th century SPECIALIST: Oak furniture GENERAL: Antiques for the country home.

J.C. Tutt Antiques, Angel Street, GU28 0BQ TEL: 43221 ASSNS: PAADA PARKING: Medium OPEN: Mon-Sat 10-5, closed some Mons MIN: £30 MAX: £8,000 PERIOD: 18th-19th century GENERAL: Furniture, smalls, china.

T.G. Wilkinson Antiques Ltd, New Street TEL: 44443 PARKING: Easy OPEN: Mon-Sat 10-5.30 MIN: £50 MAX: £20,000 PERIOD: 17th-18th century SPECIALIST: English & Continental furniture GENERAL: Pictures, decorative items, mirrors etc.

BILLINGSHURST (0403)
Tom Burton & Rod Johnston, Great Grooms Antique Centre, Parbrook TEL: 786202 PARKING: Own carpark OPEN: Seven days 9.30-5.30 MIN: £50 MAX: £500 PERIOD: 19th century SPECIALIST: Ceramics, mainly ironstone, Blue & White pottery and some porcelain.

Great Grooms Antique Centre, Great Grooms, Parbrook, RH14 9EU TEL: 786202 PARKING: Own carpark OPEN: Mon-Sat 9.30-5.30, Sun 10.30-4.30 MIN: £10 MAX: £10,000 PERIOD: 18th-20th century SPECIALIST: Variety of specialist dealers in English & Continental furniture, pictures, silver, plated ware, pottery, porcelain, jewellery, treen, flatware etc OTHER INFO: 1 mile from Sotheby's at Summers Place, Billingshurst, opposite The Gables restaurant.

Wakelin & Linfield, P.O.Box 48, RH14 0YZ TEL: 700004 FAX: 700004 ASSNS: BADA, LAPADA PARKING: Own carpark OPEN: By appt MIN: £500 MAX: £50,000 PERIOD: 17th-19th century SPECIALIST: English & Continental furniture and decorative accessories from 15th-19th centuries.

ADVERSANE (0403)
Bradley Antiques & Orchard Market, The Little Shop, Old House Antique Centre, RH14 9TT TEL: 782186 PARKING: Own carpark OPEN: 10-6 MIN: £15 MAX: £2,000 PERIOD: 18th-20th century SPECIALIST: Gramophones, pestles & mortars GENERAL: Furniture, metalware OTHER INFO: 30 dealers, tearooms & lunches on site. 1 mile from Sotheby's at Summer Place.

WASHINGTON (0903)
Chanctonbury Antiques, Clematis Cottage, School Lane, RH20 4AP TEL: 892233 PARKING: Easy OPEN: Mon, Wed-Sat 10.30-5 (dusk in winter) & by appt MIN: £3 MAX: £500 PERIOD: 18th-19th century SPECIALIST: English pottery & porcelain GENERAL: Needlework, towels & other interesting smalls, treen, small furniture.

STEYNING (0903)
David Fileman Antiques, Squirrels, Bayards, Horsham Road, BN4 3AA TEL: 813229 PARKING: Own carpark OPEN: Any time MIN: £50 MAX: £20,000 SPECIALIST: 18th-19th century glass, chandeliers, table lights, wall lights, lustres. table glass, collectors glass, French paperweights. Restoration of above OTHER INFO: Brambe Castle, old house, cottages.

WORTHING (0903)
Chinaman Godden of Worthing Ltd, 19a Crescent Road, BN11 1RL TEL: 235958 ASSNS: BADA PARKING: Own carpark OPEN: Mon-Fri by appt MIN: £50 MAX: £2,000 PERIOD: 18th-19th century SPECIALIST: English porcelain GENERAL: Ceramics only OTHER INFO: Author of 20+ standard reference books on English Ceramics, some available.

Rathbone Law, 7-9 The Arcade TEL: 200274 ASSNS: NAS PARKING: Medium OPEN: Mon, Tues, Thurs-Sat 10-5 MIN: £50 PERIOD: 19th-20th century SPECIALIST: Diamond merchants, largest & most varied stock of emerald set rings in Sussex GENERAL: Teddybears, dolls, antiques jewellery, silver, porcelain, glass OTHER INFO: Character sea-side town with beautifully cultivated bowling parks, old style cinema & lively provincial theatre nestled between shingle beaches & the rolling South Downs.

Steyne Antique Galleries, 29 Brighton Road, BN11 3EF TEL: 200079 PARKING: Medium OPEN: Tues, Thurs-Sun 9.30-5.30, Weds 9.30-1 MIN: £5 MAX: £2,500 PERIOD: 18th-20th century SPECIALIST: Walnut, rosewood & mahogany furniture GENERAL: General antiques

Rococo Antiques, 21 Warwick Road, BN11 3ET TEL: 235896 PARKING: Medium OPEN: 10.30-5 MIN: £5 MAX: £750 PERIOD: 19th-20th century GENERAL: Collectables & antiques OTHER INFO: Surrounded by pubs & restaurants.

Robert Warner & Sons Ltd, 1-13 South Farm Road TEL: 232710 FAX: 217515 PARKING: Own carpark OPEN: 9.3-5, Wed AM only PERIOD: 19th-20th century GENERAL: 30,000 sq ft shipping furniture, bric-a-brac OTHER INFO: Warehouse adjacent Orme Road.

Wilsons Antiques, 57-59 Broadwater Road, BN14 8AH TEL: 202059 ASSNS: LAPADA PARKING: Own carpark OPEN: Mon-Sat 9-5

MIN: £10 MAX: £15,000 PERIOD: 18th-20th century SPECIALIST: English furniture & fine art including, Edwardian furniture, oils & watercolours OTHER INFO: Main A24, 500 yds south of Broadwater Church, 7 showrooms.

LITTLEHAMPTON (0903)
The Round Pond, Faux Cottage, 4a Selborne Road, BN17 5NN TEL: 714261 PARKING: Easy OPEN: By appt MIN: £50 MAX: £2,000 PERIOD: 19th-20th century SPECIALIST: Vintage model pond yachts & marine models.

ARUNDEL (0903)
Armstrong-Davis Gallery, The Square, BN18 9AB TEL: 882752 PARKING: Own carpark OPEN: Mon-Sat 10-6 PERIOD: 17th-20th century SPECIALIST: International sculpture, bronzes, fountains, statuary etc OTHER INFO: Arundel Castle, Wildfowl Trust, Norfolk Arms Hotel.

Baynton-Williams, 37a High Street, BN18 9AG TEL: 883588 FAX: 883588 PARKING: Easy OPEN: Mon-Sat 10-6 MIN: £5 MAX: £5,000 PERIOD: 17th-19th century SPECIALIST: Maps & prints OTHER INFO: Arundel Castle, very attractive town, many dealers in 'small' antiques, beautiful surrounding country

Pat Golding, 6 Castle Mews, Tarrant Street TEL: 883980 PARKING: Easy OPEN: Mon-Sat 10-1, 2-5 MIN: £5 MAX: £1,000 PERIOD: 18th-20th century GENERAL: Ceramics, pottery, glass OTHER INFO: Arundel Castle & Cathedral closeby. Wild Fowl Trust 1 mile.

Richard Davidson Antiques, Romsey House, 51 Maltravers Street BN18 9BQ TEL: 883141 FAX: 883141 ASSNS: BADA PARKING: Medium OPEN: By appt MIN: £200 MAX: £25,000 SPECIALIST: Late 18th-early 19th century furniture GENERAL: Furniture, paintings, decorative items.

Serendipity Antiques, 27 Tarrant Street, BN18 9BP TEL: 882047 PARKING: Medium OPEN: Mon-Sat 10-1, 2-5.30 MIN: £5 MAX: £650+ PERIOD: 17th-19th century SPECIALIST: Early maps & engravings GENERAL: Some etchings, watercolours & oils.

Spencer Swaffer, 30 High Street, BN18 9AB TEL: 882132 FAX: 884564 ASSNS: LAPADA PARKING: Easy OPEN: 9-6, but appts welcome anytime MIN: £10 MAX: £15,000 PERIOD:

17th-20th century SPECIALIST: Decorative antiques GENERAL: English china, glass, wide stock of accessories, pine, bamboo, English furniture OTHER INFO: In top 5 of England's leading decorative antique dealers.

Sussex Fine Art, 7 Castle Mews, Tarrant Street, BN18 9DG TEL: 884055 PARKING: Easy OPEN: Fri-Sun 10.30-5.30 MIN: £150 MAX: £3,500 PERIOD: 19th century GENERAL: English watercolours.

Stuart Thompson, 39 Tarrant Street TEL: 883796 FAX: 884491 PARKING: Easy OPEN: 8.30-5.30 MIN: £10+ PERIOD: 17th-20th century SPECIALIST: Walking sticks & canes GENERAL: Umbrella stands, parasols, walking stick stands OTHER INFO: Arundel is a maze of antique shops & pubs.

Treasure House Antiques & Saturday Market, 31 High Street, BN18 9AG TEL: 883101 PARKING: Medium OPEN: Variable PERIOD: 19th-20th century GENERAL: Wide range of mainly smalls, veritable treasure trove OTHER INFO: Opposite Arundel Toy & Military Museum, Norfolk Arms Hotel.

BOGNOR REGIS (0243)
Gough Bros Art Shop & Gallery, 71 High Street TEL: 823773 ASSNS: FATG PARKING: Medium OPEN: Mon-Sat 9-5, Wed AM only MIN: £35 MAX: £1,500 PERIOD: 19th-20th century GENERAL: Watercolours, oils, drawings, miniatures, cartoons, OTHER INFO: Shop tucked away behind The Unicorn in the High Street and seafront. We also sell art materials & are framers & picture restorers.

CHICHESTER (0243)
Gems, 39 West Street, PO19 1RP TEL: 786173 PARKING: Easy OPEN: Mon-Sat 10-5.30 MIN: £5 MAX: £2,000 PERIOD: 18th-19th century SPECIALIST: Staffordshire fine china GENERAL: Furniture, glass, china OTHER INFO: Beautiful Georgian city within Roman walls, close to harbour & cathedral.

Peter Hancock, 40-41 West Street, PO19 1RP TEL: 786173 PARKING: Easy OPEN: Mon-Sat 10-5.30 MIN: £1 MAX: £2,500 PERIOD: 18th-20th century SPECIALIST: Furniture, silver, scientific instruments, books plus wide selection of general antiques OTHER INFO: Close to Cathedral & Roman Palace.

Heritage Antiques, 77d St Pancras, PO19 4LS TEL: 783796 PARKING: Easy OPEN: Mon-Sat 9-5.30 MIN: £3 MAX: £1,500 PERIOD: 18th-20th century GENERAL: Antique & older style furniture & other interesting items OTHER INFO: Goodwood House & Park, Fishbourne Roman Villa, Weald & Downland Open Air Museum.

St Pancras Antiques, 150 St Pancras TEL: 787645 PARKING: Medium OPEN: 9.30-5 MIN: £10 MAX: £3,000 PERIOD: 17th-19th century SPECIALIST: Arms & armour, furniture, fine porcelain, medals, early militaria OTHER INFO: Shop is 16th-17th century. Festival Theatre.

HAYLING ISLAND (0705)

J. Morton Lee, Cedar House, Bacon Lane, PO11 0DN TEL: 464444 ASSN: LAPADA PARKING: Own carpark OPEN: By appt MIN: £50 MAX: £10,000 PERIOD: 18th-20th century SPECIALIST: Marine watercolours GENERAL: 18th-20th century watercolours OTHER INFO: Fair exhibitions - World of Watercolours (Jan), Harrogate (Feb), NEC Birmingham (Apr & Aug), Buxton (May), Olympia (June), Northern (Sept), Surrey (Oct), Kensington (Nov). Also own Spring & Summer exhibitions in Emsworth (Mar) & Chichester (July).

HAVANT (0705)

Trentham Gallery, 40 North Street TEL: 484935 PARKING: Own carpark OPEN: Mon-Sat 10-5 MIN: £5 MAX: £2,000 PERIOD: 18th-20th century GENERAL: Maps & prints, glass, Blue & White British pottery, small furniture, books, paintings, collectors items OTHER INFO: On Chichester harbour. Excellent facilities.

PORTSMOUTH & SOUTHSEA (0705)

Affordable Antiques, 89 Albert Road, Southsea, PO7 5PL TEL: 293344 PARKING: Easy OPEN: Mon-Fri 10-3, Sat 09.30-5 MIN: £5 MAX: £3,500 PERIOD: 19th-20th century SPECIALIST: Victorian, Edwardian & 1930's furniture.

A. Fleming (Southsea) Ltd, The Clock Tower, Castle Road, Southsea, PO5 3DE TEL: 822934 ASSNS: BADA PARKING: Easy OPEN: Mon-Fri 8.30-5, Sat 8.30-1 MIN: £5 MAX: £5,000+ PERIOD: 18th-20th century GENERAL: Furniture, china, silverplate, nautical & miscellaneous OTHER INFO: Portsmouth is very inter-

esting city, Mary Rose (Henry VIII's), Warrior, Royal Marine, D Day & Submarine Museum.

Oldfield Gallery, 76 Elm Grove, PO5 1LN TEL: 838042 FAX: 838042 ASSNS: PFBA, IMCOS PARKING: Medium OPEN: Mon-Sat 10-5.30 PERIOD: 17th-19th century SPECIALIST: Antique maps, prints, sea charts.

Pretty Chairs, 189-191 Highland Road TEL: 317411 PARKING: Easy OPEN: Mon-Sat 10-4.30 MIN: £75 MAX: £1,500 PERIOD: 19th-20th century SPECIALIST:Pretty furniture GENERAL: Continental chairs, tables, desks, sofas, bedroom furniture OTHER INFO: Hilton, Queens hotels, Murrays restaurant.

Times Past, 141 Highland Road, Southsea, PO4 9EY TEL: 822701, (0831) 418488 FAX: 822701 PARKING: Medium OPEN: Mon, Tues, Thurs-Sat 10-4 MIN: £1 MAX: £2,000 PERIOD: 19th-20th century GENERAL: Antiques & shipping goods OTHER INFO: Seagull Restaurant.

Wessex Medical Antiques, 77 Carmarthen Avenue, PO6 2AG TEL: 376518 FAX: 201479 PARKING: Easy OPEN: By appt MIN: £200

MAX: £4,000 PERIOD: 18th-19th century SPECIALIST: Medical instruments & microscopes.

GOSPORT (0705)

Peter Pan's Bazaar, 105 Forton Road, PO12 4TQ TEL: 524254 PARKING: Easy OPEN: Thurs-Sat 10.15-5 MIN: £1 MAX: £2,000 PERIOD: 19th-20th SPECIALIST: Vintage cameras GENERAL: Photographic collectors items.

Toys Dolls House, Peter Pan's Bazaar, 105-107 Forton Road, PO12 4TQ TEL: 524254 PARKING: Easy OPEN: Thurs-Sat 10-5 MIN: £5 MAX: £1,000 PERIOD: 1800-1939 SPECIALIST: Victorian dolls GENERAL: House miniatures, dolls, miniature bronzes. No repro.

FAREHAM (0329)

Elizabethan Antiques, 58 High Street, PO16 7BG TEL: 234964 PARKING: Easy OPEN: Mon & Thurs 10-4.30, Sat 10-12.30 MIN: £5 MAX: £1,500+ PERIOD: 18th-20th century SPECIALIST: Certified valuations GENERAL: Furniture, pictures, jewellery, china, glass etc OTHER INFO: Fareham's High Street is best preserved Georgian street in the South.

TITCHFIELD (0329)

Gaylords Antiques, 75 West Street, TEL: 843402 PARKING: Own carpark OPEN: Mon-Sat 9-5.30 MIN: £150 MAX: £4,500 PERIOD: 18th-20th century GENERAL: Furniture & clocks, 19th century fully restored and in fine order OTHER INFO: We are retail warehouse in historic village 2 mins from M27.

Pamela Manley Antique Jewellery, 6-8 South Street, PO14 4DJ TEL: 42794 PARKING: good OPEN: Mon-Sat 9.30-5.30 MIN: £5 MAX: £1,000 PERIOD: 18th-20th century SPECIALIST: Antique jewellery GENERAL: Silver, objects of vertu.

Titchfield Antiques Ltd, 13-15 South Street, PO4 4DL TEL: 45968 PARKING: Easy OPEN: MIN: £10 MAX: £1,000 PERIOD: 19th-20th century SPECIALIST: Art nouveau & art deco GENERAL: Silver, small furniture OTHER INFO: Historic village with abbey & church where the earls of Southampton are embalmed in honey. Adjoining original 1930's teashop & gardens complete with furniture & fittings.

PETERSFIELD (0730)

Cull Antiques, 62 Station Road, GU32 3ES TEL: 263670 PARKING: Easy OPEN: Mon-Sat 10-1, 2-5 MIN: £200 MAX: £5,000 PERIOD: 18th-19th century GENERAL: Country furniture & accessories only OTHER INFO: Next door to well-known antiquarian bookshop. Harrow Inn, best pub winner. Literary: Gilbert White's house (Selborne), Jane Austen's Chawton Uppark House (Harting). Between Petworth & Winchester, airports & London 1 hour, ferries ° hour.

The Petersfield Bookshop, 16a Chapel Street, GU32 3DS TEL: 263438 FAX: 269426 ASSNS: ABA BADA PBFA PARKING: Easy OPEN: Mon-Sat 9-5.30 MIN: £1 MAX: £9,000 PERIOD: 17th-20th century SPECIALIST: Early angling books, natural history, travel & topography GENERAL: Very large stock OTHER INFO: Petersfield Lake, rowing etc, Beefeater Steak House, numerous pubs.

SOUTH HARTING (0730)

Holmes Antique Maps & Prints, South Gardens Cottage TEL: 825040 ASSNS: FATG PARKING: Own carpark OPEN: Strictly by appt MIN: £10 MAX: £1,000 PERIOD: 17th-20th century GENERAL: Antique maps & views of the British Isles 1575-1850. Old & new prints of sporting & country life, especially horses and dogs 1750-1940 OTHER INFO: B&B possible in our 16th century thatched cottage in this pretty village on the edge of the South Down Way, Excellent pubs. Near Goodwood (racing), Cowdray Park (polo), & NT houses etc.

ALRESFORD (0962)

Alresford Antiques, 49 West Street, SO24 9AB TEL: 735959 PARKING: Medium OPEN: Tues-Sat 10-12.30, 1.30-4.30 MIN: £1 MAX: £500 PERIOD: 18th-20th century GENERAL: Small unusual items, china, glass, treen, toys, all sorts OTHER INFO: Watercress steam railway, river walks, B&B in Cheriton's Flowerpots" (has own brewery).

Artemesia, 16 West Street, SO24 9AT TEL: 732277 ASSNS: LAPADA PARKING: Easy OPEN: Mon-Sat 9.30-1, 2-5 MIN: £10 MAX: £3,500 PERIOD: 17th-19th century SPECIALIST: Oriental porcelain & works of art GENERAL: English furniture, ceramics & works of art OTHER INFO: 1st century AD to 1908 Chinese from the Han to the Qing. Good food at 2 hotels & several pubs, all close.

Evans & Evans, 40 West Street, SO24 9AU

TEL: 732170 ASSNS: LAPADA PARKING: Medium OPEN: Fri & Sat 9-1, 2-5 or by appt MIN: £400 MAX: £30,000 PERIOD: 17th-20th century SPECIALIST: English & French clocks, barometers GENERAL: Musucal boxes, secondhand wristwatches OTHER INFO: Unspoilt 18th century market town

Studio Bookshop & Gallery, 17 Broad Street, SO24 9AW TEL: 732188 ASSNS: FATG ABA PARKING: Medium OPEN: Mon-Sat 9-5 MAX: £3,000 PERIOD: 18th-20th century SPECIALIST: Antiquarian & old books GENERAL: Includes India & Far East, topographical prints OTHER INFO: Mary Russell Mitford was born here, in same road.

OAKLEY (0256)

E.H. Hutchins, 48 Pardown, RG23 7DZ TEL: 780494 PARKING: Own carpark OPEN: Mon-Sat 8-5 MIN: £30 MAX: £1,000 PERIOD: 18th-19th century GENERAL: All types of furniture.

BASINGSTOKE (0256)

Squirrel Collectors Centre, 9a New Street, RG21 1DF TEL: 464885 PARKING: Medium OPEN: Mon-Sat 10-5.30 Wide price range PERIOD: 19th-20th century SPECIALIST: Antique & modern silver, gold & silver jewellery GENERAL: Small antiques, books, old postcards, dolls houses furniture, prints, dolls, toy cars, collectables OTHER INFO: Basingstoke mainly pedestrianised with good facilities, New Concert Hall, theatre etc. Overseas visitors always make point of returning to us when in UK.

ODIHAM (0256)

Odiham Gallery, 78 High Street TEL: 703415 PARKING: Easy OPEN: Mon-Sat 9.30-5.30 MIN: £100 PERIOD: 19th-20th century SPECIALIST: Room sized decorative carpets GENERAL: Antique rugs, carpets, kilims & runners OTHER INFO: Good restaurant opposite - La Foret (French).

HARTLEY WINTNEY (0252)

Nicholas Abbott, High Street, RG27 0RF TEL: 842365 PARKING: Easy OPEN: Mon-Sat 9.30-5.30 MIN: £50 MAX: £10,000 PERIOD: 17th-19th century SPECIALIST: English furniture 1600-1830 GENERAL: Furniture OTHER INFO: Stratfield Saye (House of Duke of Wellington) 5 miles. The Vyne (17th century country house) 10 miles.

Airedale Antiques, c/o Deva Antiques, High Street.

TEL: 843538 FAX: 842946 PARKING: Easy OPEN: Mon-Sat 9-5.30 MIN: £10 MAX: £6,000 PERIOD: 17th-19th century SPECIALIST: Country furniture GENERAL: Furniture, treen, metalware.

Antique House, 22 High Street, RG27 8NY TEL: 844499 FAX 844499 PARKING: Easy OPEN: Mon-Sat 9.30-6 or by appt MIN: £50 MAX: £5,000 PERIOD: 18th-20th century SPECIALIST: Watercolours, oils & prints GENERAL: Mainly Georgian - early 20th century inlaid furniture OTHER INFO: The Lamb (hotel & restaurant), Stilton Dish & The Shoulder of Mutton , The Cricketers.

Cedar Antiques Ltd, High Street, RG27 8HL TEL: 843252 FAX: 845235 ASSNS: LAPADA PARKING: Easy opposite OPEN: Mon-Sat 9-5 MIN: £25 MAX: £15,000 PERIOD: 17th-19th century SPECIALIST: French provincial country furniture & accessories. Non-period decorative furnishings but in the country style.

Brian Clisby Antique Clocks, Andwell Antiques, The Row TEL: 716436 ASSNS: LAPADA PARKING: Easy OPEN: Mon-Sat 9.30-5.30 MIN: £300 MAX: £10,000 PERIOD: 18th-19th century SPECIALIST: Longcase clocks GENERAL: Antique clocks & barometers OTHER INFO: Big centre for antiques, frequented by dealers worldwide.

Deva Antiques, The Corner House, High Street. RG27 8NY TEL:843538, 843656 FAX: 842946 PARKING: Easy OPEN: Mon-Sat 9-5.30 MIN: £50 MAX: £6,000 PERIOD: 18th-19th century GENERAL: Mahogany & walnut furniture OTHER INFO: Hotels at Fleet, Hook & Yately all closeby. Winchfield station 2 miles, collection arranged.

Colin Harris Antiques, at Deva, High Street TEL: 843538, home (0734)732580 PARKING: Easy OPEN: Mon-Sat 9-5.30 MIN: £50 MAX: £5,000 PERIOD: 18th-19th century GENERAL: Victorian & Georgian quality furniture.

Just The Thing, High Street, RG27 8NS TEL: 843393, home 842916 PARKING: Easy OPEN: Mon-Sat 9-5 MIN: £5 MAX: £3,000 PERIOD: 18th-20th century SPECIALIST: General antiques OTHER INFO: Large choice of antique shops, pubs & restaurants in village.

David Lazarus Antiques, High Street, RG27

8NS TEL: 842272 OPEN: Mon-Sat 10-5.30 PERIOD: 17th-19th century GENERAL: Period antique furniture & objets d'art.

A.W. Porter & Son, High Street, RG27 8NY TEL: 842676 FAX: 842064 ASSNS: BHI, NAG PARKING: Easy OPEN: Mon-Sat 9-5.30 MIN: £20 MAX: £5,000 PERIOD: 18th-20th century SPECIALIST: Clocks, silver, jewellery OTHER INFO: Many good local watering holes & a very nice village cricket green.

ALDERSHOT (0252)

House of Christian, 5 Vale Road, Ash Vale, GU12 5HH TEL: 314478 PARKING: Medium OPEN: Mon-Sat 10-5.30 MIN: £5 MAX: £750 PERIOD: 19th-20th century SPECIALIST: Pine furniture GENERAL: Old, new & made up pine furniture. Occasionally old mahogany & oak furniture, small pine items. Brass, china, copper etc OTHER INFO: Hogs Back Hotel (Seale), Bush Hotel (Farnham), Wings Cottage Chinese Restaurant (Farnborough).

FARNHAM (0252)

Annies Antiques, 1 Ridgeway Parade, Frensham Road (A287) TEL: 713447 PARKING: Own carpark area OPEN: Mon-Sat 9.30-5.30, Fri 10.30 start, & by appt MIN: £1 MAX: £3,000 PERIOD: 19th-20th century GENERAL: General antiques OTHER INFO: A browsing disorganised shop, never know what you may find under a table or in the cellar.

Bourne Mill Antiques, 39-43 Guildford Road, GU9 9PY TEL: 716663 PARKING: Own carpark OPEN: Seven days 10-5 MIN: £1 MAX: £3,000 PERIOD: 18th-20th century GENERAL: Bric-a-brac, pine, antique & reproduction furniture, garden stock, tea rooms, tapestries, lights, books OTHER INFO: Bush Hotel, Bishops Table, Farnham Castle, all in town centre.

Childhood Memories, 27a South Street, GU9 7QU TEL: 724475 PARKING: Own carpark OPEN: Mon-Sat 9.30-5 MIN: £5 MAX: £2,000 PERIOD: 19th-20th century SPECIALIST: Antique teddy bears, dolls, toys, games.

Farnham Antique Centre, 27 South Street, GU9 7QU TEL: 724475 PARKING: Own carpark OPEN: Mon-Sat 9.30-5 MIN: £5 MAX: £2,000 PERIOD: 18th-20th century SPECIALIST: Clocks, silver, furniture, porcelain, jewellery.

Village Pine, 32 West Street TEL: 726660 FAX: 851360 PARKING: Own carpark OPEN: Mon-Sat 10-5 MIN: £12 MAX: £1,600 PERIOD: 17th-20th century SPECIALIST: Unusual old stripped pine GENERAL: Interesting tables, chests, dressers, boxes. Interesting objects a speciality OTHER INFO: Enormous stock of restored pine.

Karel Weijand, Lion & Lamb Courtyard, GU9 7LL TEL: 726215 ASSNS: LAPADA PARKING: Own carpark OPEN: Mon-Sat 9.30-5.30 MIN: £45 MAX: £30,000+ PERIOD: 19th-20th century SPECIALIST: Antique & decorative GENERAL: Oriental carpets & rugs OTHER INFO: The largest selection of oriental carpets outside London.

FARNBOROUGH (0252)

Martin & Parke, 97 Lynchford Road TEL: 515311 PARKING: Easy OPEN: Mon-Fri 9-5, Sat 9-4 MIN: £5 MAX: £1,000 PERIOD: 18th-20th century GENERAL: Shipping goods, Edwardian, Victorian, period.

SANDHURST (0252)

Berkshire Metal Finishers Ltd, Swan Lane Trading Estate, GU17 8DD TEL: 873475 FAX: 875434 PARKING: Easy OPEN: 8.30-1, 2-6 PERIOD: 20th century GENERAL: Metalware.

CAMBERLEY (0276)

The Pedlar, 231 London Road, GU15 3EY TEL: 64750 PARKING: Own carpark OPEN: 10-5, closed Wed PERIOD: 19th-20th century GENERAL: General antiques.

WINDLESHAM (0344)

Country Antiques, at Country Garden Centre, London Road, GU20 6LL TEL: 873404 PARKING: Own carpark OPEN: Mon-Tues, Thurs-Sun 10-5 MIN: £5 MAX: £1,500 GENERAL: General antiques OTHER INFO: 20 dealers selling wide range mainly furniture in a garden centre.

Richard Kimbell Ltd, Country Gardens, London Road, GU20 6LL PARKING: Own carpark OPEN: Seven days 9-6 MIN: £1 MAX: £3,000 PERIOD: 19th century SPECIALIST: Antique & reproduction pine GENERAL: Country furniture & crafts.

SUNNINGHILL (0344)

Antiques of Ascot, 3c High Street TEL: 872282 PARKING: Easy OPEN: Mon-Sat 10-4.45 MIN: £1 MAX: £2,500 PERIOD: 20th century GENERAL: Broad range of attractive items.

CHERTSEY (0932)
Mister Gun Antiques, 96 Guildford Street, KT16 9AD TEL: 566323 PARKING: Easy OPEN: Tues-Sat 10-5.30 MIN: £50 MAX: £2,000 PERIOD: 19th-20th century GENERAL: General antiques, dolls & teddies.
Chertsey Antiques, Windsor Street, KT16 8AS TEL: 782453 PARKING: Medium OPEN: Mon, Tues, Thurs-Sat 10-5.15 MIN: £5 MAX: £1,500 PERIOD: 17th-20th century SPECIALIST: Silver & antique jewellery GENERAL: Small furniture, unusual objets d'art, small gifts & china, books OTHER INFO: Chertsey Museum, Windsor Castle & Kneedy Memorial.
Surrey Antiques Centre, 10 Windsor Street, TEL: 563313 PARKING: Medium OPEN: Mon-Sat 10-5 MIN: £1 MAX: £650 PERIOD: 17th-20th century SPECIALIST: Mainly Victorian, Edwardian furniture & china GENERAL: Silver section, book section, pictures, general goods.
WEYBRIDGE (0932)
The Clock Shop, 64 Church Street, KT13 8DL TEL: 840407, 855503 PARKING: Easy OPEN: Mon-Sat 9.30-6 MIN: £300+ MAX: £15,000+ PERIOD: 17th-19th century SPECIALIST: Quality clocks & barometers OTHER INFO: The Ship Hotel.
Church House Antiques, 42 Church Street, KT13 8DP TEL: 842190 ASSNS: LAPADA PARKING: Easy OPEN: Thurs-Sat 10-5.30 & by appt MIN: £30 MAX: £6,000 PERIOD: 18th-20th century SPECIALIST: Jewellery GENERAL: General antiques OTHER INFO: Attractive 16th-18th century building, 4 other good antiques shops, The Queen's Head.
Not Just Silver, 16 York Rd, KT13 9DT TEL: 842468 PARKING: Easy OPEN: Mon-Sat 9.30-5.30 & by appt MIN: £3 MAX: £5,000 PERIOD:18th-20th century SPECIALIST: Antique & quality silver GENERAL: Porcelain, glass & furniture.
SHEPPERTON (0932)
Crown Antiques, Russell Road, TW17 9WF TEL: 247709, 242803 PARKING: Easy OPEN: Weds-Sat 10-5, Sun 11-4 or by appt MIN: £30 MAX: £12,000 PERIOD: 17th-19th century SPECIALIST: Quality furniture GENERAL: Mirrors, lamps, silver, porcelain, boxes etc

OTHER INFO: Old Church Square on river.
Ricketts & Co Antiques, Church Square, TW17 8JN TEL: 243571 PARKING: Easy OPEN: 9-5 MIN: £40 MAX: £2,000 PERIOD: 18th-19th century SPECIALIST: Metalwork GENERAL: Brass, copper mainly for fireplaces, some furniture. No reproduction OTHER INFO: 14th century church & riverside restaurants etc.
ISLEWORTH (081)
Crowther of Syon Lodge, Bush Corner, London Road, TW7 5BH TEL: 560 7978 FAX: 568 7572 PARKING: Own carpark OPEN: Mon-Fri 9-5, Sat, Sun 11-4.30 MIN: £500 MAX: £80,000+ PERIOD: 17th-19th century SPECIALIST: Antique panelling & manufacture of period style, quality 18th century chimneypieces GENERAL: Statues, urns, fountains, seats, temples, animal figures, panelling, chimneypieces OTHER INFO: Panelling may pre-date. Syon Park (once Duke of Northumberland's estate designed by Robert Adam in 1770), Osterley House, Ham House, Kew Gardens.

New Forest, Dorset and Wiltshire

This tour starts in Hampshire passes through the historic and ecologically vital area of the New Forest, then into Dorset with its rich heritage of prehistoric and later sites and includes the major seaside resort of Bournemouth. The route turns into Wiltshire passing through picturesque market towns and the city of Salisbury, of major importance since Roman times.

First to Winchester, the county town of Hampshire, which stands on the River Itchen amidst the rolling chalk downs. The Romans built their town of *Venta Belgarum*, later to become Winchester, alongside a prehistoric settlement. The city walls and High Street still follow the Roman lines. After the Romans left, the town declined but with the emergence of the kingdom of Wessex it became of first importance as its capital.

The see of Winchester was wealthy and the bishops powerful. Its Bishop Henry of Blois, who built Wolvesey Castle, was involved in the Civil War between King Stephen and the Empress Matilda when much of Winchester was burnt including the royal palace. It was at Wolvesey Castle that the Domesday Book was compiled and it also contained the royal treasury until the end of the 12th century. Now all that remains of the castle is the Great Hall which was built by Henry III and said to be the finest aisled medieval hall in England.

Winchester Cathedral, the second longest in Europe, was started in 1079 using stone from the Isle of Wight and shows early Norman and perpendicular work. It has many notable features: 14th century carved stalls, a restored 15th century reredos, the oldest iron grill in England, coffers containing the bones of Saxon & Danish kings. The tombs of Izaak Walton, Jane Austen and King William Rufus, killed in the New Forest, can be found there. Hooks still in the cathedral pillars once held decorations for the wedding of Queen Mary Tudor and Philip of Spain in 1554.

Winchester contains many other fine and historic buildings and in parts of the town these still conform to the Saxon street pattern. Superb examples of medieval and later architecture can be found in the cathedral close, notably the Deanery, where Charles II stayed for a time, and which is partly 14th century and Cheyne Court with three timber-framed gables rising above the ground floor.

The tour continues via Twyford, Morestead and Upham to the conurbation of Eastleigh and Southampton. For nearly two thousand years Southampton has been an important port. Armies have used it as an embarkation point for invasion and foreign troops have landed here for raids on Britain. The Romans had a port here, William the Conqueror used it for ships arriving from Normandy, Richard I left from Southampton to go on his crusades, the French sacked the town in 1338 and Edward III embarked from here to win the Battle of Crécy. More recently, during the First and Second World Wars millions of troops left the port to go into battle. Southampton was also the major port for transatlantic liners like the Queen Elizabeth and the Queen Mary.

Reminders of the medieval town can be seen in the town walls and their towers. Only one section of the wall itself survives, in Western Esplanade. The towers have all survived: Polymond, Catchcold, Wind Whistle and God's House Tower stood at the four corners of the walls. God's House Tower, on the Town Quay, is now a museum of local archaeology. Other museums are housed in the 14th century Wool House, a maritime museum, and the Tudor House, a 16th century mansion with overhanging gables, half-timbered walls and mullioned windows standing in St Michael's Square.

From Southampton the route moves inland to Romsey where the Broadlands, once the home of Lord Mountbatten of Burma and now his son, is well worth a visit. Queen Elizabetth II and Prince Philip, and later the Prince and Princess of Wales, spent part of their honeymoons here. This splendid mid-Georgian mansion is set alongside the River Test, famous for its game fishing, in a park landscaped by Capability Brown. In the 19th century it was the home of Lord Palmerston, the great Victorian Prime Minister. The Mountbatten Exhibition, in the stable building, celebrates Lord Mountbatten's life and achievements. The house, with its collections of pictures, sculpture, furniture, porcelain, etc, is also open to the public.

The tour passes through rural Plaitford and Sherfield English to the New Forest village of Cadnam. The New Forest is the largest area of lowland common land in Britain, and has a history as a legal forest going back to Norman times. There is a suggestion that areas of the New Forest were part of the primeval forest once covering most of Britain after the last Ice Age. The Normans gave it the legal status of forest which was an area, not necessarily wooded, in which animals were protected by special law, i.e. forest law, aimed at preserving game for hunting by the king or his licensees. Special courts administered forest law and this is the origin of the Court of Verderers still based in Lyndhurst. There were severe penalties attached to poaching. At first a man convicted of killing a deer could be put to death or blinded but later the penalties were changed to fines. Because part of the affect of forest law meant that the land could not be used for arable farming, local people were given various common rights, for example the right to grazing. Properties in the New Forest still have their ancient common rights attached to them and it is these that allow the famous New Forest ponies to graze freely.

Gradually, though, the New Forest's role as a royal hunting ground declined, although herds of deer still roam the Forest today. Oak for building the navy's ships became important. This started the trend to commercial tree plantations that continues to this day. Because of the Forest's unique ecostructure there are strict rules on the planting of trees and their felling, for example, clear felling of a whole area is not allowed. However, there are still areas of the Forest that have

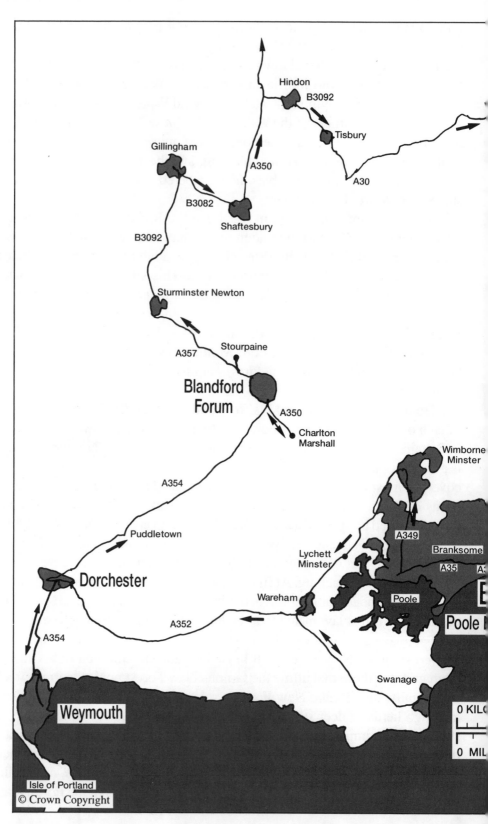

Hindon
B3092
Tisbury
Gillingham
A350
A30
B3082
Shaftesbury
B3092
Sturminster Newton
Stourpaine
A357
Blandford Forum
A350
Charlton Marshall
Wimborne Minster
A354
A349
Branksome
Puddletown
Lychett Minster
A35
Dorchester
Wareham
Poole
Poole
A352
A354
Swanage
Weymouth
0 KILO
0 MIL
Isle of Portland
© Crown Copyright

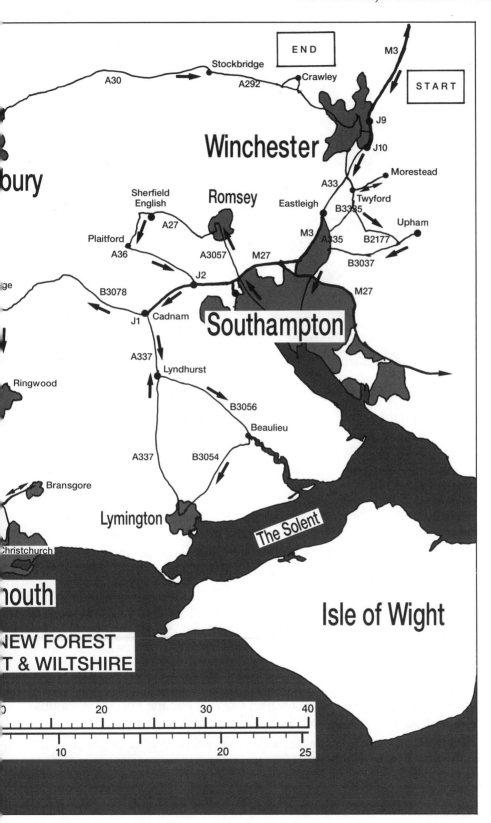

END

M3

START

Stockbridge

A30

A292

Crawley

J9

J10

Winchester

Morestead

bury

A33

Sherfield English

Romsey

Eastleigh

Twyford

B3335

Upham

A27

M3

A335

B2177

Plaitford

A3057

M27

B3037

A36

J2

M27

B3078

Cadnam

Southampton

ge

J1

A337

Ringwood

Lyndhurst

B3056

Beaulieu

A337

B3054

Bransgore

Lymington

The Solent

Christchurch

Isle of Wight

nouth

NEW FOREST
T & WILTSHIRE

20 30 40

10 20 25

New Forest Ponies. By courtesy of the New Forest District Council

not been commercially planted, amongst which are the Ancient and Ornamental Woodlands.

Nowadays the New Forest is of paramount importance for recreation and conservation. It has an unusual range of ecosystems from dry heathland to valley bogs and it contains several kinds of lowland habitat that are rare or endangered elsewhere; this is why its preservation is essential.

The Forest is extremely popular as a tourist destination and visitors can find plenty of well-maintained carparks and campsites as well as opportunities for golf, fishing and riding. Because there are few public roads through the Forest it is quite easy to enjoy the countryside without the noise and pollution found in other beauty spots. Also, the carparks, as a matter of policy, are sited close to attractions such as water, picnic areas or forest walks. As many people do not move far from their cars it is quite possible to be free of other tourists after even a relatively short walk.

Lyndhurst was the administrative centre of the New Forest and is still home to the Verderers Court, the New Forest District Council and the Forestry Commission offices. A legacy of forest law can be seen in the Tudor stirrup, kept in the Verderers' Hall, used to decide whether a dog was a threat to the king's deer. If a dog was too big to pass through the stirrup its claws were maimed so that it could no longer hunt effectively. Next door is the Queen's House, built in 1563 and a former royal hunting lodge. Another celebrated local attraction is the grave of

Alice Liddell, the original Alice in Wonderland.

Beaulieu, standing at the head of the Beaulieu River, was the site of a Cistercian Abbey founded in 1204 on land granted by King John. The abbey church was torn down during the Dissolution of the Monasteries in 1538 and the abbey gatehouse is now incorporated into Palace House, the home of Lord Montagu of Beaulieu, and built in 1870. The estate includes the National Motor Museum with over 250 vintage and historic cars on display including Donald Campbell's Bluebird.

Downstream from Beaulieu stands Bucklers Hard comprising of two rows of 18th century houses. Incredibly this tiny village was once the centre of a thriving ship building industry supplying men-of-war for the navy in the war against Napoleon. In the village there is a Maritime Museum which includes a display of how Bucklers Hard looked then. The Museum also has reconstructions of rooms in the the New Inn in 1793 and some of the village houses have also been restored to their original state so that the homes of an 18th century labourer, shipwright and master shipbuilder may be experienced.

The next town on the route is Lymington, dating from the end of the 12th century and founded by William de Redvers, Earl of Devon and Lord of the Isle of Wight. Lymington was an important market town throughout the Middle Ages with a good import and export trade. Its wide High Street is typical of a market street with ample space for stalls. Even today an open market is held every Saturday.

We next proceed to Fordingbridge with its 15th century bridge, widened in the 18th century, across the River Avon. Nearby Breamore House is worth visiting. This is an Elizabethan manor house set in parkland and with good collections of paintings, tapestries, furniture and porcelain.

The market town of Ringwood, next on the route, has interesting historical associations. It is reputed that the Duke of Monmouth, pretender to the throne of England, sheltered in a house in the High Street after the Battle of Sedgemoor. He was later caught and executed in London.

From Ringwood we move, via Bransgore, to Christchurch. Standing at the meeting of the Rivers Stour and Avon with a natural harbour, it has a history going back at least to Saxon times when it was called Twyneham. Although some of the town has been modernised evidence of its ancient past can still be seen. First and foremost is the magnificent church which gives the town its present name. At 311 feet in length, this is the longest parish church in England. Standing on the site of a 7th century church, building started in 1094 as part of Christchurch Priory. An interesting feature is the Miraculous Beam protruding through an arch in the south choir. This timber was cut a foot too short but during the night the beam was lengthened and put in place, according to legend, by Jesus Christ, hence the name Christchurch was given to the church.

To the north of the church stand the ruins of Christchurch Castle, built in the 12th century and originally owned by the de Redvers family, Earls of Devon. Some of its owners met unfortunate ends: in 1541 the Countess of Salisbury was beheaded in the Tower of London and the Lord Protector, Edward Duke of Somerset, was executed in 1552. During the Civil War the castle was held for the King by the governer, Sir John Mills, but was captured by Parliamentary forces in 1645. Five years later an order was made by Parliament for the castle to be demolished. Now all that remains are two walls of the Norman keep. However, a large part of the nearby Constable's House, dating from 1160, still stands. It is said that King Edward VI paid several visits to the house.

Bournemouth is a relative upstart in this ancient and historic area. The first house was built in 1810 on the site of the present Royal Exeter Hotel. The long sandy beaches and pleasant wooded chines have guaranteed the town's success as a holiday resort. There are two fine museums to visit: the Russell-Cotes Art Gallery and Museum, housed in a Victorian mansion on East Cliff and the Shelley Rooms Museum in Boscombe in the former home of Percy Bysshe Shelley's son.

The next place on this tour is the charming town of Wimborne with its 18th and 19th century brick buildings. The outstanding feature is the Minster with its two towers and outside walls of red sandstone and pale limestone. There has been a church on the site since AD713 when a nunnery was built here. The present church dates from Norman times although it was enlarged in the 13th and 15th centuries. The Minster has many interesting features amongst which are a 14th century astronomical clock showing the sun and moon orbiting the earth, a fine chained library with many rare books, and a 17th century sundial which used to be on a gable but was blown down and relocated below the west tower.

Wimborne has two fascinating museums. The Merley House and Model Museum is a recently restored mid 18th century house with some fine plaster ceilings. On display are over 4000 models of cars, ships and aeroplanes ranging from the 1930s to the present day. For toy train enthusiasts there are working railway layouts. The other museum is the award winning Priest's House Museum in the High Street, whose exhibits start with prehistoric finds. It also has reconstructions of a Victorian kitchen, an ironmonger's and a stationer's shop.

Our next stop, Poole, has a long history going back to at least the 13th century when it was developed on the north of its natural harbour. It became a thriving port and in the 17th and 18th century specialised in trading with Newfoundland. The 19th century church of St James illustrates this trade with its Newfoundland pine pillars. The town has houses of historic note: almshouses built in the reign of Henry V, the Guildhall from 1761 (now a museum) and the house of Sir Peter Thompson, in Market Close, built in 1746. On the Quay stands the Customs House, originally a late 18th century building but which had to be rebuilt in 1813 after a fire.

The town has several museums: the Guildhall Museum showing aspects of Poole through the ages, the Old Lifeboat House on East Quay, the Royal National Lifeboat Museum on West Quay, Scaplen's Court Museum housed in a 15th century building and concentrating on domestic history, Waterfront in the High Street, mostly devoted to the town's maritime past although there is also a reconstruction of a Victorian street.

Corfe Castle

Poole harbour, enclosed by the peninsulas of Studland and Sandbanks, is one of the largest natural harbours in the world and for centuries has been a safe haven for sailors. There are five islands within the harbour, the largest of which is Brownsea, the site of Lord Baden-Powell's first camp for 20 boys in 1907, a pre-curser to the Scout movement which he founded. The northern part is a nature reserve where red squirrels, now extinct throughout much of Britain, may be found. Brownsea can be visited by ferry from either Poole Quay or Sandbanks.

After a small detour to Lytchett Minster, the route arrives at Wareham which stands within earthworks, probably Saxon in origin and built as a defence against Viking raiders. Large parts still remain and the north west section is called "Bloody Bank" because of the executions carried out there after the Monmouth Rebellion. The town is quartered by East, West, South and North Streets which meet in the centre. The church of St Paul dates in parts from the 11th century and there is memorial to Lawrence of Arabia inside. Lady St Mary's Church contains the coffin of Edward the Martyr and an unusual six sided lead font.

Continuing on to Swanage along the A351 we pass Corfe Castle, a fortification that covers more than three acres. This Norman castle's finest hour came under the command of a woman during the Civil War. In 1643 it was besieged by Parliamentary forces but Lady Banks resisted. The besiegers made great endeavours to subdue the determined forces inside including bringing up heavy guns, some of which were mounted on a church tower. Lead from the roof was melted to make bullets. Another battery of guns was positioned on the west side of the castle. In spite of the bombardment Lady Banks and the garrison still held out. Finally the Parliamentary forces withdrew and the castle was left in peace for three years. Then Lady Banks went to London and the Parliamentary

St Aldhelm's Head west of Swanage

forces again attacked but this time the castle was betrayed and fell to the attackers. Two-thirds of the castle was blown up by the victorious army but about 60 feet of the keep may still be seen intact.

Our next stop, Swanage, was once the centre of the Purbeck stone industry which was used to decorate many English cathedrals. Now it is a popular seaside resort with sandy bathing beaches and the nearby Durlston Country Park which includes the cliffs of Durlston Head. Two of the town's attractions have been transplanted from London. Wellington Clocktower near the pier once stood at the end of London Bridge and was moved here in 1867. The facade of the Town Hall was formerly the front of the Mercers' Hall in Cheapside.

Now the tour turns west to Dorchester, a very ancient settlement and once the Roman town of *Durnovaria*. The remains of a Roman villa have been found in Colliton Park behind the Council Offices and Maumbury Rings, formerly a henge or stone circle, was converted by the Romans into an amphitheatre where gladiators fought for the gratification of the crowd.

Judge Jeffreys held his Bloody Assize here in 1685. Out of 300 prisoners who were tried, 292 were sentenced to death and 74 hung within the city walls. Almost 150 years later, in 1839, Dorchester was associated with another infamous trial, that of the Tolpuddle Martyrs. They combined to demand a wage increase but because unions and fraternities were illegal they were sentenced to transportation. The Old Shire Hall, where they were put on trial, is now the Tolpuddle Memorial.

Perhaps the most famous and finest earth fortress in Europe, Maiden Castle, stands 2 miles south-west of Dorchester and no visit to the area would be complete without seeing it. Stone Age remains have been found here although now there is no visible trace of these earliest settlers. However it was the Iron Age inhabitants that vastly expanded the settlement. Covering some 120 acres it is estimated that it could accommodate about 5000 people. Using a simple ditch and bank system, it grew in complexity as time went on. More banks were added to the original fortifications and it is suggested that these prevented attackers coming close enough to effectively use a sling. There were two gates which, by the 1st century AD, were reinforced with limestone blocks.

With the Roman invasion of Britain it became inevitable that Maiden Castle had to be subdued. Under the command of Vespasian (later to be Emperor), the 2nd Augustan Legion attacked the fortification under cover of darkness. Their aim was to break through the Eastern Gate which was the more lightly defended of the two. First it was bombarded by *ballistae* (powerful crossbow devices mounted on frames), then the legion moved in and fought from rampart to rampart until the fortress fell. Archeologists have found skeletons bearing the marks of that battle: one had an arrowhead from the *ballistae* embedded in the vertebra and others show signs of sword cuts. Although the Romans allowed the settlement to continue after the castle had been rendered defenceless, it was abandoned by about 70 AD.

Moving to the coast, we reach Weymouth with its fine Georgian buildings. A port and holiday resort, the town also has royal connections. King George III once lived in Gloucester House, now a hotel, and there is a statue of him in the town.

Turning inland, Puddletown stands on the edge of open heathland, the Egdon Heath of Thomas Hardy's novels. It has a fine perpendicular church with the west gallery supported on pillars. One of the finest medieval houses in England, Athelhampton, is situated about a mile east. Built in 1485 on the site of King Athelstan's palace, it is set in 10 acres and the house contains heraldic glass, linenfold panelling and a good collection of furniture. Nearby Dawnay House is also well worth a visit. Said by Sir John Betjeman to be the amongst his favourite Dorsetshire houses, although Georgian it is built in the Queen Anne style. It has collections of antiques, antiquities and oriental art.

Stopping first in Charlton Marshall, we continue to Blandford Forum which, despite its name, was not a Roman town. Many of the present buildings date from the 18th century as a devastating fire in 1731 destroyed much of the town, two nearby villages and caused the death of 74 people. There is a memorial outside the church of St Peter and St Paul in the form of a portico once housing a pump. On it is inscribed "in remembrance of God's dreadful visitation by fire."

This tour then passes through Sturminster Newton, Thomas Hardy's "Stourcastle" and where he wrote *Return of the Native*. The town is reputed to hold England's largest calf market although the old Market Place has been partly built upon. Well worth a visit, Sturminster Newton Mill is set on a weir on the River Stour in charming surroundings. There is a record of a mill on this site since the Domesday Book although the present building dates from the 17th century with later additions. Restoration was carried out in 1981 and it is open to the public. The mill is worked so visitors can see grain processed into flour and animal feed.

Continuing onwards via Gillingham, on the River Stour and once a royal manor and forest, we reach Shaftesbury, a small market town overlooking Blackmoor Vale. It is the site of an abbey founded in AD 880 by King Alfred for his daughter, Ethelgiva. Because Edward the Martyr's bones were interred here it became a place of pilgrimage. Until the Dissolution of the Monasteries this was one of the wealthiest Benedictine nunneries in the country. Now only the some of the foundations can be seen. The town's major tourist attraction, and much used by film makers, is Gold Hill, a steep cobbled street with old cottages on one side and the abbey wall on the other.

We next visit the small villages of Hindon and Tisbury before reaching one of the most famous stately homes in Southern England: Wilton House in the village of Wilton. The home of the Earls of Pembroke, this house was rebuilt in the mid 17th century to a design by Inigo Jones after a fire had destroyed the earlier building. The Cube Room and the Double Cube Room are said to be the most perfectly proportioned rooms in the country. It contains a superb collection of paintings and other works of art. A family of influence and power, it was the eighth Earl of Pembroke who introduced carpet weaving to the area. Later the half-brother of the twelfth Earl, Sidney Herbert, was Secretary of War during the Crimean War and was instrumental in enabling Florence Nightingale and her nurses to go to the Crimea. Her portrait can be seen in Wilton House.

Driving to Salisbury, the sight of the cathedral with its famous spire soaring to the heavens, is a quintessential English scene painted by, among others, Constable, and engraved by Whistler. The first cathedral was on the nearby hill of Old Sarum, a cold, windy and unfriendly place but which had seen the earliest settlement because it was a good defensive position at 240 feet above the River Avon. There is evidence of human habitation going back to the Iron Age, continuing through the Roman occupation and then to the Saxons with, finally, the Normans building a castle and a cathedral side by side on the hill.

In the 13th century the clerics decided they had had enough of this miserable, windy, waterless hill and moved down to the valley and the townspeople followed them. In just 40 years the magnificent cathedral that we know today was built. The foundation stones were laid in 1220 by Bishop Richard Poore who later became Bishop of Durham where he continued his interest in great cathedral building. The world-famous spire was added to Salisbury Cathedral in the 14th century and rises to a height of 404 feet. In the 15th century strainer arches had to be built to support the weight of the spire which would certainly have collapsed without them.

Amongst the treasures and items of interest in the Cathedral there is the famous dialless clock in the bell tower dating from the 14th century and thought to be one of the oldest clocks in the country. The Cathedral also has an original copy of

Magna Carta, one of only four surviving copies. The cathedral close is reputed to be one of the finest in England and contains buildings ranging from the 14th to 18th centuries. Here in the close Anthony Trollope conceived the idea for his Barchester series of novels.

The fact that Salisbury was a new town built on a green field site, albeit seven centuries ago, can be seen from the regular grid pattern of streets rather than the more usual haphazard jumble seen in cities that have grown gradually through the centuries. Historic buildings from the 14th century onwards still survive in the city today, including many of the inns.

A visit to this area would not be complete without seeing Stonehenge, perhaps the most famous prehistoric site in Europe. Considered to be some 5000 years old, the exact purpose of this incredible monument is still unclear. Its construction points to a considerable effort with some of the stones weighing up to 50 tons each and with 80 stones being brought from the Preseli Mountains in South Wales, well over 200 miles. Imagine the problems involved in such a journey. Stonehenge illustrates the sophistication of the culture in those distant times. Not only was there the organisation, and also the resources to manage a scheme of this scale, but those prehistoric builders aligned the stone avenue with sunrise on Midsummer's Day.

The last leg of the tour uses one of the many Roman roads in the area to reach the quiet town of Stockbridge on the River Test, with its unusally wide High Street, before rejoining the M3 for the journey back to London.

ANTIQUE DEALERS
WINCHESTER (0962)
Bell Fine Art, 67b Parchment Street, SO23 8AT TEL: 860439 ASSNS: FATG PARKING: Own carpark OPEN: Mon-Sat 9.30-5.30 MIN: £10 MAX: £5,000 PERIOD: 19th-20th century SPECIALIST: British watercolour & drawings OTHER INFO: Longest cathedral in Europe only 5 mins, opposite 3 star Royal Hotel.

Gallery Antiques Ltd., Gallery Corner, St Thomas Street TEL: 865039 PARKING: Easy OPEN: Mon-Fri 9-5, Sat 9-1 MIN: £200 MAX: £15,000 PERIOD: 18th century SPECIALIST:English furniture & giltwood GENERAL: Mahogany & giltwood, some unrestored OTHER INFO: Close to antiques market & cathedral.

Henry March Gilbert, 19 The Square, SO23 9EY TEL: 852832 ASSNS: ABA PARKING: Medium OPEN: Mon-Sat 9-5.30 MIN: £1 MAX: £1,000 PERIOD: 19th-20th century SPECIALIST: English Literature including library sets GENERAL: Interesting range of secondhand & rare books OTHER INFO: Located in cul-de-sac 200 yds NW of cathedral, many good pubs etc near, also other antique shops.

Gerald Marsh Antique Clocks Ltd, 32a The Square, SO23 9EX ASSNS: BADA, BHI, Clockmakers Company TEL: 844443 FAX: (0869) 40087 PARKING: Medium OPEN: Mon-Sat 9.30-5 MIN: £20 MAX: £100,000 PERIOD: 17th-20th century SPECIALIST: Fine early English clocks GENERAL: Clocks, watches & antique & new barometers. New watch stands. Full repair & restoration workshop OTHER INFO: Cathedral city with many restaurants & good museums closeby. Hotels: Wessex, Royal. Wyckham Arms pub.

Printed Page, 2-3 Bridge Street, SO23 9BK TEL: 854072 FAX: 862995 ASSNS: FATG, Institute of Paper Conservation PARKING: Medium OPEN: Tues-Sat 9.30-5.30 MIN: £5 MAX: £750 PERIOD: 19th-20th century SPECIALIST: Antique maps & prints GENERAL: Modern prints & pictures. We are also picture framers OTHER INFO: Cricketers pub nearby (very good). Youth Hostel adjacent.

Mary Roofe Antiques, 1 Stonemasons' Court, Parchment Street, SO23 8AT TEL: 840613 ASSNS: LAPADA PARKING: Medium OPEN: Wed-Sat 10-5, or by appt MIN: £20 MAX: £2,000 PERIOD: 18th-19th century SPECIALIST:Boxes GENERAL: Furniture, treen OTHER INFO: Ancient capital of England, cathedral, Winchester College. Good hotels: Wessex, Royal.

Samuel Spencers Antiques & Decorative Arts Emporium, 39 Jewry Street TEL: 867014 PARKING: Easy OPEN: Mon-Sat 10-5.30 MIN: £1 PERIOD: 17th-20th century GENERAL: All types of antiques & decorative items in 31 individual units OTHER INFO: Interior designer available. Roman sights, The Great Hall with King Arthur's Round Table.

Thompson Antiques, 20a Jewry Street TEL: 866633 PARKING: Easy OPEN: Mon-Sat 9.30-5 MIN: £5 MAX: £5,000 PERIOD: 18th-20th century SPECIALIST: Large desk, dining tables & sets of chairs GENERAL: Furniture & bric-a-brac OTHER INFO: Historic town, old capital of England.

Todd & Austin Antiques & Fine Art of Winchester, 2 Andover Road, SO23 7BS TEL: 869824 ASSNS Chartered Institute of Marketing PARKING: 6 carparks 100 yards OPEN: Mon-Fri 9.30-4.45, Sat 9.30-1 MIN: £20 MAX: £6,000 PERIOD: 18th-early 20th century SPECIALIST: Antique glass, paperweights circa 1850, (French & some English). Boxes, tea caddies, snuff boxes, card cases, ivory miniatures GENERAL: General antiques.

Webb Fine Art, 38 Jewry Street, SO23 8RY TEL: 842273 FAX: 842246 ASSNS: GMC PARKING: Own carpark OPEN: Mon-Fri 9-5, Sat 9.30-4 PERIOD: 19th century SPECIALIST: Victorian oil paintings GENERAL: Over 300 oil paintings always in stock.

MORESTEAD (0962)
The Pine Cellars, Burgess Farm, SO21 1LZ TEL: 777546 ASSNS: GMC PARKING: Own carpark OPEN: Mon-Sat 9-5 MIN: £5 MAX: £5,000 PERIOD: 17th-19th century SPECIALIST: Individual pieces of antique pine GENERAL: 20,000 sq ft stocked with antique pine (many photos in Miller's 1994 guide) OTHER INFO: Shipping worldwide available, also B&B at the farmhouse.

TWYFORD (0962)
Twyford Antiques, High Street, SO21 1WH

TEL: 713484 PARKING: Medium OPEN: Mon-Sat 9.30-5.30 MIN: £250 MAX: £3,000 PERIOD: 18th-19th century SPECIALIST: Clocks & decorative items GENERAL: Good quality, well-restored furniture OTHER INFO: Picturesque village short walk to famous Water Meadows. 2 antique shops, 3 good pubs. Close to other shops with varying stock.

UPHAM (0489)

Susanna Fisher, Spencer, SO3 1JD TEL: 291 FAX: 860291 PARKING: Own carpark OPEN: By appt only MIN: £50 MAX: £5.000 PERIOD: 17th-19th century SPECIALIST: Navigational charts & related books.

Sharbrooks, Farthing Cottages, SO3 1JJ TEL: 860267 PARKING: Own carpark OPEN: By appt PERIOD: 18th-20th century SPECIALIST: Leather bound books as literature & decoration/furnishing OTHER INFO: 7 miles SE of Winchester.

SOUTHAMPTON (0703)

Gazelles Art Deco Interiors, 31 Northam Road, SO2 0NZ TEL: 235291 PARKING: Medium OPEN: Tues, Thurs, Sat 10.30-4 MIN: £5 MAX: £6,000 PERIOD: 20th century SPECIALIST: Art Deco OTHER INFO: Broadlands Estate, Romsey, also close to Winchester, the ancient capital of England.

Highfield Antiques, 33 Highfield Lane TEL: 324101 PARKING: Own carpark OPEN: Mon-Sat 10-5.30 MIN: £5 MAX: £800 PERIOD: 18th-early 20th century SPECIALIST: Furniture GENERAL: Antiques OTHER INFO: Close to university & Moat House Hotel.

Henry March Gilbert, 2½ Portland Street, SO1 0EB TEL: 226420 ASSNS: ABA PARKING: Medium OPEN: Mon-Sat 9-5.30 MIN: £1 MAX: £1,000 PERIOD: 19th-20th century SPECIALIST: English Literature (including library sets) GENERAL: Interesting range of rare & secondhand books.

Old Curiosity Shop & Morris Gallery, 280 Shirley Road, Shirley, SO1 3HL TEL: 774772 PARKING: Own carpark OPEN: Mon-Sat 9-6 MIN: £1 MAX: £3,000 PERIOD: 19th-20th century SPECIALIST: Victorian furniture, marine art & artefacts GENERAL: Curios, paintings, china, bronzes, silver, militaria etc. Fine restored furniture OTHER INFO: Prior

phoning ensures Curator/Valuer.

EASTLEIGH (0703)

Tappers Antiques, 186 Southampton Road, SO5 5QW TEL: 643105 PARKING: Easy OPEN: Mon-Sat 10-5 MIN: £2 MAX: £2,000 PERIOD: 18th-19th century GENERAL: Postcards, furniture, china, glass chimneypots -anything & everything OTHER INFO: Large shop very interesting for buying & browsing, a museum in itself. Handy for M27

ROMSEY (0794)

Cambridge Antiques & Medal Centre, 5 Bell Street, SO51 8GY TEL: 523089, 512069 FAX: 830332 ASSNS: LAPADA, OMRS PARKING: Medium OPEN: Mon-Sat 8.30-5.30 MIN: £20 MAX: £5,000 PERIOD: 19th-20th century SPECIALIST: Medals (worldwide customer service) GENERAL: China, silver, glass, jewellery, oriental, Moorcroft OTHER INFO: Quaint market town with individual shops & friendly people. Well worth a visit.

Bell Antiques, 8 Bell Street, SO51 8GA TEL: 514719 ASSNS: Gemmological Assn PARKING: Easy OPEN: Mon-Sat 9.30-5.30, closed Wed pm in winter MIN: £1 MAX: £6,000 PERIOD: 19th-20th century SPECIALIST: Jewellery GENERAL: China, glassware, small silver, small furniture, pictures, prints OTHER INFO: Romsey Abbey & Broadlands (Home of late Earl Mountbatten), Piaf's Bar & Restaurant, good pub: The 3 Tuns.

SHERFIELD ENGLISH (0794)

Old Cottage Things, Ash Hill Workshop, Broxmore Park TEL: 884538 PARKING: Own carpark OPEN: Mon-Sat 8.30-4.30 MIN: £1 MAX: £1,000 PERIOD: 17th-19th century SPECIALIST: Architectural materials, pine doors, cast iron gates, baths, original cast iron fires GENERAL: Staddle stones, pine furniture, pine & oak flooring OTHER INFO: pre 1920-30, also many unusual items, all stock is original antiques. Florence Nightingale site.

PLAITFORD (0794)

Plaitford House Gallery, Pound Lane, SO51 6EH TEL: 22221 PARKING: Own carpark OPEN: Anytime to suit clients' convenience MIN: £200 MAX: £15,000 PERIOD: 19th-20th century GENERAL: Oil paintings & watercolours, some bronzes.

CADNAM (0703)

Hingstons, Minstead Cottage, Romsey Road TEL: 812301, 812637 PARKING: Own carpark OPEN: Mon-Fri 9-5 MIN: £25 MAX: £4,500 PERIOD: 19th-20th century SPECIALIST: Quality oak GENERAL: Large selection quality pre 1930's furniture OTHER INFO: On edge of New Forest, good French restaurant, accommmodation opposite.

LYNDHURST (0703)

Peter Humphries, 6 High Street, SO43 7BD TEL: 282754 PARKING: Easy OPEN: Mon-Sat 9.30-5 GENERAL: 2nd hand various OTHER INFO: Mad Hatter tearoom next door to Bow Windows restaurant.

Lita Kaye of Lyndhurst, 13 The High Street TEL: 282337 PARKING: Easy OPEN: Mon-Sat 9.30-5 MIN: £150 MAX: £15,000 PERIOD: 18-19th century GENERAL: Upmarket furniture, decorative porcelain, clocks OTHER INFO: New Forest Visitors Centre, Lyndhurst Church burial place of Alice Hargreaves (Alice in Wonderland). Church also contains fresco by Lord Leighton and windows by Burne Jones.

BEAULIEU (0590)

Beaulieu Fine Arts, The Malt House, High Street, SO42 7YA TEL: 612089 PARKING: Easy OPEN: Mon-Sat 9.30-5.15 MIN: £5 MAX: £7,000 PERIOD: 18th-20th century SPECIALIST: Marine watercolours GENERAL: Wide range of paintings, prints & contemporary works in five gallery rooms OTHER INFO: Good hotel opposite. Village set in New Forest, Marine Museum & Motor Museum near

LYMINGTON (0590)

Captain's Cabin Antiques, 1 Quay Street, SO41 9AS TEL: 672912 PARKING: Easy OPEN: Mon, Tues, Thurs-Sat 10-5.30, Sun 11-4 MIN: £10 MAX: £3,000 PERIOD: 18th-20th century SPECIALIST: Marine items GENERAL: Small furniture, objets d'art, paintings, ceramics, silver, clocks, barometers OTHER INFO: Lymington is one of the largest yacht centres in England, the Quay area is ancient & attractive. Cid restaurant, Stanwell House Hotel in High Street, Peders in Gosport Street. Chewton Glen Hotel (national prize-winner), New Milton & La Poussin, (prize winner) Brockenhurst.

Hughes & Smeeth Ltd, 1 Gosport Street,

SO41 9BG TEL: 676324 ASSNS: ABA PFBA PARKING: Medium OPEN: Mon-Sat 9.30-5 PERIOD: 18th-20th century SPECIALIST: Books on sailing, natural history & topography GENERAL: Old & secondhand books, topographical prints & British county maps.

The Lymington Antique Centre, 76 High Street, SO41 9AL TEL: 670934 PARKING: Medium OPEN: Mon-Fri 10-5, Sat 9-5 PERIOD: 18th-20th century SPECIALIST:Lamps, books, jewellery, toys GENERAL: Kitchen equipment, paintings, coins + medals, line & lace OTHER INFO: We have a coffee shop, selection of hotels, bars & restaurants. Lymington has a lovely harbour, boating marina & quay.

Barry Papworth, 28 St.Thomas Street, SO41 9NE TEL: 676422 PARKING: Easy OPEN: Mon-Sat 9-5 MIN: £5 MAX: £10,000 PERIOD: 18th-20th century SPECIALIST:Antique silver, jewellery GENERAL: All small to medium size jewellery, silver OTHER INFO: Pretty town, best hotel: Stanwell House Hotel.

Robert Perera Fine Art, 19 St Thomas Street, SO41 9NB TEL: 678230 FAX: 678230 PARKING: Easy OPEN: Mon-Fri 10-5, Sat 9-5.30 MIN: £50 MAX: £7,500 PERIOD: 19th-20th century SPECIALIST: Marine paintings including work by Norman Wilkinson CBE GENERAL: Over 200 paintings, watercolours & etchings. Also studio pottery & Worcester porcelain.

Triangle Books, Lymington Antiques Centre, 76 High Street, SO41 9ZK TEL: 670934 ASSNS: PBFA PARKING: Easy OPEN: Mon-Fri 10-5, Sat 9-5 MIN: £1 MAX: £250 PERIOD: 19th-20th century SPECIALIST: Art, antiques, cookery, horse racing, topography GENERAL: 2500 good quality books + ephemera, prints & sheet music OTHER INFO: 30 dealers under one roof selling a range of general antiques. Good restaurants, railway station

FORDINGBRIDGE (0425)

Quatrefoil, Burgate, SP6 1LX TEL: 653309 PARKING: Own carpark OPEN: Resident, anytime MIN: £30 MAX: £10,000 PERIOD: 17th-18th century SPECIALIST: Oak, English & Continental furniture. Medieval & Renaissance carvings & sculpture antiquities & classical coins.

Millers Antiques Ltd

Large selection of English and Continental country Furniture, treen, Majolica, Quimper and Decorative items.

Netherbrook House, 86 Christchurch Road, Ringwood, Hants. BH24 1DR

Tel: 0425 472062   Fax: 0425 472727

RINGWOOD (0425)

Barbara Davies Antiques, 30a Christchurch Road, BH24 1.. TEL: (0860) 690744 shop, (0202) 872260 home PARKING: Easy OPEN: Tues 10-1, Wed & Fri 10-3 MIN: £i MAX: £250 PERIOD: 18th-20th century SPECIALIST: Porcelain GENERAL: Smalls and small furniture

Millers Antiques, Netherbrook House, 86 Christchurch Road, BH24 1DR. Tel: 472062 FAX: 472727 ASSNS: LAPADA PARKING: Own carpark OPEN: Mon-Fri 9-5.30, Sat 10-4 MIN: £25 MAX: £3,500 PERIOD 18th-19th century SPECIALIST: Large stocks of English & Continental furniture with emphasis on the country look. Quimper & majolica GENERAL: Wide range of all types of antiques including furniture, gilt, treen, faience & metalware OTHER INFO: Near prize-winning Chewton Glen Hotel (New Milton), Tyrell's Ford Hotel (3 star, reasonable).

The Pine Company, 104 Christchurch Road TEL: 476705 FAX: 480467 PARKING: Own carpark OPEN: Mon-Sat 9-6 MIN: £5 MAX: £2500 PERIOD: 18th-19th century SPECIALIST: Antique pine and leading importer of antique Chinese furniture.

Glen Robinson Interiors & Antiques, 82 Christchurch Road, BH24 1DR TEL: 480450 PARKING: Easy OPEN: Mon-Sat 10-5 PERIOD: 18th-19th century SPECIALIST: Decorative pieces and objects GENERAL: Small pieces of furniture.

BRANSGORE (0425)

The Old Stores, West Road, BH23 8BG TEL: 672616 PARKING: Own carpark OPEN: Thurs & Fri 9-7 or by appt MIN: £1 MAX: £800 PERIOD: 19th-20th century GENERAL: General antiques.

CHRISTCHURCH (O202)

Christchurch Carpets, 55-57 Bargates TEL: 482712 PARKING: Own carpark OPEN: Mon-Sat 9-5.30 MIN: £30 MAX: £5,000 PERIOD: 19th-20th century SPECIALIST: Persian old oriental rugs GENERAL: Rugs & carpets.

H.L.B. Antiques, 139 Barrack Road TEL: 482388 PARKING: Easy OPEN: Mon-Sat 10-4 but anytime by appt PERIOD: 19th-20th century SPECIALIST: Art Deco GENERAL: Collectables, old dolls.

M & R Lankshear Antiques, 149 Barrack Road, BH23 2AP TEL: 473091 PARKING: Own carpark (large forecourt) OPEN: Mon-Sat 9.30-5.30 PERIOD: 19th-20th century SPECIALIST: Militaria, swords & uniforms GENERAL: Furniture, clocks, pictures, china, glass, copper, walking sticks.

BOURNEMOUTH (0202)

Michael Andrews Antiques, 916 Christchurch Road, Boscombe, BH7 6DL TEL: 427615 PARKING: Medium OPEN: Mon, Tues, Thurs-Sat 10-5 £5 MAX: £2,000 PERIOD: 19th-20th century GENERAL: Furniture, glass, ceramics.

The Antique Centre, 837-839 Christchurch Road, Boscombe East TEL: 421052 FAX: 391950 PARKING: Own carpark OPEN: Mon-Sat 9.30-5.30 £5 MAX: £2,000+ PERIOD: 18th-20th century GENERAL: Silver & plate, Art Deco, collectables, furniture, pictures, etc OTHER INFO: Elysée Restaurant.

The Antique Shop, 646 Wimborne Road, Winton, BH9 2EH TEL: 527205 PARKING:

Medium OPEN: Non-Sat 10.15-5.15 MIN: £1 MAX: £200 PERIOD: 19th-20th century GENERAL: China, glass, silver, flatware.

Boscombe Militaria, 86 Palmerston Road, Boscombe, BH7 4HU TEL: 304250 PARKING: Medium OPEN: Mon, Tues, Thurs-Sat 10-1, 2.45-5 MIN: £1 MAX: £1,000 PERIOD: 19th-20th century SPECIALIST: De-activated guns, Third Reich militaria GENERAL: Any militaria from the 180's to the present day.

Boscombe Models & Collectors Shop, 802c Christchurch Road, Boscombe, BH7 6DD TEL: 398884 PARKING: Medium OPEN: Mon, Tues, Thurs-Sat 10-1, 2-4.30 £1 MAX: £1,000 PERIOD: 19th-20th century SPECIALIST: Collectors toys OTHER INFO: Shop just off main road, 3 doors inside Somerset Road.

Collectors Corner, 63 Seabourne Road, Southbourne TEL: 420945 FAX: 0425 620794 PARKING: Medium OPEN: Mon, Tues, Thurs-Sat 10-4.45 £3 MAX: £800 PERIOD: 19th-20th century SPECIALIST: Old advertising, Doulton goods GENERAL: General antiques, OTHER INFO: 30 antique shops within half a mile, many hotels and good eating.

Peter Denver Antiques, 36 Calvin Road, Winton BH9 1LW TEL: 532536 PARKING: Easy OPEN: Mon-Sat 10.30-4.30 MIN: £10 MAX: £1,000 PERIOD: 19th-20th century GENERAL: Anything good quality including 1920-40's reproduction OTHER INFO: 100 yds from main shopping area.

Richard Dunton Antiques, 920 Christchurch Road, Boscombe, BH7 6DL TEL: 425963 FAX: 418456 PARKING: Easy OPEN: Mon-Sat 9-6 £5 MAX: £10,000 PERIOD: 18th-19th century GENERAL: Furniture, china, glass, metalware, paintings, garden urns & statues.

Lionel Geneen Ltd, 781 Christchurch Road, Boscombe, BH7 6AW TEL: 422961 ASSNS: LAPADA, BDADA PARKING: Easy OPEN: Mon-Fri 9-5 Sat 9-12 (not lunchtime) & by appt £50 MAX: £3,500. PERIOD: 18th-20th century GENERAL: Decorative European & Oriental furniture, china, glass, bronzes, objects OTHER INFO: Some 20th century Art Deco.

Hampshire Gallery, 18 Lansdowne Road, BH1 1SD TEL: 551211 ASSNS: LAPADA PARKING: Own carpark OPEN: By appt MIN: £250 MAX: £10,000 PERIOD: 19th century to 1930 SPECIALIST: English & Continental pictures OTHER INFO: Some earlier pictures.

Kebo Antiques, 823 Christchurch Road, Boscombe TEL: 417052 PARKING: Medium OPEN: 10-4.30 £5 MAX: £500 PERIOD: 19th-20th century SPECIALIST: Pocket watches & jewellery GENERAL: All general antiques.

Geo. A Payne & Son Ltd, 742 Christchurch Road, Boscombe TEL: 394954 ASSNS: NAG PARKING:Medium OPEN: Mon-Sat 9-5.30 MIN: £10 MAX: £4,000 PERIOD: 19th century GENERAL: Jewellery & silverware OTHER INFO: New jewellery & silverware.

Pegasus Antiques, 13 Gladstone Road West, Boscombe PARKING: Medium OPEN: 9-5 MIN: £1 MAX: £500 PERIOD: 18th-20th century GENERAL: Linen, lace, textiles, porcelain, glass, jewellery, small furniture OTHER INFO: Antique centre, 8 to 12 dealers.

Shickell Antiques, 869 Christchurch Road, Boscombe, BH7 6AT TEL: 418497 PARKING: Medium OPEN: Mon-Sat 9-5 MIN: £5 MAX: £2-3,000 PERIOD: 17th-20th GENERAL: Furniture, porcelain, jewellery, silver items OTHER INFO: 30 other antique shops in same street, nice beaches, conference & holiday area, mild weather year round.

Shippeys, 15-16 Royal Arcade, Boscombe, BH7 4BT TEL: 396548 PARKING: Easy (multistorey) OPEN: Mon, Tues, Thurs-Sat 9-5 MIN: £5 MAX: £1,000 PERIOD: 19th-20th century GENERAL: General antiques OTHER INFO: We are an old-fashioned shop in a Victorian arcade.

Peter Stebbing, 7 Post Office Road, BH1 1BB TEL: 552587 PARKING: Easy OPEN: Mon-Sat 9.30-5 MIN: £5 MAX: £5,000 PERIOD: 18th-19th century GENERAL: Mixed - furniture, glass, porcelain, brass, copper etc OTHER INFO: Russell-Coates Museum (original house used in film *Valentino*. Excellent hotels, theatre, beautiful gardens, safe clean beach.

Mark C. Taylor, 995 Christchurch Road, BH7 6BB TEL: 429718 ASSNS: Guild of Master Craftsmen PARKING: Easy OPEN: 8-6 £150 MAX: £5,000 PERIOD: 19th century SPECIALIST: English longcase & dial clocks GENERAL: Antique clocks.

Victorian Parlour Antiques, 874 Christchurch Road, BH7 6DJ TEL: 433928 PARKING: Easy OPEN: Mon-Sat 9-5.30 MIN: £1 MAX: £700 PERIOD: 19th century SPECIALIST: Stripped pine GENERAL: Victorian furniture OTHER INFO: You can spend a day passing from one antique shop to the next in this area.

York House Gallery, York House, 32 Somerset Road, Boscombe TEL: 391034, 394275 PARKING: Own carpark OPEN: Mon-Sat 2.15-4.30 & by appt £25 MAX: £5,000 PERIOD: 19th century SPECIALIST: Watercolours, oils.

BRANKSOME (0202) •

Allens (Branksome) Ltd, 447-449 Poole Road, BH12 1DH TEL: 763724 FAX: 763724 PARKING: Medium OPEN: Mon-Sat 9-5.30 MIN: £20 MAX: £7,500 PERIOD: 19th-20th century GENERAL: Clean good quality Victorian, Edwardian & 1920's OTHER INFO: Main road between Bournemouth & Poole

Branksome Antiques, 370 Poole Road, BH12 1AW TEL: 763324 PARKING: Medium OPEN: Mon, Tues, Thurs, Fri 10-4.30 £20 MAX: £10,000 PERIOD: 18th-20th century SPECIALIST: Marine & scientific instruments GENERAL: Georgian & Victorian furniture, china, copper, brass, clocks OTHER INFO: Many antique shops in area.

David Mack Antiques, 434-437 Poole Road TEL: 760005 FAX: 765100 PARKING: Own carpark OPEN: Mon-Sat 9-5.30 £200 MAX: £7,000 PERIOD: 18th-20th century SPECIALIST: Dining room furniture GENERAL: Furniture and all aspects thereof OTHER INFO: In Bournemouth/Poole conurbation with excellent transport facilities. Next to railway station.

POOLE (0202)

Capricorn, 15 Parr Street, Ashley Cross, Lower Parkstone TEL: 429712 PARKING: Easy OPEN: Mon, Tues, Thurs, Fri 9.30-4 £5 MAX: £500 PERIOD: 19th-20th century SPECIALIST: Porcelain & silver GENERAL: Small furniture, glass etc

D.J. Jewellery, 166-168 Ashley Road, Parkstone, BH14 9BY TEL: 745148 ASSNS: BWCMG PARKING: Easy OPEN: Mon-Sat 9-5 MIN: £5 MAX: £2,000 PERIOD: 19th-20th century SPECIALIST: Antique & modern jewellery & clocks repaired & restored OTHER

INFO: Next to excellent Chinese restaurant, The Canton, and few doors from the only Austrian restaurant, The Edelweiss (both fully licensed). Excellent Twin Cedars Hotel (pet lovers).

Wiffen's Antiques & Furnishings, 95-101 Bournemouth Road, Parkstone, BH14 0ER TEL: 736567 FAX: 717305 PARKING: Own carpark OPEN: Mon-Sat 9-5.30 MIN: £35 MAX: £15,000 PERIOD: 17th-20th century GENERAL: General antiques & replicas.

WIMBORNE MINSTER (0202)

Antiqua Tat Antiques, Antiqua Tat House, Hanham Road, BH21 1AS TEL: 887496 FAX: 888424 ASSNS: LAPADA PARKING: Own carpark OPEN: Mon-Sat 9-5 £500 MAX: £30-40,000 PERIOD: 18th-19th century GENERAL: Furniture, large stock of dining tables & chairs, chests of drawers etc OTHER INFO: Good restaurant above showrooms (Sorrels).

Barnes House Antiques, 11a West Row TEL: 886275 PARKING: Easy OPEN: Mon-Sat 10-4.30 MIN: £5 MAX: £5,000+ PERIOD: 17th-20th century GENERAL: Period oak and mahogany furniture, porcelain, silver, glass OTHER INFO: Kings Head Hotel, Priest's House Museum.

Brights of Nettlebed, 61-63 Leigh Road, BH21 1AE TEL: 884613 FAX: 885679 PARKING: Own carpark OPEN: Tues-Sat 9-5.30 MIN: £500 MAX: £12,000 PERIOD: 18th century SPECIALIST: English furniture OTHER INFO: We have a small antiques area in large replica furniture showroom. The antiques on display are to high standard.

Victoriana, 3 Leigh Road TEL: 886739 PARKING: Easy OPEN: Tues, Thur, Sat 10-1, 2.30-4 MIN: £12 MAX: £300 PERIOD: 19th-20th century GENERAL: Silver, jewellery, glass, brass, china & small antiques OTHER INFO: Beautiful minster, Kingston Lacey House (NT), Good restaurants, Trust House.

LYTCHETT MINSTER (0202)

The Old Button Shop, Dorchester Road, BH16 6JF TEL: 622169 PARKING: Medium OPEN: Tues-Fri 2-5, Sat 11-1 £1 MAX: £500 PERIOD: 17th-20th century SPECIALIST: Dorset buttons, antique buttons GENERAL: Antiques & curios OTHER INFO: The only place in the world where Dorset buttons can be bought at any time (in small numbers). These buttons are sometimes available at auctions etc but most come from this collection. Shop itself from 17th century & historically connected with the 300 year old Dorset Button Industry.

WAREHAM (0929)

Georgina Ryder Textiles, Rempstone Hall, Corfe Castle, BH20 6LD TEL: 480382 FAX: 480382 ASSNS: LAPADA PARKING: Own carpark OPEN: By appt MIN: £250 MAX: £15,000 PERIOD: 17th-19th century SPECIALIST: Textiles & 18th & 19th century painted French furniture, tapestries & decorative items OTHER INFO: Heart of Hardys beautiful historic Dorset, next to Corfe Castle, close Poole Harbour. A wonderful day out.

SWANAGE (0929)

Georgian Gems, 28 High Street, BH19 2NU TEL: 424697 FAX: 426200 ASSNS: NAG, Gemmological Assn PARKING:Medium OPEN: Mon-sat 9.30-1, 2.30-5 (Thurs halfday) or by appt MIN: £2 MAX: £5,000 PERIOD: 18th-20th century SPECIALIST: Antique & secondhand jewellery & small silver OTHER INFO: We are the smallest jewellers in UK in the smallest shop, a 16th century building.

Reference Works, 12 Commercial Road, BH19 1DF TEL: 42443 FAX: 422597 PARKING: Medium OPEN: By appt MIN: £2 MAX: £600 PERIOD: 18th-20th century SPECIALIST: Reference books on antique pottery & porcelain of all countries. New & out of print. Small range of porcelain OTHER INFO: Steam railway, art galleries, The Galley, award-winning restaurant.

DORCHESTER (0305)

Box of Porcelain, 51d Icen Way, DT1 1EW TEL: 250851 PARKING: Medium OPEN: Mon-Sat 10-4 MIN: £1 MAX: £1,000 PERIOD: 19th-20th century SPECIALIST: Jeswick animals GENERAL: Quality porcelain: Worcester, Coalport, Derby etc OTHER INFO: Collectors finder service

WEYMOUTH (0305)

Books Afloat, 66 Park Street, DT4 7DE TEL: 779774 PARKING: Easy OPEN: Mon-Sat 9.30-5.30 MIN: £1 MAX: £650 PERIOD: 19th-20th century SPECIALIST: Naval & maritime books, nautical hardware & ephemera GENERAL: Out of print books on all subjects, diecast toys, prints, pictures OTHER INFO: Close railway station, 5 pubs in Park Street, plenty to see and do for the day or long weekend.

Nautical Antique Centre, Old Harbour Passage, 3a Hope Square, DT4 8TR TEL: 777838, home 783180 PARKING: Easy OPEN: Tues-Sat 10-5.30 or by appt MIN: £1 MAX: £850 PERIOD: 19th-20th century SPECIALIST: All nautical OTHER INFO: Opp. Brewers Quay Timewalk & Museum complex with full facilities. 3 other antique shops.

PUDDLETOWN (0305)

The Antique Map & Bookshop, DT2 8RU TEL: 846633 FAX: 848992 ASSNS: ABA PBFA PARKING: Medium OPEN: Mon-Sat 9-5 MIN: £1 MAX: £2,000 PERIOD: 17th-20th century SPECIALIST: Thomas Hardy/Dorset material, local antique maps & prints GENERAL: OTHER INFO: Various subjects such as illustraed books, English literature & Modern Firsts, UK & foreign travel etc.

BLANDFORD FORUM (0258)

A & D Antiques, 21 East Street, TEL: 455643 PARKING: Easy OPEN: Tues, Thurs-Sat 10-5, Wed 10-1 MIN: £10 MAX: £5,000 PERIOD: 18th-20th century SPECIALIST: 18th century drinking glasses to Lalique, silver + plate.

Ancient & Modern Bookshop/Garrets Antiques, 84 Salisbury Street DT11 7QE TEL: 455276 PARKING: Medium OPEN: Mon, Tues, Thurs-Sat 9.30-12.30, 1.30-5.30 £1 MAX: £500 PERIOD: 18th-20th century GENERAL: Books, antiques OTHER INFO: Crown hotel, small street markets Thurs & Sats.

CHARLTON MARSHALL (0258)

Zona Dawson Antiques, The Old Club House, 2 The Close, DT11 9PA TEL: 453146 PARKING: Easy OPEN: Tues-Sat 10-5, Sun by appt (Closed June & closed September) MIN: £50 MAX: £2,500 PERIOD: 18th-19th century GENERAL: Mahogany, oak, walnut furniture (mainly small) OTHER INFO: Some quality reproduction. Diagonally opposite to Charlton Inn, on the corner of the main A350.

STOURPAINE (0258)

Havelin Antiques, Stourpaine House, Manor

Road TEL: 452431 FAX: (0725) 4283 PARKING: Own carpark OPEN: Seven days by appt only MIN: £10 MAX: £6,000 PERIOD: 18th-20th century SPECIALIST: Decorative furniture, carpets, textiles, china.

STURMINSTER NEWTON (0258)
Branksome Antiques, Toll house, Bagber Lane, Bagber, DT10 2HS TEL: 72296 PARKING: Own carpark OPEN: Mon-Sat 9-6 MIN: £20 MAX: £3,000 PERIOD: 18th-20th century GENERAL: Georgian & Victorian furniture, general shipping goods OTHER INFO: Facilities available for packing containers.

Quarter Jack Antiques, Bridge Street, DT10 1BZ TEL: 472558 PARKING: Medium OPEN: Mon-Sat 9.5.30 MIN: £1 MAX: £1,500 PERIOD: 18th-19th century SPECIALIST: Glass, walking sticks, corkscrews, brasses GENERAL: Furniture, pictures OTHER INFO: Thomas Hardy's house, Monday Market.

Tom Tribe & Son, Bridge Street, DT10 1BZ TEL: 472311 PARKING: Easy OPEN: Mon-Fri 9-1, 2-5, Sat 9-1 MIN: Eng. longcase £1,500 MAX: £8,000 PERIOD: 18th-19th century SPECIALIST: English longcase clocks (20-30 always in stock) GENERAL: French carriage & mantel clocks, English bracket clocks. Mercurial barometers OTHER INFO: Working mill, town museum & our shop which has many horological items displayed but not for sale. Plumber Manor Hotel, high class food & accommodation. Swan Hotel.

GILLINGHAM (0747)
Talisman, The Old Brewery, Wyke, SP8 4NW TEL: 824423 FAX: 823544 ASSNS: LAPADA PARKING: Easy OPEN: Mon-Fri 9-6, Sat 10-5 MIN: £5 MAX: £50,000 PERIOD: 17th-20th century GENERAL: English & Continental furniture, mirrors, paintings, garden furniture & statuary, decorative & unusual objects.

SHAFTESBURY (0747)
The Book in Hand, 17 Bell Street, SP7 8AB No telephone PARKING: Medium OPEN: Mon-Sat 10-1, 2-4.30 MIN: £1 MAX: £200 PERIOD: 19th-20th century GENERAL: Medium OTHER INFO: Very small amount antiquarian. Bell Street. Abbey Ruins, wonderful views from Park Walk, very good restaurants: Fleur-de-Lys, Vesters.

HINDON (0747)
Monkton Galleries, High Street, SP3 6DR TEL: 89235 PARKING: Own carpark OPEN: Mon-Sat 9-5.30 MIN: £25 MAX: £10,000 PERIOD: 17th-18th century SPECIALIST: Early oak & country furniture & metalwork GENERAL: Pottery, treen & other decorative items OTHER INFO: Opp. famous country hotel & restaurant: The Lamb.

TISBURY (0747)
Edward Marnier Antiques, 17 High Street, SP3 6HF TEL: 870213 PARKING: Easy OPEN: Mon-Sat 10-5.30 MIN: £4 MAX: £4,000 PERIOD: 18th-20th century SPECIALIST: Old rugs, carpets GENERAL: Furniture, pictures, mirrors & interesting decorative objects OTHER INFO: Howards House Hotel, Teffont. BR Station, Wardour Castle, Stourhead House, Fonthill Abbey.

Carol Pearson Antiques, 2-3 High Street, SP3 6PS TEL: 870710 PARKING: Easy OPEN: Mon-Sat 10-5, Wed by appt MIN: £15 MAX: £20,000 PERIOD: 18th-19th century SPECIALIST: Oil paintings GENERAL: Furniture, porcelain, oils & watercolours OTHER INFO: Wardour Castle, Howards Hotel, ancient Dower House for meals & accommodation. Lovely pubs & countryside

WILTON (0722)
Ian J. Brook Antiques & Fine Art, 26 North Street, SP2 OHJ TEL: 743392 PARKING: Own carpark OPEN: Mon-Sat 8.45-6 MIN: £10 MAX: £5,000 PERIOD: 18th-19th century SPECIALIST: Fine oil paintings & watercolours. Fine mahogany & oak furniture & small items OTHER INFO: Wilton House (April-Oct) 400

yds. Wilton Royal Carpet Factory

Earle, 47 North Street, SP2 0HE TEL: 743284 PARKING: Easy OPEN: Mon, Tues, Thurs-Sat 9-5 PERIOD: 20th century GENERAL: Small furniture & china OTHER INFO: 6 antique shops & 1 secondhand dealer.

Pamela Lynch, 18 West Street, SP2 0DF TEL: 744113 PARKING: Easy (Market Square) OPEN: Mon-Sat 10-5 but resident MIN: £48 MAX: £2,000 PERIOD: 18th-19th century SPECIALIST: Enamel boxes, needlework pictures & watercolours GENERAL: Furniture & some porcelain OTHER INFO: Wilton House (seat of Earl of Pembroke & site of Shakespeare's plays), carpet factory due to Huguenot refugees, church & newly refurbished hotel: The Pembroke Arms

SALISBURY (0722)

John Amos Antiques, 7a St. John Street, SP1 2SB TEL: 330888 PARKING: Medium OPEN: Mon, Tues, Thur, Fri 9.30-1.30, 2.30-5, Sat 9.30-1.30 MAX: £400 PERIOD: 19th-20th century GENERAL: Mainly porcelain & china with small furniture & some brass, copper, glass & silver.

Antique & Collectors Market, 37 Catherine Street, SP1 2DH TEL: 326033 PARKING: Easy OPEN: Mon-Sat 9-5.30 MIN: £1 MAX: £300 PERIOD: 19th-20th century GENERAL: All type antiques & collectables OTHER INFO: 3 floors & 20 dealers

Robert Bradley Antiques, 71 Brown Street, SP1 2BA TEL: 333677 PARKING: Easy OPEN: Mon-Fri 9.30-5.30 MIN: £200 MAX: £50,000 PERIOD: 17th-18th century GENERAL: English furniture & related objects.

Ronald Carr, 6 St. Francis Road, SP1 3QS TEL: 328892 FAX: 328593 PARKING: Easy OPEN: Anytime by appt MIN: £5 MAX: £1,000 PERIOD: 19th-20th century SPECIALIST: Modern British etchings 1850-1940 GENERAL: Wood-engravings & woodcuts OTHER INFO: Pleasant countryside, Cathedral, interesting city with many good English pubs for meals.

Castle Galleries, 81 Castle Street, SP1 3SP TEL: 333734 PARKING: Easy OPEN: Tues, Thurs, Fri 9-5, Sat 9-1 PERIOD: 19th-20th century SPECIALIST: Coins, medals GENERAL: Small antiques OTHER INFO: Parking outside.

The Jerram Gallery, 7 St John Street, SP1 2SB TEL: 412310 PARKING: Easy OPEN: Mon-Fri 9.30-5.30, Sat 10-4 MIN: £100 MAX: £15,000 PERIOD: mid 19th-20th century SPECIALIST: Figurative etchings, watercolours, oils & sculpture including contempory artists.

Micawber's, 53 Fisherton Street, SP2 7SU TEL: 337822 PARKING: Easy OPEN: Mon, Tues, Thurs-Sat 9.30-5 MIN: £1 MAX: £700 PERIOD: 19th-20th century SPECIALIST: Jewellery, clothes, military, prints GENERAL: General antiques OTHER INFO: Market is on 4 floors. Many restaurants & B&B's close.

Chris Wadge Clocks, 142 Fisherton Street, SP2 7QT TEL: 334467 FAX: 334467 PARKING: Medium OPEN: Tues-Sat 9-1, 2-5 MIN: £1 MAX: £2,500 PERIOD: 19th-20th century SPECIALIST: 400 day clocks GENERAL: Assorted clocks: longcase, Vienna regulators, carriage plus barometers OTHER INFO: New clocks & barometers also. 10 mins from Tourist Advice Centre, bus station, 5 mins from Cathedral, 2 mins from railway station.

STOCKBRIDGE (0264)

George Hoffman, At The Sign of The Black Cat, High Street, SO20 6EY TEL: 810570 PARKING: Easy OPEN: Mon-Sat 9.30-5.30, 3% off on Weds MIN: £1 MAX: £2,500 PERIOD: 17th-20th century SPECIALIST: Furniture GENERAL: Brass, pottery, lamps etc - no jewels or silver OTHER INFO: River walks plenty of ducks and fish, Pleasant street.

Stockbridge Antiques, High Street, SO20 6EX TEL: 810829 ASSNS: LAPADA PARKING: Easy OPEN: 9.30-5 MIN: £10 MAX: £9,000 PERIOD: 18th century SPECIALIST: Georgian glass/silver GENERAL: Mahogany furniture, interesting gilts, early Victorian porcelain OTHER INFO: Something for all tastes. Very small historic town. Centre of trout fishing on River Test. Good restaurants, beautiful walks, Danebury Hill Fort. Halfway between Winchester & Salisbury. Wide main street.

Somerset to the South Coast

The ruins of Glastonbury Abbey

This tour moves from the Severn estuary to the south coast and passes through parts of Avon, Somerset, Devon, Dorset and Wiltshire. This is an area that has been inhabited by man for thousands of years and is full of busy market towns and charming stone-built villages as well as remains from our prehistoric past.

The first stop, Clevedon, stands at the junction of two hill ranges. A pleasant seaside resort, it is also in the middle of good walking country. It was the birthplace of Hartley Coleridge and the poem *In Memoriam* by Tennyson was inspired by the death of Arthur Hallam who is buried in St Andrew's Churchyard. Arthur Hallam lived at the 14th century Clevedon Court, now a National Trust property. The house incorporates a 12th century tower and 13th century hall and has important collections of Nailsea Glass and Eltonware.

The village of Yatton, inland from Clevedon, has a large perpendicular church with an odd truncated spire and contains the splendid 15th century tomb of Sir John Newton.

Moving to the coast again, Weston-super-Mare is a popular resort on the Bristol Channel which has two piers, one of which is also used as a jetty and lifeboat station. It has sandy bathing beaches and the other amenities usual to a good seaside town. Our next stop is the resort of Burnham-on-Sea which really began in the 19th century when a curate sank two wells to turn the area into a spa. Unfortunately the water was so unpleasant that the idea failed. Instead the town has become a pleasant holiday

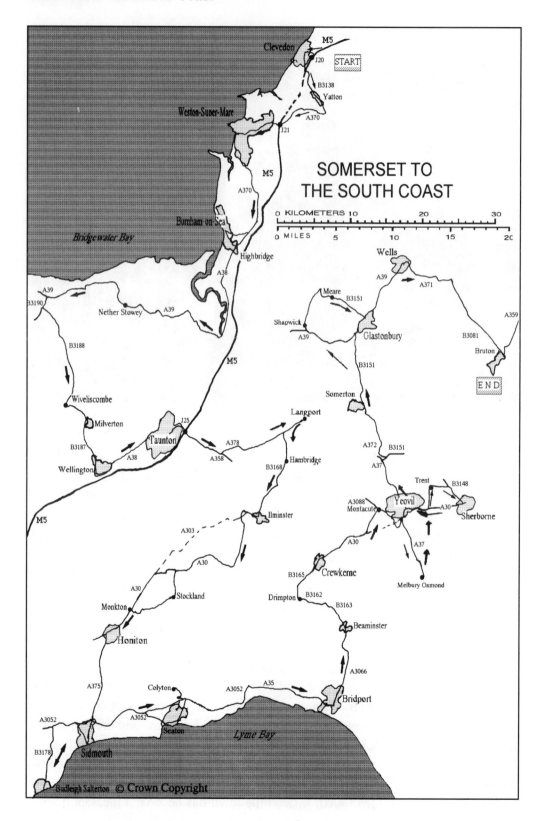

SOMERSET TO
THE SOUTH COAST

town with about seven miles of sandy beaches. The church contains a white marble altar originally carved by Grinling Gibbons for the chapel in the Palace of Whitehall.

Continuing south west, our next visit is to Highbridge. This town was a busy port during the 18th and 19th centuries and then later it repaired railway engines for the Somerset and Dorset Railway. Now turning westward along the A39 we come to Nether Stowey where Samuel T. Coleridge wrote *The Ancient Mariner* at his cottage here. Near the village stands Dodington Hall, a small Tudor manor house.

Carrying on via Wiveliscombe and the ancient village of Milverton with its pleasing Georgian houses, we come to Wellington, the town from which the Duke of Wellington took his title. Just three miles south of the town, on the crest of the Blackdown Hills, is an obelisk erected to commemorate the Iron Duke.

Now on to the cider making town of Taunton on the River Tone. Strategically placed in the centre of the river valley, it was fortified in the 8th century. Its Noman castle was built on the site of an early earthwork fortification by Henry of Blois although it has been altered considerably since then. Various parts of the castle date from as early as the 12th century with others as late as the 18th century.

To the north east of the town, near Bridgwater, lies the battlefield of Sedgemoor. On the death of Charles II, James II, a Roman Catholic, became King. The Duke of Monmouth, illegitimate son of Charles II, and his supporters felt this was their chance to seize the throne. Monmouth had been in Holland but he sailed for England landing in Lyme Regis. There he found he had much popular support. Two of Monmouth's supporters had also landed in Scotland to rally the people there but had been caught and executed. From then on Monmouth had no chance of success. Meanwhile, royal troops under the command of John Churchill, later first Duke of Marlborough, were marching to the West Country to put down the rebellion. On 5th July 1685 battle was joined; the makeshift army stood no chance against the royal troops and was slaughtered. The Duke of Monmouth escaped but only for a few days before he was brought to London and executed.

Survivors from the rebel army were ruthlessly hunted down and the Lord Chief Justice, the notorious Judge Jeffreys, was sent to the West Country to deal with them. In the Great Hall of Taunton Castle in September 1685 he held his 'Bloody Assizes' in which he sentenced between 150 and 300 people to death by hanging and numerous others, possibly up to 800, to transportation and slavery in the West Indies. It is said that the ghost of Judge Jeffreys walks the castle on September nights.

In addition to that bloody and tragic episode in English history, Taunton contains other more peaceful reminders of the past. There are three public schools, one of which was founded in the 13th century, and a thatched leper hospital, now restored to serve as rural district offices. There is also a Tudor house in Fore Street and 17th century almshouses.

Moving onwards we come to Langport, on the River Parrett, which has certainly existed since Saxon times and possibly earlier. Its church has some fine stained glass and nearby can be found the curious Hanging Chapel built by a merchants' guild above the town gate in 1353.

The route now takes us, via Hambridge, to Ilminster, once a centre of flax and lace making. It has a 15th century church with a fine perpendicular central tower. The Wadham family, founders of Wadham college in Oxford, have their tomb here. The town also has a grammar school founded in 1586. Five miles north east of Ilminster stands the Tudor house, Barrington Court, with its lovely garden laid out as a series of three rooms. A well known local family, the Spekes, suffered in the Monmouth Rebellion. The elder son survived the Battle of Sedgemoor after leading a troop of soldiers and managed to escape abroad afterwards. In retribution, Judge Jeffreys hanged his younger brother instead from a tree in the market place.

Now moving into Devon, we come to Honiton, best known for its lace making. Because much of it was rebuilt in the late 18th century after a catastrophic fire in 1765, the buildings are mostly Georgian. Some earlier buildings did survive however, including the 14th century Hospital of St Margaret and Marwood House from 1619.

Moving to the coast, we call first at Sidmouth, a small unspoilt seaside resort on the mouth of the River Sid with lovely terraces of Regency houses. Then we visit Budleigh Salterton. Situated at the mouth of the River Otter, this is a small seaside resort with a shingle bathing beach.

Retracing our route, the next stop is in Colyton, an important wool town in Tudor times. The lord here was Henry Courtenay who, unfortunately, came into disfavour with Henry VIII and was beheaded. The manor was then bought from the Crown by twenty local merchants and yeoman farmers under a Deed of Feoffment and to this day Colyton is still run by sixteen feoffees. Buildings of note are the Old Church House and The Great House in South Street which has a chequerboard front.

Calling first at Seaton, a small quiet resort situated on the estuary of the River Axe, we next visit Bridport. In Thomas Hardy's novels this ancient town was called Port Bredy. Rope-making has been the principal industry for 750 years and the streets were fashioned to accommodate ropes. The pavements, known as rope-walks, are unusually wide and were once used to lay out and dry new rope. There are many fine Georgian houses and the Town Hall is also Georgian. Bridport Museum, which tells the story of the town, is housed in a Tudor building. There is a story that Charles II, after the battle of Worcester, came to Bridport before escaping to Normandy.

Moving inland, the tour now comes to Beaminster. Set in an designated area of outstanding natural beauty, the town retains many of its older buildings. Much of the town was rebuilt in the 18th century after a fire although it still has its beautiful 15th century church of St Mary. The story goes that victims of Judge Jeffreys 'Bloody Assizes' were hung from this church tower. Close to the town there are two large houses of note: Mapperton and Parnham. Mapperton is a Tudor manor house set in lovely terraced gardens. Parnham is a restored Elizabethan manor surrounded by gardens designed by Inigo Jones. Inside there is a display of the best of 20th century craftmanship covering furniture, paintings, glass, textiles and ceramics.

The ancient town of Crewkerne, next on the route, was a Roman settlement then later a Saxon one when the town had a royal mint. As well as being the market town for the surrounding agricultural area, Crewkerne had a thriving sail-making industry and made sails for the ships at Trafalgar including Nelson's Victory. The 15th century church is extremely beautiful with a particularly fine west facade.

Going north east along the A30, we take a small detour to visit the magnificent Elizabethan Montacute House standing in the lovely village of Montacute. Built in local Ham stone during the latter part of the 16th century, its Long Gallery, measuring 189 feet, is reputed to be the longest in England. It has fine collections of heraldic glass, tapestries, panelling, furniture and Elizabethan and Jacobean portraits.

The nearby town of Yeovil was once a Roman settlement and an Iron Age fort stands on nearby Hamdon Hill. The market town for the area, Yeovil became prosperous through the manufacture of gloves, glass and cheese. Now it is the home of Westland Helicoptors; the original company was founded here during the First World War. The town has a medieval church with a 15th century brass lectern engraved with the figure of a monk. The church's lofty arches and windows make it so light and airy that it has been called The Lantern of the West.

Stopping first in the small village of Trent, where Charles II hid for three weeks in the local manor house, we go next to Sherborne, whose history covers over 1200 years and has been home, at different times, to several famous men. The first of these was Bishop Aldhelm who built a church and famous school here in the 8th century. Two of King Alfred's brothers were buried here and it is said that Alfred himself may have been educated here for a time.

Perhaps the most famous of the men associated with Sherborne is Sir Walter Raleigh, the Elizabethan explorer and writer who ended on the scaffold. Sir Walter Raleigh was given Sherborne's 12th century castle by Elizabeth I, and he decided to build a new house a few hundred yards from the old castle on the site of a former hunting lodge. This is why Sherborne now has two castles. It is said that it was in the grounds of the new castle that a servant came across Sir Walter sitting on a seat smoking. Thinking his master was on fire, he threw a bucket of water over him.

In the early 17th century, Sir Walter's castle was enlarged by its new owner, Sir John Digby, and in the 18th century Capability Brown laid out the grounds. The Old Castle was slighted (partly demolished to prevent further military use) by Parliamentary troops after being involved in two sieges in the Civil War, the second of which was severe with fierce fighting. Nowadays there are some remains still to be seen.

Sherborne itself is a pleasant town in a rural setting on the River Yeo. The buildings are mainly Georgian, Regency and Victorian. Its main attraction is St Aldhelm's Abbey with its wonderful 15th century fan vaulting and Gothic monument to the Digby family. It also contains all the 35 available colours (flags) of the Dorsetshire

Regiment. Nearby there are 15th century almshouses and The Conduit, a roofed house where monks shaved their heads and washed.

The next stops are Somerton, on the River Cherwell, the village of Meare, and then the literally legendary town of Glastonbury. One of the legends tells the story of Joseph of Arimathea landing in Somerset with the Holy Grail and coming inland to Glastonbury. He stuck his staff in the ground while he rested and the staff took root and flowered, a sign that his travels should end and he should build a church here. Glastonbury is also a centre of Arthurian legends and is reputedly where King Arthur and Queen Guinevere are buried.

There is evidence of settlement here in prehistoric times although little is known of this early period. The famous abbey was probably originally Celtic with later Saxon additions. It was attacked by Vikings but St Dunstan, who became abbot in 943, repaired it and also presided over its rise to become a wealthy and influential establishment. At about this time the abbey expanded, and was still further enlarged after the Norman Conquest. This expansion continued until the Dissolution of the Monasteries which left the building in ruins. The remains of the abbey give an idea of its size and grandeur. The Abbot's Kitchen is a notable feature with the famous flowering thorn tree near by which is reputed to be from a cutting of the one planted by Joseph of Arimathea. The town has two museums: Glastonbury Lake Village in the High Street showing a collection of prehistoric antiquities and the award winning Somerset Rural Life Museum, Chilkwell Street.

We proceed onward to the beautiful cathedral city of Wells at the foot of the Mendip Hills. There were holy wells here in Saxon times and a monastery was founded in the 8th century. Near the site of the present cathedral there was probably a small Saxon church until a large Norman one replaced it which was consecrated in 1148. However, in the last quarter of that century the bishop, Reginald de Bohun, started the present cathedral. The building was continued by Bishop Jocelyn through most of the first half of the 13th century.

During this time there was a political struggle over which town should be the seat of the diocese of Bath and Wells. The monks in Bath abbey were campaigning to have the bishopric there. However, when Bath made a final attempt to obtain it in the mid 13th century, the bishop of Wells was able to inform the Pope that a worthy cathedral already existed in Wells.

This wonderful cathedral has many beautiful features; amongst the most notable is the 24 hour dial clock from 1390 where the earth is shown as the centre of the universe and the sun is the hour hand. Every quarter hour knights on horseback rotate. Perhaps the greatest work in the cathedral is the West Front, designed as a sculpture gallery and housing 293 medieval statues, two-thirds of which are life-size. This is, without doubt, a magnificent medieval cathedral. The Bishop's Palace is also quite splendid and set within a moat on which the swans ring a bell for food. Also the original holy well of St Andrew stands within the bishop's garden.

Stalagmites and stalagtites in Cheddar Caves

The city of Wells has a number of other places of interest including both the Archdeacon's house, the Deanery, the cathedral school and the organist's house. There is also a fine medieval tithe barn and William Penn once preached from an upper window of the Crown Hotel.

Wells is also the ideal place from which to make a detour to visit Wookey Hole, quite close by, and Cheddar Gorge, about eight miles away. Wookey Hole is a great cavern with a number of chambers carved by water in the carboniferous limestone. Through it runs part of the River Axe and there is evidence that this series of caves was inhabited between 250BC and 450BC. On the site is a museum, a papermill with an exhibition about handmade paper and another exhibition of fairground figures.

Cheddar Gorge may be reached by taking the A371 from Wells which, nearing the Gorge, changes from a gradual descent to a breathtaking plunge down to the valley floor with the cliffs rising to a height of 450 feet in places. The village of Cheddar is now very commercialised with cafes, gift shops, etc but nothing can spoil the beauty and wonder of the caves. Inhabited by Paleolithic man, 10,000 years ago, the rock formations and the effects caused by minerals colouring the rocks are quite dramatic as are the numerous stalagmites and stalagtites (tites grow down, mites grow up).

Our final call is on the old town of Bruton. It has a fine Gothic parish church with two towers, a 16th century grammar school, a 16th century roofless dovecote and some 12th century abbey walls.

ANTIQUE DEALERS

CLEVEDON (0275)

John & Carol Hawley Antique Clocks, The Orchard, Clevedon Lane, Clapton Wick, BS21 7AG TEL: 852052 ASSNS: BHI, BWCMG PARKING: Own carpark OPEN: By appt MIN: £100 MAX: £4,000 PERIOD: 18th-19th century SPECIALIST: Clocks - English, longcase, fusee wall, bracket, Vienna regulators, carriage. OTHER INFO: Victorian seaside town close to Bath and Bristol

YATTON (0934)

Glenville Antiques, 120 High Street. BS19 4DH TEL: 832284 ASSNS: LAPADA PARKING: Easy OPEN: Mon-Sat 10.30-1, 2.15-5 or by appt MIN: £1 MAX: £2,225 PERIOD: 18th-20th century SPECIALIST: Sewing tools GENERAL: General antiques OTHER INFO: Near good garden centre with café.

WESTON-SUPER-MARE (0934)

Sterling Books, 43a Locking Road, BS23 3DG TEL: 625056 ASSNS: ABA, PBFA PARKING: Own carpark OPEN: Mon-Sat 9-6 MIN: £1 MAX: £1,500 PERIOD: 17th-20th century SPECIALIST: Books - antiquarian, travel, topography arts & crafts GENERAL: Prints, bookbinding, restoration, picture framing OTHER INFO: Railway station nearby.

Tobys Antiques, 47 Upper Church Road, BS23 2DY TEL: 623555 PARKING: Medium OPEN: Mon-Sat 9-5 MIN: £2 MAX: £900 PERIOD: 19th century

BURNHAM ON SEA (0278)

Heape's, 39 Victoria Street, TA8 1AN TEL: 782131 PARKING: Easy OPEN: Mon-Sat 10-4

MIN: £5 MAX: £2,000 PERIOD: 19th-20th century SPECIALIST: China, silver plate GENERAL: General antiques OTHER INFO: New Promenade, leaning tower parish church, lighthouse, Mitre restaurant.

HIGHBRIDGE (0278)

C.W.E and R.I. Dyte, The Old Bacon Factory, Huntspill Road TEL: 788590 FAX: 788604 ASSNS: LAPADA PARKING: Own carpark OPEN: Mon-Sat 8-6 MIN: £10 MAX: £10,000 PERIOD: 18th-20th century SPECIALIST: Furniture GENERAL: Large stock shipping - Georgian furniture OTHER INFO: 5 antique traders buying daily.

Terence Kelly Antiques, Huntspill Court, West Huntspill, TA9 3QZ TEL: 785052 PARKING: Own carpark OPEN: By appt MIN: £20 MAX: £3,000 PERIOD: 17-19th century (some 20th and occasionnally 16th) SPECIALIST: Mainly oak & country furniture, metalware GENERAL: Wide range including pottery, glass, pictures etc

NETHER STOWEY (0278)

House of Antiquity (Antique Books), 12 St Mary Street, Nether Stowey, TA5 1LJ TEL: 732426 ASSNS: PTS PARKING: Easy OPEN: Mon-Sat 9-5.30 MIN: £1 MAX: £500 PERIOD: 19th-20th century SPECIALIST: Philatelic Literature GENERAL: Fiction, non-fiction, large selection old and new.

WIVELISCOMBE (0984)

Heads 'n' Tails, Bournes House, Church Street, TA4 2LT TEL: 623097 FAX: 624445 PARKING: Easy OPEN: By appt MIN: £10 MAX: £5,000 PERIOD: 19th-20th century SPECIALIST: Taxidermy GENERAL: Full mount animals, including bears. Also birds, insects, cased fish, skulls, big game trophies.

MILVERTON (0823)

Milverton Antiques, Fore Street, TA4 1JU TEL: 400597 PARKING: Easy OPEN: Mon-Sat 9.30-6 MIN: £20 MAX: £3,500 PERIOD: 18th-19th century SPECIALIST: Oak & well finished stripped pine GENERAL: China, brass & copper interesting country bygones OTHER INFO: Conservation village with fine Georgian house - church with early benchends.

WELLINGTON (0823)

M & A Lewis Oriental Carpets & Rugs, 8 North Street, TA21 8LT TEL: 667430 ASSNS:

LAPADA PARKING: Easy OPEN: Tues-Fri 10-1, 2-5.30 or by appt MIN: £25 MAX: £12,000 PERIOD: 19th-20th century GENERAL: Old and antique rugs and carpets, restoration and cleaning, valuations OTHER INFO: Rummage pile £100 and under

TAUNTON (0823)

Staplegrove Lodge Antiques, TEL: 331153 PARKING: Own carpark OPEN: By appt PERIOD: 17-19th century GENERAL: Furniture, china.

Taunton Antiques Market Silver Street, 27-29 Silver Street, TA1 3DH TEL: 289327 FAX: 289327 PARKING: Easy OPEN: Mondays 9-4 including Bank Holidays MIN: £1 MAX: £500 about PERIOD: 18th-20th century GENERAL: 130 dealers in West Country's largest one day market OTHER INFO: Park in Sainsbury's town centre carpark, buy your groceries there to avoid fee - we are adjacent across the road. 2 cafés serving real food.

Windsor House Antiques, 35b East Reach, TA1 3ES TEL: 325012 PARKING: Medium OPEN: To be arranged, Mon-Sat MIN: £5 MAX: £1,000 PERIOD: 19th-20th century GENERAL: All in good condition & well presented OTHER INFO: Taunton is the gateway to the West. 30 mins to Exeter, Bath, Wells, Honiton etc, B&B available on premises.

LANGPORT (0458)

King's House Antiques, The King's House, Bow Street, TA10 9PS TEL: 250350 FAX: 250350 PARKING: Easy OPEN: Tues-Sat 10-4 MIN: £5 MAX: £100 PERIOD: 19th-20th century GENERAL: Good quality bric-a-brac, smalls etc OTHER INFO: Lots of pubs and good places to eat.

HAMBRIDGE (0458)

Chalow UK Ltd, Hambridge Hill, TA10 0BP TEL: 252374 ASSNS: LAPADA PARKING: Own carpark OPEN: Mon-Sat 9-5 MIN: £100 MAX: £7,500 PERIOD: 18th-19th century GENERAL: European country and decorative handmade furniture OTHER INFO: Touring guide available, weekend breaks may be booked.

ILMINSTER (0460)

Ray Best Antiques, North Street House, TA19 0DG TEL: 52194 ASSNS: LAPADA PARKING: Easy OPEN: Mon-Fri 9.30-6, Sat 11-3 or

by appt MIN: £10 MAX: £10,000, PERIOD: 17th-19th century SPECIALIST: Furniture GENERAL: Copper, brass, porcelain, pottery, silver + plate, clocks OTHER INFO: Montacute House, Barrington Court, Brympton D'Evercy, Forde Abbey, Cricket St Thomas Wildlife Park and nearby forest trail. Good restaurants - B&B possiblity inhouse.

Dowlish Wake Antiques, Dowlish Wake Village, TA19 0NY TEL: 52784 PARKING: Easy OPEN: Mon-Sat 10-1, 2.30-5.30 MIN: £1 MAX: £10,000 but average range £20-£200 SPECIALIST: Ceramics GENERAL: Mostly 19th century English & Continental porcelain and pottery, 18th century porcelain, some 17th-18th century delftware & pottery. No Art Deco or Oriental. OTHER INFO: Very pretty village, Egon Ronay listed pub, real Somerset cider mill & museum, 13th century church with 19th century tomb and memorial to explorer John Hanning Speke, discoverer of the Nile source.. Stone-arched pack bridge over (now dry) ford. Dowlish means damp and Wake from the Plantagenet Lady Isobel Wake whose sculpted tomb is in the church.

James Hutchison, 5 West Street, TA19 9AA TEL: 21066 PARKING: Easy OPEN: Mon-Sat 11-5 MIN: £5 MAX: £1,000 PERIOD: 19th-20th century SPECIALIST: Paintings and antique frames GENERAL: Prints, furniture, collectables OTHER INFO: 15th century Minster, ample hotels, B&B's, restaurants.

Moolham Mill Antiques, Moolham Lane, Moolham Mill, TA19 0PD TEL: 52834 ASSNS: BADA PARKING: Own carpark OPEN: By appt MIN: £50 MAX: £8,000 PERIOD: 17th-early 19th century SPECIALIST: 17th century oak,

Pugh's Antiques

**Pugh's Farm, Monkton,
Nr. Honiton, Devon EX14 9QH**

A30 – LONDON

Open Monday – Saturday 9am–6pm

Five barns furniture, Edwardian–Victorian
Antique beds & tables, farmhouse, etc.
Imported monthly from France.

Tel: 0404 42860

18th century mahogany, samplers, treen, brass
OTHER INFO: N.T. Montacute House, N.T.
Lytes Carey Manor.

West End House Antiques, 34-36 West Street,
TA9 9AB TEL: 52793 PARKING: Easy OPEN:
Mon-Sat 10-5.30 MIN: £1 MAX: £5,000
PERIOD: 18th-20th century SPECIALIST:
Clarice Cliff, darkwood furniture up to Deco era
GENERAL: General antiques OTHER INFO:
Minster. 500+ dealers within 15 mins.

MONKTON (0404)

Pugh's Antiques, Pugh's Farm, EX14 9GH TEL:
42860 FAX: 47782 PARKING: Own carpark
OPEN: Mon-Sat 9-6 MIN: £10 MAX: £1,000
PERIOD: 19th-20th century SPECIALIST: Beds
& furniture imported from France GENERAL:
Victorian & Edwardian furniture.

HONITON (0404)

The Angel Antique Centre - Abingdon House,
136 High Street TEL: 42108 PARKING: Easy
OPEN: 10-5 PERIOD: 18th-20th century
SPECIALIST: General antiques and furniture
OTHER INFO: Centre containing 15 dealers.

J. Barrymore & Co. 73-75 High Street, EX14
8PG TEL: 42244 FAX: 47071 PARKING: Easy
OPEN: Mon-Sat 10-5, but Thurs by appt only.
MIN: £50 MAX: £20,000 PERIOD: 18th-19th
century SPECIALIST: Canteens and part sets of
flatware GENERAL: Silver, Victorian silver
plate & jewellery.

Bramble Cross Antiques, Exeter Road, EX14 8XX
TEL: 47085 PARKING: Own carpark OPEN: Mon-
Sat 10-5.30 MIN: £40 MAX: £10,000 PERIOD:
18th-20th century GENERAL: Georgian, Victorian & Edwardian furnishings. 9 showrooms.

Roderick Butler, Marwood House, EX14 8PY

ASSNS: BADA TEL: 42169 PARKING: Own
carpark OPEN: Mon-Sat 9.30-5.30, closed public holidays PERIOD: 17th, 18th & Regency
19th century SPECIALIST: Furniture, early
metalwork OTHER INFO: Usually some rare,
unusual or amusing items. Good food close by.

Elizabeth Gilmore Antiques, 126 High Street
TEL: 43565 ASSNS: LAPADA PARKING:
Medium OPEN: 10-5 or by appt SPECIALIST:
Oak and country furniture and paintings.

Fountain Antiques Centre, 132 High Street,
EX14 8JP TEL: 42074 PARKING: Medium
OPEN: Mon-Sat 9.30-5.30 MIN: £1 MAX:
£2,000 PERIOD: 18th-20th century GENERAL:
Wide range of furniture, pottery, china, books,
line & lace, etc OTHER INFO: 25 dealers.

Honiton Antique Centre, Abingdon House, 136
High Street, EX14 8JP TEL: 42108, 850464
PARKING: Medium OPEN: Mon-Sat 10-5 MIN:
£1 MAX: £1,500 PERIOD: 18th-20th century
SPECIALIST: Country & sporting goods
GENERAL: Comprehensive range of antiques.
20+ dealers

Honiton Clock Clinic, 167 High Street, EX14
8LQ TEL: 47466 ASSNS: FSB PARKING:
Medium OPEN: Mon-Sat 10-4.30 MIN: £30
MAX: £3,000 PERIOD: 17th-20th century
SPECIALIST: Clocks & barometer spares, cabi-
net fittings, restoration materials GENERAL:
Clocks & Barometers OTHER INFO: Honiton
is the largest antiques centre in the West Country.

Honiton Fine Art, 189 High Street, EX14 8LQ
TEL: 45942 PARKING: Easy OPEN: Mon-Sat
9.30-5 MIN: £300 MAX: £7,000 PERIOD: 18th-
19th century SPECIALIST: Old Master drawings GENERAL: English & European paintings
& watercolours.

Honiton Junction, 159 High Street, EX14 8LJ
TEL: 43436 PARKING: Easy OPEN: Mon-Sat
10-5 MIN: £1 MAX: £1,000 PERIOD: 19th century SPECIALIST: Collectables GENERAL:
Country pine & oak, kitchenalia, copper, brass,
door & window hardware etc OTHER INFO:
Honiton - the antique centre of the Southwest
with some 30 shops and 3 antique centres.
B&B's.

Honiton Lace Shop, 44 High Street, EX14 8PJ
TEL: 42416 FAX: 47797 PARKING: Easy

OPEN: Mon-Sat 9.30-1, 2-5 MIN: £1 MAX: £4,000 PERIOD: 17th-19th century SPECIALIST: Collectors & rare lace, textiles OTHER INFO: Good winebar & pubs, Museum has superb collection of Honiton lace.

Honiton Old Bookshop, Felix House, 51 High Street, EX14 8PW TEL: 47180 FAX: 47180 ASSNS: ABA, PBFA PARKING: Easy OPEN: Mon-Sat 10-30-5.30 PERIOD: Antiquarian to modern out of print GENERAL: Good quality general stock, cleanly & comfortably presented OTHER INFO: 5 other secondhand bookshops nearby, all with interesting, changing stock.

House of Antiques, 195 High Street, EX14 8LQ TEL: 41648 PARKING: Medium OPEN: Mon-Sat 10-6 MAX: £10,000 PERIOD: 19th-20th century SPECIALIST: Fine quality Victorian & Edwardian furniture.

L.J. Huggett & Son, Stamps Building, King Street, EX14 8AG TEL: 42403 PARKING: Own carpark OPEN: Mon-Sat 9.30-5 PERIOD:18th-19th century SPECIALIST: Period furniture.

Kings Arms Antiques Centre, 56 High Street TEL: 46269 PARKING: Easy OPEN: Mon-Sat 10-4.30, Thurs AM only MIN: £2 MAX: £1,000 PERIOD: 18th-20th century GENERAL: 10+ dealers with comprehensive range of antiques.

Kingsway House Antiques, Kingsway House, 3 High Street TEL: 46213 PARKING: easy OPEN: Mon-Sat 10-5.30 MIN: £20 MAX: £5,000 PERIOD: 1780-1850 SPECIALIST: Large stock of clocks GENERAL: Chests of drawers, toilet mirrors, decorative items, soft furnishings etc

Micklem Antiques, 126 High Street, EX14 8JP TEL: 43565 ASSNS: BADA PARKING: Easy OPEN: Mon-Sat 10-5 MIN: £25 MAX: £15,000 PERIOD: 17th-20th century SPECIALIST: Walnut veneered & early furniture. GENERAL: Mostly before 1720 & some later decorative. Separate rooms OTHER INFO: Lots of good hotels & restaurants including Bittesham Park highly recommended.

Otter Antiques, 69 High Street, EX14 8PW TEL: 42627 PARKING: Medium OPEN: Mon-Wed, Fri, Sat 9-5. Thurs by appt MIN: £1 MAX: £1,000 PERIOD: 18th-20th century SPECIALIST: Tableware GENERAL: Silver, silverplate OTHER INFO: 25 antique shops in High Street

+ 3 auction rooms.

Pilgrim Antiques, 145 High Street, EX14 8LJ TEL: 41219 FAX: 45317 PARKING: Medium OPEN: Mon-Sat 9-5.30 MIN: £100 MAX: £10,000 PERIOD: 17-19th century SPECIALIST: English & Continental furniture, longcase clocks GENERAL: Shipping services OTHER INFO: 16,000 sq ft trade warehouse.

Upstairs Downstairs, 12 High Street, EX14 8PU TEL: 42140 PARKING: Easy OPEN: Mon-Sat 10-5.30 PERIOD: 18th-20th century GENERAL: General antiques.

Wickham Antiques, 191 High Street, EX14 8LQ TEL: 44654 PARKING: Medium OPEN: Mon-Sat 9.30-5 MIN: £100 MAX: £2,000 PERIOD: 18th-19th century SPECIALIST: Georgian & Victorian furniture GENERAL: Decorative items.

John Wignall Fine Books, 174 High Street, EX14 8LA TEL: 43460 FAX: 47377 PARKING: Medium OPEN: 10-5.30 MIN: £8 MAX: £800 PERIOD: 18th-20th century SPECIALIST: Antiquarian & sporting books, particularly field sports OTHER INFO: 1st floor picture gallery, ceramics & antiques. Constant coffee.

Geoffrey Woodhead Antiques, 53 High Street, EX14 8PW TEL: 42969 PARKING: Easy OPEN: Mon-Sat 9.30-1, 2.15-5.30 MIN: £2 MAX: £5,000 PERIOD: 18th-20th century GENERAL: Antiques & collectors items, antique & secondhand books.

SIDMOUTH (0395)

Bygones, 2 Old Fore Street, EX10 8LS TEL: 512086 PARKING: Easy OPEN: Summer seven days 9-5.30, Winter Mon-Sat 9-5 MIN: £1 PERIOD: 18th-20th century GENERAL: Veri-

```
┌─────────────────────────────────────────────────────────────┐
│                                                             │
│      DEVONSHIRE HOUSE ANTIQUES CENTRE                       │
│            15 Fore Street, Sidmouth, Devon                  │
│   Situated in the centre of this delightful Georgian        │
│                    seaside resort.                          │
│  20 dealers selling a variety of antiques and collectors    │
│   items, antiquarian books, linen and lace, collectors      │
│     records 1920s–80s, pictures and prints, etc.            │
│                                                             │
│      *Open daily Monday – Saturday, 10am–5pm.*              │
│      *Easter to end of September, Sundays 1pm–5pm.*         │
│           *Tearoom open from Easter.*                       │
│           **Enquiries: 0935 512588**                        │
│                                                             │
└─────────────────────────────────────────────────────────────┘
```

table cornucopia, a bit of everything.

Devonshire House Antiques Centre, 15 Fore Street TEL: 512588 PARKING: Easy OPEN: Mon-Sat 10-5; Easter to end of Sept Sun 1-5 MIN: £2 MAX: £1,500 PERIOD: 18th-20th century GENERAL: 2 good book dealers, Goss & crested ware, oak & pine furniture, pictures, china, glass & collectors items OTHER INFO: Tearoom in Centre during summer. 20+ dealers. England's biggest International Folk Festival in early August.

Dorothy Hartnell Antiques, 21 Fore Street TEL: 515291 PARKING: easy in Winter OPEN: Mon-Sat 10-5, Winter Thurs halfday MIN: £1 MAX: £5,000 PERIOD: 18th-20th century GENERAL: General antiques OTHER INFO: Charming Regency resort, relaxed atmosphere, wealth of individual shops, large & small first class hotels, winner of the Britain in Bloom Floral Town.

The Little Shop Vintage Toy & Train Museum Shop, Market Place, EX10 8LU TEL: 513399 ext 208 Assn of Indep. Museums PARKING: Easy OPEN: 1st Apr-31st Oct 10-2.45 MIN: £2 MAX: £500 PERIOD: 20th century SPECIALIST: Tinplate toys & trains GENERAL: Hornby Gauge 0 & 00, Meccano, Dinky toys, Corgis, Matchbox, Britains, wooden puzzles OTHER INFO: Sidmouth is one of the fairest places in the kingdom. Seafront quite unspoilt with Regency terraces.

BUDLEIGH SALTERTON (0395)

New Gallery, 9 Fore Street, EX9 6NG TEL: 443768 ASSNS: FRSA PARKING: Easy OPEN: Easter to Christmas Tues-Sat 10-1, 2-5 otherwise by appt MIN: £10 MAX: £1,000 PERIOD: 19th-20th century SPECIALIST: Fine watercolours GENERAL: Oils, prints OTHER INFO: Gallery is in ballroom of an elegant Edwardian house set in a colourful garden.

Wendy Cook, Budleigh House, East Budleigh, EX9 7ED TEL: 445368 PARKING: Easy OPEN: Tues, Thur-Sun 10-5 MIN: £5 MAX: £1,500 PERIOD: 18th-19th century SPECIALIST: Country furniture GENERAL: Porcelain, pottery, metalware, decorative items OTHER INFO: Opposite Sir Walter Raleigh pub. Village is his birthplace.

David J Thorn, 2 High Street, EX9 6LQ TEL: 442448 PARKING: Easy OPEN: Tues & Fri 10-1, 2-5, Sat 10-1 MIN: £2 MAX: £10,000 PERIOD: 17th-20th century SPECIALIST: Ceramics: English, Continental & Oriental.

SEATON (0297)

Etcetera Etc Antiques, 12 Beer Road TEL: 21965 PARKING: Own carpark OPEN: Mon-Wed, Fri, Sat 10-1, 2-5 PERIOD: 18th-20th century GENERAL: Furniture, china, glass, brass, bric-a-brac, reproduction OTHER INFO: Lovely coastline walks, 18 hole links, tramway beside Axe Estuary, B&B's etc.

COLYTON (0297)

Colyton Antiques Centre, Dolphin Street, EX13 6NA TEL: 552339 PARKING: Own carpark OPEN: Mon-Sat 10-5 MIN: £1 MAX: £2,000 PERIOD: 19th-20th century GENERAL: General antiques OTHER INFO: Colyton dating from Saxon times, a unique town with a village atmosphere. Interesting church with octagonal lantern tower.

BRIDPORT (0308)

Pic's Bookshop, 11 South Street, DT6 3NR TEL: 25689 PARKING: Easy OPEN: 9-4.30 MIN: £1

MAX: £200+ PERIOD: 18th-20th century GENERAL: Rare & general stock of secondhand books, 50 classifications. Reference libray to Dorset.

Tudor House Antiques, 88 East Street, DT6 3LL TEL: 27200 PARKING: Easy OPEN: Mon-Sat 9-5.30 MIN: £10 MAX: £3,000 PERIOD: 17th-19th century GENERAL: Antique furniture. Some oils paintings, porcelain, silver, clocks etc OTHER INFO: Very good hotel & restaurant Whitefriars at Winterbourne Abbas (8 miles).

Westdale Antiques, Bridport Antique Centre, West Allington TEL: 27271 PARKING: Medium OPEN: Mon-Sat 9-5 PERIOD: 19th century GENERAL: Taxidermy studies, lace, linen, jewellery.

BEAMINSTER (0308)

Beaminster Antiques, 4 Church Street, DT8 3AZ TEL: 862591 PARKING: Easy OPEN: Mon-Sat 10-4.30 MIN: £15 MAX: £1,000 PERIOD: 18th, 20th century GENERAL: Small items, silver, sewing implements, porcelain, general collectors pieces OTHER INFO: A small shop packed with curiosity pieces. 3 other antique shops with a monthly antique fair (same phone).

Good Hope Antiques, 2 Hogshill Street, DT8 3AE TEL: 862119 PARKING: Easy OPEN: Mon, Tues, Thurs-Sat 9.30-5 PERIOD: 18th-19th century SPECIALIST: Longcase, bracket & wall clocks. Barometers GENERAL: Furniture.

DRIMPTON (0308)

Drimpton Antiques, The Old Barn, Netherhay, DT8 3RH TEL: 867597 PARKING: Own carpark OPEN: By appt (Mondays only) MIN: £5 MAX: £1,000 PERIOD: 17th-20th century SPECIALIST: Garden, country items GENERAL: Pictures, furniture, china, metalwork, farming items OTHER INFO: Old milking parlours with holes in roof, general antiques and junk.

CREWKERNE (0460)

Crewkerne Furniture Emporium, Viney Bridge, South Street, TA18 8AE TEL: 75319 FAX: 75122 PARKING: Own carpark OPEN: Mon-Sat 8.30-5.30, Sun 10-5 MIN: £1 MAX: £1,000 PERIOD: 19th-20th century SPECIALIST: House clearance GENERAL: Good used furniture, shipping pieces, some antiques

OTHER INFO: 6 secondhand, pine, antique shops, auction room. B&B's and hotels including vegetarian.

MONTACUTE (0935)

Montacute Antiques, South Street, TA15 6XD TEL: 824786 PARKING: Medium OPEN: Mon-Sat 8.30-6.30 MIN: £10 MAX: £1,000 PERIOD: 18th-19th century SPECIALIST: Old oak furniture, porcelain GENERAL: Brass, copper, pewter, collectables etc OTHER INFO: Montacute House (NT) 100 yards.

YEOVIL (0935)

Fox & Co, 30 Princes Street, BA20 1EQ TEL: 72323 FAX: 411026 ASSNS: Antiquity Dealers Assn. PARKING: Medium OPEN: Mon-Sat 9-5.30 MIN: £1 MAX: £2,000 SPECIALIST: Antiquities, coins, militaria, ethnographia OTHER INFO: 250 million BC to date.

MELBURY OSMOND (0935)

Hardy County, Holt Mill Farm, DT2 0LX TEL: 873361 PARKING: Own carpark OPEN: Mon-Sat 9-4 MIN: £20 MAX: £1,500 PERIOD: 19th-20th century SPECIALIST: Antique pine GENERAL: Old country furniture OTHER INFO: Hotels & B&B's in surrounding villages.

SHERBORNE (0935)

Abbas Antiques, 17 Newlands, DT9 3JG TEL: 0963-371019 PARKING: Rasy OPEN: Mon-Sat 9.30-5 MIN: £5 MAX: £2,000 PERIOD: 19th century GENERAL: Antiques.

Antiques of Sherborne, 1 The Green, DT9 5HZ TEL: 816549 PARKING: Easy OPEN: Mon-Sat 9.45-5 £2 MAX: £5,000 PERIOD: 19th century SPECIALIST: Furniture, bed linen GENERAL: General antiques OTHER INFO: Superb old buildings in the town.

Dodge & Son, 28-33 Cheap Street, DT9 3PU TEL: 815151 FAX: 816902 ASSNS: LAPADA PARKING: Own carpark OPEN: Mon-Sat 9-5.30 MIN: £10 MAX: £10,000 PERIOD: 18th-19th century SPECIALIST: Dining tables & chairs GENERAL: Furniture & pictures.

Steven Ferdinando, The Swan Gallery, 51 Cheap Street, DT9 3AX TEL: 814465 PARKING: Easy OPEN: Mon-Sat 9.30-5 (Weds halfday) MIN: £5 MAX: £2,000 PERIOD: 19th-20th century SPECIALIST: Antiquarian books GENERAL: Old & out of print books. Maps, prints, watercolours OTHER INFO: The nicest

THE SWAN GALLERY

51 Cheap Street, Sherborne, Dorset DT9 3AX
Tel: 0935 814465   Fax: 0308 868195

A very large stock of fine
Victorian watercolours, antique prints & maps
on numerous subjects including sporting,
natural history, military, topography, etc.

9.30am–5pm Monday to Saturday

town in Old Dorset, excellent facilities.

Greystoke Antiques, Swan Yard, Cheap Street, DT9 3AX TEL: 812833 PARKING: Easy OPEN: Mon, Tues, Thurs-Sat 10-4.30 MIN: £5 MAX: £5,000 PERIOD: 18th-20th century GENERAL: Silver OTHER INFO: Next to Old Market carpark.

Heygate Browne, South Street, DT9 3NG TEL: 815487 PARKING: Own carpark OPEN: Mon-Sat 10-5 £20 MAX: £10,000 PERIOD: 18th-19th century GENERAL: General antiques OTHER INFO: 12th century abbey & 2 castles.

The Nook Antiques, The Nook, South Street, DT9 3LX TEL: 813987 ASSNS: NADA, LAPADA PARKING: Easy OPEN: Thurs-Sat 10-5 £5 MAX: £600 PERIOD: 19th-20th century GENERAL: General antiques.

The Swan Gallery, 51 Cheap Street, DT9 3AX TEL: 814465 FAX: 0308 868195 PARKING: Easy OPEN: Mon-Sat 9.30-5, (Wed halfday) MIN: £10 MAX: £2,500 PERIOD: 18th-20th century SPECIALIST: Victorian watercolours GENERAL: Antique maps, prints. Antiquarian & out of print books OTHER INFO: Fine medieval abbey church, 2 castles, Eastbury Hotel recommended. On rail network.

TRENT (0935)

Old Barn Antiques, Flamberts Trent, DT9 4SS TEL: 850648 PARKING: Own carpark OPEN: By appt MIN: £200 MAX: £10,000 PERIOD: 18th-19th century GENERAL: Good mahogany furniture.

SOMERTON (0458)

London Cigarette Card Co. Ltd, Sutton Road, TA11 6QP TEL: 73452 PARKING: Own carpark OPEN: Mon-Sat 9-1, Mon,Tues.Thurs, Fri 2-5

MIN: £2 MAX: £10,000 PERIOD: 19th-20th century SPECIALIST: Over 100 million cigarette and picture cards.

Westville House Antiques, Littleton, TA11 6NP TEL: 73376 FAX: 73376 PARKING: Own carpark OPEN: Mon-Sat 9-6 MIN: £100 MAX: £3,000 PERIOD: 18th-19th century SPECIALIST: Pine GENERAL: Country oak, mahogany.

SHAPWICK (0458)

King's Farm Antiques, The Old Farmhouse, School Lane TEL: 210021 PARKING: Own carpark OPEN: By appt MIN: £50 MAX: £1,500 PERIOD: 17th-19th century SPECIALIST: Oak and country furniture GENERAL: General antiques OTHER INFO: 15/16th century hotel in village, 4 miles to Street (Clarke's Village factory shops).

GLASTONBURY (0458)

Antiques Fair, St. Dunstan's, Market Place, BA6 9EL TEL:32939 PARKING: Own car park OPEN: Mon-Sat 9.30-6 MIN: £3 MAX: £2,000 PERIOD: 19th-20th century SPECIALIST: Unusual quality & decorative items GENERAL: No furniture but all quality variety of smalls, OTHER INFO: Shop is in carpark of Glastonbury Abbey, burial place of King Arthur.

The Lace & Linen Shop, 1 The Monarch Mews, 15 High Street,(next to Midland Bank) TEL: 835422 PARKING: Easy OPEN: Mon,Tues, Thurs-Sat 10-4, closed Mons in winter MIN: £1 MAX: £500 PERIOD: 18th-20th century SPECIALIST: Victorian christening gowns, bonnets, samplers GENERAL: Linens, lace, quilts & costume jewellery OTHER INFO: We are at rear of a 17th century inn. 3 antiques shops in mews, tourists love it. Tea room in the old wine cellar, cobblestones, flowers.

BRUTON (0749)

Michael Lewis Gallery, 17 High Street, BA10 0AB TEL: 813557 PARKING: Own carpark OPEN: Mon-Sat 9-6 MIN: £20 PERIOD: 18th-20th century GENERAL: Maps, prints, paintings.

M.G.R. Exports, Unit 1, Riverside, Station Road, BA10 0EH TEL: 812460 FAX: 812882 PARKING: Own carpark OPEN: 9-5.30, Sat 9-12.30 & by appt MIN: £5 MAX: £5,000 PERIOD: 17th-20th century GENERAL: Victoriana, shipping, pine, etc 15,000 sq ft, packing service also available.

Devon

This tour of Devon is one of contrasts. It moves from windswept granite moorlands to rolling hills, popular seaside resorts to picturesque villages. Prehistoric remains testify to early settlements and evidence shows that simple tin extraction was carried out 4000 years ago. Along the South Devon coast we see a much kinder milder land, popular for family holidays. However move inland to Dartmoor and

Exeter Cathedral

Exmoor and see the wilder face of Devon, unchanged for centuries but, even there the landscape has been altered by man.

Leaving the M5 at Junction 28 we first arrive in the villages of Cullompton and then Hele before continuing onwards to Exeter. Once the Roman town of *Isca Dumnoniorum*, remains of the Roman city walls may still be seen in Southernhay. Exeter has the distinction of being the last English town to hold out against the Norman invasion. It only surrendered in the winter of 1068 after promises that no reprisals would be taken against the townsfolk.

The city has many buildings of note including the Guildhall dating from 1330 with later alterations and additions, Wynyard's Hospital of 1436 and the restored Tudor St Nicholas' Priory.

Above all there is the cathedral with its two Norman transeptal towers. Built between the 13th and 14th centuries its west front has the largest surviving collection of 14th century sculpture in Britain. Inside, it is said, that the ceiling has the longest stretch of 13th century Gothic vaulting in the world. There is also the 59 foot high Bishop's Throne and a minstrel's gallery displaying angels with musical instruments.

The tour detours along the A337 to Newton St Cyres before visiting the pretty Dartmoor town of Chagford, once important as a tin mining centre and standing in an area rich in prehistoric remains. Nearby Moretonhampstead is a small town ideally situated as a touring centre for Dartmoor. A group of colonnaded 17th

Devon

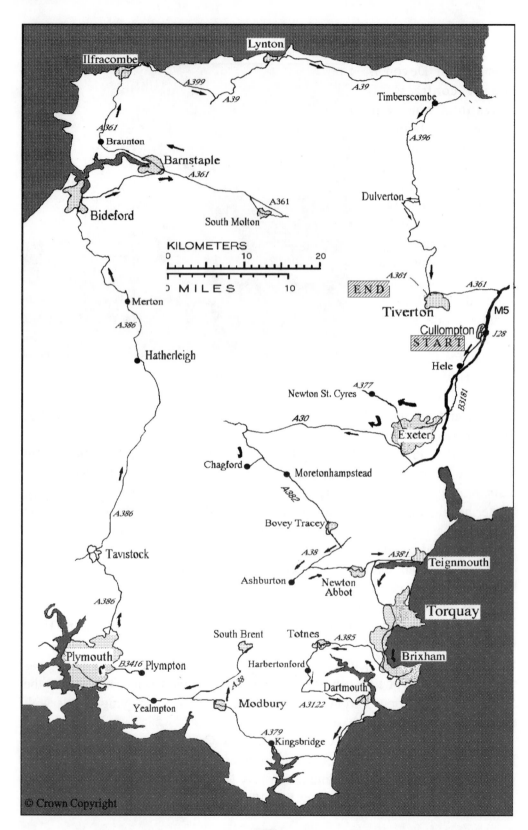

century almshouses may be seen by the churchyard.

Bovey Tracey, the next town, stands on the eastern edge of Dartmoor and is now an important centre for tourists exploring the moors. The original church is said to have been built by Sir William de Tracey in 1170 to atone for his part in the murder of Thomas à Becket. This was burnt down in the early 14th century and later rebuilt.

Our next stop, Ashburton, is an attractive small town on the River Yeo. It has some old slate hung houses, the most notable of these, in North Street, is called The House of Cards because diamonds, spades, hearts and clubs are depicted on the hanging tiles. The route now continues to Newton Abbot, a typically busy English market town. It's most noteworthy features are the 14th century St Leonard's Tower and the 15th century Bradley Manor, a National Trust property. The Manor still shows many of the features, inside and outside, of a typical medieval building although there have been some 19th century alterations.

Now moving on to the coast, we arrive in Teignmouth (pronounced Tinmouth) standing at the mouth of the River Teign. There has been a settlement here since prehistoric times and its importance from then until the Middle Ages was for panning and exporting salt. Fishing also developed as an important industry in the town and boats went out from here to fish the Newfoundland Grand Banks. As fishing became less profitable the town then began to export potter's clay and granite. Nowadays it is a fairly typical seaside resort although signs of its history may still be found.

The popular seaside resort of Torquay, next on the tour, is famous for its mild weather and palm trees growing along the seafront. The public gardens behind the main beach were, in the Middle Ages, part of farmland belonging to Torre Abbey. The Abbey was founded in 1196 but after the Dissolution of the Monasteries in 1539 it became a private residence. It was extensively remodelled in the 18th century and contains a family chapel, furniture, paintings and works of art as well as the Dame Agatha Christie Memorial Room with many mementos of the writer who was born in Torquay. There are also ruins of the original medieval abbey and its church.

Our next stop is the pretty fishing village of Brixham, popular with artists who can be seen painting the picturesque harbour in the summer. It was here that William of Orange landed in 1688 to take the throne of England. A statue stands on the edge of the quay to commemorate the event - often with a seagull on its head. Brixham's other claim to fame is that Henry Lyte wrote the hymn *Abide with Me* in Berry Head House while he was vicar of All Saints Church.

Moving inland now, we arrive in Totnes situated on the River Dart. It claims to be one of the oldest boroughs in England and it was the site of the Royal Mint during the 10th century. The line of the walls once surrounding the town may still be seen as well as two of the gates, one of which, the 15th century East Gate, has

Church Street, Modbury, part of the town's Conservation Area

been restored. There are also several Elizabethan and Georgian houses in the town as well as a picturesque Butterwalk.

Totnes Castle was built after the town surrendered to the Normans and is a good example of a motte and bailey castle. It stands on a hill overlooking the River Dart where three valleys meet. What remains of the castle is mostly 14th century although the huge mound on which it was built is Norman.

Back to the coast, the route now reaches Dartmouth which has been closely associated with the navy for centuries. In medieval times it was used by fleets sailing for the Crusades and vessels from this port took part in the siege of Calais. Later nine ships from Dartmouth joined in the repulsion of the Spanish Armada. This importance as a naval port led to attacks on the town which accounts for the defences - the castles of Dartmouth, Kingswear, Bearscove and Gallants Bower which were used again as defensive positions during the Second World War. In 1944 it was from the Dart estuary that the great fleet departed for the invasion of Normandy and the eventual liberation of Europe. Nowadays it is the Royal Naval College that is most closely identified with the town and which has trained many of the highest ranking naval officers this century.

Our next stop is Kingsbridge, a misleading name for a town that has no river and no bridge but instead is at the head of a deep inlet on the coast. It has a number of interesting buildings: The Shambles, a late 16th century arcade,

Dodbrooke Church also 16th century and the Grammar School dating from 1670.

Following the A379 the tour now reaches Modbury, a pretty town consisting of three main steep streets which converge near the Exeter Inn. There are a number of elegant 18th century houses and the town is well known for the large number of antique shops and art galleries. South Brent, the next village on the route, is situated on the southern edge of Dartmoor and has a carved Norman font inside its church which is also Norman in parts.

We now move on, via Plympton to Plymouth. This city has been an important port and navy dockyard for centuries. It was here that Sir Francis Drake is reputed to have played bowls as the Spanish Armada approached. The Pilgrim Fathers sailed from Plymouth aboard the Mayflower to settle in the New World and, more recently, Sir Francis Chichester arrived in Plymouth at the end of his round the world voyage in 1967.

Much of the centre of Plymouth has been rebuilt after wartime bombing but some of the old town still survives most notably around the harbour. The Elizabethan House in New Street is authentically furnished as an Elizabethan merchant's house and there is another Merchant's House in St Andrew's Street furnished in 16th century style.

Standing on the Rame Peninsular, to the west of Plymouth, is Mount Edgcumbe House and Country Park which contains one of the only three Grade 1 Historic Gardens in Cornwall. It was designed 240 years ago and contains formal gardens in Italian, French and English styles, a deer park, woodland walks and wonderful views. Two new gardens, the New Zealand Garden and the American Plantation, have also been established. The house itself, owned by the Edgcumbe family for over 400 years, is a restored Tudor building now furnished and decorated in late 18th century style.

Turning north, Tavistock, on the western fringe of Dartmoor is a good touring centre for the beautiful country surrounding it. In the late 13th century Tavistock became a Stannary town, that is a centre for the weighing and stamping of tin which came from the mines on Dartmoor. Although there are a few Georgian cottages by the Canal Basin the town centre shows a more Victorian influence. In the mid-19th century the Duke of Bedford used some of his wealth to rebuild it along

A cromlech (prehistoric burial chamber)
on Dartmoor

more spacious lines. His statue stands in the square named after him.

Via the villages of Hatherleigh and Merton we next come to Bideford on the River Torridge with its 677 foot long, 24 arch bridge across the river in which some 15th century stonework may still be seen. The town was the main port for North Devon from 16th to 18th centuries. Nowadays the island of Lundy may be reached by launch from here. Charles Kingsley wrote *Westward Ho!* in the Royal Hotel and there is statue of him at the park gates.

Barnstaple, the next stop, has been the administrative centre of North Devon since Saxon times and may well be the oldest borough in England. Only the mound remains of an ancient castle once standing in Barnstaple but Castle House was built in its grounds and stones from the castle were used for its construction. The town was an important port and market for wool but the port declined with the improvement in the roads and the coming of the railways in the mid 19th century. However the town has continued to grow as new industries have moved into the area.

The route now detours inland along the A361 to South Molton which contains a number of antique shops. The town has some Georgian houses and its Guildhall was built in 1743 with an arcaded lower storey.

Moving back towards the coast we come to Braunton, said to be the largest village in England. The church is of particular interest. Reputedly founded by St. Brannock, a 6th century Welsh missionary, legend has it that he sailed to Braunton in a stone coffin. The present building dates from the 13th century and stands on the site of the church he founded. Nearby there is Braunton Burrows, a 560 acre national nature reserve.

Now to Ilfracombe, a simple fishing village until Victorian times when it developed into a holiday resort. Nowadays it is still popular and is a good centre for exploring Exmoor and North Devon. Pleasure cruisers ply between Ilfracombe and Swansea and Bristol and there are also boat trips to Lundy Island.

Continuing along the coast we arrive in Lynton. The town is perched high on the cliffs above the small picturesque harbour town of Lynmouth and a visit to one usually includes a visit to the other. From Lynton, Lynmouth is reached either by a very steep road (1 in 4) or by a water-powered cliff railway which rises up almost vertically. Both were tiny villages until the early 19th century when the poet, Shelley, stayed in Lynmouth. Later both Wordsworth and Coleridge also visited the village. In 1952 there was a disastrous flood in Lynmouth when the East and West Lyn Rivers burst their banks and hundreds of tons of rocks were brought down by the floodwaters. A total of 34 people were killed and great damage was done. In spite of this the original fishing village cottages alongside the harbour survived.

The tour continues along the coast until it reaches the A396 when it turns inland to visit Timberscombe and Dulverton in Somerset before reaching the final des-

Lynmouth

tination of Tiverton. This is a charming country market town whose wealth, since the 12th century, was founded on the wool trade. Amongst the buildings of note are the Jacobean Great House, now used as council offices, St. Peter's Church founded in in 1073 but greatly endowed by 15th and 16th century wool merchants and the ruins of Tiverton Castle built in 1106. The castle has a magnificent medieval gatehouse and tower which contains an important Civil War armoury, furniture, pictures, tapestry and a fine collection of clocks. The town also has the award-wining Tiverton Museum which contains a Railway Gallery and Lace Machine Gallery.

From Tiverton it is a short drive to the M5 back to London.

Devon

ANTIQUE DEALERS

CULLOMPTON (0884)
Cullompton Antiques, The Old Tannery, EX15 1DT TEL: 38476, home (0395) 279253 PARKING: Own carpark OPEN: 7 days 10-5 MIN: £1 MAX: £5,000 PERIOD: 18th-20th century SPECIALIST: 6,000 sq ft of country furniture GENERAL: Antiques, smalls.

HELE (0392)
Fagins Antiques, Old Whiteways Cider Factory TEL: 882062 FAX: 882194 PARKING: OPEN: Mon-Fri 9.15-5, Sat 11-5 MIN: £1 MAX: £5,000 PERIOD: 19th-20th century SPECIALIST: Stripped pine, mahogany, oak GENERAL: Bric-a-brac, pictures, taxidermy, architectural items. OTHER INFO: 40,000 sq ft showrooms - The Aladdins Cave of the Southwest.

EXETER (0392)
Coombe Street Galleries, Coombe Street, EX1 1DB TEL: 496464 PARKING: Easy OPEN: Mon-Sat 10-6 MIN: £3 MAX: £3,000 PERIOD: 19th-20th century SPECIALIST: Persian carpets, longcase clocks, oriental porcelain GENERAL: Furniture, decorative items, collectables OTHER INFO: Next to popular 15th century White Hart Hotel recently voted best hotel bar in Britain.

Exeter Rare Books, Guildhall Shopping Centre, EX4 3HG TEL: 436021 ASSNS: ABA, PBFA PARKING: Easy OPEN: Mon-Sat 10-1, 2-5 MIN: £1 MAX: £500 PERIOD: 19th-20th century SPECIALIST: Devon & West Country topography GENERAL: Out-of-print, antiquarian & secondhand books on most subjects. Fine bindings & illustrated books OTHER INFO: In heart of city with first floor gallery of restored Georgian market building, close to cathedral, museums.

Gold & Silver Exchange, Eastgate House, Princesshay, EX4 3JT TEL: 217478 PARKING: Easy OPEN: Mon-Sat 9.30-3 MIN: £5 MAX: £2,500 PERIOD: 19th-20th century GENERAL: Silver, antique & secondhand jewellery.

Pennies, Unit 2, Wessex Estate, Station Road, Exwick, EX4 4NZ TEL: 71928, 76532 PARKING: Own carpark OPEN: Mon-Sat 9-6 MIN: £1 MAX: £2,000 PERIOD: 20th century

GENERAL: General antiques OTHER INFO: 1930's, 40's & 50's and secondhand furniture. Directly behind main railway station.

McBains of Exeter, Adj. Exeter Airport, EX5 2BA TEL: 366261 FAX: 365572 ASSNS: LAPADA PARKING: Own carpark OPEN: Mon-Fri 9-5 or by appt MIN: £50 MAX: £5,000 PERIOD: 18th-19th century SPECIALIST: Good furniture GENERAL: Furniture OTHER INFO: Long established family business.

Quay Gallery Antiques Emporium, 43 The Quay TEL: 213283 PARKING: Easy OPEN: seven days 10-5 MIN: £1 MAX: £2,500 PERIOD: 19th-20th century SPECIALIST: Furniture, marine items, silver + plate GENERAL: Collectables, pine, small decorative items OTHER INFO: View onto the Exeter Ship Canal, used filming *The Onedin Line*, in a very well kept part of Exeter. Shop with 8 dealers is in a bonded warehouse c.1530 with excellent café below. Customs House next door.

Strip & Wax, Exe Street, EX4 3HD TEL: 52476 PARKING: Own carpark OPEN: Mon-Wed, Fri, Sat 10-6 MIN: £25 MAX: £800 PERIOD: 19th-20th century SPECIALIST: Cane chairs with stripping & caning service GENERAL: Furniture OTHER INFO: Overlooking River Exe, 30 seconds from The Mill on the Exe, pub (coverted paper mill), and the Papermakers winebar.

NEWTON ST CYRES (0392)
Gordon Hepworth Gallery, Hayne Farm, EX5 5PE TEL: 851351 PARKING: Own carpark MIN: £150 MAX: £5,000 PERIOD: 20th century SPECIALIST: Postwar & contemporary paintings, St Ives School and Cornish paintings with regular exhibitions in 15th century longhouse OTHER INFO: Phone for opening times, directions and gallery brochure.

CHAGFORD (0647)
Mary Payton Antiques, Old Market House, TQ13 8AB TEL: 432428 PARKING: OPEN: Tues-Sun 10-1,2.30-5 MIN: £5 MAX: £300 PERIOD: 19th-20th century SPECIALIST: English pottery & porcelain.

MORETONHAMPSTEAD (0647)
Herbert Clark, 2-4 Fore Street, TQ13 8LN TEL: 40334 PARKING: Easy OPEN: Mon-Wed, Fri, Sat 9.30-1, 2.15-5.30 MIN: £1 MAX:

£200 PERIOD: 19th-20th century GENERAL: Glass & pottery OTHER INFO: White Hart Hotel, B&B Post House (recommended).

BOVEY TRACEY (0626)

Thomas & James Antiques, Station Road TEL: 835350 PARKING: Own carpark OPEN: Mon-Sat 10-4.30 MIN: £20 MAX: £5,000 PERIOD: 17th-20th century SPECIALIST: Period furniture, ceramics & works of art OTHER INFO: Gateway to Dartmoor, good facilities & hotels.

ASHBURTON (0364)

Ashburton Marbles, Great Hall, North Street, TQ13 7QD TEL: 653189 FAX: 654075 PARKING: Own carpark OPEN: Mon-Fri 8-5, Sat 10-4 MIN: £25 MAX: £10,000 PERIOD: 18th-19th century SPECIALIST: Antique fireplaces, marble & wooden GENERAL: Extensive stock 19th century furnishings, lighting, mirrors etc.

Moor Antiques, 19 North Street, TQ13 7QH TEL: 653767 PARKING: Easy OPEN: Mon-Sat 10-5, Wed mornings only MIN: £20 MAX: £2,500 PERIOD: 18th-19th century SPECIALIST: Furniture & clocks GENERAL: Silver, porcelain, metalware, lighting OTHER INFO: Very ancient Stannary town. Lots of Civil War history. Plenty of accommodation with good access to other areas.

NEWTON ABBOTT (0626)

The Attic, 9 Union Street, TQ12 2JX TEL: 55124 PARKING: Difficult OPEN: Tues, Wed, Fri, Sat 9.15-5.30 MIN: £1 MAX: £2,000 PERIOD: 18th-20th century GENERAL: Could be anything-bric-a-brac, tools, antiques, you name it I sell it OTHER INFO: Newton Abbott centre of tourism trade so many good hotels etc.

Newton Abbott Antiques Centre, 55 East Street TEL: 54074 PARKING: Own carpark OPEN: Tuesdays 9-3 OTHER INFO: 45+ dealers

Old Treasures, 126 Queen Street TEL: 67181 PARKING: Medium OPEN: Mon-Wed, Fri, Sat 10-4 MIN: £1 MAX: £2,000 PERIOD: 19th-20th century GENERAL: Antique jewellery.

TEIGNMOUTH (0626)

Charterhouse Antiques, 1b Northumberland Place TEL: 54592 home PARKING: Easy OPEN: Tues, Wed, Fri, Sat 11-1, 2.30-4.30 MIN: £5 MAX: £500 PERIOD: 19th century SPECIALIST: Royal & political commemoratives GENERAL: General an-

tiques OTHER INFO: Sometimes 18th & 20th century. Handy for Dartmoor and coast.

Timepiece Antiques, 125 Ritton Park Road, TQ14 9BZ TEL: 770275 PARKING: Medium OPEN: Mon-Sat 10-5.30 MIN: £1 MAX: £2,000 PERIOD: 18th-20th century SPECIALIST: Pine and clocks GENERAL: Kitchenalia, brass, copper, brown furniture OTHER INFO: Beautiful coastline & estuary with easy access to Dartmoor, Torquay & Exeter.

TORQUAY (0803)

Perchance Ltd. 21 Walnut Road TEL: 528506 PARKING: Easy OPEN: Mon, Tues, Thurs & Fri AM MIN: £3 MAX: £300 PERIOD: 19th-20th century SPECIALIST: Ceramics GENERAL: Other small items OTHER INFO: Close to Conference Centre and Torre Abbey.

Spencers Antiques, 187 Higher Union Street, Torre, TQ1 4BY TEL: 296598 PARKING: Easy OPEN: Mon-Sat 10-4 MIN: c £10 MAX: £3,000 PERIOD: 18th but usually 19th-20th century OTHER INFO: Central for English Riviera, Dartmoor, the beautiful South Harns & historic Totnes.

Torre Antique Traders, 264-266 Union Street, Torre, TQ2 5QU TEL: 292184 PARKING: Easy OPEN: Mon-Sat 10-5 MIN: £2 MAX: £1,000 approx. PERIOD: 18th-20th century GENERAL: General antiques.

G A Whiteway, Sunsea, Teignmouth Road, Maidencombe, TQ1 4TD TEL: 329692 PARKING: Own carpark OPEN: By appt PERIOD: 18th-20th century GENERAL: Most fields except silver OTHER INFO: Lovely gardens, coastal area of great beauty.

BRIXHAM (0803)

John Prestige Antiques, 1-2 Greenswood Court, TQ5 9BH TEL: 856141, 853739 (home) FAX: 851649 PARKING: Own carpark OPEN: (appt advisable) Mon-Fri 8.45-6 or by appt MIN: £100 MAX: £10,000 PERIOD: 17th-19th century GENERAL: Large stock of period Victorian & Edwardian furniture & some interesting smaller items OTHER INFO: Most markets suited including better shipping furniture. One of the most beautiful fishing villages where Henry Lyte wrote *Abide with Me*.

TOTNES (0803)

Collards Bookshop, 4 Castle Street, TEL:

Home 0548-550246 OPEN: Mon-Sat 10-5 but restricted Nov-March MAX: £200 PERIOD: 18th-20th century GENERAL: Antiquarian & out-of-print books OTHER INFO: Nestling under historic Totnes Castle. 3 other bookshops in this Elizabethan town. Keith Floyd's restaurant a few miles.

James Sturges Antiques, Past & Present, 94 High Street, TQ9 5SN TEL: 866086 PARKING: Medium OPEN: Normal MIN: £5 MAX: £5,000 PERIOD: 18th-20th century GENERAL: Georgian, Victorian & Edwardian collectables etc OTHER INFO: Charming Elizabethan town & second oldest borough in England.

HARBERTONFORD (0803)
Fine Pine, Woodland Road, TQ9 7SX TEL: 732465 PARKING: Own carpark OPEN: Mon-Sat 9.30-5, Sun 11-4 MIN: £5 MAX: £1,500 PERIOD: 18th-19th century SPECIALIST: Antique pine & country pine GENERAL: Furniture OTHER INFO: Crowdy Watermill in village, Good local hotel & B&B at Church House Inn (childrens room).

DARTMOUTH (0803)
Chantry Bookshop & Gallery, 11 Higher Street, TQ6 9RB TEL: 832796, 834208 PARKING: Medium OPEN: Mon-Sat 10.30-5 PERIOD: 17th-20th century GENERAL: Books, watercolours, sea charts, maps, town plans, prints.

KINGSBRIDGE (0548)
Avon House Antiques, 13 Church Street, TQ7 1BT TEL: 853718 PARKING: Medium OPEN: Mon-Sat 10-5 MIN: £5 MAX: £3,000 PERIOD: 19th-20th century GENERAL: General antiques.

Quay Antiques, The Promenade, TQ7 1JG TEL: 856567 PARKING: carpark opposite OPEN: Summer Mon-Sat 10-5 MIN: £1 MAX: £3,000 PERIOD: 19th-20th century GENERAL: General antiques.

MODBURY (0548)
Country Cottage Antiques, The Old Chapel, Church Street, PL21 0QR TEL: 831079 FAX: 831081 PARKING: Medium OPEN: Mon-Sat 9-6 MIN: £30 MAX: £3,500 PERIOD: 19th-20th century SPECIALIST: Country furniture OTHER INFO: Quaint traditional small Devon town, quality shops. Beaches nearby.

Fourteen A, 14a Broad Street, PL21 0PU TEL: 830732 PARKING: Easy OPEN: Mon-Sat 10-5 MIN: £1 MAX: £300 PERIOD: 19th-20th century SPECIALIST: Antique lace & linen GENERAL: General antiques OTHER INFO: Total of 8 antique shops & 1 s/h shop here. Good B&B (£14) at Little Orchard Farm.

Welsh Dresser, 64 Brownston Street TEL: 842589 PARKING: Easy OPEN: Mon, Tues, Thurs-Sat 10-5 MIN: £50 MAX: £5,000 PERIOD: 17th-19th century SPECIALIST: Oak & country furniture GENERAL: Decorative china, pictures & prints.

Wild Goose Antiques, 34 Church Street, PL21 0PD TEL: 830715, 830238 PARKING: Easy OPEN: Tues-Sat 9.30-5 or by appt MIN: £5 MAX: £5,000 PERIOD: 18th-early 20th century GENERAL: Furniture, paintings, silver.

Ye Little Shoppe Antiques & Restoration, 1a Broad Street, PL21 0PS TEL: 830732 PARKING: Easy OPEN: Mon-Sat 10-5 PERIOD: 19th-20th century SPECIALIST: Woodworking tools, bookbinding implements, writing boxes, trinkets and workboxes. Oil lamps. GENERAL: Occasionally small furniture, copper, brassware etc Treen.

SOUTH BRENT (0364)
Philip Andrade, White Oxen Manor, near Rattery, TQ10 9JX TEL: 72454 FAX: 73061 ASSNS: BADA, LAPADA PARKING: Own carpark OPEN: Mon-Sat 9-5.30, Sat pm by appt MIN: £50 MAX: £10,000 SPECIALIST: English 18th-early 19th century furniture GENERAL: General stock 17th-19th century OTHER INFO: Inside Dartmoor National Park

YEALMPTON (0752)
Colin Rhodes Antiques, 15 Fore Street TEL: 862232, 881170 ASSNS: LAPADA PARKING: Own carpark OPEN: Tues, Thurs, Sat 10-5, Fri 2-5 MIN: £40 MAX: £5,000 PERIOD: 17th-early 19th century GENERAL: Furniture & paintings, silver, pottery + small interesting items OTHER INFO: Only 15 mins from Plymouth on Kingsbridge Road.

PLYMPTON (0752)
Alan Jones Antiques, Applethorn Slade Farm, Sparkwell PL7 5AS TEL: 338188 PARKING: Own carpark OPEN: By appt MIN: £5 MAX: £2,000 PERIOD: 17th-19th century SPECIALIST: Nautical, scientific, clocks GENERAL:

Collectors, decorative. OTHER INFO: Close to eastern Plymouth.

PLYMOUTH (0752)

Annterior Antiques, 22 Molesworth Road, Millbridge, PL1 5LZ TEL: 558277 FAX: 558277 PARKING: Easy OPEN: Mon-Sat 9.30-5.30 MIN: £1 MAX: £3,000 PERIOD: 18th-20th century SPECIALIST: Antiques stripped pine GENERAL: Mahogany, rosewood, jewel & writing boxes, mirrors, decorative accessories OTHER INFO: Full range of designer fabrics, wallpapers & interesting things for home. Plymouth has wonderful waterfront, the Barbican, NT properties and Dartmoor on its doorstep

Barbican Antiques Centre, 82-84 Vauxhall Street, PL4 0EX TEL: 255752 PARKING: Own carpark OPEN: Seven days 9.30-5 MIN: £1 MAX: £500 SPECIALIST: Silver & jewellery GENERAL: Porcelain, glass, furniture, coins, pictures OTHER INFO: Quayside position in historic old surroundings, close to steps where *The Mayflower* with the Founding Fathers set sail for America in 1620

Upstairs Downstairs, 30 Camden Street, Greenbank TEL: 261015 PARKING: Medium OPEN: Mon-Sat 10-5 MIN: £2 PERIOD: 19th-20th century SPECIALIST: Period costume - Victorian to 1950's GENERAL: China, furniture, jewellery, lace, linen OTHER INFO: We are old fashioned curio shop hidden away in back street of Old Plymouth, phone for directions.

TAVISTOCK (0822)

King Street Curios, 5 King Street, PL19 0DS TEL: 615193 PARKING: Easy OPEN: Mon-Sat 9-5 MIN: £1 MAX: £300 PERIOD: 19th-20th century SPECIALIST: Postcards & cigarette cards.

Pendar Antiques, 8 Drake Road, PL19 0AX TEL: 617641, 612207 PARKING: Medium OPEN: Mon-Sat 9-5 MIN: £1 MAX: £1,500 PERIOD: 18-20th century SPECIALIST: Furniture GENERAL: Some china, granite troughs, bric-a-brac, mostly Victorian, Edwardian, 1920's furniture OTHER INFO: Buctor Guest House excellent B&B (£12+). Very good breakfast (I cook it).

HATHERLEIGH (0837)

Hatherleigh Antiques, 15 Bridge Street, EX20 3HY TEL: 810159 ASSNS: BADA PARKING: Easy OPEN: Mon, Tues, Thurs-Sat 9-5 MIN: £300+ MAX: £30,000+ PERIOD: 17th century SPECIALIST: Furniture & works of art.

MERTON (0805)

Barometer World, Quicksilver Barn, EX20 3DS ASSNS: BAFRA, UKIC listed TEL: 3443 FAX: 3344 PARKING: Own carpark OPEN: Mon-Sat 8-5 MIN: £50 MAX: £3,000 PERIOD: 19th-20th century SPECIALIST: (recognised worldwide) Antique barometers & restoration GENERAL: Barometers OTHER INFO: Between Great Torrington and Okehampton on A386

BIDEFORD (0237)

J. Collins & Son, (est 1953), The Studio, 43 High Street, EX39 2AN TEL: 473103 FAX: 475658 ASSNS: LAPADA PARKING: Easy OPEN: Mon-Sat 9.30-5 MIN: £30 MAX: £20,000 SPECIALIST: Georgian to Regency furniture. 19th century oil paintings and watercolours OTHER INFO: Burton Art Gallery. 3 hotels, all very good.

Red House Antiques, 25-26 Bridgeland Street, EX39 2PZ TEL: 470686 PARKING: Medium OPEN: Tues, Thurs-Sat 10-4 or by appt MIN: £5 MAX: £2,000 PERIOD: 19th-20th century SPECIALIST: Furniture & decorative items from the Arts & Crafts period GENERAL: Victorian, Edwardian furniture & smalls.

Scudders Emporium, Bridge Street, EX39 2BU TEL: 479567, 451665 PARKING: Easy OPEN: Mon-Sat 9.30-5.30, (Suns admission 50p 10.30-4.30) MIN: £1 MAX: £1,500 PERIOD: 19th century SPECIALIST: Collectables & architectural GENERAL: 6,000 sq ft of browsers & dealers delights in antique, restored and revival furniture OTHER INFO: High turnover allows us to cover all periods. Shop runs as 'organised chaos' on 3 floors including "hi & lo" callers, a children friendly shop to be enjoyed. Loads of stuffed animals & museum items.

BARNSTAPLE (0271)

Nostalgia, 48b Bear Street, EX32 9AJ TEL: 327783 shop, 73751 home PARKING: Easy OPEN: Mon, Tues, Thurs-Sat 10-4 MIN: £5 MAX: £500 PERIOD: 19th-20th century SPECIALIST: Commemoratives, local pottery, period clothes GENERAL: Linen, lace & fabrics, furniture, china & glass OTHER INFO: Barnstaple is the regional centre for North Devon and Exmoor.

SOUTH MOLTON (0769)

The Furniture Market, 14a Barnstaple Street TEL: 573401 PARKING: Easy OPEN: Mon-Sat 10-5, Wed closed pm MIN: £5 MAX: £10,000 PERIOD: 17th-20th century SPECIALIST: Pine, oak & mahogany furniture GENERAL: Antiques OTHER INFO: 2,000 sq ft of large varied stock. Trade very welcome. Good restaurants.

Memory Lane Antiques, 100 East Street, EX36 3DF TEL: 574288 PARKING: Easy OPEN: Mon-Sat 9.30-5.30. Suns by appt MIN: £1 MAX: £3,000 PERIOD: 18th-19th century SPECIALIST: Large stock of general antiques (4 rooms) OTHER INFO: Heart of Exmoor, many good B&B's, hotels. Corndolly teashop well known.

South Molton Antiques, 103 East Street, EX36 3DF TEL: 573478 PARKING: Easy OPEN: Mon-Sat 9-5 MIN: £20 MAX: £3,000 PERIOD: 18th-20th century SPECIALIST: Victorian & Edwardian furniture GENERAL: Furniture, trade & shipping goods.

J.R. Tredant, 50-50a South Street TEL: 573006 PARKING: Medium OPEN: Mon, Tues, Thurs-Sat 10-4 MIN: £1 MAX: £3,000 PERIOD: 18th-20th century GENERAL: Smalls & furniture.

BRAUNTON (0271)

Eileen Cooper Antiques, Challoners Road, EX33 2ES TEL: 813320, 816005 PARKING: Easy OPEN: Usually Tues, Thurs, Sat 10-30-1, 2-4.30, sometimes other days MIN: £1 MAX: £1,000 PERIOD: 18th-20th century SPECIALIST: Fine linen & textiles, North Devon pottery GENERAL: General antiques OTHER INFO: This old established shop is a 1920's timberclad cottage. Beside Shell gas station on main road to Victorian Ilfracombe. Next to popular Agricultural Inn.

Timothy Coward Fine Silver, Marisco, Saunton, EX33 1LG TEL: 890466 PARKING: Own carpark OPEN: By appt MIN: £30 MAX: £5,000 PERIOD: 17th-20th century SPECIALIST: Silver. OTHER INFO: Saunton Sands Hotel 200 yds.

ILFRACOMBE (0271)

Relics, 113 High Street TEL: 865486 PARKING: Easy OPEN: Mon-Sat 9.30-5.30 MIN: £1 MAX: £500 PERIOD: 19th-20th century SPECIALIST: Pine furniture GENERAL: Small collectables, cigarette cards, china, jewellery, bottles, paperback books (20p+) OTHER INFO: Good walking area, edge of Exmoor. Old relics bought & sold but not 'her indoors' we've heard that one before!

LYNTON (0598)

Vendy Antiques. 29a Lee Road, EX35 6BS TEL: 53327 PARKING: Easy OPEN: Mon-Sat 10-5 MIN: £1 MAX: £4,000 PERIOD: 17th-20th century GENERAL: Widest range of antiques of all descriptions.

TIMBERSCOMBE (0643)

Zwan Antiques, TA24 7TG TEL: 841608 PARKING: Easy OPEN: Tues, Thurs, Sun 2-5 or by appt MIN: £1 MAX: £5,000 PERIOD: 18th-20th century SPECIALIST: Sporting pictures and jewellery GENERAL: All sorts of small items OTHER INFO: 5 miles inland from Minehead. Wonderful Exmoor views, Close to Snowdrop Valley, 15th century church, super B&B's within sight.

DULVERTON (0398)

Acorn Antiques, 39 High Street, TA22 9DW TEL: 23286 PARKING: Medium OPEN: Mon-Sat 9.30-5.30 MIN: £10 MAX: £5,000 PERIOD: 17th-19th century SPECIALIST: 18th & 19th century decorative antiques OTHER INFO: Information centre, country sports, good hotels, restaurants, pubs.

Faded Elegance, 39 High Street, TA22 9DW TEL: 23286 PARKING: Medium OPEN: Mon-Sat 9.30-5.30 MIN: £15 MAX: £5,000 PERIOD: 17th-19th century SPECIALIST: Textiles, decorative antiques OTHER INFO: Right in centre of Exmoor National Park.

TIVERTON (0884)

Bygone Days Antiques, 40 Gold Street, EX16 6PY TEL: 252832 PARKING: Easy OPEN: Mon-Wed, Fri, Sat 10-5 MIN: £250 MAX: £3,500 PERIOD: 18th-19th century GENERAL: Furniture, longcase clocks, soft furnishings OTHER INFO: Castle Museum Knighthayes (NT House), restaurants, tearooms, B&B's etc

Cornwall

Bodmin Moor. By courtesy of Cornwall Tourist Board

Cornwall is a land of legend and magic. Stories of King Arthur and his knights abound, as do others dealing with giants and piskies. There are grimmer tales that tell of smugglers and wreckers, who lured ships on to rocks to steal their cargo. This is also the land where tin brought prosperity from earliest times until it became uneconomic in the 19th century. Now tourism sustains the Cornish economy. With its mild climate, picturesque villages and dramatic scenery it has much to offer the visitor.

Our first stop is on the coast in Looe. This comprises of two small towns, East and West Looe standing either side of the Looe River and joined by a bridge. Both are small fishing towns and holiday resorts.

Taking the B3369 we arrive in Lostwithiel, situated on the River Fowey, once a centre of the tin trade and capital of Cornwall. It has a number of features of note including a medieval bridge, the 14th century Duchy House and various Georgian buildings. The 12th to 13th century Restormel Castle lies about a mile north of the town.

St. Austell, next on the tour, has now swapped tin-mining for china clay both of which have turned this once small village into a thriving market town. Its past can be seen in the narrow streets and stone-built cottages. We move on via the villages of Grampound and Tregony to Portscatho, a picturesque village popular

Cornwall

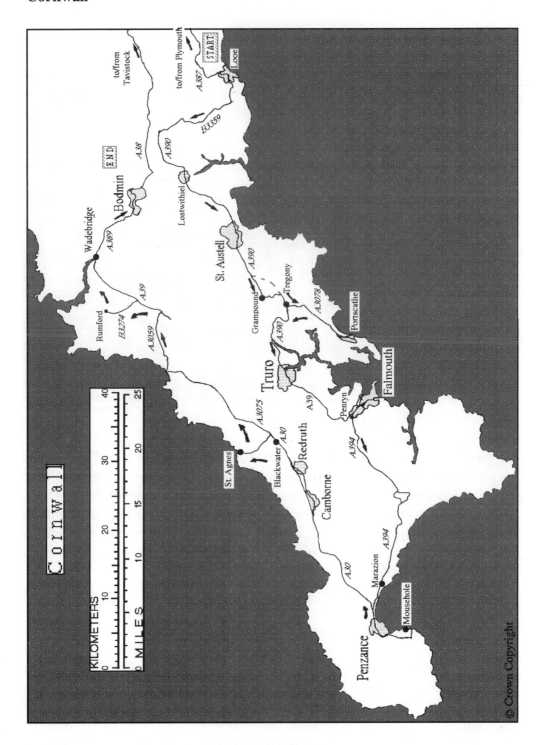

START

to/from Plymouth

Looe

to/from
Tavistock

A.387

B3359

A.390

A38

END

Bodmin

Wadebridge

A.389

A.39

Lostwithiel

St. Austell

A.390

Grampound

Tregony

A3078

Portscatho

Rumford

B3274

A3059

A.390

Truro

Falmouth

A39

Penryn

A3075

A30

Redruth

St. Agnes

Blackwater

Camborne

A394

Penzance

Marazion

A30

A394

Mousehole

Cornwall

KILOMETERS

40 30 20 10 0

25 20 15 10 0

MILES

© Crown Copyright

Falmouth. By courtesy of Cornwall Tourist Board

with artists. Situated on Gerrans Bay and with good sandy beaches, there are late Georgian houses on the promenade.

Now turning inland again we arrive in Truro standing on the convergence of the Rivers Allen and Kenwyn to form the River Truro. A town made prosperous by tin, the streets are lined with Georgian and Regency houses. However the town is dominated by the cathedral, the only one in Cornwall and the first Anglican cathedral built since St. Paul's. It was started in 1879 after the diocese of Devon and Cornwall was split in two. At the time building a cathedral in Cornwall was not an easy business. The local economy was in decline with the tin mines closing. Also Anglicanism had lost ground in the county to non-conformist faiths. In spite of this the cathedral was built in just thirty years, probably due to the determination of the Bishop, E.W. Benson, who wanted a centre for the revival of the Anglican Catholic tradition of worship in Cornwall.

The tour continues to Penryn which stands in a sheltered position thereby giving it a milder climate than the surrounding area and so this Georgian town has many sub-tropical plants. Falmouth, the next town, combines the roles of port, marina and holiday resort. Its harbour is the largest in Cornwall and receives shipping from all over the world. Overlooking the harbour, Pendennis Castle was built by Henry VIII in 1545 to guard against a French invasion. Its finest hour was probably in 1646 when it resisted a six month siege during the Civil War. Commanded at that time by the 70 year old Colonel Arundell, it was cut off by Parliamentary troops on the landward side and by a blockade on the seaward

St Michael's Mount.
By courtesy of Cornwall Tourist Board

side. The siege started in March and by July things were getting so desperate that troops in the castle unsuccessfully attempted to break out to get supplies. By 17th August Colonel Arundell realised that he could hold out no longer and so surrendered. He was honoured for his bravery by being allowed to march out of the castle with the full honours of war.

Following the A394 we come to Marazion, a nice holiday resort with sandy beaches and an ideal spot for a sight of St. Michael's Mount. The town is connected to the Mount by a half mile long causeway. St Michael's Mount was originally built as a priory for Benedictine monks by Edward the Confessor. However, it has had a troubled history over the centuries and has been seized a number of times during rebellions and the Civil War.

Penzance, situated at the head of Mount's Bay, is a holiday resort and port. There are Georgian and Regency buildings in Church Street, the oldest street in Penzance, and sub-tropical plants in Morrab Gardens. Chysauster Ancient Village stands about 3 miles north of Penzance. This village was already in existence two centuries before the Romans arrived in Britain.

Moving onwards to the most south-westerly point of this tour, we arrive in Mousehole, a very pretty village and once a busy fishing port with over a 1000 boats using it. Now, however, that has changed and only a few trawlers are left. The nearby village of Paul has two Celtic crosses that are believed to be more than 1000 years old. Mousehole is only about five miles from Land's End, the most south westerley point in England.

Turning north east, Camborne was important as a centre of tin-mining and the Camborne School of Mines Geological Museum and Art Gallery displays a collection of minerals and ores. At Pool, about two miles east of the town on the A3047, there is the National Trust property of Cornish Engines. The largest of the great beam engines used in tin mining still left in Cornwall stands at the East

Pool and Agar Mine. This engine weighs about 52 tons and could lift 450 gallons of water a minute from a depth of 1700 feet. There are other impressive engines in the area, some used for removing water from the mines and others for men and materials.

Continuing onwards the route comes to Redruth, once an important mining town. This was the home of William Murdock, an inventor, who had the first gas-lit house in Britain. About two miles south west of the town lie the remains of prehistoric Carn Brea Castle. Next we visit the village of Blackwater then St. Agnes, on the coast and another former centre of Cornish tin-mining. Now it is a good holiday resort with attractive sandy bathing beaches.

After stopping in Rumford and Wadebridge the tour ends in Bodmin, the county town of Cornwall. Standing on the edge of the beautiful Bodmin Moor, it is the only Cornish town to be recorded in the Domesday Book. The National Trust house, Lanhydrock, can be found about $2^1/_2$ miles away on the B3268. Originally built between 1630 and 1642, now most of the house is a reflection of the High Victorian style because a disastrous fire in 1881 destroyed all but the North Wing. Four miles to the north west of Bodmin, on the A389, stands another fine property, Pencarrow House and Garden. Set in listed gardens, this superb Georgian house contains a wonderful collection of 18th century furniture, pictures and china.

We now take the A30 to Exeter and then the M5 motorway for the journey home.

Cornwall

ANTIQUE DEALERS

LOOE (0503)

West Quay Curios, 6 The Quay, West Looe, PL13 2BX TEL: 264411 PARKING: Easy OPEN: Mon-Sat 10-7 (Summer), 10-5 (Winter) MIN: £1 MAX: £500 PERIOD: Mostly 19th-20th century but occasionally earlier SPECIALIST: Postcards, cigarette cards, china GENERAL: Wide range general antiques & collectors items. Virtually anything e.g. furniture, china, books, jewellery etc OTHER INFO: Idyllic setting right by the river and sea in beautiful Cornish fishing village. Several other antiques and collectors shops in area. Wonderful range of hotels etc. Most of the pubs and restaurants are well known to me and come personally recommended.

LOSTWITHIEL (0208)

John Bragg, 35 Fore Street, PL22 0RA TEL: 872827 PARKING: Easy OPEN: Mon-Sat 10-1, 2-5 or by appt MIN: £50 MAX: £11,000 PERIOD: 17th-19th century SPECIALIST: Furniture OTHER INFO: Smallest & oldest capital town of Cornwall, fine selection of restaurants including Trewithan.

Old Palace Antiques, The Old Palace, Quay Street, PL22 0BS TEL: 872909 PARKING: Easy OPEN: Mon, Tues, Thurs-Sat 10-1, 2-5, Wed 10-1 MIN: £1 MAX: £600 PERIOD: 19th-20th century SPECIALIST: Mostly pine furniture GENERAL: China, brass, cast iron, jewellry, postcards, collectors items OTHER INFO: Many specialist shops. Four antique shops & several good pubs.

ST AUSTELL (0726)

Margaret Chesterton Antiques, 33 Pentewan Road, PL25 5BU TEL: 72926 PARKING: Own carpark OPEN: Mon-Sat 9.30-5.30 or by appt MIN: £1 MAX: £750 PERIOD: 19th-20th century SPECIALIST: Porcelain, pottery, Victoriana GENERAL: 19th century watercolours, small furniture OTHER INFO: Cliff Head Hotel (Carlyon Bay) - ° price lunches for 2, Mon-Fri.

St Austell Antiques Centre & Radnor House Antiques, 37-39 Truro Road, PL25 5JE TEL: 63178 PARKING: Easy OPEN: Mon-Sat 10-5 MIN: £1 MAX: £5,000 PERIOD: 18th-20th century GENERAL: General antiques.

GRAMPOUND (0726)

Radnor House Antiques, Radnor House, TR2 4PT TEL: 882921 PARKING: Medium OPEN: Mon-Sat 10-6 MIN: £20 MAX: £2,000 PERIOD: 18th-19th century GENERAL: Furniture.

TREGONY (0872)

Clock Tower Antiques, TEL: 53225 PARKING: Easy OPEN: Mon-Sat 10-6 or by appt MIN: £15 MAX: £2,500 PERIOD: Early 19th-early 20th century SPECIALIST: Watercolours, Doulton stoneware GENERAL: General antiques OTHER INFO: In centre of historic medieval village with wide main street. Next to the picturesque Roseland peninsular where pretty coves, safe bathing beaches, country inns, restaurants and hotels abound.

PORTSCATHO (0872)

Curiosity Antiques, The Square TEL: 580411 PARKING: Easy OPEN: Mon-Sat 10.30-12.30, 2.30-5.30 - but not necessarily MIN: £1 MAX: £1,000+ PERIOD: 18th-20th century SPECIALIST: Small collectables & general antiques OTHER INFO: Odd & flexible hours so please phone first if making special journey.

Turnpike Cottage Antiques & Tearooms, The Square, St Gerrans, TR2 5EB TEL:580853 PARKING: Easy OPEN: Tues-Sat 11-1, 3-6 but winter afternoons only MIN: £2 MAX: £1,000 PERIOD: 18th-20th century GENERAL: General antiques OTHER INFO: We are a small tearoom amidst the antiques and we open for bookings as a licensed Cornish restaurant.

TRURO (0872)

Alan Bennett, New Bridge House, New Bridge Street, TR1 2AA TEL: 73296 PARKING: Easy OPEN: Mon-Sat 9-5.30 MIN: £20 MAX: £20.000 PERIOD: 18th-19th century SPECIALIST: Good furniture GENERAL: General antiques.

Pydar Antiques, Peoples Palace off Pydar Street, TR1 2AZ TEL: 510485 PARKING: Medium OPEN: Mon-Sat 10.30-5 MIN: £5 MAX: £2,500 PERIOD: 19th century SPECIALIST: Decorative soft furnishing GENERAL: Furniture OTHER INFO: Pine furniture made from reclaimed wood.

Richard Winkworth Antiques, Calenick Street TEL: 40901 PARKING: Easy OPEN: Mon-Sat 10-5 MIN: £2 MAX: £5,000 PERIOD: 18th-20th century (occasionally 17th) SPECIALIST: Furniture & anthing unusual or interesting OTHER INFO: Vast quantities of stock. Trade very welcome. Containers & shipping arranged worldwide.

PENRYN (0326)

Duchy Antiques, 7 The Praze TEL: 372767 PARKING: Easy OPEN: Mon-Sat 10.30-5.30 MIN: £1

MAX: £6,000 PERIOD: 18th-20th century SPECIALIST: Furniture GENERAL: General antiques OTHER INFO: 20 other antique/junk shops.

FALMOUTH (0326)

John Maggs Antiquarian Prints & Maps, 54 Church Street TEL: 313153 FAX: 313153 PARKING: Easy OPEN: Mon-Sat 10-5 PERIOD: 17th-19th century SPECIALIST: Entirely antiquarian.

MARAZION (0736)

Antiques, The Shambles, Market Place, TR17 0AR TEL: 711381 PARKING: Easy OPEN: Mon-Sat 10-5.30 MIN: £1 MAX: £200 PERIOD: 19th-20th century GENERAL: General antiques & collectors items OTHER INFO: On main street of small old Cornish seaside town opposite St Michael's Mount.

PENZANCE (0736)

Ken Ashbrook Antiques, Redbrick Warehouse, Leskinnick Place TEL: 330914 PARKING: Difficult OPEN: Mon-Sat 10-1, 2.15-5 MIN: £5 MAX: £5,000 PERIOD: 19th-20th century SPECIALIST: Furniture.

Catherine and Mary, 1-2 Old Brewery Yard, Bread Street, TR18 2SL TEL: 51053 PARKING: Easy OPEN: Mon-Sat 10-5 MIN: £1 MAX: £500 PERIOD: 19th-20th century SPECIALIST: Textiles & lace GENERAL: General antiques.

Kitts Corner Antiques, 51 Chapel Street TEL: 64507 (shop hours) PARKING: Easy OPEN: Mon, Tues, Thurs-Sat 10-1, 2-4.30 MIN: £1 MAX: £200 PERIOD: 19th-20th century GENERAL: General antiques OTHER INFO: Chapel Street is the oldest street in Penzance. Full of antique shops, restaurants, best pubs. Interesting buildings.

Penzance Gallery and Antiques, 14 Chapel Street, TR19 4AW TEL: 66620, after hours 68461 PARKING: Easy OPEN: Mon-Sat 9-5.30 MIN: £10 MAX: £4,000 PERIOD: 19th-20th century SPECIALIST: Newlyn copper, cranberry glass GENERAL: Newlyn & St Ives schools paintings, contemporary sculpture & paintings, small furniture.

MOUSEHOLE (0736)

Vanity Fayre, Commercial Road, TR19 6QG (est 1963) No phone PARKING: OPEN: Mon-Sat 10-1, 2-5 (outside season restricted) MIN: £1 MAX: £500 PERIOD: 18th-20th century GENERAL: Quality to bric-a-brac always changing OTHER INFO: Charming unspoilt Cornish coast village.

CAMBORNE (0209)

Victoria Gallery, 28 Cross St TEL: 719268 PARKING: Easy OPEN: Mon-Wed, Fri 10-5.15, Sat 10-1 MIN: £8 MAX: £2,000 PERIOD: 19th-20th century GENERAL: General antiques & books OTHER INFO: 10 minutes drive from beautiful unspoilt North Coast.

REDRUTH (0209)

Richard Winkworth Antiques, Station Approach TEL: 216631 PARKING: Easy OPEN: Mon-Sat 10-5 MIN: £2 MAX: £5,000 PERIOD: 18-20th (occasionally 17th) century SPECIALIST: Furniture OTHER INFO: Vast quantities and variety of stock. Trade welcome. Containers & shipping arranged worldwide.

BLACKWATER (0872)

Blackwater Pine Antiques, TR4 8ET TEL: 560919 FAX: 560919 ASSNS: GMC PARKING: Easy OPEN: Mon-Sat 9-6, usually Sun 2-6 PERIOD: 19th century SPECIALIST: Furniture made to order GENERAL: Original stripped pine furniture, etc OTHER INFO: Pennypots Restaurant one of best in Cornwall, several farm B&B's

ST AGNES (0872)

Ages Ago Antiques, 1b Churchtown TEL: 553820 PARKING: Easy OPEN: Mon-Sat 10-1 MIN: £1 MAX: £560 GENERAL: 19th-early 20th century furniture, late 18th-19th century ceramics.

RUMFORD VILLAGE (0841)

Henley House Antiques, Rumford, PL27 7SS TEL: 540322 PARKING: no restrictions OPEN: Thurs-Sat or anytime (resident) PERIOD: Mostly 19th century GENERAL: General antiques OTHER INFO: Small pretty village easily reached via St Merryn. This is a small shop but well & very interestingly stocked.

WADEBRIDGE (0208)

St Breock Gallery, TEL: 812543 FAX: (071) 243 8300 PARKING: Easy OPEN: Mon-Sat 10-5 MIN: £50 MAX: £2,500 PERIOD: 19th-20th century SPECIALIST: Watercolours.

BODMIN (0208)

Clocks, Art & Antiques, 9 St Nicholas Street, PL31 1AA TEL: 74408 FAX: 74408 PARKING: Easy OPEN: Tues, Thurs, Fri 12-5 or anytime by appt MIN: £5 MAX: £3,000 PERIOD: 17th-20th century SPECIALIST: Clocks & good English furniture OTHER INFO: We have an idyllic cottage where customers may stay during their visit, with salmon & trout fishing.

Avon and North Wiltshire

Castle Combe

On this tour we visit some of the country's most historic towns as well as pass through beautiful countryside. The route takes in parts of the spectacular Mendip Hills and, in contrast, the gentler scenery of Avon and Wiltshire

Our first stop, Swindon, is closely associated with the railways. Although this town is growing rapidly it still has some interesting features to offer the visitor. Because the railways have been so important to the town, the Great Western Railway Museum in Faringdon Road is fascinating with exhibits ranging from locomotives through to posters and tickets. Also in Faringdon Road is the Railway Village Museum which is an original Great Western Railway Company village restored to its turn of the century appearance. The Museum and Art Gallery in Bath Road displays items of local historical and archeological interest.

Next, Wootton Basset lies beside the M4 motorway. It contains some fine Georgian buildings and a half timbered town hall built on stone pillars in 1700 by the Earl of Rochester. Stocks, a ducking stool and a small wooden fire-engine may be seen inside.

The tour turns north via the villages of Upper Minety and Hankerton to visit Malmesbury, standing between two branches of the River Avon. It has a long history with the present town built on the site of a fortified Saxon town and granted its charter by Alfred the Great in AD880.

The Market Cross, standing in the centre of the town, is actually a building with a fine vaulted roof and was designed to shelter people from the rain. The older buildings are built of local stone, including the 17th century St John's Almhouse. Another notable feature is Tolsey Gate which has two cells on either side and served as the local prison during the 18th and 19th centuries.

There is a story that an 11th century monk at Malmesbury Abbey, called Elmer, tried to fly. He made wings and fitted them to his hands and feet and then leapt off the abbey tower, thrashing wildly. He is said to have flown some 200 yards before crashing, breaking both legs and crippling himself for life. Brother Elmer's flight is commemorated in the abbey by a modern stained-glass window.

The abbey was probably founded in the 7th century by St Aldhelm who was its first abbot. It was rebuilt in the 13th century and largely escaped destruction at the Dissolution of the Monasteries by being sold to a local wool merchant who used the buildings for weaving. Two years after he bought it, he presented the town with the abbey's nave for use as the parish church. Much of what remains is impressive. There is a fine, highly decorated, Norman porch and a 15th century monument to the Saxon King Athelstan, the first to rule all of England and who, it is said, was interred here.

Across the motorway stands Castle Combe, described as the prettiest village in England. It is certainly picturesque with its stone-built cottages, church and covered market set against a background of trees.

The tour now passes through the small villages of North Wraxall, West Yatton, Kington St Michael, Christian Malford and Langley Burrell before coming to Corsham, on the southern most edge of the Cotswolds. Evidence indicates there was a settlement here in pre-Roman times and it grew through the centuries to be a thriving market town and also part of the medieval Cotswold weaving industry; weavers' cottages may be seen in the High Street. Another building of interest is the 17th century almshouses. The Elizabethan Corsham Court, built on the site of a Saxon royal manor, contains a wonderful collection of paintings and furniture and is set in a park designed by Capability Brown.

Another manor house stands between Chippenham and Corsham: Sheldon Manor. Parts of the building date from as early as 1282 with the main part rebuilt in the 17th century. Unfortunately, this house has known many different owners who allowed the house to deteriorate. Its fortunes have changed and today it contains collections of oak furniture, porcelain, paintings and Nailsea glass.

Onwards, via Atworth, to Melksham on the River Avon, a town whose history goes back to before the Norman Conquest. This town also contains some fine old coaching inns from the days it was on the main coach road between London and Bath. Some of the town's oldest houses, from the 16th to 18th centuries, stand in

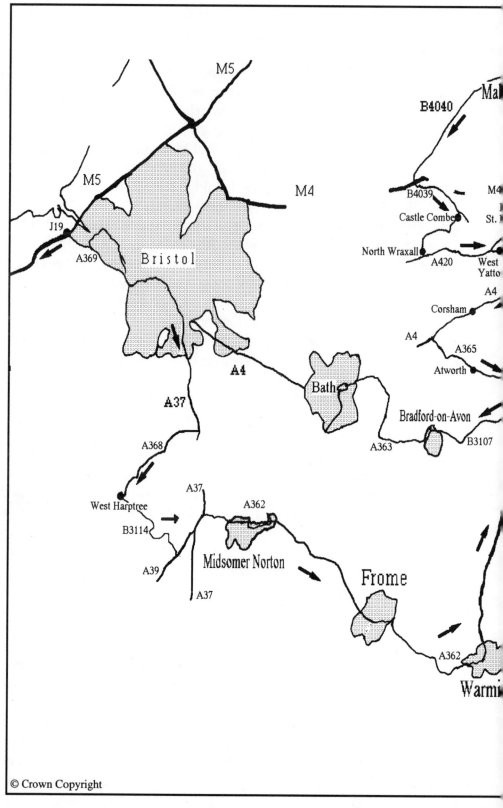

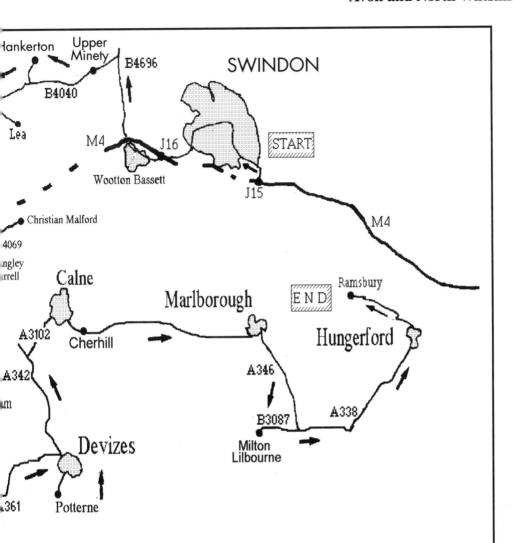

AVON & NORTH WILTSHIRE

Canon Square and adjoining Church Walk.

Bradford-on-Avon, the next stop, is mentioned in the Domesday Book and also has a history that goes back beyond the Norman Conquest. The town is built on a steep slope of the Avon valley and its streets rise in terraces on the hillside. Built of local limestone, they give the feeling of having grown in position over the centuries. The highest of the main terraces, Tory from the word Tor meaning high place, was originally 18th century weavers' cottages, many of which have been restored. Some of these cottages were first built with kitchens excavated from caves in the hillside. On a lower terrace, Middle Rank, there are late 17th century weavers' cottages, also mostly renovated. In Bradford's centre lies the medieval shopping area of The Shambles, a narrow lane joining Market Street and Silver Street.

A find of major historic interest was made in the town in the 1850s. The vicar of the parish, Canon William Jones, noticed the cruciform shape of some cottages under repair. The workmen uncovered two carved angels and this confirmed Canon Jones' suspicions that there was a forgotten Saxon church here. The chancel had been converted into a cottage and the nave into a school. Other buildings had been built against the church so that it was no longer recognisable. It was only in 1870 that these adjoining buildings were removed and the clear shape of the Saxon church, the most complete in the country, could be seen.

Nearby Bath was a famous spa even in Roman times, then called *Aquae Sulis* as the Romans built a temple here to Sulis (Sul was a Celtic goddess), and their own goddess, Minerva. It was in the 18th century that Bath became extremely fashionable and the town's distinctive Regency architecture dates from this time. Bath's greatest tourist attraction, of course, is the Pump Room. It is here that one can see the remains of the Roman baths, remarkably complete, and the Roman Temple Precinct. Another outstanding landmark is Bath Abbey. Started in 1499 on the site of a 7th century church, there is an unusual carving on the west front of angels ascending and descending a ladder from heaven.

There are numerous museums in the town; perhaps one of the most interesting to visitors is the Building of Bath Museum in The Paragon. This recounts the story of how the town grew from the 18th century onwards. On display are pattern books, tools and architectural fragments. Another fascinating museum, housed at Claverton Manor, just over three miles from the town, is the American Museum in Britain exhibiting American decorative arts from the late 17th to mid 19th centuries including furniture, paintings, glass, textiles, folk art and much more besides. In Julian Road there is quite an unusual museum: Mr Bowler's Business Bath Industrial Heritage Centre. It consists of the entire stock of a J.B. Bowler, a Victorian brass founder, engineer and mineral water manufacturer and is displayed in authentic settings with some working machinery.

The last two museums of especial note are No.1 Royal Crescent and Sally Lunn's

House. The first is a Georgian townhouse in Bath's most splendid terrace, redecorated and furnished in late 18th century style. Sally Lunn's House in North Parade Passage is the oldest house in Bath with a cellar museum showing the ancient kitchen and excavations of Roman, Saxon and medieval buildings on the same site. It was here that the famous Sally Lunn bun was created. There are many other museums in Bath and again the Tourist Information Centre is the place to find out more about them.

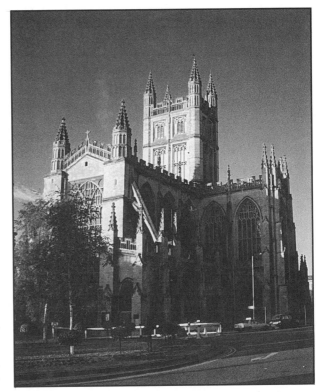

Bath Abbey

The tour now goes on to the city of Bristol, not only a busy commercial and industrial centre, but also rich in history. Bristol has been a port for over 800 years. First trading with Europe, it was the trade with the Americas for which Bristol is famous. Cabot Tower on Brandon Hill commemorates the expedition from Bristol to discover the mainland of America, led by John Cabot.

Another reminder of Bristol's seafaring past is found in the SS Great Britain built by Isambard Kingdom Brunel and the first iron, screwdriven steamship. Brunel's work can also be seen in part of Temple Meads railway station. He also designed the Clifton Suspension Bridge but this was only constructed after his death.

Unfortunately, much of the old centre of the city was destroyed by bombing in the Second World War but there are remnants left. The oldest working theatre in the country, the Theatre Royal dating from 1766, can be found in King Street. In the same street stands the 17th century Llandoger Trow, possibly used by pirates and the inn that is said to be the "Spyglass Inn" in Robert Louis Stevenson's novel *Treasure Island*.

The city has numerous other interesting and historic buildings. Perhaps one of the most important is the Cathedral, originally an abbey church dating from 1148. In the 16th century the nave was demolished to build a new one but they could not afford to proceed with the work. It was only in 1868 that construction started.

Fortunately, the architect, G.E. Street, designed the nave to harmonise with the 14th century east arm of the cathedral without falling into the trap of building a 19th century pastiche.

The route now reaches West Harptree with its Norman church, Jacobean Gournay Manor and the 17th century Tilly Manor. Now going south east we first come to Midsomer Norton and then the riverside market town of Frome, much of whose centre is a conservation area. In Cheap Street there is still a watercourse running down the centre of the street. This is another place affected by Judge Jeffreys who had twelve local men hanged. From Frome the route passes on to Warminster, a royal manor in the time of King Alfred. The town has many inns, survivors of the days when it was on a coach road. One of its most interesting building is probably the parish church, dating from the 14th century with a 15th century tower and some later 18th and 19th century work.

To the west of Warminster lies Longleat House with its famous safari park. The house was built in 1580 and is still owned by the same family, the Thynnes. The house and park have many attractions including Victorian kitchens, Lord Bath's Bygones, Dolls Houses, Butterfly Garden, etc.

The next stop is in the market town of Devizes, surrounded by rich farming country. The first fortifications here were pre-Norman earthworks although a castle was constructed in the reign of Henry I. During the Civil War it was besieged by Parliamentary troops and it eventually surrendered and was slighted. The present building was constructed in the 19th century. The Devizes Museum in Long Street has an important collection of local antiquities including finds from Wiltshire neolithic, bronze, and iron age sites. There are many good Georgian buildings and a 16th century timbered house can be seen in St John's Alley. The Kennet and Avon Canal, passing near the town, rises with the aid of 29 locks and connects London and Bristol. The town has a museum in Couch Lane devoted to telling the story of the canal.

On now to Calne, a town of great antiquity. Originally it prospered as a weaving centre but when this declined it turned to the curing of bacon with the Harris Bacon factory. This developed because droves of Irish pigs passed regularly on their way from Bristol to London. Unfortunately, this factory has now closed but is still commemorated by a bronze pig near the shopping mall. The town also has a fine coaching inn. The 18th century Bowood House and Gardens, again lands-caped by Capability Brown, stands near the town. The house has fine collections of silver, porcelain, paintings and Victoriana.

Cherhill, the next stop on the tour, has two nice stories attached to it. A white horse, dating from 1780, was cut into the hillside above the village by a Dr Alsop from Calne. The story goes that he stood more than a mile away from the site and shouted instructions through a megaphone to his workmen. The finished work can be seen for about 40 miles. The other story concerns a group of thieves, called the Cherhill Gang, who used to strip naked before attacking to make it harder to identify them.

The route proceeds on to the the ancient town of Marlborough with one of the widest High Streets in the country and many historic buildings ranging from Tudor to Victorian. In the grounds of the 19th century Marlborough College there was a prehistoric barrow on which the Normans built a castle, often used by the monarch when hunting in the nearby Savernake Forest. It was here that King John was

Thatching a typical Wiltshire stone cottage

married and Henry III summoned Parliament. Edward VI, son of Henry VIII and Jane Seymour, gave the castle to his mother's family and later the diarists, Samuel Pepys and John Evelyn, both stayed here. In the 18th century the castle was used as an inn on the coach road between London and Bath. Finally it became the centre of the public school, Marlborough College.

Next is Hungerford, built on the old Roman road to Bath. In the 18th and 19th centuries it was on the major coach road between London and Bath and so had many inns. Today one survives, The Bear, which was used by William of Orange and King James II in 1668 for holding a meeting to discuss the future of the monarchy.

Many of the buildings date from the 17th and 18th centuries and line the elegant High Street. It is also a centre for anglers because, apart from the Kennet and Avon Canal which cuts through the town, Hungerford also has the Rivers Kennet and Dunn, famous for their trout.

Three miles to the west of Hungerford stands the unspoilt Tudor manor, Littlecote House. It has a complete Cromwellian chapel, stark in its simplicity, and a collection of Cromwellian arms and armour from the local Parliamentary force. There is a Roman villa in the grounds where visitors can see the restored Orpheus Mosaic, said to be the largest coloured Roman mosaic in the country.

Continuing westward, we come to our last stop, Ramsbury, a small village on the River Kennet, contains some Jacobean and Georgian buildings and an early English church which displays some ancient sculptured stones.

ANTIQUE DEALERS
SWINDON (0793)
Allan Smith Antique Clocks, Amity Cottage, 162 Beechcroft Road, Upper Stratton, SN2 6QE TEL: 822977 PARKING: Own carpark OPEN: MIN: £995 MAX: £7,950 PERIOD: 17th-19th century SPECIALIST: Longcase clocks usually 30+ in stock GENERAL: Bracket, lantern, fusee dial, weight driven Vienna. Barometers OTHER INFO: 100 yards from Baker Arms pub.

Antiques & All Pine, 11 Newport Street TEL: 520259 PARKING: Easy OPEN: Mon,Tues, Thurs-Sat 10-5.30 MIN: £3 MAX: £1,000 PERIOD: 20th century SPECIALIST: Antique & reproduction pine country furniture GENERAL: General antiques & special size mattresses for old pine beds OTHER INFO: In Old Town with many restaurants & pubs.

Marlborough Bookshop & Sporting Gallery, Unit 22, Cheney Manor, SN2 2PJ TEL: 421458 FAX: 421640 PARKING: Own carpark OPEN: Mon-Fri 9-4.30 MIN: £10 MAX: £5,000

PERIOD: 19th-20th century SPECIALIST: We are country's biggest dealers in racing, hunting & other equestrian prints and watercolours.

WOOTTON BASSETT (0793)
Tubbjoys Antiques Market, 118 High Street, SN4 7AY TEL: 849499 PARKING: Own carpark OPEN: Seven days 10-5 MIN: £5 MAX: £1,000 PERIOD: 19th-20th century GENERAL: 15 units. General antiques OTHER INFO: Good coffee shop in market, B&B in town (out of hours opening).

MINETY (0666)
Sambourne House Antiques, Sambourne House, SN16 9RQ TEL: 860288 PARKING: Own carpark OPEN: Mon-Sat 8.30-5.30 MIN: £10 MAX: £1,500 PERIOD: 19th-20th century SPECIALIST: Antique pine furniture, Irish GENERAL: Stripping & restoration on premises OTHER INFO: B&B at White Horse Inn 500 yds.

HANKERTON (06667)
North Wilts Exporters, Cloatley Manor TEL: 7870 PARKING: Own carpark OPEN: Mon-Sat 9-5 or by appt MIN: £1 MAX: £5,000 PERIOD: 19th-20th century SPECIALIST: Pine & shipping goods.

MALMESBURY (0666)
Andrew Britten, 48 High Street TEL: 823376 FAX: 825563 PARKING: Medium OPEN: Mon-Sat 9.30-5.30 MIN: £15 MAX: £1,500 PERIOD: 18th-19th century GENERAL: Decorative furniture & accessories, particularly brass & boxes OTHER INFO: This is England's oldest borough (AD 880).

Cross Hayes Antiques, The Antique & Furniture Warehouse, 19 Bristol Street, SN16 0AY TEL: 824260 day, 822062 evening FAX: 823020 ASSNS: LAPADA PARKING: Medium OPEN: 9-5 Closed Thurs & Sat, or by appt MIN: £2 MAX: £2,000 PERIOD: Generally 1860-1930 SPECIALIST: Furniture GENERAL: Bric-a-brac, shipping goods.

Dovetail Antiques, 67-69 High Street, SN16 9AG TEL: 822191 PARKING: Medium OPEN: Mon-Sat 10-5.30 PERIOD: 17th-19th century GENERAL: Country furniture, metalware, needlework & some mahogany furniture OTHER INFO: The Old Bell Hotel, Le Flambé restaurant.

CASTLE COMBE (0249)

Combe Cottage Antiques, SN14 7HU TEL: 782250 ASSNS: BADA PARKING: Medium OPEN:Mon-Sat 10-5.30 (closed Thursday over lunch), phone if coming any distance MIN: £20 MAX: £10,000 PERIOD: 17-19th century but also some earlier SPECIALIST: Medieval furniture, early oak, metalware GENERAL: Country antiques OTHER INFO: England's prettiest village. Hotel + B&B.

Unicorn Gallery, The Street, SN14 7HU TEL: 782291 PARKING: Easy OPEN: Seven days 9.30-5.30 MIN: £5 approx MAX: £1,000 PERIOD: 17th-18th century SPECIALIST: Hand crafts, gifts, antiques OTHER INFO: Manor Hotel is rather formal country house style, beautiful rooms etc but expensive, White Hart Hotel at Ford (5 mins) has very good dining & accommodation.

NORTH WRAXALL (0225)

Delomosne & Son Ltd, Court Close, SN14 7AD TEL: 891505 FAX: 891907 ASSNS: BADA, BABADA PARKING: Easy OPEN: Mon-Fri 9.30-5.30, Sat 9.30-1 MIN: £20 PERIOD: 17th-20th century GENERAL: 18th-19th century English & Continental glass, porcelain, chandeliers & other light fittings. Some decorative items.

KINGTON ST MICHAEL (0249)

Lantern Gallery, Hazeland House, SN14 6JJ TEL: 750306 FAX: 758896 ASSNS: BADA, ABA PARKING: Own carpark OPEN: Mon-Fri 9-4 & by appt MIN: £10 MAX: £4,500 PERIOD: 17th-19th century SPECIALIST: Botanical, natural history, 18th century stipples GENERAL: Old engravings OTHER INFO: Excellent pub in village.

CHRISTIAN MALFORD (0249)

Harley Antiques, The Comedy, SN15 4BS TEL: 720112 PARKING: Own carpark OPEN: Seven days 9-6 MIN: £20 MAX: £3,000 PERIOD: 18th-19th century GENERAL: Largest stock of decorative accessories & the more unusual furniture OTHER INFO: We are converted stables amid 7 acres landscaped parkland. Stunning Fullmans Restaurant (Crudwell) & Bell Hotel at Sutton Benger.

LANGLEY BURRELL (0249)

Fairfax Fireplaces & Antiques, Langley Green,

SN15 4LL TEL: 652030 FAX: 652030 PARKING: Easy OPEN: Mon-Sat 10-5 MIN: £20 MAX: £2,000 PERIOD: 18th-20th century SPECIALIST: Fireplaces & architectural GENERAL: Antique fixtures for restoring house, Listed Building advice OTHER INFO: Langley Green, a country village hamlet is mostly 16th century, but listed from 12th century.

CORSHAM (0249)

Matthew Eden Antiques, Pickwick End TEL: 713335 FAX: 713644 PARKING: Own carpark OPEN: Mon-Sat 9-7, resident MIN: £5 MAX: £4,000 PERIOD: 17th-20th century SPECIALIST: Country house furniture & garden items, makers of garden furniture.

ATWORTH (0225)

Peter Campbell Antiques, 59 Bath Road, SN12 8JY TEL: 709742 PARKING: Own carpark OPEN: Mon-Wed, Fri, Sat 10-5 MIN: £10 MAX: £450 PERIOD: 19th century GENERAL: English & Continental furniture & decorative arts OTHER INFO: 2 B&B's in village & 2 other antique shops.

MELKSHAM (0225)

Jaffray Antiques, 16 The Market Place, SN12 6EX TEL: 702269 FAX: 790413 PARKING: Own carpark OPEN: Mon-Sat 9-5.30 MIN: £15 MAX: £3,000 PERIOD: 18th-20th century SPECIALIST: Staffordshire & decorative items GENERAL: Large - Linen presses, chests, boxes on stand. Restoration facilities available OTHER INFO: Good hotels & restaurants, courier service, transport to & from nearest station (Chippenham) available every hour.

BRADFORD-ON-AVON (0225)

Avon Antiques, 25-27 Market Street, BA15 1LL TEL: 862052 ASSNS: BADA PARKING: Own carpark OPEN: Mon-Sat 9.45-5.30 PERIOD: 17th-mid 19th century SPECIALIST: Furniture GENERAL: Longcase clocks, metalwork, needlework OTHER INFO: Saxon church, medieval Tithe Barn, Woolley Grange Hotel (864705), Priory Steps (862230).

Harp Antiques, 17 Woolley Street, BA15 1AD TEL: 865770 ASSNS: LAPADA, BABADA PARKING: Easy OPEN: Mon-Sat 9-6 or by appt (resident) MIN: £10 MAX: £10,000 PERIOD: 18th-19th century GENERAL: George III mahogany & Regency furniture, silver, ceramics

OTHER INFO: Small town of exceptional beauty & historic interest. 5 good antique shops & no rubbish.

MacHumble Antiques, 7-9 Woolley Street, BA15 1AD TEL: 866329 ASSNS: BADA, BABADA PARKING: Easy OPEN: Mon-Sat 9-6 MIN: £25 MAX: £6,000 PERIOD: 18th-19th century SPECIALIST: Samplers, needlework, metalware GENERAL: English mahogany furniture, small pieces of excellent colour & patination OTHER INFO: One of the best small town in England with strong historic interest. 2 BADA & 3 LAPADA members with excellent quality items, no junk or rubbish. Woolley Grange Hotel, Leigh Park Hotel

Moxham's Antiques, 17, 23-24 Silver Street, BA15 1JZ TEL: 862789 FAX: 867844 ASSNS: LAPADA PARKING: Own carpark OPEN: Mon-Sat 9-5.30 MIN: £300 MAX: £20,000 PERIOD: 17th-19th century SPECIALIST: Georgian brown furniture GENERAL: Period stock, ceramics, metalware, decorative & garden items OTHER INFO: Old woollen historic town near Bath with many other dealers in the town.

BATH (0225)

Adam Gallery, 13 John Street, BA1 2JL TEL: 480406 ASSNS: FATG, Inst of Paper Conservators PARKING: Easy OPEN: Mon-Sat 9.30-5.30 MIN: £200 MAX: £15,000+ PERIOD: 19th-20th century SPECIALIST: Fine oils, watercolours 1880-1940, contemporary works GENERAL: Paintings and watercolours OTHER INFO: Splendid Georgian city, Bath Spa-5 star hotel.

Alderson, 23 Brock Street, BA1 2LW TEL: 421652 FAX: 421652 ASSNS: BADA PARKING: Easy OPEN: Mon-Sat 9.30-5.30 MIN: £25 MAX: £20,000 PERIOD: 18th-19th century SPECIALIST: English furniture and accessories OTHER INFO: World Heritage city surrounded by NT properties.

Antique Linens and Lace, 11 Pulteney Bridge, BA2 4AY TEL: 465782 PARKING: Easy OPEN: Seven days 10-6 MIN: £4 MAX: £450 PERIOD: 19th century SPECIALIST: Christening gowns, baby bonnets, table linen GENERAL: Pillow cases, bedspreads, wedding veils, shawls etc

Bath Antiques Market, Guinea Lane off Lansdown Road TEL: 337638 FAX: 445118 PARKING: Easy OPEN: Wednesdays 6.30-2.30 PERIOD: 18th-20th century GENERAL: 60 Dealers - antiques, furniture, silver, jewellery, porcelain, china, paintings, prints, textiles etc OTHER INFO: Arrive early for best deals as primarily trade market. Café serving quality homemade food, unrestricted parking above Hedgemead Park.

Bath Stamp & Coin Shop, 12 Pulteney Bridge, BA2 4AY TEL: 463073 ASSNS: Philatelic Trade Society PARKING: Medium OPEN: Mon-Sat 9.30-5.30 MIN: £1 MAX: £200 PERIOD: Roman times-20th century GENERAL: Stamps, coins, medals, banknotes OTHER INFO: Excellent views, sited on the world-famous Pulteney Bridge.

George Bayntun, 21 Manvers Street, BA1 1JW TEL: 466000 FAX: 482122 ASSNS: ABA PARKING: Own carpark OPEN: Mon-Fri 9-1, 2-5.30, Sat 9.30-1 MIN: £10 MAX: £5,000 PERIOD: 17th-20th century SPECIALIST: Fine bindings, first editions of English literature OTHER INFO: Our centenary year. Book Museum specialising in Jane Austen, Dickens & other famous authors local or visited. Small book-binding exhibition.

Beau Nash, 1st floor, Union Passage, BA1 1RD TEL: 447806 FAX: 447806 PARKING: Difficult OPEN: Mon-Sat 10-5 MIN: £500 MAX: £15,000 PERIOD: 18th-early 19th century SPECIALIST: Regency and George III furniture GENERAL: Decorative objects, oil paintings OTHER INFO: Grade I listed house close to Roman Baths and Abbey.

Blyth Antiques, 28 Sydney Buildings, BA2 6BX TEL: 469766 PARKING: Easy OPEN: By appt MIN: £50 MAX: £2,000 PERIOD: 18th-19th century SPECIALIST: Brass GENERAL: Treen & small furniture.

Bryers Antiques, First Stall, Guildhall Market, TEL: 466352 PARKING: Difficult OPEN: Mon-Sat 9.30-5 MIN: £5 MAX: £5,000 PERIOD: 18th-20th century SPECIALIST: Antique silver, Sheffield plate GENERAL: Some porcelain & glass OTHER INFO: Close to historic Bath Guildhall & Bath Abbey.

Carr Linford, 10-11 Walcot Buildings, London Road, BA1 6AD TEL: 317516 PARKING: Medium OPEN: Mon-Sat 9-5 MIN: £100 MAX:

£5,000 PERIOD: 18th-19th century SPECIAL-IST: Period painted furniture GENERAL: Decorative furniture & objects.

Chelsea Interiors, 9 Chelsea Road, Lower Weston TEL: 426717 PARKING: Easy OPEN: Mon 12-2, 3-6, Tues-Fri 10-2, 3-6 or by appt MIN: £5 MAX: £5,000 PERIOD: 18th-19th century GENERAL: Decorative furniture, lighting, prints & ceramics OTHER INFO: Royal Crescent and Newbridge hotels nearby.

Brian & Caroline Craik Ltd, 8 Margaret's Buildings TEL: 337161 PARKING: Medium OPEN: Mon-Sat 9.30-5.30. Resident MIN: £10 MAX: £1,000 PERIOD: 19th-20th century SPECIALIST: Candlesticks GENERAL: Small objects, wood metal, brass, glass OTHER INFO: Between the circus of the Royal Crescent.

Corridor Stamp Shop, 7a The Corridor, BA1 5AP TEL: 463368 PARKING: Medium OPEN: Tues-Sat 9.30-5 MIN: £1 PERIOD: 18th-20th century SPECIALIST: GB, Dominions, Western Europe GENERAL: Worldwide, plus albums and accessories OTHER INFO: B&B at Sherford House, Lansdown Road.

John Croft Antiques, 3 George Street, BA1 2EH TEL: 466211 ASSNS: LAPADA PARKING: Medium PERIOD: 18th-19th century GENERAL: Furniture, decorative objects, barometers.

Andrew Dando, 4 Wood Street, Queen Square, BA1 2JQ TEL: 422702 ASSNS: BADA PARKING: Medium OPEN: Mon-Fri 9.30-5.30, Sat 10-1 MIN: £5 MAX: £5,000 PERIOD: 18th-19th century SPECIALIST: Large stock of fine pottery & porcelain 1700-1860 GENERAL: Selection of antique prints including local topography, furniture.

D & B Dickinson, 22 New Bond Street, BA1 1BA TEL: 466502 ASSNS: BADA, PARKING: Easy OPEN: Mon-Fri 9.30-1, 2-5, Sat 9.30-1 MIN: £10 MAX: £5,000 PERIOD: 18th-20th century SPECIALIST: Silver, old Sheffield plate, antique and secondhand jewellery OTHER INFO: 5 star Bath Spa Hotel, Museum of Costume.

Frank Dux Antiques, 33 Belvedere, Lansdown Road, BA1 5HR TEL: 312367 FAX: 312367 ASSNS: BBADA PARKING: Easy OPEN: Mon-Sat 10-6 MIN: £1 MAX: £5,000 PERIOD:

17th-19th century SPECIALIST: Georgian glass GENERAL: Period oak and fruitwood furniture, Georgian and later glass, pewter, rugs, pictures etc OTHER INFO: Good bistro closeby.

Paul Michael Farnham, 27a 27b Belvedere, Lansdown, BA1 5HR TEL: 428256 PARKING: Easy OPEN: Mon-Sat 10-5.30 or by appt MIN: £20 PERIOD: 17th-20th century SPECIALIST: Beyond description OTHER INFO: Prehistoric bones.

Simon Freeman Antiques, 11 Walcot Buildings, London Road, BA1 6AD TEL: 317516 PARKING: Medium OPEN: Mon-Sat 9-5 MIN: £50 MAX: £5,000 PERIOD: 18th-19th century GENERAL: Period & decorative furniture & objects.

The Galleon, 33 Monmouth Street, BA1 2AN TEL: 312330 PARKING: Easy OPEN: Tues-Fri 10-5.30, Sat 10-6 MIN: £5 MAX: £3,000 PERIOD: 18th-20th century GENERAL: General antiques OTHER INFO: Established 21 years. Close to Roman Baths, Costume Museum, theatre, river trips.

David Gibson, 4 Wood Street, Queen Square, BA1 2JQ TEL: 446646 ASSNS: BADA, LAPADA PARKING: Easy OPEN: Tues-Sat 10-5.30 MIN: £2,500 MAX: £25,000 PERIOD: 18th century SPECIALIST: Clocks & Barometers.

Graylow & Co, 7 Princes Building, George Street TEL: 469859 FAX: 215405 PARKING: Easy OPEN: Mon-Sat 10-5.30 MIN: £100 MAX: £8,000 PERIOD: 18th-19th century SPECIALIST: Georgian furniture GENERAL: Paintings, silver, oriental.

George Gregory, Manvers Street, BA1 1JW TEL: 466055 FAX: 482122 ASSNS: ABA PARKING: Own car park OPEN: 9-1, 2-5.30, Sat 9.30-1 MIN: £1 MAX: £2,000 PERIOD: 18th-20th century SPECIALIST: English Literature, antique engravings, views and portraits.

Great Western Antique Centre, Bartlett Street, BA1 2QZ TEL: 424243 FAX: 424243 PARKING: Medium OPEN: Mon, Tues, Thurs, Fri 10-5, Sat 9.30-5.30, Weds 8.30-5, Wednesday Market 7.30-4 SPECIALIST: Buttons, linen, lace, stamps, railwayiana, jewellery, paintings, prints, furniture, ceramics, coins etc OTHER INFO: 50 stalls with various stock.

Haliden Oriental Rug Shop, 98 Walcot Street, BA1 5BG TEL: 469240 PARKING: Easy (multi storey) OPEN: Mon-Sat 10-5 MIN: £20 MAX: £2,000 PERIOD: 19th & some early 20th century SPECIALIST: Chinese porcelain, Ming & earlier, some textiles GENERAL: Old & antique Caucasian, Persian, Turkish, Turcoman, tribal rugs & carpets OTHER INFO: 250 yards Hilton Hotel, next to Walcot Reclamation. Cleaning, repairs, conservation, restoration.

Ann King, 38 Belvedere, Lansdown Road TEL: 336295 PARKING: Medium OPEN: Mon-Sat 10.30-4.30 MIN: £1 MAX: £100+ PERIOD: 17th-20th century SPECIALIST: Clothes, linen, lace, textiles, quilts, old cushions, curtains.

Lansdown Antiques, 23 Belvedere, Lansdown Road, BA1 5ED TEL: 313417 ASSNS: BBADA PARKING: Medium OPEN: Mon-Sat 9-6 MIN: £1 MAX: £2,000 PERIOD: 17th-19th century SPECIALIST: Painted pine & country furniture, unusual & decorative items OTHER INFO: From A4/A46 junction, turn right at 3rd set of lights, 300 yds up hill on left.

Looking Glass, 96 Walcot Street TEL: 461969 PARKING: Own carpark OPEN: Mon-Sat 9-6 PERIOD: 20th century SPECIALIST: Mirrors & frames GENERAL: Replica mirrors & picture frames.

Mallory of Bath, 1-4 Bridge Street, BA2 4AP TEL: 465885 FAX: 442210 ASSNS: BADA, NAG PARKING: Medium OPEN: Mon-Sat 9.30-5.15 MIN: £10 MAX: £20,000 PERIOD: 18th-20th century SPECIALIST: Fine antique silver & jewellery GENERAL: Modern jewellery, silver, watches, china, glass & gifts OTHER INFO: Also at 5 Old Bond Street. Spa Hotel, Grove Hotel, The Francis Hotel. Wednesday Antique Market & 40 local dealers in the association.

Paragon Antiques Market, 3 Bladud Buildings, The Paragon TEL: 463715 PARKING: Easy OPEN: Wed 6.30-3.30 OTHER INFO: 60 stalls of antiques & collectables

William Pelly at the Kingsley Gallery, 16 Margaret's Buildings, Brock Street, BA1 2LP TEL: 448432, 421714. ASSNS: BBADA PARKING: Easy OPEN: Mon-Sat 10-5.30. After hours & Sundays by appt MIN: £50-100 MAX: £8-10,000 PERIOD: 17th-20th century

SPECIALIST: Mainly oil paintings GENERAL: Watercolours, figures (bronzes), English, Continental & Scandinavian OTHER INFO: Sometimes early old masters, sometimes contemporary art. Near Royal Crescent, opposite excellent Lebanese restaurant: Cedars.

Pennard House Antiques, 3-4 Piccadilly, London Road, BA1 6PL TEL: 313791 FAX: 448196 ASSNS: LAPADA, BABADA PARKING: Own carpark OPEN: Mon-Sat 9.30-5.30 OTHER INFO: We are 6 dealers under one roof and we are particularly geared to assisting overseas customers. MIN: £10 MAX: £5,000 PERIOD: 18th-19th century SPECIALIST: French provincial fruitwood, pine furniture GENERAL: Decorative items, original paintwork OTHER INFO: Queensberry Hotel, New Moon Pub.

Quiet Street Antiques, 3 Quiet Street, BA1 2JS TEL: 315727 ASSNS: BABADA PARKING: Easy OPEN: Mon-Sat 10-6 MIN: £100 MAX: £5,000 PERIOD: 18th-19th century SPECIALIST: Interesting boxes and caddies, good clocks, Royal Worcester porcelain GENERAL: General antiques OTHER INFO: 4 showrooms, every item priced and fully described. Well known on tour circuit as friendly, helpful and knowledgable. Exports arranged. Happy to listen to amusing anecdotes on any subject.

Michael and Jo Saffell, 3 Walcot Buildings, London Road, BA1 6AD TEL: 315857 PARKING: Medium OPEN: Mon-Fri 9.30-5 or by appt. Best phone first anyway MIN: £5 MAX: £2,000 PERIOD: 19th-20th century SPECIALIST: British tins mainly, other advertising items GENERAL: Decorative and collectors items.

Saville Row Gallery, 1 Saville Row, Alfred Street, BA1 2QP TEL: 334595 ASSNS: FATG PARKING: Easy OPEN: Mon-Sat 10-4 MIN: £25 MAX: £15,000 PERIOD: 17th-19th century GENERAL: Antiques, oil paintings, water colours OTHER INFO: 20th century early British paintings. Next to Georgian Assembly Rooms.

Walcot Reclamation Ltd. 108 Walcot Street, BA1 5BG TEL: 444404 FAX: 448163 PARKING: Own carpark OPEN: Mon-Fri 8.30-5.30, Sat 9-5 PERIOD: 17th-20th century SPECIALIST: Architectural salvage and antiques OTHER INFO: One of largest dealers in UK, two sites. Phone first for directions. Minutes from centre of Bath, accommodation guides on request.

Glenda Wallis - Antiquarian & Secondhand Booksellers, 6 Chapel Row, Queen Square, BA1 1HN TEL: 424677 ASSNS: PBFA, ABA PARKING: Easy OPEN: Mon-Sat 10-5.30 MIN: £1 MAX: £1,000 PERIOD: 18th-20th century SPECIALIST: Victorian childrens, illustrated, Canadian & folklore GENERAL: Large general stock on most subjects OTHER INFO: Next door to good French bistro (The Beaujolais).

Widcombe Antiques, 9 Claverton Buildings, Widcombe, BA2 4LE TEL: 428767 PARKING: Own carpark OPEN: Mon-Sat 10.30-5.30 PERIOD: 18th-19th century GENERAL: Period pine & brass, dressers, tables, chests-brass & iron fenders.

BRISTOL (0272)
Alexander Gallery Partnership, 122 Whiteladies Road, BS8 2RP TEL: 734692 FAX: 466991 ASSNS: FATG PARKING: Medium OPEN: Mon, Tues, Thurs-Sat 9-5.30, Weds 9-

1 MIN: £100 MAX: £10,000 PERIOD: 19th-20th century SPECIALIST: Oils & watercolours.

Antique Beds, 3 Litfield Place, Clifton BS8 3LT TEL: 735134 FAX: 744450 PARKING: Own carpark OPEN: Anytime by appt MIN: £950 MAX: £5,000 PERIOD: 18th-19th century SPECIALIST: Four poster beds only GENERAL: Antique four posters, custom-made mattresses, fabrics, making up service OTHER INFO: 100 yards Clifton Suspension Bridge, SS Great Britain, Bristol Zoo, Moat House Hotel, Swallow Royal Hotel. Excellent Marwicks Restaurant in City

The Barometer Shop, 2 Lower Park Row, BS1 5BJ TEL: 272565 ASSNS: BHI PARKING: Own carpark OPEN: Mon, Wed, Fri 10-4, Sat 10-1 MIN: £45 MAX: £8,500 PERIOD: 18th-20th century SPECIALIST: Clocks, barometers GENERAL: Period furniture.

Robin Butler, 20 Clifton Road, BS8 1AQ TEL: 733017 FAX: 733017 ASSNS: BADA PARKING: Own carpark OPEN: Mon-Fri 9.30-5.30, Sat 10-3 MIN: £20 MAX: £50,000 PERIOD: 18th-19th century SPECIALIST: Furniture, wine antiques glass, silver, clocks OTHER INFO: For information or a map on how to find us, please telephone or write. Exhibitor at Bath & Olympia. Harveys Wine Museum, SS Great Britain, Suspension Bridge. Many attractions, lots of good food - ask me.

Clifton Antiques Market, 26-28 The Mall, Clifton TEL: 734531, 734698 PARKING: Difficult OPEN: Tues-Sat 10-6 PERIOD: 19th-20th century GENERAL: Approx 30 dealers covering jewellery, silver, gold, furniture, textiles, porcelain, china, prints, pictures, linen, lace, glassware, book binding, picture framing & restoration OTHER INFO: We are housed in a historic building in the heart of Georgian Clifton Village, close to famous Clifton Suspension Bridge.

David Cross Fine Art, 7 Boyces Avenue, Clifton, BS8 4AA TEL: 732614 ASSNS: BAG PARKING: Easy OPEN: Mon-Sat 9.30-6 MIN: £5 MAX: £50.000 PERIOD: 18th-20th century SPECIALIST: British marine, landscape, figurative, sporting, topographical GENERAL: Oils, watercolours and local prints and contemporary OTHER INFO: Old Clifton, 100 yards to Clifton Suspension Bridge and Avon Gorge.

Flame & Grate, 159 Hotwells Road, Hotwells, BS8 4RY TEL: 252560 PARKING: Easy OPEN: Mon-Sat 9-5 MIN: £3 MAX: £8,000 PERIOD: 17th-20th century SPECIALIST: Original fireplaces, marble surrounds GENERAL: All makes of original and modern fireplaces, stones, handcarved surrounds OTHER INFO: Close to historic harbour and SS Great Britain.

Grey-Harris & Co Ltd, 12 Princess Victoria Street, Clifton, BS8 TEL: 737365 ASSNS: BADA, NAG PARKING: Medium OPEN: Mon-Sat 9.30-5.30 MIN: £50 MAX: £15,000 PERIOD: 18th-20th century SPECIALIST: Jewellery, silver OTHER INFO: One of the finest 19th century jewellers shop interiors in the provinces (restored to c. 1860).

John Martin Antiques, Bristol Antiques Centre, Broad Plain TEL: 297739 PARKING: Easy OPEN: Tues-Sat 10-4.30 MIN: £5 MAX: £3,000+ PERIOD: 18th-20th century GENERAL: Clocks, furniture, oil lamps, copper and brass OTHER INFO: Close to Marriott Hotel and city centre.

Robert Mills Ltd, Unit 2, Satellite Business Park, Blackswarth Road, Redfield, BS5 8AX TEL: 556542 FAX: 558146 PARKING: Own carpark OPEN: Mon-Fri 9.30-5.30 MIN: £100 MAX: £50,000 PERIOD: 18th-20th century SPECIALIST: Architectural antiques, stained glass, bars, panelled rooms, church woodwork.

No. 74 Antiques & Collectables, 74 Alma Road, Clifton, BS8 3BA TEL: 733821 PARKING: Medium OPEN: Mon-Sat 10.30-5.30 MIN: £20 MAX: £3,000+ PERIOD: 18th-19th century SPECIALIST: Period town house furniture GENERAL: Clocks, decorative items OTHER INFO: Antique finders and interior design service upholsterer on premises. Close to Brunel's famous suspension bridge

Period Fireplaces, The Old Railway Station, Station Road, Montpelier TEL: 412258 42409 PARKING: Own carpark OPEN: Mon-Sat 9-5.30 MIN: £10 MAX: £1,000 PERIOD: 19th-20th century SPECIALIST: Genuine antique fireplaces OTHER INFO: Good restaurants within 3 minutes walk.

Potters Antiques & Coins, 60 Colston Street, BS1 5AZ TEL: 262551 PARKING: Medium OPEN: Mon-Sat 10.30-5 MIN: £1 MAX: £500 PERIOD: 17th-20th century SPECIALIST:

Coins & antiquities GENERAL: Brass, copper,commemoratives, glass, silver etc OTHER INFO: Antiquities from 1500BC to 400AD.Near famous Christmas Steps and Red Lodge, ° mile from Museum & Art Gallery.

Relics Pine Furniture, 109 Street, Georges Road, College Green, BS1 5UW TEL: 268453 PARKING: Easy OPEN: Mon-Sat 10-5.30 MIN: £16 MAX: £685 PERIOD: Early 20th century SPECIALIST: Pine furniture - old and reproduction GENERAL: Large selection of repro, Victorian jugs & basins sets OTHER INFO: Local pub has excellent food at low price.

John Roberts Bookshop, 43 Triangle West. Clifton, BS8 1ES TEL: 268568 PARKING:- OPEN: Mon-Sat 9.30-5.30 PERIOD: 18th-20th century GENERAL: Antiquarian and 2nd hand books.

The Wise Owl Bookshop, 26 Upper Maudlin Street, BS2 8DJ TEL: 262738, after hours 246936 ASSNS PBFA PARKING: Medium OPEN: Mon-Sat 10.30-5.30 MIN: £3 MAX: £100 PERIOD: 19th-20th century SPECIALIST: Books on performing arts, music GENERAL: Secondhand and antiquarian books on all subjects OTHER INFO: WE also sell sheet music, records, tapes and cds.

WEST HARPTREE (0761)

Tilly Manor Antiques, Tilly Manor, BS18 6EB TEL: 221888 PARKING: Own carpark OPEN: Tues-Sat 10-5 no bank holidays MIN: £5 MAX: £5,000 PERIOD: 18th-20th century SPECIALIST: Antique furniture (town & country) GENERAL: Metalware, decorative collectors items OTHER INFO: Wealth of treasures in beautiful 17th century manor house 25 mins from Bath on A368

MIDSOMER NORTON (0761)

Somervale Antiques, 6 Radstock Road, BA3 2AJ TEL: 412686 (24 hours) ASSNS: BADA, LAPADA, CINOA, BBADA PARKING: Own carpark OPEN: By appt only MIN: £20 MAX: £5,000 PERIOD: 17th-19th century SPECIALIST: English drinking glasses, decanters, cut and coloured Bristol and Nailsea glass. Also bijouterie, scent bottles OTHER INFO: Coal Mining Museum nearby Sats only. Trains from Bath met by arrangement.

FROME (0373)

Sutton & Sons, 15 & 33 Vicarage Street, BA11 1PX TEL: 462062, 462526 PARKING: Good OPEN: Mon-Sat 9-5 MIN: £18 MAX: £2,800 PERIOD: 18th-19th century GENERAL: English furniture OTHER INFO: Longleat 4 miles, quaint town of Frome.

WARMINSTER (0985)

Bishopstrow Antiques, 55 East Street, BA12 9BZ TEL: 212683 PARKING: Easy/medium OPEN: Mon-Sat 10-1, 2-5.30 MIN: £3 MAX: £3,000 PERIOD: 18th-20th century GENERAL: Mahogany & oak furniture, country and painted, china, small silver & decorative items OTHER INFO: Good pubs in lovely villages.

Britannia Antiques, 7 Silver Street, BA12 8PS TEL: 217465 PARKING: Easy OPEN: Mon-Sat 9-5.30 MIN: £50 MAX: £3,000 PERIOD: 19th century SPECIALIST: Victorian.

Century Antiques, 10 Silver Street TEL: 217031 FAX: 846253 ASSNS: FATG PARKING: Easy OPEN: Mon-Sat 10-1, 2-5.30 MIN: £20 MAX: £4,500 PERIOD: 18th-20th century GENERAL: Paintings, furniture & decorative smalls.

Choice Antiques, 4 Silver Street, TEL: 218924 PARKING: Easy OPEN: 10-1, 2-5.30 MIN: £25 MAX: £2,500 PERIOD: 18th-19th century GENERAL: Small pieces mahogany and country furniture & decorative items.

Peter Houghton Antiques, 33 Silver Street, BA12 8PT TEL:213451, 216288 ASSNS: LAPADA PARKING: Easy OPEN: Mon-Sat 10.30-12.30, 2-5.30 MIN: £50 MAX: £12,000 PERIOD: 17th-19th century SPECIALIST: 18th & early 19th century English furniture GENERAL: Accessories, watercolours, maps & prints OTHER INFO: Bishopstrow Hotel (superb country house hotel) 2 miles.

Emma Hurley Antiques & Textiles, 3 Silver Street TEL: 219726 PARKING: Medium OPEN: Mon-Sat 10-5 MIN: £5 MAX: £1,000 PERIOD: 19th century SPECIALIST: Textiles GENERAL: Home embellishments (mirrors, lighting, paintings, French beds OTHER INFO: Good restaurant & B&B 2 doors away.

Isabella Antiques, 16a Silver Street TEL: 218933 PARKING: Easy OPEN: Mon-Sat 10-5.30 MIN: £25 MAX: £5,000 PERIOD: late 18th-19th century GENERAL: Mahogany (especially inlaid) furniture, gilt mirrors, boxes, small clocks OTHER INFO: 12 antique shops.

Obelisk Antiques, 2 Silver Street, BA12 8PS TEL: 846646 FAX: 219901 PARKING: Easy OPEN: Mon-Sat 10-1, 2-5.30 MIN: £10 MAX: £10,000 PERIOD: 18th-20th century GENERAL: Large stock English & Continental furniture, chandeliers & decorative items OTHER INFO: 18 dealers in town. Bishopstrow House Hotel, The Angel, Heytesbury (good country pub with restaurant & accommodation).

Swans Antiques, 8 Silver Street TEL: 219726 PARKING: Medium OPEN: Mon-Sat 9.30-5 MIN: £25 MAX: £1,000 PERIOD: 19th century SPECIALIST: Textiles & decorative furnishings GENERAL: Lighting, mirrors & pictures etc

Vernon Antiques, 16a Silver Street TEL: 218933 PARKING: Easy OPEN: 10-12.45, 2.15-5.30 MIN: £5 MAX: £5,000 PERIOD: 18th-19th century SPECIALIST: Georgian and Victorian furniture OTHER INFO: Export arranged.

DEVIZES (0380)

Cross Keys Jewellers, The Ginnel, The Market Place, SN10 1HN TEL: 726293 ASSNS: IJL PARKING: Easy OPEN: Mon-Sat 9.30-5.30 MIN: £1 MAX: £3,000 PERIOD: 20th century SPECIALIST: Antique (mainly rings & amber) jewellery GENERAL: Jewellery & watches OTHER INFO: Avebury Stone Circle & Stonehenge, Longleat House.

Sussex House Antiques, 1a Bath Road, SN10 2AP TEL: 720916 FAX: 720916 PARKING: Own carpark OPEN: Tues-Sat 10-12.30, 1.30-5 MIN: £20 MAX: £3,000 PERIOD: 18th-20th century SPECIALIST: Mainly 19th century furniture GENERAL: General antiques OTHER INFO: Beer Hotel reasonable prices with good food & accommodation.

POTTERNE (0380)

The Antique Gallery, 17 High Street, SN10 5NA TEL: 728007 PARKING: Easy OPEN: Fri-Sat 10-5 & by appt PERIOD: 17th-19th century SPECIALIST: Looking glasses, antique picture frames GENERAL: Furniture, architectural items, decorative antiques.

CALNE (0249)

Calne Antiques, 2a London Road TEL: 816311 PARKING: Own carpark OPEN: Seven days 10-5 or by appt MIN: £10 MAX: £2,000 PERIOD: 19th-20th century GENERAL: Stripped pine, mahogany, satinwalnut, oak. Smalls 1800-1950

OTHER INFO: Largest selection of furniture in the area priced £100-500. Help gladly given for local accommodation & visits.

Sophie Dupre & Clive Farahar, XIV The Green, SN11 8DQ TEL: 821121 FAX: 821202 ABA, ILAB, Manuscript Society PARKING: Easy OPEN: By appt MIN: £5 MAX: £5,000 PERIOD: 17th-20th century SPECIALIST: Rare books on voyages & travels, autograph letters, signed photos, manuscripts, especially royalty & literature OTHER INFO: Attractive area in Wiltshire Downs near Bath, close to Bowood House & Lacock Abbey.

MARLBOROUGH (0672)

The Antique & Book Collector, Katharine House, The Parade, SN8 1NE TEL: 514040 ASSNS: PBFA PARKING: Easy OPEN: Mon-Sat 9.45-5.30 MIN: £10 MAX: £2,000 PERIOD: 18th-20th century (antiquities 1500 BC-500 AD) SPECIALIST: Modern British pictures, Roman glass & other antiquities GENERAL: General antiques. Antiquarian & secondhand books.

Nigel Cracknell (Antiques) Ltd., 138 High Street, SN8 1HN TEL: 512912 ASSNS: BADA PARKING: Medium OPEN: By appt MIN: £500 MAX: £30,000 PERIOD: 17th-19th century GENERAL: Quality furniture OTHER INFO: Avebury, Silbury Hill, Long Barrows. Pollys Restaurant, country house hotels.

Cross Keys Jewellers, 21a High Street. Hilliers Yard, SN8 ILW TEL: 516260 ASSNS: IJL PARKING: Easy OPEN: Mon-Sat 9.30-5.30 MIN: £1 MAX: £3,000 PERIOD: 20th century SPECIALIST: Antique (mainly rings & amber) jewellery GENERAL: Jewellery & watches OTHER INFO: We are in main carpark entrance just round from Polly Tearooms.

The Marlborough Parade Antique Centre, The Parade, SN8 1NE TEL: 515331 PARKING: Easy OPEN: Seven days 10-5 MAX: £5,000 PERIOD: 18th-20th century GENERAL: Very high quality stock, we have 50+ dealers covering almost everything OTHER INFO: Historic town of great character. We are frequently told by the public and trade that we have the best antique centre in Britain.

Principia Fine Art, 5 London Road, SN8 1PH TEL: 512072 FAX: 511551 PARKING: Easy OPEN: Mon-Sat 9.30-5.30 PERIOD: 2000 BC to 19th century GENERAL: Wide range of collectors items including pottery, fabrics, objets de vertu, scientific & decorative.

Stuart Gallery, Loncraines, 4 London Road, SN8 1PH TEL: 513593 PARKING: Easy OPEN: Thurs-Sat 9-6.30 MIN: £1 MAX: £1,000 PERIOD: 18th-20th century SPECIALIST: Glasses, pictures GENERAL: General antiques.

Annmarie Turner Antiques, 22 Salisbury Road, SN8 4AD TEL: 515396 PARKING: Own carpark at rear OPEN: Mon-Sat 10-6 or by appt (resident so ring side door bell) MIN: £5 MAX: £1,500 PERIOD: 18th-19th century SPECIALIST: Welsh items GENERAL: Country furniture, allied decorative items & the unusual OTHER INFO: Some 20th century items.

HUNGERFORD (0488)

Ashley Antiques, Hungerford Arcade TEL: (0672) 20481(ANS) PARKING: Easy OPEN: Mon-Sat 9.30-5.30, Sun 10-6 MIN: £5 MAX: £1,500 PERIOD: 17th-20th century GENERAL: General antiques OTHER INFO: Apart from Arcade, over 20 shops a walk away. Hotels: Three Swans, Bear.

Below Stairs, 103 High Street, RG17 0NB TEL: 682317 PARKING: Easy OPEN: Seven days 10-6 MIN: £10 MAX: £2-3,000 PERIOD: 19th century SPECIALIST: Kitchen antiques, quality bedroom furniture, lighting, decorative garden items, taxidermy, interior fittings, interesting collectables OTHER INFO: No modern or re-pro, emphasis on good English items.

Sir William Bentley Billiards, Standen Manor Farm, RG17 0RB TEL: 681711 FAX: 685197 PARKING: Own carpark OPEN: Mon-Fri 9-5 or by appt MIN: £10 MAX: £75,000 PERIOD: 18t-20th century SPECIALIST: Largest stock in Europe. Some 100 tables all sizes, all beautifully coloured, both simple & elegant.

The Fire Place (Hungerford) Ltd, The Old Fire Station, Charnham Street, RG17 0EP TEL: 683420 PARKING: Easy OPEN: Mon-Sat 10-1, 2.15-5 MIN: £10 MAX: £2,000 PERIOD: 19th-20th century SPECIALIST: Fireplace furnishings especially fenders GENERAL: Paintings.

Robert & Georgina Hastie, 35a High Street, RG17 0NF TEL: 682873, (0860)641560 ASSNS: LAPADA PARKING: Easy OPEN: Mon-Sat

9.30-5 (closed August) MIN: £40 MAX: £5,000 PERIOD: 18th-20th century GENERAL: Furniture & objects OTHER INFO: Hungerford is a long established antiques centre with more than 20 shops and an arcade.

Roger King Antiques, 111 High Street, RG17 0NB TEL: 682256 PARKING: Easy OPEN: Mon-Sat 9.30-5 MIN: £50 MAX: £2,000 PERIOD: 19th century GENERAL: Late Georgian & Victorian furniture.

Medalcrest Ltd, Charnham House, 29-30 Charnham Street TEL: 684157 PARKING: Easy OPEN: Mon-Fri 9.30-5, Sat 10-6 MIN: £2-300 MAX: £10,000 PERIOD: 17th-19th century SPECIALIST: Barometers and clocks GENERAL: Extensive stock of good antique furniture OTHER INFO: The Bear Hotel, Behind the Green Door, The John of Gaunt, Dundas Arms.

The Old Malthouse, 15 Bridge Street, RG17 0EG TEL: 682209 ASSNS: BADA, CINOA PARKING: Easy OPEN: Mon-Sat 10-5.30 MIN: £25 MAX: £30,000 PERIOD: 18th-19th century SPECIALIST: Walnut furniture GENERAL: General antiques OTHER INFO: Nearby Littlecote House is open to public.

Riverside Antiques Ltd, Riverside House, RG17 0EP TEL: 682314 PARKING: Own carpark OPEN: Mon-Sat 10-5.30 MIN: £100 MAX: £5,000 PERIOD: 18th-19th century SPECIALIST: Georgian GENERAL: Accessories

Styles Silver, 12 Bridge Street, RG17 0EH TEL: 683922 ASSNS: LAPADA PARKING: Easy OPEN: Mon-Sat 9.30-5.30 (closed school holidays) MIN: £5 MAX: £5,000 PERIOD: 18th-20th century SPECIALIST: Silver of all periods OTHER INFO: On receipt of SAE will send out leaflet *Guide to Antiques in Hungerford*, listing 22 dealers and antique market.

RAMSBURY (0672)

Heraldry Today, Parliament Piece, SN8 2QH TEL: 20617 FAX: 20183 ASSNS: ABA PARKING: Own carpark OPEN: Mon-Fri 9-4.30 MIN: £3 MAX: £6,000 PERIOD: 18th-20th century SPECIALIST: Heraldic & genealogical books in all languages, also peerage, family history, biography, history, topography and reference OTHER INFO: Good hotel & pub, The Bell. Nice tea & light meals at The Dolls House.

Thames Valley to the Chilterns

Oxford

The first half of this tour follows part of the M4 motorway, calling at the historic towns and pretty villages that lie close by it. It then moves north to go to the world famous city of Oxford as well as other charming villages and market towns in Oxfordshire and the southern part of Buckinghamshire.

The first stops on the tour are on the edge of London. First we visit Staines where Sir Walter Raleigh stood trial, was found guilty and condemned to death. The trial took place here because London was in the grip of plague. From here we move northwards to Uxbridge and then west to the pleasant village of Iver.

The next place to visit on this tour is the lovely, rose-pink, 15th century manor house of Dorney Court in the village of Dorney. *Country Life* said that this was one of the finest Tudor manor houses in England. Built in 1440, successive owners have resisted the urge to drastically alter this beautiful house. It was given to Sir James Palmer by Elizabeth I and has remained in that family ever since. The Palmer family kept strong links with royalty for Sir Roger Palmer stayed loyal to Charles II before the Restoration and was made Earl of Castlemaine on Charles' accession to the throne. The King was also close to Sir Roger's wife, Barbara, who was his mistress for ten years and bore him several children.

Now on for two miles to the linked towns of Eton and Windsor, the former is famous for its school and the latter for its royal castle. On the opposite bank of the Thames from Windsor, Eton's High Street still retains many of its charming 18th century shop fronts and timber-framed buildings, many of which are now antique shops or antiquarian bookshops. Eton College, founded by Henry VI in 1440, is probably the most well-known of English public schools and it has some buildings surviving from its foundation.

Crossing the river by the 18th century bridge in Eton High Street we arrive in Windsor, dominated by its castle. There was a Saxon palace at Old Windsor but William the Conquerer decided to build a castle on top of a hill overlooking the river about two miles away. By 1086 the castle was listed in the Domesday Book. It was from here, in June 1215, that King John went to Runnymede for the meeting with his barons to put his seal to the Magna Carta. Although the barons were principally concerned with their own interests, Magna Carta enshrined, for the first time, a citizen's rights before the law. The 39th article stated, "No free man shall be arrested or imprisoned or dispossessed or outlawed or harmed in any way save by the lawful judgement of his equals under the law of the land. Justice will not be sold to any man nor will it be refused or delayed."

The castle continued in royal use until Edward III made it his principal residence, building the Round Tower in 1348 and making alterations in other parts of the castle. As well as the residence of the Kings of England, Windsor Castle was used for keeping eminent prisoners, for example, David Bruce, King of Scotland, and John, King of France in the 14th century. During the Civil War, the castle was held by Parliament and many of its treasures were melted down.

Today some areas of the castle are open to the public: the famous State Apartments (only when the Queen is not in residence), Queen Mary's Dolls' House and the Exhibition of the Queen's Presents and Royal Carriages. St George's Chapel is a building of particular note with its magnificent perpendicular structure displaying fine fan vaulting. In the choir are the stalls and brasses of Garter Knights, and many royal tombs include those of Henry VIII, Charles I and Edward VII. Also nearby is the Albert Memorial Chapel, originally built by King Henry VII but now used to commemorate Queen Victoria's beloved Albert.

In the Home Park of Windsor Castle stands Frogmore House, also open to the public. It was built in the latter part of the 17th century and was the home of Queen Charlotte and Queen Victoria's mother, the Duchess of Kent. Now it has been restored and many of its original contents returned. Frogmore Gardens, only open for two days a year, contains the Mausoleum in which Queen Victoria and Prince Albert are buried.

The tour now reaches Maidenhead, the popular Thames-side town. Amongst the more interesting features are a railway bridge built in 1838 by Isambard Kingdom Brunel which spans the river, 17th century almshouses and the beauty spot, Boulter's Lock, a mile upriver.

From here we go, via Wargrave, to Henley-on-Thames, a popular Thames Valley

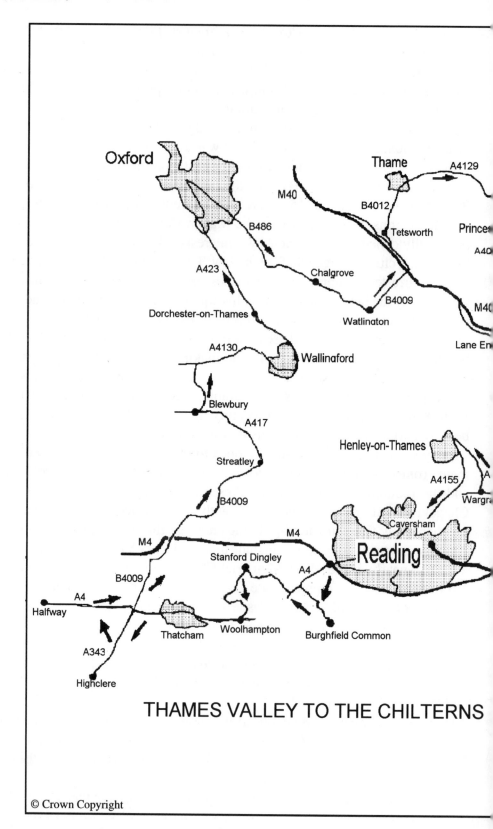

THAMES VALLEY TO THE CHILTERNS

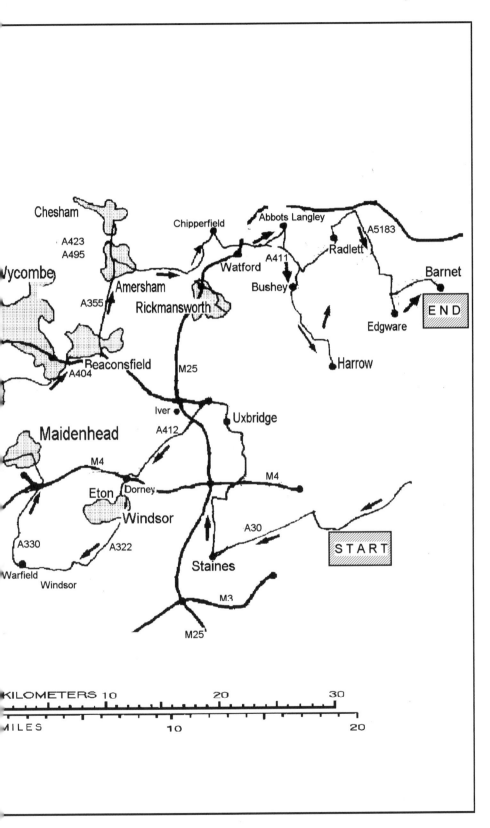

resort, famous for its regatta held annually in the first week of July. The town contains many Georgian and older houses, of particular note is the Chantry House dating back to 1400 which was formerly a school. Fawley Court is another striking building designed by Sir Chrisopher Wren and built in 1684. Inside the work of Grinling Gibbons can be seen and the beautiful park was designed by Capability Brown. A museum is housed in Fawley Court particularly devoted to documents of the Polish kings, historical sabres and military objects of the Polish army. There are also many classical sculptures, paintings and works of art. Since 1953 the house has been in the care of a religious community, the Congregation of Marian Fathers.

We come now to Reading, situated on the junction of the Rivers Thames and Kennet, and a busy commercial and university town. In spite of this, it has a long history, traces of which may still be found, for example, the few remains of the once-famous 13th century abbey where King Henry I was buried. This was so completely destroyed in the Dissolution that little is left apart from the restored abbey gateway. It was once a school and, in 1786, Jane Austen was a pupil. Inscribed on a stone tablet in the former chapter house was the part-song entitled *Sumer is icumen in* written by a monk in about 1240. It was also here that Edward IV made the announcement of his marriage to the hugely unpopular Elizabeth Woodville. Coming to more modern times, Oscar Wilde was imprisoned in Reading where he wrote *De Profundis* and *The Ballad of Reading Gaol*.

The tour continues to the villages of Stanford Dingley, Burghfield Common and Woolhampton before reaching Thatcham, in the Kennet valley, which boasts a 14th century chapel, converted into a school in 1707, and a church with a Norman doorway and a pinnacled tower from the 15th century.

The next call, the small village of Highclere is the site of the High Victorian home of the Earls of Carnavon, Highclere Castle. Built in the 1830s and designed by Charles Barry who was also the architect of the Houses of Parliament, its extravagant style shows all the self-confidence of the Victorian era. Inside there is a good collection of paintings and furniture including Napoleon's desk and chair, brought from St. Helena after his death. The 5th Earl discovered the tomb of Tutankhamun and there is also collection of his early Egyptian finds.

The route passes through Streatley where the hill above this pleasant village on the River Thames gives a wonderful panoramic view over the surrounding area.

Now on the A417, the tour arrives in Blewbury which contains some charming half-timbered houses and a trans-Norman to perpendicular church. Next we visit the small town of Wallingford, again on the banks of the Thames. This town has several interesting features. There are slight remains of a castle, probably Saxon, a 17th century town hall mounted on stone pillars, and a fine bridge with fourteen arches crosses the river. It has two interesting churches. St Leonard's, in spite of mid 19th century alterations, still shows some Norman architectural fea-

Christchurch College, Oxford

tures and St Peter's, rebuilt in 1860, has an unusual openwork spire designed by Sir Robert Taylor in 1777. There are also several notable Georgian buildings in the High Street and Thames Street.

Dorchester-on-Thames, our next stop, is an ancient settlement dating back to the Bronze Age. At one time a Roman station and then a Saxon town, its main claim to fame is that it was here that Christianity was first introduced into Southern England by St Birinus. The glorious abbey dates mostly from the 12th century although there is small section that survives from an earlier Saxon church. Some of the windows contain 13th century coloured glass and there is a fine Jesse window.

Now to Oxford. The first visit on arrival should be paid to the Tourist Information Centre because it is impossible in the space available here to cover even a small part of the glories of this ancient university town.

The origins of Oxford are definitely pre-Norman with a reference to the town in the Saxon Chronicle of AD912 and it is possible that there was a prosperous settlement for some four to five hundred years before that date. Similarly, the origins of the University are unclear, although it appears likely that it sprung out of monastic schools attached to the priory here. There are over thirty University Colleges, one of the earliest is New College founded by William of Wykeham in 1379 and noted for its chapel, hall and cloisters. Another early College was Queen's, founded in 1340 although much of it was rebuilt in the 18th century. It is claimed that University College is the oldest and was first endowed in 1249. One of the best known is Magdalen (pronounced Maudlen), founded in 1448. Its wonderful tower dates from the end of the 15th century.

So much of Oxford is of architectural importance that it is almost invidious to single out particular buildings. However, amongst the most notable are the Bodleian Library, the Ashmolean Museum which, in 1683, was the first museum in Europe to be opened to the public, and the Sheldonian Theatre designed by Sir Christopher Wren.

Oxford is also well-endowed with museums. Apart from the Ashmolean Museum of Art & Archaeology in Beaumont Street, already mentioned, the others include the Museum of the History of Science, Broad Street, the Museum of Oxford in St. Aldates, the Oxford Story also in Broad Street, the Museum of Modern Art, Pembroke Street and the Rotunda Museum of Antique Dolls' Houses in Grove House, Iffley Turn.

Taking the B480 out of Oxford, the route passes through the small village of Chalgrove, the scene of a Civil War battle in 1643 in which John Hampden was fatally wounded. John Hampden, it could be said, was a catalyst in bringing about the Civil War. It was his refusal to pay a King's tax, the so called Ship Money and the court case which went against him, that crystallised the sense of grievance at the King's autocratic rule. He was also one of the five Members of Parliament that King Charles I seeked to arrest when he went in person with his swordsmen to Parliament but the five had been warned and were not there. The outrage that this episode provoked caused Charles to withdraw from London to Hampton Court. The next time he saw London was at his trial and execution. A monument commemorates John Hampden's death in the village.

Nearby Watlington, at the foot of the Chiltern escarpment, contains several Georgian houses as well as the market hall which dates from 1664. One mile north east of the town stands the 14th century moated Shirburn Castle. The splendid viewpoint of Watlington Hill, rising to 800 feet, stands about a mile and a half south east of the town and gives good views of the surrounding area.

The next stop, Thame, has an exceptionally wide and long main street with buildings that range from medieval timber-framed to Georgian. The largely 15th century church has a 13th century chapel with interesting brasses and the 16th century tomb of Lord Williams of Thame and his wife.

On to Princes Risborough which stands on the edge of the Chiltern escarpment and has several picturesque old houses including the 17th century Princes Risborough Manor House with its Jacobean staircase with an openwork balustrade cut from solid oak. Then on to High Wycombe, sited on a gap in the Chiltern Hills. Famous for the manufacture of furniture, particularly chairs, there is an interesting museum, The Wycombe Local History & Chair Museum, which looks at the crafts and history of the region. The town also has many notable buildings including a greatly restored 13th century church, Little Market House from 1604 but rebuilt by Robert Adam in 1761, the Guildhall dating from 1757 and the remains of the 12th century St John's Hospital.

One of High Wycombe's most famous former residents was the great British Victorian Prime Minister, Benjamin Disraeli, whose home, Hughenden Manor, stands one and half miles north of the town. Now owned by the National Trust, Hughenden Manor holds many reminders of Disraeli and his wife, Mary Anne. They lived here from 1847 until they died; Benjamin Disraeli in 1881 and his wife nine years earlier. It was in this house that they entertained many of the great and powerful figures of the day including Queen Victoria herself. Disraeli and Lord Melbourne were the only Prime Ministers that Victoria honoured with a visit. Amongst the items of interest in the house are an autographed copy of Queen Victoria's only published work, portraits of Disraeli's parents in his study and the black-edged writing paper that he used after his wife's death. There is also a Gallery of Friendship lining the stairs and hall which is a collection of portraits of statesmen the Disraelis knew.

The next stop on this tour is Lane End and then the Thames-side town of Marlow which contains many charming Georgian buildings. The poet, Shelley, wrote the *Revolt of Islam* in a house in West Street and Mary Shelley wrote *Frankenstein* in the same house. The Old Parsonage and Deanery were once part of a great 14th century house and parts of the original building have survived.

We now come to Beaconsfield with its wide main street, old inns, timbered cottages, and red-brick Georgian houses. In the restored 15th century church lie Edmund Burke, the 18th century writer and politician, and Edmund Waller a poet. The writer, G.K. Chesterton, lived at Top Meadow on the outskirts of the town.

The next town is Amersham. This ancient market town consists of two parts: Old Amersham and new Amersham-on-the-Hill. Old Amersham lies in the valley of the River Misborne and was once a staging post on the coach road which ran from London to Aylesbury. The old coaching inns of the Crown Hotel, The Griffin, the Red Lion, the Elephant and Castle, The Swan and The King's Arms are evidence of the town's past and all date back from between the 16th to the 18th centuries. The broad High Street was once a coach road and it goes past the medieval market place where produce has been sold since the early 13th century when King John granted the town its charter. There is also an annual two-day fair, held on September 19 and 20, when the stalls and attractions stretch the length of the old town and this has also been held each year since the 13th century.

The old part of the town contains many timbered buildings dating from the the 16th and 17th centuries. Some of these were modernised in the 18th century and given brick fronts so disguising their true age. A notable building is Shardeloes

House completed in 1766 and it is an example of some of Robert Adams earliest work.

The newer Amersham-on-the-Hill developed around the railway station, built in the 1890s. Near here is the first house in Britain built incorporating the ideas of the architect Le Corbusier. It is call High and Over and is built of concrete and glass.

Now, via Chesham, the tour arrives in Rickmansworth, on the River Colne and the home of William Penn. The great Palladian mansion of Moor Park, just a mile south east of the town, was built in the late 17th century for the Duke of Monmouth. It was reconstructed in 1720 by Sir James Thornhill and Giacomo Leoni. The estate is the home of the well-known Moor Park Golf Club.

We now arrive on the edge of London and our last stops in the suburbs. The next visit is to Chipperfield and then Watford, situated on the Rivers Colne and Gade. Watford has a number of interesting buildings including the late 16th century Essex Chapel and the Elizabethan Fuller Free School from 1704. Moving on, the tour proceeds to Abbot's Langley and Bushey and then Harrow. Standing high on a hill, the town, with its 13th century spired church, is a notable landmark in the area. Harrow public school is the best known feature of the town. Founded in 1572 by John Lyon, the school has had some very famous pupils: Sir Winston Churchill, Sir Robert Peel, Lord Byron and Anthony Trollope are just a sample.

From Harrow we continue on to Radlett, Edgware and, our last stop, Barnet. Situated on the Great North Road, Barnet stands on a major route out of London which has contributed greatly to its growth over the centuries. It was the scene of a great battle in the Wars of the Roses when the Earl of Warwick was killed. An obelisk on Hadley Green marks the site of the battle.

ANTIQUE DEALERS
STAINES (0784)
K.W. Dunster Antiques, 23 Church Street, TW19 5DL TEL: 453297 PARKING: Easy OPEN: Mon-Wed, Fri-Sat 9-5 PERIOD: 19th-20th century GENERAL: Wide range of interesting antiques.

UXBRIDGE (0895)
Antiques Warehouse, 34-36 Rockingham Road, UB8 2TZ TEL: 256963 PARKING: Own carpark OPEN: Mon-Sat 10-6 MIN: £1 MAX: £4,000+ PERIOD: 19th-20th century GENERAL: General antiques.

IVER (0753)
Yesteryear, 12 High Street, SL0 9NG TEL: 652072 PARKING: Easy OPEN: Mon-Sat 10-6 MIN: £1 MAX: £500+ PERIOD: 18th-20th century GENERAL: China, glass, metalwork, pictures & furniture OTHER INFO: Our Georgian shop close to village centre and 17th century inn and Norman church.

DORNEY (0753)
The Old School Antiques, Dorney, SL4 6QW TEL: 0628-603247 ASSNS: LAPADA, TVADA PARKING: Own carpark OPEN: Mon-Sat 9.30-5.30 MIN: £20 MAX: £6,000 PERIOD: 17th-19th century SPECIALIST: 18th century English porcelain.

WINDSOR & ETON (0753)
Guy Bousfield, 58 Thames Street, SL4 1QW TEL: 864575 ASSNS: BADA PARKING: Easy OPEN: Mon-Sat 8.30-5 MINIMUM: £300 MAXIMUM: £7,000 PERIOD: 18th century SPECIALIST: Only Georgian furniture, pre-1830 OTHER INFO: Thirty feet from Thames Bridge & opposite Wren's Old House Hotel (said to have been built by Wren).

The Compton Gallery, 42 Thames Street, SL4 1PR TEL: 830100 FAX: 832278 PARKING: Own carpark OPEN: Mon-Fri 10.30-5, Sat, Sun by appt MINIMUM: £5 MAXIMUM: £15,000 PERIOD: 18th-20th century SPECIALIST: Jewellery, ceramics, glassware, silver GENERAL: General antiques.

Country Furniture, 79 St Leonards Road, SL4 3BZ TEL: 830154 PARKING: Easy OPEN: Mon-Sat 9.30-6 MIN: £5 MAX: £5,000 PERIOD: 18th-19th century SPECIALIST: French provincial furniture GENERAL: Farmhouse tables, painted furniture, antique beds

Dee's Antiques, 89 Grove Road, SL4 1HT TEL: 865627 ASSNS: CC PARKING: Easy OPEN: Mon-Sat 10-6 MIN: £5 MAX: £1,000 PERIOD: 19th century GENERAL: Victorian, Edwardian furniture, pictures etc.

Peter Martin Antiques, 40 High Street, Eton TEL: 864901 ASSNS: TVADA PARKING: Easy OPEN: Mon-Fri 10-1 & 2-5, Sat 10-1 MIN: £50 MAX: £20,000 PERIOD: 18th-early 20th century GENERAL: 3,500 sq ft of period, Victorian & later furniture OTHER INFO: Adjacent to Eton College, and in the shadow of Windsor Castle, River Thames.

Mostly Boxes, 92 High Street, Eton TEL: 858470 PARKING: Medium OPEN: Mon-Sat 9.30-6 MIN: £10 MAX: £700 (average £200) PERIOD: 18th-19th century SPECIALIST: Largest stock in UK of wooden boxes: tea caddies, writing, vanity, apothecary, etc OTHER INFO: Eton High Street is a good general trade call, over 25 dealers in a compact street.

O'Connor Bros, 59 St Leonards Road TEL: 866732 PARKING: Own carpark OPEN: Mon-Sat 8-5 PERIOD: 18th-20th century SPECIALIST: Antiques warehouse

Ulla Stafford, 41 High Street, Eton, SL4 6BD TEL: 859625 FAX: 833924 ASSNS: BADA, LAPADA, TVADA PARKING: Easy OPEN: Tues-Sat 10-5 MIN: £50 MAX: £20,000 PERIOD: 18th century SPECIALIST: European & English furniture GENERAL: Porcelain, Oriental works of art 1700-1820.

Turks Head Antiques, High Street, Eton, SL4 6AF TEL: 863939 PARKING: Easy OPEN:

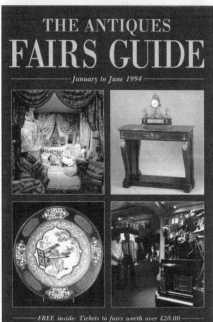

Tues-Sat 10.30-5 MIN: £5 MAX: £2,000 PERIOD: 18th-20th century SPECIALIST: Antique jewellery, silver + plate, cigarette cards, sporting memorabilia.

WARFIELD (0344)

Moss End Antique Centre, Moss End (A3095), RG12 6ES TEL: 861942 PARKING: Own carpark OPEN: Tues-Sun 10.30-5 MIN: £1 MAX: £5,000 PERIOD: 18th-20th century SPECIALIST: Large furniture & china GENERAL: China matching service, general antiques OTHER INFO: Coffee shop. Unlimited parking. We are in large garden centre with over 3,000 sq ft of antiques.

MAIDENHEAD (0628)

Miscellanea, 71 St Marks Road, SL6 2DP TEL: 23058 PARKING: Easy OPEN: Mon-Sat 10.30-5.30 MIN: £1 MAX: £2,000 PERIOD: 19th-20th century GENERAL: Antique & later furniture, collectable items & books.

WARGRAVE (0734)

Wargrave Antiques, 66 High Street TEL:

402914 PARKING: Easy OPEN: Wed-Sun 10-5.30 MIN: £1 MAX: £1,000 PERIOD: 19th-20th century GENERAL: General antiques.

HENLEY-ON-THAMES (0491)

The Country Seat, Huntercombe Manor Barn, RG9 5RY TEL: 641349 FAX: 641533 ASSNS: BADA, LAPADA, TVADA, CINOA PARKING: Own carpark OPEN: Mon-Sat 9-5.30 MIN: £10 MAX: £100,000 PERIOD: 17th-19th century SPECIALIST: Signed 19th century furniture, garden ornaments, furniture & statuary, panelled rooms.

Friday Street Antique Centre, 2 Friday Street, RG9 1AH TEL: 574104 PARKING: Easy weekdays OPEN: Mon-Sat 9.30-5.30, Sun 11-5 MIN: £1 MAX: £1,000 PERIOD: 19th-20th century GENERAL: 20 dealers, specialising in kitchenalia, small furniture, jewellery, prints & pictures, china, silver & the unusual. Occasional pre 19th century finds OTHER INFO: Friday Street (originally a Friday fish market) is on riverside, near town centre. Carpark in Greys Road.

Henley Antiques Centre, Rotherfield Arcade, 2-4 Reading Road, RG9 1AG TEL: 411468 PARKING: Easy OPEN: Mon-Sat 9.30-6, Sun 12-6 MIN: £3 MAX: £22,500 PERIOD: 17th-20th century SPECIALIST: Art Deco figures, etc GENERAL: General antiques

Barry Keene Gallery, 12 Thameside, RG9 1BH TEL: 577119 ASSNS: FATG, TVADA PARKING: Medium OPEN: Mon-Sat 9.30-5.30, Sun 10-5.30 MIN: £15 MAX: £15,000 PERIOD: 18th-20th century SPECIALIST: Fine English watercolours GENERAL: Paintings, etchings, prints & contemporary sculpture OTHER INFO: Red Lion, White Hart & Edwardian hotels,

Crispin's Restaurant, River trips: Hobbs & Sons.

R.J. Kingston Antiques, 95 Bell Street, RG9 2BD TEL: 574535 ASSNS: BADA, LAPADA, TVADA PARKING: Easy OPEN: Mon-Sat 9.30-5 PERIOD: 18th-19th century SPECIALIST: Period furniture & general antiques OTHER INFO: Home of the Royal Regatta.

B.R. Ryland, 75 Reading Road TEL: 573663 PARKING: Medium OPEN: Mon, Tues, Thurs-Sat 9-5 MIN: £1 MAX: £1,500 PERIOD: 18th-20th century GENERAL: General antiques.

Thames Gallery, Thames Side, RG9 2LJ TEL: 572449 FAX: 410273 ASSNS: TVADA PARKING: Medium OPEN: Mon-Sat 10-1, 2-5 MIN: £25 MAX: £3,500 PERIOD: 18th-20th century SPECIALIST: Silver & Sheffield plate OTHER INFO: On riverfront between 2 major hotels.

Thames Oriental Rug Co, 48-56 Reading Road, RG9 1AG TEL: 574676 FAX: 577877 ASSNS: National Carpet Cleaners Assn, GMC PARKING: Own carpark OPEN: Mon-Fri 9-5, Sat 9-12.30 MIN: £15 PERIOD: 19th-20th century SPECIALIST: Antique Oriental carpets GENERAL: Modern & semi-antique rugs of all regions & origins, needlework.

CAVERSHAM (0734)

The Clock Workshop, 17 Prospect Street, RG4 8JB TEL: 470741 FAX: 474194 ASSNS: BHI, TVADA PARKING: Own carpark OPEN: Mon-Fri 9.30-5.30, Sat 10-1 MIN: £200 PERIOD: 18th-19th century SPECIALIST: English longcases GENERAL: French clocks, including carriage, bracket clocks, barometers.

The Collectors Gallery, 8 Bridge Street Caversham, RG4 8AA TEL: 483663 ASSNS: TVADA PARKING: Medium OPEN: Mon-Fri 10-5, Sat 10-4 MIN: £15 MAX: £4,500 PERIOD: 18th-19th century SPECIALIST: English Victorian GENERAL: 18th-early 20th century watercolours & oils, prints.

READING (0734)

P.D. Leatherland Antiques, 68 London Street, RG1 4SQ TEL: 581960 ASSNS: TVADA PARKING: Own carpark OPEN: Mon-Sat 9-5 MIN: £5 MAX: £4,500 SPECIALIST: 19th century furniture GENERAL: Vast range of china & small collectables, including silver + plate, furniture from 18th century to 1920 OTHER INFO: Picturesque Thames Valley. Several excellent new hotels, good transport connections.

BURGHFIELD COMMON (0734)

Graham Gallery, Highwoods, RG7 3BG TEL: 832320 FAX: 832320 PARKING: Own carpark OPEN: Anytime by appt MIN: £50 MAX: £2,000 PERIOD: 19th-early 20th century GENERAL: Watercolours, oils & prints (mainly landscapes of Britain) OTHER INFO: 3 miles from M4 & 30 mins from Heathrow. Highwoods also listed in *Best B&B's in the World.*

STANFORD DINGLEY (0734)

Eliot Antiques, RG7 6LX TEL: 744649, 744346 PARKING: Easy OPEN: Mon-Sat 10.30-1 or by appt PERIOD: 18th-19th century SPECIALIST: 18th century English enamel boxes GENERAL: Porcelain OTHER INFO: Royal Oak, Yattendon, hotel & good food 2 miles from shop.

WOOLHAMPTON (0734)

The Old Bakery Antiques, RG7 5RE TEL: 712116 PARKING: Easy OPEN: Mon-Sat 9-5.30 MIN: £10 MAX: £600 PERIOD: 18th-20th century SPECIALIST: Furniture GENERAL: Country items & collectables.

THATCHAM (0635)

Richard Kimbell Ltd, Country Gardens, Turnpike Road, RG13 3AN TEL: 874822 FAX: 874388 PARKING: Own carpark OPEN: Seven days 9-6 MIN: £1 MAX: £3,000 PERIOD: 19th century SPECIALIST: Antique & reproduction pine country furniture and crafts.

HIGHCLERE (0635)

Griffons Court Antiques, RG15 9QS TEL: 253247 PARKING: Own carpark OPEN: anytime by appt only MIN: £60 MAX: £8,000 PERIOD: 18th-19th century SPECIALIST: Georgian furniture GENERAL: Porcelain, brass OTHER INFO: Abundance of good pubs with good food, Yew Tree Inn 1 mile.

HALFWAY (0488)

Walker & Walker, Halfway Manor TEL: 58693 ASSNS: TVADA PARKING: Easy OPEN: By appt MIN: £100 MAX: £100,000 PERIOD: 18th-19th century SPECIALIST: Fine barometers OTHER INFO: Restoration undertaken.

STREATLEY (0491)

Vine Cottage Antiques, High Street, RG8 9JD TEL: 872425 PARKING: Medium OPEN: Mon-sat 9.30-5.30 MIN: £10 MAX: £3,000 PERIOD: 18th-20th century GENERAL: General antiques OTHER INFO: Hotel/restaurant: The Swan. Diplomat 200 yds on Thames.

BLEWBURY (0235)

Blewbury Antiques, London Road, OX11 9NX TEL: 850366 PARKING: Own carpark OPEN: Mon, Wed-Sat 10-6 MAX: £1,000 PERIOD: 19th-20th century GENERAL: General antiques & collectables OTHER INFO: Nearby teashop, 4 village pubs.

WALLINGFORD (0491)

De Albuquerque Antiques, 12 High Street, OX10 0BP TEL: 832322 ASSNS: TVADA PARKING: Easy OPEN: Mon-Sat 10-5 MIN: £10 MAX: £5,000 PERIOD: 18th-19th century GENERAL: English furniture & objects of the period OTHER INFO: We have one of the largest & oldest medieval castles in England.

The Lamb Antiques Arcade, High Street TEL: 835166 PARKING: Easy nearby OPEN: Mon, Tues, Thurs, Fri 10-5, Wed 10-4, Sat 10-5.30 PERIOD: 18th-20th century GENERAL: 25+ shops & showcases offering wide selection, including furniture, porcelain, silver, jewellery, brass bedsteads, pictures, books & crafts OTHER INFO: The Lamb itself is an old coaching inn dating back to the 16th century with excellent coffee shop & winebar.

O'Donnell Antiques, 26 High Street TEL: 839332 PARKING: Easy OPEN: Mon-Sat 10-1, 2-5 MIN: £1 MAX: £2,000 PERIOD: 17th-20th century SPECIALIST: Maps, clocks GENERAL: Silverplate & inexpensive jewellery, worldwide curios, antiquities, collectables OTHER INFO: 16th century inn just opposite.

Second Time Around Antiques, 6 St. Peters Street, OX10 8EJ TEL: 839345 ASSNS: TVADA PARKING: Easy OPEN: Tues, Thurs-Sat 9.30-5, but anytime by appt MIN: £5 MAX: £2,000 PERIOD: 19th century SPECIALIST: Clocks & Oriental GENERAL: 4 showrooms of Georgian to Edwardian furniture & lots of smalls OTHER INFO: 11th century St Leonards Church, castle ruins, Riverside restaurant.

Summers Davis & Son, Calleva House, 6 High Street, OX10 0BP TEL: 836284 FAX: 833443 ASSNS: BADA, LAPADA, CINOA, TVADA PARKING: Own carpark OPEN: Mon-Sat 8-5.30 MIN: £50 MAX: £150,000 PERIOD: 18th-19th century SPECIALIST: English & Continental furniture OTHER INFO: Courier service available.

DORCHESTER-ON-THAMES (0865)

Giffengate Fine Art Ltd, 16 High Street, OX10 7HL TEL: 340068 FAX: 341149 ASSNS: LAPADA, TVADA PARKING: Easy OPEN: Mon-Sat 9-1, 2-5 MIN: £30 MAX: £30,000 PERIOD: 17th-19th century GENERAL: English & Continental furniture, lamps, porcelain, pictures.

Hallidays (Fine Antiques) Ltd, The Old College, OX10 7HL TEL: 340028 FAX: 341149 ASSNS: LAPADA, TVADA PARKING: Easy OPEN: Mon-Sat 9-1, 2-5 MIN: £10 MAX: £50,000 PERIOD: 17th-19th century GENERAL: General antiques OTHER INFO: One of largest showrooms in the South. Hotels: George, White Hart.

Shambles Antiques, 3 High Street, OX10 7HH TEL: 341373 ASSNS: TVADA PARKING: Easy OPEN: Tues-Sun 10-5 MIN: £10 MAX: £4,000 PERIOD: 18th-19th century SPECIALIST: Chairs & upholstery OTHER INFO: Directly opposite medieval abbey in an 18th century shambles. Probably the most beautiful village in the Thames valley.

OXFORD (0865)

Blackwell's Rare Books, 38 Holywell Street, OX1 3SW TEL: 792792 FAX: 248833 ASSNS: ABA PARKING: Medium OPEN: Mon-Sat 9-6 (Tues open at 9.30) MIN: £30 MAX: £10,000 PERIOD: 16th-20th century SPECIALIST: Modern Firsts & antiquarian literature, childrens books sets, private pressbook, bibliography OTHER INFO: Our main shop (48-51 Broad Street) handles general secondhand material.

Christopher Legge Oriental Carpets, 25 Oakthorpe Road, Summertown, OX2 6RU TEL: 57572 FAX: 54877 PARKING: Easy OPEN: Mon-Sat 9.30-5 MIN: £50 MAX: £7,500 but most stock £275-£3,500 PERIOD: 19th-20th century GENERAL: Old & antique tribal & village rugs, etc OTHER INFO: Brown's restaurant & Old Parsonage Hotel.

Magna Gallery, 41 High Street, OX1 4AP TEL: 245805 ASSNS: ABA PARKING: Medium OPEN: Mon-Sat 10-5.30 MIN: £5 MAX: £3,000 PERIOD: 17th-19th century SPECIALIST: Oxford topography & English county maps GENERAL: Maps & topographical prints. OTHER INFO: Oxford University, Blenheim Palace. Old Parsonage Hotel & Eastgate Hotel.

Oxford Antiques, 10 North Parade, OX2 6LX TEL: 512816 PARKING: Easy OPEN: Mon-Sat 10-1.30 MIN: £1 MAX: £1,500 PERIOD: 18th-20th century SPECIALIST: 19th century pottery & porcelain GENERAL: Small antiques OTHER INFO: Fourth generation antique dealers. Area of Oxford where it is still possible to park. Famous Rose & Crown pub

Oxford Architectural Antiques, The Old Depot, Nelson Street, Jericho TEL: 53310 PARKING: Own carpark OPEN: Mon-Fri 10-4, Sat 9.30-5 PERIOD: 19th century SPECIALIST: Wide selection salvaged items GENERAL: Architectural antiques, Victorian fixtures & fittings OTHER INFO: Close to town centre.

Payne & Son (Goldsmiths) Ltd, 131 High Street, OX1 4DH TEL: 243787 FAX: 793241 ASSNS: BADA, NAG PARKING: Difficult OPEN: Mon-Fri 9-5 MIN: £50 MAX: £10,000 PERIOD: 17th-20th century SPECIALIST: Antique silver & jewellery.

Sanders of Oxford, 104 High Street, OX1 4BW TEL: 242590 FAX: 721748 ASSNS: ABA OPEN: Mon-Fri 9-1, 2.15-5.15, Sat 9-1 MIN: £1 MAX: £2,000 PERIOD: 17th-20th century GENERAL: Antique & rare prints, maps, fans & cards OTHER INFO: Right in very centre of Oxford so perfect for visitors.

Titles Old & Rare Books, 15/1 Turl Street, OX1 3DQ TEL: 727928 FAX: 727928 ASSNS: ABA, PBFA OPEN: Mon-Sat 9.30-5.30 MIN: £1 MAX: £10,000 PERIOD: 17th-20th century SPECIALIST: Environment including natural history GENERAL: Travel, illustrated books, fine bindings, the arts, science & earth sciences OTHER INFO: We also help customers build their collections. Book search.

CHALGROVE (0865)

Rupert Hitchcox Antiques, Antique Warehouse, Warpsgrove TEL: 890241 FAX: 890241 PARKING: Own carpark OPEN: Mon-Sat 9-5, Sun 2-5 MIN: £25 MAX: £2,500 PERIOD: 18th-20th century GENERAL: Furniture only, (600-800 pieces), mostly oak & walnut, all in original condition, housed in 6 barns. No smalls.

WATLINGTON (0491)

Stephen Orton Antiques, The Antiques Warehouse, Shirburn Road, OX9 5BZ TEL: 613752 FAX: 613875 ASSNS: TVADA PARKING: Own carpark OPEN: Mon-Fri 9-5 & by appt PERIOD: 18th-19th century GENERAL: Quality furniture.

TETSWORTH (0844)

Tetsworth Antiques, 42a Old Stores, High Street, OX9 7DU TEL: 281636 PARKING: Easy OPEN: Tues, Thurs-Sun 11-5 MIN: £1 MAX: £4,000 PERIOD: 18th-20th century GENERAL: General antiques and some jewellery OTHER INFO: Good food at village pub next door.

THAME (0844)

Rosemary and Time, 42 Park Street, OX9 3HR TEL: 216923 PARKING: Easy OPEN: Mon-Sat 9-6 MIN: £50 MAX: £5,000 PERIOD: 18th-20th century SPECIALIST: Antique clocks of all types OTHER INFO: Picturesque historic town. Spread Eagle, famous coaching inn.

PRINCES RISBOROUGH (08444)

Bell Street Antiques Centre, 20-22 Bell Street, HP17 0AD TEL: 3034 PARKING: Medium OPEN: Mon-Sat 9.30-5.30, Sun 12-5 MIN: £1 MAX: £2,000 PERIOD: 19th-20th century SPECIALIST: We are a medium size antique

centre with 19 dealers GENERAL: General antiques OTHER INFO: We also have a beautiful conservatory tearoom & garden.

HIGH WYCOMBE (0494)

Burrell Antiques, Kitchener Works, Kitchener Rd TEL: 523619 ASSNS: Guild of Master Craftsmen PARKING: Own carpark OPEN: Mon-Fri 8.30-5 MIN: £50 MAX: £3,000 PERIOD: 19th century SPECIALIST: Victorian wind-out tables GENERAL: Furniture.

LANE END (0494)

Bach Antiques, Essex House. Finings Road, HP14 3EY TEL: 882683, 881695 PARKING: Easy OPEN: Tues, Thurs, Fri 11-5, Wed 10-3, Sat 10-5, Suns summer only MAX: £5,000 PERIOD: 18th-19th century GENERAL: Mainly furniture, stripped pine & decorative items OTHER INFO: West Wycombe House & farmhouse B&B's.

MARLOW (0628)

Coldstream Military Antiques, 55a High Street, SL7 1BA TEL: 822503 Fax: 822503 OPEN: by appt only MIN: £5 MAX: £5,000 PERIOD: 19th-20th century SPECIALIST: Fine original helmets, headdresses, badges of the British Army OTHER INFO: Insurance valuations, probate & sale by private treaty.

BEACONSFIELD (0494)

Grosvenor House Interiors, 51 Wycombe End, Old Town, HP9 1LX TEL: 677498 ASSNS: TVADA PARKING: Own carpark OPEN: Mon, Tues, Thurs-Sat 9.15-1, 2-5.30 MIN: £50 MAX: £8,000 PERIOD: 17th-19th century SPECIALIST: Victorian upholstered furniture GENERAL: Pictures, clocks, fireplaces & porcelain.

Norton Antiques, 56 London End, HP9 2JH

TEL: 673674 ASSNS: TVADA PARKING: Easy OPEN: Tues, Thurs-Sat 10-1, 2.15-5 MIN: £1 MAX: £5,000 PERIOD: 17th-20th century SPECIALIST: Georgian mahogany furniture GENERAL: Clocks, oil & water colour paintings, woodworking tools OTHER INFO: Fine selection of coaching inns & restaurants (including Wheeler's fish restaurant).

Period Furniture Showrooms, 49 London End, HP9 2HW TEL: 674112 PARKING: Easy OPEN: Mon-Sat 9-5.30 MIN: £5 MAX: £3,000 PERIOD: 18th-20th century GENERAL: General antiques.

The Spinning Wheel, 86 London End, HP9 2JD TEL: 673055 PARKING: Own carpark (1 space) OPEN: Mon-Sat 10-5 MIN: £5 MAX: £2,500 PERIOD: 18th-19th century SPECIALIST: Glass GENERAL: Furniture & china OTHER INFO: Interesting street of 17th-19th century houses.

AMERSHAM (0494)

Amersham Antiques & Collectors Centre, 20-22 Whielden Street, Old Amersham, HP7 0NT TEL: 431282 PARKING: Difficult OPEN: Mon-Sat 9.30-5.30 MIN: £1 MAX: £1,650 PERIOD: 19th-20th century SPECIALIST: Diecast model vehicles GENERAL: General antiques.

The Cupboard Antiques, Baileys, 80 High Street TEL: 722882 PARKING: Easy OPEN: 10-5, closed Fri & Sun SPECIALIST: Georgian, Regency and early Victorian furniture and decorative items.

Michael Quilter Antiques, 38 High Street TEL: 433723 PARKING: Easy OPEN: Mon-Sat 10-5 PERIOD: 19th-20th century SPECIALIST: Stripped pine GENERAL: Brass, copper.

Partridges, 67 High Street, Old Amersham HP7

0DT TEL: 728452 PARKING: Easy OPEN: Tues-Thurs, Sats 10.30-5, Fri 1-5 MIN: £10 MAX: £1,200 PERIOD: 18th-20th century SPECIALIST: Fine porcelain GENERAL: China, glass, Sheffield plate, 18th-19th century framed engravings, mainly people, fashion prints, small furniture OTHER INFO: The Pheasant Inn, Ballinger (very good food 10 mins away), The Eton Wine Bar, Elephant & Castle, Kings Arms & The Crown-all in Amersham.

Sundial Antiques, 19 Whielden Street, Old Amersham HP7 0HU TEL: 727955 PARKING: Medium OPEN: Mon-Sat 9.30-5.30 MIN: £5 MAX: £1,500 PERIOD: 18th-20th century SPECIALIST: Metalware, horse brasses GENERAL: General antiques OTHER INFO: Museum open weekends/bank holidays.

CHESHAM (0494)

Albert Bartram, 177 Hivings Hill, HP5 2PN TEL: 783271 PARKING: Own carpark OPEN: By appt MIN: £50 MAX: £8,000 PERIOD: 17th-19th century SPECIALIST: Antique pewter & early metalwork OTHER INFO: Illustrated lists of antique pewter issued.

Chess Antiques, 85 Broad Street, HP5 2PG TEL: 783043 FAX: 791302 ASSNS: LAPADA PARKING: Own carpark OPEN: Mon-Sat 9-5 MIN: £100 PERIOD: 18th-19th century SPECIALIST: Clocks, furniture OTHER INFO: Restoration.

Omniphil Prints Ltd, Germains Lodge, Fullers Hill, HP5 1LR TEL: 771851 PARKING: Own carpark OPEN: Mon-Sat 9-5.30 MIN: £2 MAX: £100 PERIOD: 19th century SPECIALIST: Illustrated London News only.

Queen Anne House Antiques, 57 Church Street, HP5 1HY TEL: 783811 PARKING: Easy OPEN: Weds, Fri, Sat 9.30-5 & by appt MIN: £1 MAX: £2,000 PERIOD: 19th-20th century GENERAL: Quality furnishing antiques for the home, also china, glass, Persian rugs OTHER INFO: On Metropolitan Line out of London.

RICKMANSWORTH (0923)

The Whitestocks Collections Ltd, The Barn, Whitestocks Farm, Loudwater Lane, WD3 4AL TEL: 710960 FAX: 710960 ASSNS: LAPADA,

BADA PARKING: Own carpark OPEN: Thurs-Sat 10-5 MIN: £15 MAX: £6,000 PERIOD: 17th-19th century SPECIALIST: Halcyon Days Porcelain GENERAL: English furniture, objets d'art OTHER INFO: Lovely setting in beautiful gardens where the coffee is always hot.

CHIPPERFIELD (0923)

Frenches Farm Antiques, Tower Hill TEL: 265848 PARKING: Easy OPEN: Mon-Sat 11-6 MIN: £1 MAX: £800 PERIOD: 19th-20th century GENERAL: General antiques.

ABBOTTS LANGLEY (0923)

Dobson"s Antiques, 53 High Street, WD5 0AA TEL: 763186 PARKING: Easy OPEN: Mon-Sat 8.30-5.30 MIN: £1 MAX: £1,000 PERIOD: 19th-early 20th century GENERAL: Pre 1914 furniture & bric-a-brac OTHER INFO: The only English pope, Pope Adrian IV born here.

BUSHEY (081)

Country Life Antiques, 33a High Street TEL: 950 8575 FAX: 950 8575 PARKING: Easy OPEN: Mon-Sat 9-5 MIN: £5 MAX: £2,500 PERIOD 19th-20th century SPECIALIST: Antique pine from all over Europe GENERAL: Oils, watercolours, collectables etc OTHER INFO: Very interesting olde worlde shop on 3 floors. Export/shipping arranged.

RADLETT (0923)

Hasel-Britt Ltd. Antiques, 157 Watling Street, WD7 7NQ TEL: 854477 PARKING: Medium OPEN: Mon-Sat 10-5.30, (Wed ° day) PERIOD 19th-20th century GENERAL: Stock changeable OTHER INFO: Bric-a-brac also.

BARNET (081)

C. Bellinger Antiques, 91 Wood Street, EN5 4BX TEL: 449 3467 PARKING: Easy OPEN: Thurs-Sat 10-5 MIN: £10 MAX: £1,000 PERIOD: 19th-20th century GENERAL: Antique furnitures & general antiques.

EDGWARE (081)

Edgware Antiques, 19 Whitchurch Lane, HA8 6JZ TEL: 952 1606, 952 5924 PARKING: Easy OPEN: Thurs-Sat 10-5 or by appt MIN: £3 MAX: £1,000 PERIOD: 19th-20th century GENERAL: Furniture, paintings, porcelain, silver + plate, bric-a-brac.

Northern Home Counties

Much of this tour covers the Chiltern Hills, part of the chalk belt that stretches from Dorset through to Yorkshire. It has given a scenery of rounded hills and beechwoods. Nowadays many of the towns and villages serve as dormitories for London but most have retained their ancient charm.

The first visit is to Sawbridgeworth with it fine Georgian houses and decorated and perpendicular church containing many monuments and brasses. After that we carry on to Hatfield Broad Oak and Stansted Mountfitchet before arriving in Bishops Stortford, the birthplace of Cecil Rhodes. The house of his birth, now a Memorial Museum and Commonwealth Centre, is one of the town's interesting and historic buildings. Others include two inns, the Black Lion and the Boar's Heads. The National Trust property of Hatfield Forest lies about 3 miles east of Bishops Stortford and covers some 1000 acres. This is the remnants of the great Forest of Essex, a royal hunting preserve since before the Norman Conquest.

The unspoilt village of Much Hadham is next, with its Georgian and earlier buildings, which has been the manor of the Bishop of London for 900 years. The Bishop's Palace is largely Jacobean and there are Elizabethan and Regency houses in the High Street.

Continuing west along the B1004 the route reaches the ancient town of Hertford, standing on the River Lea. The ruins of its original castle, built in the early 12th century, may still be seen. The present castle was built between 1500 and 1800. There are a number of other interesting and historic buildings dating from the same period.

Hatfield New Town, our next stop, was built in 1947 and has doubled the population of the area. However Old Hatfield retains its charm and historic appearance. It is the site of the palatial Hatfield House built between 1607 and 1611 by Robert Cecil, first Earl of Salisbury. The Cecil family have lived in the house ever since. It contains wonderful collections of rare tapestries, furniture, paintings and armour. A surviving wing of the old royal palace of Hatfield may be seen in the grounds. It was here that Elizabeth I spent much of her youth and some of her relics may be seen.

Turning north we come to Knebworth and Knebworth House. Home of the same family, the Lyttons, for over 500 years, the original Tudor manor house was altered in the 19th century to reflect the high Gothic style fashionable at that period. The beautiful rooms contain portraits, furniture and a collection of manuscripts and letters.

On to Hitchin, a market town with considerable charm and built around its market place. The streets contain Georgian and earlier houses including the 15th century Church of St Mary and the Priory built from 1770 with small parts surviving from an earlier 14th century Carmelite building.

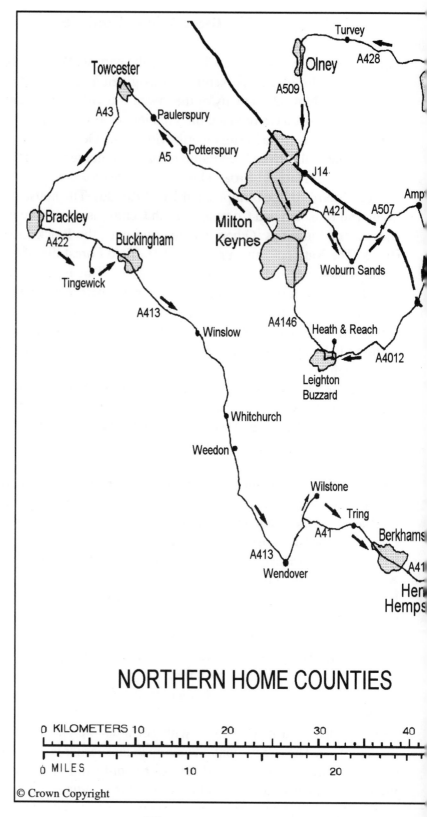

NORTHERN HOME COUNTIES

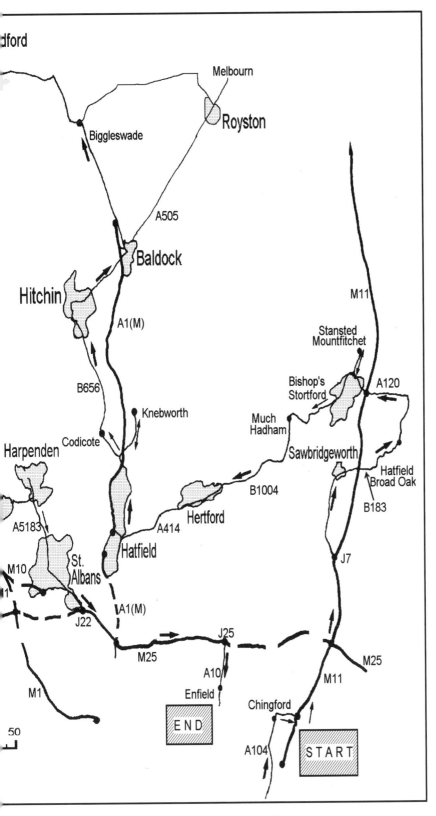

The route continues through the ancient town of Baldock, with several fine Georgian buildings in the High Street, and Royston which grew up on the intersection of the Roman Ermine Street and the Icknield Way soon after the Norman Conquest. The town's church has a rare pentagon shaped oriel window.

Next is Melbourn and then Biggleswade, on the River Ivel. It was once a stopping place for coaches on the Great North Road as its numerous inns show. The oldest of the coaching inns is the White Hart, while The Sun has been restored and converted into houses.

The tour then comes to the county town of Bedford which has been in existence since Saxon times. Sacked and burned by the Danes in 1010, a castle was built here by the Normans of which only the mound remains. St Peter's Church still has some Saxon stonework which bear burnmarks, said to have been caused in the Danish attack. John Bunyan was imprisoned in Bedford gaol and wrote *The Pilgrim's Progress* whilst there. The Bunyan Meeting Library and Museum in Mill Street contains all the surviving relics of John Bunyan as well as copies of *The Pilgrim's Progress* in 169 languages.

Passing first through the pretty village of Turvey we next visit Olney, on the River Ouse. This town has long been associated with the making of boots. William Cowper lived here between 1768 and 1786 and his home in Market Place is now the Cowper and Newton Museum.

The route now turns south to Milton Keynes, a new town established in 1967 which has engulfed some of the small villages in the area. Known for its grid-like street plan and concrete cows, after some 25 years it is now establishing its own identity. It is the home of the Open University and also has an extremely good shopping centre.

Nearby Woburn Abbey, home of the Dukes of Bedford for over 350 years, is probably the most famous of the great English houses open to the public. It contains collections of furniture, silver and pictures including works by Canaletto, Van Dyck, Rembrandt, Gainsborough, Velazques, etc. Also on display is a wonderful Sevres dinner service presented to Duke of Bedford by Louis XV. In the grounds there is a wildlife park and an antiques centre.

The tour crosses the motorway to arrive in Ampthill, once the site of a 15th century castle and a pleasant town with many fine Georgian buildings, before turning south west to Leighton Buzzard. Prehistoric and Roman remains have been found in this ancient town as well as three Saxon cemeteries. The town's most notable building is its church, All Saints. Started at the end of the 13th century its spire rises to a height of 190 feet. Unfortunately parts of the building were damaged by fire in 1985 although some of its best features escaped. Amongst these is the 13th century oak lectern, said to be the oldest in Britain. The font and the sanctus bell, both possibly older than the church itself, also survived.

Turning north west along the A5 via Potterspury and Paulerspury we next visit

Towcester (pronounced Toe-ster) standing astride the old Roman road of Watling Street. Although once the Roman settlement of Lactodorum, it was as a coaching town in the 18th and 19th centuries that it really prospered. It has a number of coaching inns and one of them, the Saracen's Head, was featured in Dickens' *Pickwick Papers*.

Now on to the small town of Brackley which has a number of 18th century houses in the High Street and a church with an early-English tower. Buckingham, our next call, was the county town from 888AD until 1725 when a disastrous fire destroyed much of the town and the county administration was transferred to Aylesbury. Because of the fire the town's buildings are mostly Georgian although a few older ones did survive. The Chantry Chapel is one survivor. It was originally 13th century but rebuilt in 1475 although it still retains a Norman doorway. Four miles from Buckingham stands Stowe, now a school. It was the 18th century home of the Dukes of Buckingham and it is set in superb landscaped gardens with the largest collection of garden buildings in the country.

Moving along the A413 via Winslow, with a 17th century hall that is one of the few private buildings that can definitely be attributed to Sir Christopher Wren, and then on to Whitchurch. An earthmound is all that is left of the castle of Bolebec on the west side of Whitchurch. The village has a fine church with a 15th century painting in the north aisle.

The route continues to Weedon, a canal boat centre, and then to Wendover, beautifully situated in the Chiltern Hills, this small town includes several Georgian and older houses and the decorated style can be seen in the local church.

Tring is the next stop on the tour. The Grand Union Canal climbs through 65 locks between here and Brentford on the outskirts of London to one of its summit levels near the town. Tring Steps are a series of six locks that enable the canal to rise to a height of 500 feet above sea level. Near to the canal lie the Tring Reservoirs which form a national nature reserve.

Also situated on the Grand Union Canal, Berkhamsted is an old market town with some surviving buildings of interest. The Saxons submitted to William the Conqueror here after the Battle of Hastings. William's half-brother was given a grant of land and he started work on the castle, ruins of which may still be seen. The castle has been associated with many historic figures. Amongst it previous owners have been Katherine of Aragon, Anne Boleyn, Jane Seymour and Queen Elizabeth I before she ascended the throne.

Passing through the small town of Redbourn with its Norman church and Georgian houses, we move on to the residential town of Harpenden before arriving in St Albans. The most notable feature of this city is its hilltop cathedral. It has an exceptionally long nave dating from the Norman period and was built as an abbey church. At that time building materials were in short supply in the area and so Roman bricks and tiles were used in the main fabric of the building. The abbey was wealthy and the abbots powerful. However, they were unpopular in the town and at the Dissolution of the Monasteries almost all of the abbey buildings were destroyed. The church was only saved because the townspeople intended to use it as their parish church. The Lady Chapel was turned into the town's grammar school. The upkeep of such a large building as the church was too much and gradually it was left to decay and reached a ruinous condition by 1877 when it was needed as a cathedral for the counties of Hertfordshire and Bedfordshire. At this point the millionaire, Lord Grimthorpe, came on stage and rescued the church. He paid for the restoration of the building but he insisted that everything should be done to his own designs. Much of what he did has been criticised and led to the formation of the Society for the Protection of Ancient Monuments. While it might be possible to sympathise with those people who founded the Society, one is left with the question: what would have happened to St Albans Cathedral without Lord Grimthorpe?

In the city of St Albans itself there are many interesting and historic buildings. The ancient Fighting Cocks Inn is one of the oldest inns in the country and there are numerous good Georgian houses including Romeland House, one of the finest of these. Several fine churchs also survive: the perpendicular St Peter's with old glass, St Stephen's displaying an inscribed 16th century lectern and St Michael's with its monument to Francis Bacon who died here in 1626 and lived at Gorhambury House. Ruins of the old house survive near the later mansion built between 1777 and 1784. In 1455 and 1461 St Albans was also the site of two great battles in the Wars of the Roses.

From St Albans we travel along the M25 eastwards to Junction 25 where we take the A10 to Enfield, our last visit on this tour.

ANTIQUE DEALERS
CHINGFORD (081)
Nicholas Salter Antiques, 8 Station Approach, E4 7AZ TEL: 529 2938 PARKING: Own carpark OPEN: 10-5, closed Thurs MIN: £10 MAX: £2,000 PERIOD: 19th-20th century GENERAL: Antiques & collectables OTHER INFO: Shop part of Victorian station that Queen Victoria visited, hunting lodge nearby.
SAWBRIDGEWORTH (0279)
Herts & Essex Antiques Centre, The Maltings, Station Road, CM21 9JX TEL: 722044 PARKING: Own carpark OPEN: Tues-Fri 10-5, Sat-Sun 10.30-6 MIN: £1 MAX: £2,000 PERIOD: 18th-20th century GENERAL: Antiques & collectables.
HATFIELD BROAD OAK (0279)
Tudor Antiques, High Street, CM22 7HQ TEL: 718557 PARKING: Easy OPEN: Seven days 9.30-5.30 MIN: £1 MAX: £1,000 PERIOD: 18th-20th century GENERAL: Porcelain, china, furniture (wide range). Unusual & interesting items OTHER INFO: We live opposite so easy access out of hours. Good pub/restaurant next door.
STANSTED MOUNTFITCHET (0279)
Valmar Antiques, Croft House, High Lane, CM24 8LQ TEL: 813201 FAX: 816962 ASSNS: LAPADA OPEN: By appt MIN: £100 MAX: £10,000 PERIOD: 18th-19th century SPECIALIST: Furniture, decorative furnishings GENERAL: Large stock of quality antiques in 18th century barn.
BISHOPS STORTFORD (0279)
Northgate Antiques, Northgate House, 21 Northgate End, CM23 2ET TEL: 656957 FAX: 755873 PARKING: Own carpark OPEN: Mon-Fri 9-5, Sat 9.15-3.30 MIN: £5 MAX: £3,500 PERIOD 18th-20th century SPECIALIST: Oils & watercolours GENERAL: General antqiues OTHER INFO: Close to auction rooms. Good hotels: Donn Hall, Watfield Heath, Manor of Groves, High Wych. Sawbridgeworth.
MUCH HADHAM (0279)
Careless Cottage Antiques, High Street, SG10 6DA TEL: 842007 PARKING: Easy OPEN: Mon-Sat 9-5 MIN: £10 MAX: £1,500 PERIOD: 18th-19th century SPECIALIST: Oak & country furniture GENERAL: China, glass, rugs, decorative items OTHER INFO: Henry Moore Sculpture Park 1 mile, Working Forge Museum.

HERTFORD (0992)
Beckwith & Son, Street, St Nicholas Hall, St Andrew Street, SG14 1HZ TEL: 582079 PARKING: Easy OPEN: Mon-Sat 9-1, 2-5.30 MIN: £1 MAX: £10,000 PERIOD 17th-early 20th century SPECIALIST: Furniture & clocks GENERAL: We deal in anything old & interesing except stamps & coins. Very large varied stock OTHER INFO: Shop is very large & fascinating 15th century timbered building near centre town.
Robert Horton Antiques, 13 Castle Street, SG14 1ER TEL: 587546 ASSNS: BWCMG PARKING: Medium OPEN: Mon-Sat 9-5.30 MIN: £150 MAX: £4,000 PERIOD 18th-19th century SPECIALIST: Clocks, watches GENERAL: Furniture.
HATFIELD (0707)
Old Cathay Fine Books & Prints, 48 Park Street, Old Hatfield, AL9 5BA TEL: 274200 FAX: 270730 PARKING: Own carpark OPEN: Seven days 10.30-6 MIN: £1 MAX: £1,000 PERIOD: 19th-20th century SPECIALIST: Edwardian & Victorian colourplate, picture books, travel & topography, childrens books, postcards, printed ephemera, many prints OTHER INFO: 200 yds from 3 old pubs.
KNEBWORTH (0438)
Hamilton & Tucker Billiard Co. Ltd., Park Lane TEL: 811995 FAX: 814939 ASSNS: BSAIF & Billiard Snooker Trade Assn (BSTA) PARKING: Own carpark OPEN: Mon-Fri 9-5 or by appt MIN: £250 MAX: £20,000 PERIOD 19th-20th century SPECIALIST: Billiard tables, dining tables, traditional games GENERAL: Game accessories, chairs etc OTHER INFO: Knebworth House, Hatfield House, Brocket Hall. Our showrooms are outside Knebworth Station.
CODICOTE (0438)
Richard Kimbell Ltd, Country Gardens, High Street, SG4 8XA TEL: 821616 FAX: 821756 PARKING: Own carpark OPEN: Seven days 9-6 MIN: £1 MAX: £3,000 PERIOD: 19th century SPECIALIST: Antique & reproduction pine country furniture and crafts.
HITCHIN (0462)
Bexfield Antiques, 13-14 Sun Street TEL: 432641 PARKING: Medium OPEN: Mon, Tues, Thurs-Sat 9.30-5 MIN: £10 MAX: £2,500 PERIOD 18th-20th century SPECIALIST: Sil-

ver GENERAL: General antiques OTHER INFO: Sun Hotel.

Countrylife Galleries, 41-43 Portmill Lane, SG5 1DJ TEL: 433267 PARKING: Own carpark OPEN: By appt MIN: £50 MAX: £30,000 PERIOD: 18th-19th century SPECIALIST: Garden, flower & landcape subjects.

Eric T Moore, 24 Bridge Street, SG5 2DF TEL: 450497 ASSNS: ABA PARKING: Own small carpark OPEN: Mon-Sat 9.30-1, 2.15-5.30 MIN: £1 MAX: £200 PERIOD: 18th-20th century GENERAL: Books, antiquarian maps & prints.

R.J. Perry Antiques at the Hitchin Antiques Gallery, 38 Bridge Street, SG5 2DF TEL: 434525 ASSNS: LAPADA PARKING: Medium OPEN: Mon-Sat 10-5.30 MIN: £5 MAX: £3,000 PERIOD 18th-early 20th century GENERAL: General antiques & collectables OTHER INFO: Delightful market town with many period buildings. Our own dates back to 1580. Excellent selection of shops, hotels & restaurants. Market day Tuesday. Full overseas shipping service. All major credit cards

Phillips of Hitchin Antiques Ltd, The Manor House, SG5 1JW TEL: 432067 FAX: 441368 ASSNS: BADA PARKING: Easy OPEN: Mon-Sat 9-5.30 MIN: £500 MAX: £10,000 PERIOD 18th-19th century SPECIALIST: English furniture, mainstream but also including unusual pieces: eg metamorphic, campaign, travelling furniture with makers names, library furniture etc, reference books on furniture & antiques.

BALDOCK (0462)

Anthony Butt Antiques, 7-9 Church Street, SG7 5AE TEL: 895272 PARKING: Easy OPEN: Tues-Sat usual hours or by appt (resident) MIN: £100 MAX: £3,000 PERIOD: 17th-19th century GENERAL: Furniture & decorative objects OTHER INFO: Close to the centre of this small market town, near M1/M25 junction.

Howard Antique Clocks, 33 Whitehorse Street, SG7 6QF TEL: 892385 PARKING: Own carpark OPEN: Tues-Sat 9.30-5 MIN: £150 MAX: £4,000 PERIOD 18th-20th GENERAL: Clocks: longcase, bracket, wall & carriage.

Ralph & Bruce Moss, 26 Whitehorse Street, SG7 6QQ TEL: 892751 PARKING: Own carpark OPEN: Mon-Sat 9-6 MIN: £15 MAX: £10,000 PERIOD 17th-20th century SPECIAL-

IST: Musical boxes occasionally held in stock GENERAL: General antiques OTHER INFO: Historic market town with fine 12th century church, many Georgian houses.

Graham Porter Antiques, 31 Whitehorse Street TEL: 895351 PARKING: Easy OPEN: Mon-Sat 9-5, Sun 11-4 MIN: £5 MAX: £1,500 PERIOD 18th-20th century SPECIALIST: Victorian & earlier pine GENERAL: Furniture, clean retail stock OTHER INFO: Many hotels & excellent restaurants in the area.

ROYSTON (0763)

Royston Antiques, 29 Kneesworth Street, SG8 5AB TEL: 243876 PARKING: Own carpark OPEN: Mon-Wed, Fri-Sat 09.30-5 MIN: £1 MAX: £2,000 PERIOD: 19th-20th century SPECIALIST: Victorian & Edwardian furniture GENERAL: General antiques & collectables OTHER INFO: Next to King James I Palace and opposite Royston Museum. Royston market days Wed & Sat. The medieval Cave was once used by the Knights Templar for worship. The Bull is 17th century hotel/restaurant.

MELBOURN (0763)

P.N. Hardiman, 62 High Street, SG8 6AJ TEL: 260093 PARKING: Own carpark OPEN: Mon-Sat 9-5 MIN: £300 MAX: £4,000 PERIOD: 18th-20th century GENERAL: Furniture.

BIGGLESWADE (0767)

Shortmead Antiques, 46 Shortmead Street, SG18 0AP TEL: 601780 PARKING: Easy OPEN: Mon-Wed, Fri, Sat 10-4 MIN: £5 MAX: £1,500 PERIOD: 18th-20th century GENERAL: General antiques OTHER INFO: Very picturesque village ° mile from A1, 5 mins drive from Old Warden Aircraft Museum.

BEDFORD (0234)

D.H. Stapleton Antiques, 51 Ford End Road TEL: 211087 PARKING: Easy OPEN: Mon-Sat 9-5.30 MIN: £5 MAX: £20,000 PERIOD: 18th-20th century GENERAL: Oak, mahogany & pine furniture OTHER INFO: Home of John Bunyan. Shakespeare Hotel.

WILSTEAD (0234)

Manor Antiques, The Manor House, Cottonend Road, MK45 3BT TEL: 740262 PARKING: Own carpark OPEN: Mon-Sat 10-5 MIN: £45 MAX: £6,000 PERIOD: 19th century SPECIAL-IST: Furniture & good quality accessories

OTHER INFO: 15 mins drive to Woburn Abbey & large antique centre.

TURVEY (0234)

Fenlan Antiques, Old Working Men's Room, High Street, MK43 8DE TEL: shop 888916, home 342775, 713524 PARKING: Own carpark OPEN: Mon-Fri 8.30-5.30, Sat 9.30-1 MIN: £20 MAX: £3,500 PERIOD: 19th-20th century SPECIALIST: Furniture & restoration products & sundries OTHER INFO: Mainly workshop for restoration/cabinet making. Trade & public welcome. Village atmosphere, reasonably close to other antique outlets 12-15 mile radius.

OLNEY (0234)

Market Square Antiques, 20 Market Place, MK46 4BA TEL: 712172 PARKING: Easy OPEN: Mon-Sat 10-5, Sun 1-5 MIN: £10 MAX: £5,000 PERIOD: 18th-20th century GENERAL: General antiques OTHER INFO: Market town (market Thursdays). Also Cowper Museum, Church Park etc

Olney Antique Centre, Rose Court, Market Place, MK46 4BA TEL: 712172 PARKING: Easy OPEN: Mon-Sat 10-5, Sun 1-5 MIN: £1 MAX: £1,000 PERIOD: 18th-20th century GENERAL: General antiques.

John Overland Antiques, Rose Court, Market Place TEL: 712351 PARKING: Own carpark OPEN: Mon-Sat 10-5, closed Wed MIN: £5 MAX: £5,000 PERIOD: 17th-19th century SPECIALIST: Country oak, mahogany, antique pine, clocks & very unusual items OTHER INFO: Market town, 10 mins from M1.

Pine Antiques, 10 Market Place, MK46 4EA TEL: 711065 PARKING: Easy OPEN: Mon, Tues, Thurs-Sat 10-5, Sun 12-5 MAX: £800 PERIOD: 19th-20th century GENERAL: Pine & reclaimed timber furniture, no reproduction OTHER INFO: Adjacent to centre of town noted for many antique shops.

MILTON KEYNES (0908)

Restall Brown & Clennell Ltd, Cosgrove Hall, Cosgrove, MK19 7JB TEL: 565888 FAX: 564353 PARKING: Own carpark OPEN: Mon-Fri 9-5.30 or by appt MIN: £100 MAX: £25,000 PERIOD: 18th-19th century GENERAL: Full range of antique furniture OTHER INFO: Many other dealers in area. Good hotels & restaurants nearby. Woburn Abbey 15 miles. We can collect

and return to local rail station. We also manufacture high quality reproduction furniture.

WOBURN (0525)

Applecross Antiques, Woburn Abbey Antiques Centre, MK43 0TP TEL: 290350 OPEN: Normal PARKING: Own carpark OPEN: Nov-Easter 11-5, Easter Sunday - Oct 10-6 MIN: £50 MAX: £1,000 PERIOD: 17th-19th century SPECIALIST: Blue & White transfer ware, Staffordshire figures GENERAL: Silver, ceramics, prints, needlework OTHER INFO: All stock pre-1860, Woburn Abbey Stately Home open to public, together with Safari Park.

Sefton Antiques, Woburn Abbey Antique Centre, MK43 0TP TEL: 290350 OPEN: Normal PARKING: Own carpark OPEN: Nov-Easter 11-5, Easter Sunday-Oct 10-6 MIN: £50 MAX: £3,000 PERIOD: 17th-19th century SPECIALIST: Brass candlesticks, papier maché, Tunbridge Ware, pewter GENERAL: General antiques OTHER INFO: All stock pre-1860.

Christopher Sykes Antiques, The Old Parsonage, Bedford Street, MK17 9QL TEL: 290259 FAX: 290061 ASSNS: American Breweriana Assn Inc, member Canadian Corkscrew Club PARKING: Easy OPEN: Mon-Sat 9-.30 MIN: £10 MAX: £5,000 PERIOD: 18th-19th SPECIALIST: Corkscrews illustrated catalogue £7 or $15 GENERAL: Collectors antique items specialising in wine-related pieces, scientific and medical instruments OTHER INFO: Bedford Arms & The Bell hotels, Paris House restaurant (1 mile), Black Horse pub.

Town Hall Antiques, Market Place TEL: 290950 PARKING: Easy OPEN: Tues-Sun 11-5.30 MIN: £1 MAX: £5,000 PERIOD: 19th-early 20th century SPECIALIST: Early porcelain, furniture. Toys, prints, childrens books, pine.

Woburn Abbey Antiques Centre, South Stables, Woburn Abbey, MK43 0TP TEL: 290350 FAX: 290271 PARKING: Own carpark OPEN: Seven days Easter Sunday-31st Oct 10-6, 1st Nov-Easter Saturday 11-5, closed Christmas MIN: £1 MAX: £5,000 GENERAL: 17th-19th century furniture in mahogany, oak, walnut, fruitwood etc, paintings, prints, silver, clocks, glass, porcelain, objets d'art OTHER INFO: 40 shops and 12 fitted showcases on 2 floors all in a beautiful village street setting.

Stately home of the Dukes of Bedford and currently home of the Marquess & Marchioness of Tavistock and family.

WOBURN SANDS (0908)

Haydon House Antiques, Station Road, MK17 8RX TEL: 582447 ASSNS: LAPADA PARKING: Own carpark OPEN: Mon-Fri 10-5.30, Sat-Sun 10-1 MIN: £5 MAX: £6,000 PERIOD: 18th-19th century GENERAL: General antiques OTHER INFO: 2 miles from Woburn Abbey & Bedford Arms Hotel, Woburn.

Woburn Sands Antique Centre, Nevilles Antiques, The Old Bakery, 1 Russell Street TEL: 584827, 583024 PARKING: Own carpark OPEN: Mon-Sat 10-5 or by appt MIN: £1 MAX: £4,000 PERIOD: 18th-20th century GENERAL: Furniture, pictures, silver, china, lighting.

AMPTHILL (0525)

Ampthill Antiques, Market Square, TEL: 403344 PARKING: Easy OPEN: Tues-Sat 9.30-5, Sun 2-5 MIN: £1 MAX: £2,500+ PERIOD: 19th-20th century GENERAL: General antiques, Art Deco including Clarice Cliff OTHER INFO: Bunyan Country & Houghton House.

Robert Harman, 11 Church Street, MK45 2DL TEL: 402322 ASSNS: BADA PARKING: Own carpark OPEN: Mon-Sat 9.30-5 MIN: £300 MAX: £35,000 PERIOD: 18th-early 19th century SPECIALIST: Fine 18th century English furniture & works of art.

The Pine Parlour, 82A Dunstable Street, MK45 2JS TEL: 403030 PARKING: Easy OPEN: Tues-Sun 10-5 MIN: £5 MAX: £800 PERIOD: 19th-20th century SPECIALIST: Georgian & Victorian pine furniture GENERAL: Kitchenalia, country bygones & interesting cast iron objects including Victorian mangles.

Ann Roberts Antiques, 1 Kings Arms Yard TEL: 403394 PARKING: Easy OPEN: Wed-Sat 11.30-4.30, Sun 2-5 MIN: £30 MAX: £750 PERIOD: 18th-20th SPECIALIST: Victorian & Georgian original fenders, cast iron fires GENERAL: Furniture, wood fire surrounds, chests, cupboards, tables, chairs, oil lamps, clocks.

S & S Timms Antiques Ltd, 20 Dunstable Street, MK45 2JT TEL: 403067, (0860) 482995 ASSNS: LAPADA PARKING: Medium OPEN: Mon-Fri 9.30-5, Sat 10-4 or by appt MIN: £30 MAX: £5,000 PERIOD: 18th-20th century GENERAL: Furniture, copper, brass & fine art

HEATH & REACH (0525)

Brindleys, Woburn Road, LU7 0AR TEL: 237750, home 240448 PARKING: Own carpark OPEN: Mon-Sat 10-5 MIN: £5 MAX: £4,500 PERIOD: 18th-20th century GENERAL: Pottery, porcelain, paintings & furniture.

Charterhouse Gallery Ltd, 26 Birds Hill, LU7 0AQ TEL: 237379 FAX: 237379 ASSNS: LAPADA, FATG PARKING: Own carpark OPEN: Mon-Thurs, Sat 10-1, 2-5 MIN: £25 MAX: £8,000 PERIOD: 19th-early 20th century SPECIALIST: Watercolours GENERAL: Fine art restoration & framing.

LEIGHTON BUZZARD (0525)

David Ball Antiques, 59 North Street, LU7 7EQ TEL: 210753, 382954 ASSNS: LAPADA PARKING: Easy OPEN: Mon 10-5 or by appt MIN: £10 MAX: £3-4,000 PERIOD: 18th-20th century GENERAL: Georgian & Victorian furniture, clocks, barometers, and unusual items.

Linslade Antiques, 1 New Road, Linslade TEL: 378348 PARKING: Own carpark OPEN: Mon-Sat 9.30-5.30, Sun 1-5 MIN: £1 MAX: £3,000 PERIOD: 17th-20th century GENERAL: General antiques OTHER INFO: 200 yards mainline station, close Woburn Abbey.

Linslade Antiques, 16 Wing Road, Linslade TEL: 378348 PARKING: Own carpark OPEN: Mon-Sat 9.30-5.30, Sun 1-5 MIN: £1 MAX: £3,000 PERIOD: 17th-20th century GENERAL: General antiques OTHER INFO: 200 yards mainline station, close Woburn Abbey.

POTTERSPURY (0908)

Reindeer Antiques Ltd, 43 Watling Street, NN12 7QD TEL: 542407, 542200 FAX: 542121 ASSNS: BADA, LAPADA PARKING: Own carpark OPEN: Mon-Sat 9-6 MIN: £50 MAX: £65,000 PERIOD 17th-19th century SPECIALIST: English furniture GENERAL: Oak, statuary, period accessories, mirrors etc OTHER INFO: Large showrooms. Near Althorp House & Cock Inn. Also Bull Inn at Stony Stratford-both famous for Cock & Bull story.

PAULERSPURY (0327)

Malcolm Cameron, The Antique Galleries, Watling Street, NN12 7LQ TEL: 811238 ASSNS: BADA PARKING: Own carpark OPEN: Mon-Sat 9-5.30 MIN: £400 MAX:

£8,000 PERIOD 17th-18th century SPECIAL-IST: English furniture & barometers only.

TOWCESTER (0327)

Clark Galleries, 215 Watling Street, NN12 6BX TEL: 352957 ASSNS: Ass. British Picture Restorers PARKING: Medium OPEN: Mon-Fri 9-5.30, Sat 9.30-4 MIN: £150 MAX: £25,000 PERIOD 18th -20th century SPECIALIST: Oil paintings of all types OTHER INFO: Some watercolours & prints. Fine art (oils) reliners & restorers. Excellent hotel: Saracen's Head, Pickwick restaurant, a good coffee shop.

Ron Green Antiques, 209, 227 & 239 Watling Street TEL: 350387 PARKING: Easy OPEN: Mon-Sat 8.30-5.30 MIN: £25 MAX: £10,000 PERIOD 17th-19th century SPECIALIST: English & Continental furniture, decorative items OTHER INFO: Early coaching inn: Saracens Head lies between our shops and was used by Charles Dickens.

Shelron Collectors Shop, 9° Brackley Road, NN12 6DH TEL: 350242 ASSNS: Postcard Traders Assn, Cartophilic Society PARKING: Easy OPEN: Wed-Sat 10-4 MIN: £1 MAX: £200 PERIOD 19th-20th century GENERAL: Mostly paper. Bric-a-brac, models, books, all types of cards (playing, cigarette, post, trade etc) maps, prints OTHER INFO: Saracen's Head Hotel (mentioned in Dicken's Pickwick Papers) 1 min. walk.

BRACKLEY (0280)

Brackley Antiques, Hollywood House, 69 High Street, NN13 7BW TEL: 703362 PARKING: Own carpark OPEN: Mon-Sat 10-6 MIN: £1 MAX: £2,000 PERIOD 19th-20th century GENERAL: Traditionally upholstered 19th century chairs & sofas, china, pottery, furniture, collectables.

The Old Hall Bookshop, 32 Market Place TEL: 704146 ASSNS: ABA, PBFA PARKING:Easy OPEN: Mon-Sat 9.30-1, 2-5.30 MIN: £1 MAX: £1,000+ PERIOD: 19th-20th century SPECIAL-IST: Local topography, travel, art, literature, sporting, children GENERAL: Large general stock OTHER INFO: Pleasant small market town, 20 miles north of Oxford. The Old Hall is a fine 18th century house set in the middle of the Market Place. The Gardens at Stole nearby.

Right Angle, 24 Manor Road, NN13 6AJ TEL:

702462 FAX: 701228 ASSNS: FATG PARKING: Easy OPEN: Mon-Sat 9.30-1, 2-5.30, (Weds am only) MIN: £4 MAX: £1,500 PERIOD: 18th-20th century SPECIALIST: Engravings GENERAL: Watercolours, oils, etchings, chromolithographs OTHER INFO: 3 good antique shops + excellent bookshop.

TINGEWICK (0280)

Tim Marshall Antiques, The Antique Shop, Main Street, MK18 4NL TEL: 848546 PARKING: Easy OPEN: Mon-Sat 10-6 MIN: £5 MAX: £2,000 PERIOD: 17th-19th century SPECIAL-IST: Longcase clocks GENERAL: Oak & pine country furniture etc OTHER INFO: Stowe School & Stowe Landscape Gardens (NT) 3 miles.

Tingewick Antiques Centre, Heritage House, Main Street, MK18 4RB TEL: 848219 PARKING: Easy OPEN: Mon-Thurs, Sat 10-5.30, Sun 11-5 MIN: £1 MAX: £2,000 PERIOD: 18th-20th century SPECIALIST: Roll top desks GENERAL: Furniture, china, collectables.

WINSLOW (0296)

Medina, 8 High Street, MK18 3HF TEL: 712468 OPEN: Mon-Sat 9.30-6 MIN: £5 MAX: £1,000 SPECIALIST: Antiquarian maps & prints GENERAL: Watercolours, oils, prints etc OTHER INFO: Ancient market town with church built c.1260 & Queen Anne-style hall built in 1700. Bell Hotel & restaurants.

Winslow Antiques Centre, 15 Market Square, MK18 3AB TEL: 714540 FAX: 714928 PARKING: Easy OPEN: Mon-Sat 10-5 MIN: £1 MAX: £3,000+ PERIOD: 17th-20th century GENERAL: Silver, jewellery, furniture, porcelain, glass, earthenware etc OTHER INFO: Winebar, bistro, good coffee shop opposite. Close to Winslow Hall & Clayden House (NT).

WHITCHURCH (0296)

Deerstalker Antiques, 28 High Street, HP22 4JT TEL: 641505 PARKING: Easy OPEN: Tues, Wed, Thurs, Sat 10-5.30 MIN: £1 MAX: £3,000 PERIOD: 19th-20th century SPECIALIST: Georgian chests of drawers GENERAL: Bric-a-brac, smalls, furniture OTHER INFO: Tudor Hotel in village.

WENDOVER (0296)

Antiques at...Wendover, The Old Post Office, HP22 6DU TEL: 625335 PARKING: Own carpark OPEN: Mon-Sat 10-5.30, Sun 11-5.30 MIN: £1 MAX: £3,000+ PERIOD: 20th century (dateline 1930) GENERAL: 30+ dealers in a Tudor building (pine spiral staircase & wall prints, a ghost & Hamish the Scottie dog) with very wide range of town & country items OTHER INFO: Red Lion Hotel (17th century coaching inn). Wendover is of general historic interest with cottages given by Henry VIII to Anne Boleyn.

Bowood Antiques, Bowood Lane (nr. Wendover), HP22 6PY TEL: 622113 PARKING: Own carpark OPEN: Mon-Sat 9-5 MIN: £15 MAX: £12,000 PERIOD: 17th-19th century SPECIALIST: Mainly period furniture & related items GENERAL: Mirrors, rugs, porcelain OTHER INFO: Shop is situated off the A413 halfway between Gt. Missenden & Wendover. Showrooms are in the buildings of an old farmhouse.

Sally Turner Antiques, Hogarth House, High Street, HP22 6DU TEL: 624402, Mobile: 0860 201718 ASSNS: LAPADA PARKING: Own carpark OPEN: Mon-Sat 10-5.30 MIN: £5 MAX: £5,000 PERIOD: 17th-19th & some 20th century SPECIALIST: Furniture, ceramics & decorative smalls OTHER INFO: Close to residential hotels & pubs, coffee shops, centre of town with further shops, boutiques etc Library. Village setting & good country rambles.

Wendover Antiques, 1 South Street, HP22 6EF TEL: 622078 ASSNS: LAPADA PARKING: Medium (in lane opposite) OPEN: Mon-Sat 9-5.30 MIN: £25 MAX: £6,000+ PERIOD: 17th-19th century SPECIALIST: Portraits, old Sheffield plate, decanters GENERAL: Furniture, fine pictures, silhouettes, 18th century engravings OTHER INFO: Hotels: Hartnell House, Aylesbury, The Bell (Aston Clinton), Places of Interest: Waddesdon Manor, Amersham Old Town, Wendover Old Town.

WILSTONE (0442)

Michael Armson Antiques, 34 Tring Road, TEL: 8900990 FAX: 891167 PARKING: Easy OPEN: Mon, Tues, Thurs-Sat 8.30-5.30 MIN: £25 MAX: £10,000 PERIOD: 17th-19th century SPECIALIST: Georgian furniture & small items.

TRING (0442)

John Bly, 50 High Street, HP23 5AG TEL: 823030 FAX: 890237 PARKING: Easy OPEN: Mon-Sat 9-5.30 MIN: £100 MAX: £10,000 PERIOD 17th-19th century SPECIALIST: English furniture

GENERAL: Old fashioned antiques.

Country Clocks, 5 Pendley Bridge Cottages, Tring Station, HP23 5QU TEL: 825090 PARKING: Easy OPEN: Mon-Sat 9.30-5.30, Sun 2-5 MIN: £100 MAX: £5,000 PERIOD 18th-19th century SPECIALIST: Wall, mantel, carriage & longcase clocks OTHER INFO: Next to Grand Union Canal, near picturesque village of Aldbury & Ashridge Forest (NT).

BERKHAMSTED (0442)

Park Street Antiques, 350 High Street, HP4 1HT TEL: 864790 FAX: 864790 ASSNS: BADA PARKING: Own carpark OPEN: Tues-Sat 9.30-5.30 MIN: £50 MAX: £40,000 PERIOD: 18th-19th century GENERAL: General antiques.

REDBOURN (0582)

J.N. Antiques, 86 High Street, AL3 7BD TEL: 793603 PARKING: Own carpark OPEN: Mon-Sat 9-6 MIN: £1 MAX: £1,500 PERIOD 19th-20th century SPECIALIST: Furniture 1760-1930 GENERAL: General antiques OTHER INFO: Close exit 9 of M1. Moat House, Harpenden & Markyate, Aubrey Hotel, Hempstead Rd.

Tim Wharton Antiques, 24 High Street TEL: 794371 PARKING: Easy OPEN: Tues, Wed, Fri 10-5, Sat 10-4 MIN: £10 MAX: £10,000 PERIOD 17th-19th century GENERAL: Oak, country , mahogany furniture & general antiques.

HARPENDEN (0582)

Meg Andrews Antique Costume & Textiles, 28 Cowper Road, AL5 5NG TEL: 460107 FAX: 768627 PARKING: Easy OPEN: Anytime by appt PERIOD: 18th-20th century SPECIALIST: Chinese costume, Arts & Crafts, paisley shawls, English costume for collectors. Archive fabrics OTHER INFO: Luton Hoo, Hatfield House, Verulamium (Roman) Museum in St Albans.

HEMEL HEMPSTEAD (0442)

Abbey Antiques & Fine Art, 97 High Street, Old Town, HP1 3AH TEL: 64667 ASSNS: LAPADA PARKING: Easy OPEN: Mon-Sat 9.30-5.30 , Weds halfday MIN: £5 MAX: £3,000 PERIOD 18th-20th century SPECIALIST: Jewellery, silver, watercolours GENERAL: Furniture, small antiques OTHER INFO: Modern jewellery & silver. Valuations, repairs.

ST ALBANS (0727)

By George, 23 George Street, AL3 4DS TEL: 853032 PARKING: Medium OPEN: Mon-Fri 10-

5, Sat 10-5.30 hours MIN: £2 MAX: £6,000+ PERIOD: 18th-20th century GENERAL: 25+ dealers with a good range.

The Clock Shop, 161 Victoria Street (on City Station bridge), AL1 3TA TEL: 856633 ASSNS: BWCMG PARKING: Easy OPEN: Mon-Weds, Fri 10.30-6.30, Sat 10.30-4 MIN: £50 MAX: £6,000 PERIOD 18th-20th century SPECIALIST: Clocks, watches, barometers. Repairs OTHER INFO: Open market Weds & Sat, St Michaels Manor, The Noke. Michelino's restaurant next door.

Magic Lanterns, By George, 23 George Street, AL3 4ES TEL: 865680, 853032 PARKING: Medium OPEN: Mon-Wed, Fri 10-5, Thurs 11-5, Sat 10-5.30, Sun 1-5 MIN: £18 MAX: £1,000+ PERIOD: 19th-20th century SPECIALIST: Over 500 antique, period & decorative light fittings: Converted gas lights, Art Nouveau & Art Deco OTHER INFO: Author of *Lamps & Lighting*. Situated in 15th century antique centre with craft arcade and restaurant. Near the Fighting Cock, one of oldest pubs in England.

Oriental Rug Gallery Ltd, 42 Verulam Road, AL3 4DQ TEL: 841046 FAX: 841046 PARKING: Easy OPEN: Mon-Sat 9-6, Sun 10.30-4 MIN: £50 MAX: £5,000+ PERIOD 19th-20th century SPECIALIST: Carpets, rugs, kelim, old & new, from Iran, Turkey, Afghanistan, Russia OTHER INFO: 20 mins by train to London. Open Sunday.

St Albans Antique Fair, The Town Hall, Chequers Street TEL: 844957 PARKING: Easy OPEN: Mon-Sat 10-4 (admission 20p) 8-4 MIN: £2 MAX: £600 PERIOD 18th-19th century SPECIALIST: Records, books, 1930's jewellery Deco costume GENERAL: General antiques & collectables OTHER INFO: Town Hall is above Tourist Info Centre.

Stuart Wharton, 1 George Street, AL3 4EB TEL: 59489 FAX: 55474 ASSNS: NAG, FGA PARKING: Medium OPEN: Mon-Sat 9.30-6 MIN: £10 MAX:£1,000 PERIOD some 18th, 19th-20th century SPECIALIST: I only have small stock of small & medium silver tableware, flatware.

ENFIELD (081)

Richard Kimbell Ltd, Country World, Cattlegate Road, Crews Hill, EN2 9DP TEL: 364 6661 FAX: 364 5455 PARKING: Own carpark OPEN: Seven days 9-6 MIN: £1 MAX: £3,000 PERIOD: 19th century SPECIALIST: Antique & reproduction pine GENERAL: Country furniture & crafts.

La Trouvaille, 1a Windmill Hill, EN2 6SE TEL: 367 1080 PARKING: Medium OPEN: Mon-TuesThurs-Sat 9.30-5.30 MIN: £5 MAX: £2,000 PERIOD: Late 18th-20th century GENERAL: General antiques OTHER INFO: 1 modern & 3 antique showrooms, Unusual & exclusive gifts housed in 200 year old building overlooking attractive greens & historic Elizabethan Gentlemans Row.,

Essex and Suffolk

Away from London's northwest sprawling suburbs, this tour, never rising beyond 400 feet above sea level, passes through the gently undulating countryside north of the Thames Estuary where the sea has made numerous and often long, intricate inlets in the coast. Some of the coastal settlements were Victorian resorts for work-weary Londoners, others small river ports. The whole route is characterised by the host of quaint timbered buildings and leafy lanes.

We start the tour in Chipping Ongar on the River Roding. This was the site of a Saxon castle, the moat and mound of which may still be seen. Nearby Blackmore village has a 12th-15th century restored church with good timbers and a tower of note. Onwards to Ingatestone which is famous for its main street full of timber-framed Georgian houses and Ingatestone Hall, the seat of the Petrie family who have lived there for over 400 years.

We then head for the Thames Estuary, via the village of Stock, to Grays before turning east to Leigh-on-Sea. Now a holiday resort, its inhabitants once earnt their living by fishing and smuggling. The adjoining town of Westcliff-on-Sea is also popular with holiday makers. It is, however, overshadowed in popularity by its next door neighbour, Southend, which is the epitome of a seaside town, with a pier, amusement arcades, cockle and whelk stands, fish and chip shops, etc.

Moving from the delights of the popular English coastal towns, we come next to Rayleigh, once the site of a castle, and then on, via Purleigh, to the harbour town of Maldon on the mouth of the rivers Chelmer and Blackwater. A very pretty town, it has a number of medieval houses in the High Street and its 13th century church has a most unusual triangular tower.

From Maldon we rejoin the A12 for a short distance before taking the B1024 to Coggeshall, on the River Blackwater. This is a charming village noted particularly for its lacemaking and wool. Wool particularly helped make Coggeshall prosperous in medieval times. The most famous attraction in the village is Paycocke's, built by wool merchant, John Paycocke, at the beginning of the 16th century. It is a fine half-timbered house, with a long pink and white, brick and timber facade. An intricately carved beam runs the whole width of the front the house just above the ground floor windows. From the latter part of the 16th century the house had a series of owners and was allowed to deteriorate. In 1890 it was in such bad condition that it was sold for demolition. However, it was saved and at the beginning of this century the Buxton family bought and restored it. In 1924 they gave the house and its garden to the National Trust.

Continuing along the route, the next villages of Felstead, Great Bardfield and Sible Hedingham retain many medieval features as does the market town of Halstead. The tour now reaches Colchester. This is one of the best known of English Roman towns although its history starts much earlier. There is evidence

Maldon

Paycockes, Coggeshall

of settlement from at least the 5th century BC and by the 1st century AD it was the capital of King Cunobelin, Shakespeare's Cymbeline, of the Trinovantes. After the Roman invasion in AD43 Colchester was soon taken and developed as an important centre. The town quickly grew especially as retired Roman soldiers were given grants of land and settled there. About twenty years after the invasion, Queen Boudicca (Boadicea) of the Iceni led her rebellion and in the process sacked Colchester. Many of the Roman veterans joined the fight to protect the town but to no avail. Some fled before the Iceni and took shelter inside the great temple built in honour of the Emperor Claudius. Within a few days, though, this was also captured and burnt. The surviving foundations still bear the marks of that fire. The rebellion could not succeed, however, and afterwards the Romans rebuilt Colchester. In the 2nd century AD the stone walls, much of which can still be seen, were built.

After the Roman withdrawal from Britain the fortunes of Colchester temporarily declined with repeated raids by the Saxons and Vikings. In the late 11th century the Normans built a castle on the foundations of the Claudian temple. Apart from a brief spell of military action during the barons' revolt against King John, the castle's principal role was as a prison until the Civil War when it was held for the King by two Royalists, Sir Charles Lucas and Sir George Lisle. They resisted the Parliamentary forces for some three months but in August 1648 they surrendered. The two Royalist leaders were put on trial and executed by firing

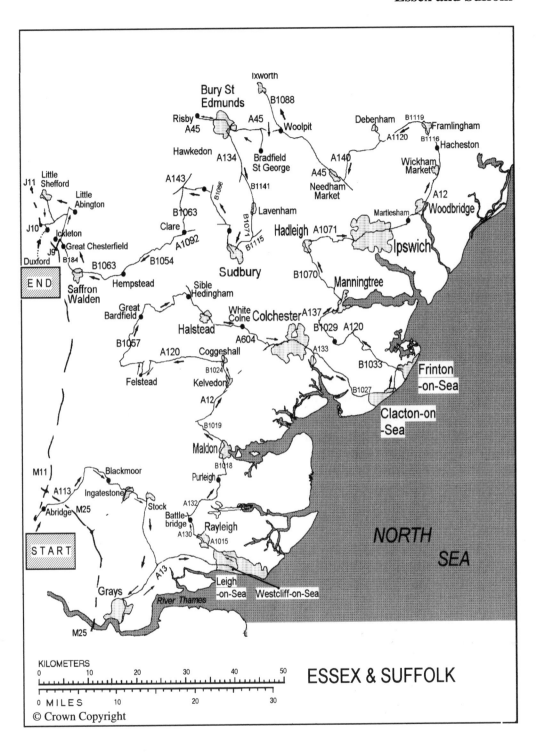

ESSEX & SUFFOLK

© Crown Copyright

squad on the 28th August 1648. There is a stone to commemorate their execution. After the Civil War the castle, like so many others, was left to decay until the 18th century when it was purchased by a Mr Charles Gray. In 1920 it was bought by Viscount Cowdray who presented it to the borough and it has been managed by them since.

The castle keep is the largest surviving in the country at 151 feet by 110 feet. Originally the keep was three storeys high but today only two storeys survive. The prisoners kept here have left their mark with graffitti and carvings still be to be seen on the walls.

As might be expected in a town with such a rich heritage, Colchester has several museums. The Castle Museum, housed in Colchester Castle, has a wonderful collection with particular emphasis on the Roman period. A fine collection of clocks can be found in the aptly named Clock Museum in a 16th century house in Trinity Street. There is the Natural History Museum in the High Street and Hollytrees Museum is virtually opposite with displays of toys, costume and decorative arts. Again in Trinity Street, Trinity Museum illustrates Essex rural life over the past two hundred years. Finally, the Minories Art Gallery in the High Street has exhibitions of 20th century art.

This is just a small taste of the many fascinating attractions that Colchester has to offer the visitor. The Tourist Information Centre in Queen Street really is an essential place to go upon arrival in the town.

The route takes the B1027 to take in the small riverside town of Wivenhoe, damaged by the 1884 Essex earthquake, then continues on to the sedate seaside town of Frinton-on-Sea. Now turning inland the tour passes through Great Bromley and Manningtree before reaching the market town of Hadleigh. Here stand the remains of a 13th century castle started by the powerful baron Hubert de Burgh in 1231 although within a year he was in disgrace and Henry III had seized his lands. Edward III rebuilt the castle in the mid 14th century as a defence against the French. By the 16th century the castle was deteriorating and was used as a source of building material. Two towers and the curtain wall still survive and give splendid views across the Thames Estuary and Essex Marshes.

From Hadleigh we go to Ipswich, the largest town in Suffolk and standing at the head of the Orwell Estuary. It has long been a thriving port having trading links with the Continent going back over centuries. It was the birthplace of Cardinal Wolsey, Henry VIII's Lord Chancellor and favourite for many years until he was disgraced. Ipswich still has some interesting and historic buildings. Christchurch Mansion, near the centre of the town, is one of the most striking. This is a fine Tudor house set in beautiful parkland and containing superb collections of ceramics, pictures, clocks and glass as well as having rooms furnished in styles ranging from the 16th to 19th centuries.

After visiting the village of Martlesham we reach another town standing at the head of an estuary, nearby Woodbridge on the Deben. The town has been a centre for boatbuilding and sailmaking since the 14th century when they built warships here for Edward III. The town has many fine, old buildings. One of these on the Quayside, now a private house, was the Boat Inn built in 1530 and nearby is the 17th century Ferry House. Another 16th century inn has been converted to private use and is now the row of cottages at 1-5 Quayside. The most noteworthy riverside building is the weatherboarded tide mill still working until 1957 when the oak drive shaft snapped.

Seckford Hall, a mile south of Woodbridge and a fine Elizabethan mansion, was the family home of Thomas Seckford, Woodbridge's great 16th century benefactor. He was an MP and barrister and he commissioned the first systematically surveyed maps of England. In the town he founded the Seckford Almshouses to care for thirteen poor men, although the present buildings only date from the 19th century. He also built Shire Hall on Market Hill which is heavily ornamented and has curly gables in the Dutch fashion. Seckford Hall was once connected by secret tunnel to another family home, the Abbey, just below the church. Now the Hall has been converted into an hotel and is said to be haunted by Thomas Seckford's ghost.

The tour continues through Wickham Market and Hacheston until it reaches Framlingham with its 12th century castle standing just outside the town. The owners of this castle had an unfortunate habit of rebelling against the monarch of the day. In 1173, Hugh Bigod, Earl of Norfolk, rebelled against Henry II but had to surrender in 1175. Most of the castle was levelled in reprisal but Hugh Bigod's son, Roger, rebuilt it. It seems that Roger Bigod had not learnt by his father's mistakes because he rebelled against King John. He fared no better and the castle was taken by the King in 1215. In the 14th century the castle passed out of the possession of the Bigod family but the new owners were no luckier. In 1405 the owner, Thomas Mowbray, was beheaded by Henry IV and in 1572 yet another went to the block because Elizabth I suspected him of supporting Mary, Queen of Scots. This unlucky building was left to Pembroke College, Cambridge in 1636, later much of the inside was destroyed to make a poorhouse. Now there are extensive remains with towers, walls and chimneys still standing. The Prison Tower is the most notable as it has no outside entrance to the ground floor, the only way in is by a door on the floor above and then through a trapdoor to the lower storey.

In Framlingham itself, Mansion House on Market Hill is a building of note. It is 16th century with later additions and faced with tiles that resemble bricks. A connection with the castle's history is found in the narrow lane at the top of Market Hill running down to Fore Street, called Queens Head Passage. The queen was Mary Tudor who was staying at the castle when she heard news of her succession in 1553. She later visited the town with her husband, Philip II of Spain.

We now turn west to visit Ashfield and Debenham, then Needham Market and Woolpit which both have interesting churches. The one in Needham Market includes a unique 15th century wooden hammerbeam nave roof. In Woolpit the decorated and perpendicular church, St Mary's, has a double hammerbeam roof which is richly carved with angels and has a splendid south porch and modern tower.

Next, Bury St Edmunds, county town of West Suffolk, takes its name from the shrine of St Edmund, the last king of East Anglia, who died about 870AD. According to legend he was killed by marauding Danes who shot him full of arrows then cut off his head. His soldiers recovered his body but his head was only found by following the howls of a she-wolf who was guarding it. His shrine was a place of pilgrimage before the Normans arrived until well into the Middle Ages. The 11th century Benedictine abbey built here became one of the greatest in England and occupied about six acres of ground. Now all that is left is a splendid 14th century gateway and the 13th century Abbot's Bridge. The county of Suffolk was declared a new diocese in 1914 and Bury St Edmunds was the choice for the cathedral. The town had the fine restored church of St James, which includes a nave begun in 1438 plus a new porch, cloister, walk and chancel, to serve as the cathedral. Inside there are a thousand hassocks to represent all the parishes of Suffolk.

The city itself has some interesting buildings. The 12th century Moyse's Hall, perhaps originally a Jewish merchant's house, is now a museum containing local antiquities. Amongst the many buildings of architectural interest are the 17th century town hall, remodelled by Robert Adam, the fine Unitarian Chapel, built in 1711 and Cupola House, an outstanding late 17th century town mansion. A most interesting exhibition is The Gershom-Parkington Memorial Collection of Clocks and Watches in a Queen Anne house on Angel Hill. On display are timepieces from the 16th century onwards.

The route now follows the A134 to Lavenham, one of the most prosperous of East Anglia's medieval wool towns. It contains over 300 listed buildings including many from the Tudor period. Stopping first in Hawkesdon, we next visit Long Melford, a particularly pretty village with an impressive main street, absolutely packed with antique shops. It still retains its medieval character with features like the timber-framed 16th century Bull Inn, a picturesque village green and an almshouse, restored in the 19th century, but founded by Sir William Cordell in 1593. There is a fine perpendicular church which includes a late 15th century chapel and stained glass from the same period. In the churchyard of the congregational church there is a typical crinkle-crankle (or undulating) brick wall with the church itself dating from 1724.

The Elizabethan Melford Hall stands on the east side of the village green. This National Trust property is a magnificent creation with turrets crowned by onion

Saffron Walden

domes yet still retaining a particularly English flavour. Amongst the many fascinating items is a survey of the estate done in 1580 by Sir William Cordell, owner of the Hall, with all the fields named. A later owner of the house was the fifth Baronet, Vice Admiral Sir Hyde Parker who ran away to sea as a boy and worked his way up through the ranks to become an admiral. His son also became an admiral and their influence can be seen in the vivid paintings of naval battles lining the walls of the library. The Chinese porcelain and ivories in the house were taken by the fifth Baronet from a captured Spanish galleon in 1762.

Continuing along the route, Clare, on the River Stour, has many medieval buildings. From Clare we follow the B1054 to the village of Hempstead and then the B1063 to Saffron Walden. Although the saffron crocus is no longer grown commercially in the district, it has given Saffron Walden its name and carvings of it can be seen in many places in the area. This is not surprising as the saffron crocus brought prosperity to the region for four hundred years. Until the late 18th century this valuable plant was grown for the bright yellow dye extracted from the golden stigma of purple crocus and used to colour cloth.

The town's finest medieval building was once a malt house but now serves as a youth hostel. It is timber framed and was built around 1500. Much of its plasterwork has worn off, revealing the original window frames. In the middle of the town are the Market Square and the mid 19th century Corn Exchange which was converted in the 1970s into a library and arts centre.

Essex and Suffolk

On the outskirts of the town are two of its most famous attractions: on the common the largest earth maze in England, and the mansion of Audley End. The maze, is about 40 yards in diameter but its path coils and twists for almost a mile and dates from prehistoric times. It is suggested that it was used in some kind of fertility ceremony to ensure a good harvest.

Audley End was started in 1603 by the first Earl of Suffolk, Lord Treasurer to James I. It was so big that it was never fully occupied or furnished. Charles II bought it in 1668 but could not afford to complete the purchase so it reverted back to the family in 1701. Because of the impossible size of the mansion parts of it were demolished to bring it down to a more realistic scale. Still magnificent, the grounds were landscaped by Capability Brown and the interior of the house shows the work of Robert Adams.

We finish the tour by visiting the small villages of Great Chesterfield, Ickleton, Little Abington, Pampisford, Little Shelford and finally Duxford. The airfield here was used during the Second World War and is now owned by the Imperial War Museum. There is a very good collection of First and Second World War aircraft and also the first Concorde to have flown.

ANTIQUE DEALERS

ABRIDGE (0992)

Revival, Coach House, Market Place, RM4 1VA TEL: 814000 FAX: 814300 PARKING: Easy OPEN: Mon-Thurs, Sat-Sun 11-5.30 MIN: £1 MAX: £3,000 PERIOD: 18th-20th century SPECIALIST: Clocks & barometers GENERAL: General antiques. Furniture restoration & upholstery OTHER INFO: Small village but 3 pubs & excellent restaurant.

BLACKMORE (0277)

Haygreen Antiques, The Farmhouse, Hay Green Lane TEL: 821275 FAX: 821275 PARKING: Own carpark OPEN: Tues-Sun 9.30-5 MIN: £100 MAX: £1,500 PERIOD: 18th-19th century SPECIALIST: English & Continental pine furniture GENERAL: Victorian furniture OTHER INFO: 2,000 sq ft showrooms in historic listed barns on our estate.

INGATESTONE (0277)

Meyers Gallery, 66 High Street, CM4 9DW TEL: 355335 ASSNS: LAPADA PARKING: Own carpark OPEN: 10-5 closed Weds MIN: £5 MAX: £5,000 PERIOD: 19th-20th century SPECIALIST: Continental watercolours & oils GENERAL: General antiques OTHER INFO: Oils restoration on premises. Ingatestone Hall (open). Art Deco shop nearby & other small interesting shops in street. Moat House Hotel

STOCK (0277)

Sabine Antiques, 38 High Street TEL: 840553 PARKING: Easy OPEN: Tues-Sat 10-5.30 MIN: £50 MAX: £2,000 PERIOD: 18th-19th century

GRAYS (0375)

Grays Galleries Collectors Centre, 6 London Road, RM17 5XY TEL: 374883 PARKING: Easy OPEN: on-Sat 10-5 MIN: £1 MAX: Sky's the limit PERIOD: 19th-20th century SPECIALIST: Goss & crested china, childrens' books, militaria GENERAL: Glass, various collectables, china all in 25 individually rented lockup cabinets. Furniture OTHER INFO: 5 mins from town centre & main (Fenchurch Street line) station. Another collectors shop 2 doors away (books, jewellery, post cards, cigarette cards, etc).

LEIGH-ON-SEA (0702)

Castle Antiques, 72 Broadway, SS9 1AE TEL: 75732 PARKING: Own carpark OPEN: 10-5.30 MIN: £10 MAX: £2,000 PERIOD: 18th-20th century SPECIALIST: Tribal, military, pottery GENERAL: General antiques OTHER INFO: Good pubs in Leigh Old Town.

WESTCLIFF-ON-SEA (0702)

It's About Time, 563 London Road, SS0 9SZ TEL: 72574 FAX: 715400 PARKING: Medium OPEN: 9-5.30 closed Weds MIN: £200 MAX: £5,000 PERIOD: 17th-19th century SPECIALIST: Longcase & Vienna wall clocks GENERAL: Bracket clocks, Victorian, Edwardian furniture OTHER INFO: World's longest pleasure pier.

RAYLEIGH (0268)

F.G. Bruschweiler (Antiques) Ltd, 41-67 Lower Lambricks, SS6 YEN TEL: 773761, 773932 FAX: 773318 PARKING: Own carpark OPEN: Mon-Fri 8.30-5 MIN: £30 MAX: £3,000 PERIOD: 18th-19th century SPECIALIST: Georgian, Victorian, Edwardian, 1920's reproduction GENERAL: Mixed furniture.

BATTLESBRIDGE (0268)

Battlesbridge Antiques Centre, TEL: 769392 ASSNS: LAPADA PARKING: Own carpark OPEN: Wed-Sun MIN: £1 MAX: £3,000 PERIOD: 19th-20th century SPECIALIST: Old telephones, fireplaces, clocks, carnival glass, musical boxes GENERAL: Victorian, Edwardian, 20's furniture & collectables OTHER INFO: 70 dealers in 5 large interesting complexes on River Crouch with tearooms etc. 17th century pub. Motorcycle Museum open Suns AM or by appt.

Battlesbridge Mills, Chelmsford Road, SS11 8TT TEL: 570090 FAX: 768844 PARKING: Own carpark OPEN: Mon-Fri 9-5, Sat-Sun 10-2 MIN: £1 MAX: £5,000 PERIOD: 19th century SPECIALIST: Stripped pine doors, Victorian fireplaces GENERAL: Cast iron baths, lamp posts, radiators, butlers sinks, pine furniture etc.

PURLEIGH (0621)

David Lloyd Gallery, The Studio, Turnstone (opp Bell Inn) TEL: 828093, weekends 828330 PARKING: Easy OPEN: By appt MIN: £50 MAX: £1,000 PERIOD: 19th-20th century GENERAL: Watercolours, oils, etchings.

MALDON (0621)

Abacus Antiques, 105 High Street, CM9 7EP TEL: 850528 PARKING: Easy OPEN: Tues, Thurs-Sat 10-4.30 MIN: £1 MAX: £1,000 PERIOD: 18th-19th century GENERAL: General antiques. No reproduction OTHER INFO: In centre of historic town. Medieval Moot Hall's 42ft long embroidery celebrating the millenium of Battle of Maldon (992 AD).

The Antique Rooms, 630 High Street, CM9 7EB TEL: 856985 PARKING: Easy OPEN: 10-4 MIN: £1 MAX: £500 PERIOD: 19th-20th century GENERAL: General antiques OTHER INFO: Good café opposite. Scandinavian spoken.

Clive Beardall Antiques, 104b High Street, CM9 7ET TEL: 857890 PARKING: Own carpark OPEN: Mon-Fri 7.30-5.30, Sat 8.30-4.30 MIN: £45 MAX: £6,000 PERIOD: 18th-20th century GENERAL: Quality furniture, oils, watercolours & prints OTHER INFO: Full restoration service.

KELVEDON (0376)

Kelvedon Antiques, 90 High Street TEL: 570557 ASSNS: BADA PARKING: Easy OPEN: Mon-Sat 9.30-5.30 MIN: £20 MAX: £10,000 PERIOD: 17th-early 19th century SPECIALIST: Furniture OTHER INFO: 6 antique shops in historic village.

G.T. Ratcliff Ltd, Whitebarn, Coggeshall Road, (and Menai House), 41 High Street, CO5 9PH TEL: 570234 FAX: 571764 PARKING: Own carpark OPEN: Mon-Sat 10-5 (Menai House), Mon-Fri 9-5, Sats by appt (Whitebarn) PERIOD: 18th-19th century SPECIALIST: Lacquer and decorative items for the interior design market GENERAL: Quality furniture and small collectables. Decorative a speciality. Wholesale warehouse OTHER INFO: Close to Dedham and Constable country, Sir Alfred Munnings home, 45 mins from London by train.

Millers Antiques Kelvedon, 46 High Street, CO5 9AG TEL: 570098 FAX: 572186 ASSNS: LAPADA PARKING: Own carpark OPEN: Mon-Fri 9-5.30, Sat 10-4 MIN: £100 MAX: £20,000 PERIOD: 17th-19th century SPECIALIST: Largest showrooms in Essex stocked with furniture GENERAL: Restoration work & desktop leathers service.

Thomas Sykes Antiques, 16 High Street, CO5 9AG TEL: 571969 ASSNS: LAPADA PARKING: Own carpark OPEN: Mon-Sat 10-5 & by appt MIN: £200 MAX: £25,000 PERIOD: 18th-early 19th century SPECIALIST: Georgian furniture OTHER INFO: Chambers guest house at Earls Colne. Mainline station in village.

Templar Antiques, 6 Peters House, High Street, CO5 9AA TEL: 572101 FAX: (0621) 818033 Templar PARKING: Own carpark OPEN: Mon,

Tues, Thurs-Sat 10-5 MIN: £25 MAX: £5,000 PERIOD: 18th-19th century SPECIALIST: 18th century wines decanters GENERAL: General antiques (no reproductions whatsoever) OTHER INFO: Owner's separate B&B from £18.

Times Past, 110 High Street TEL: 571858 PARKING: Easy OPEN: Tues, Thurs-Sat 10-5 MIN: £2 MAX: £900 PERIOD: 19th-20th century SPECIALIST: Decorative arts 1890-1940 GENERAL: General antiques (no reproductions), many unusual items OTHER INFO: 2 mins from A12, near Messing, the ancestral home of George Bush, US ex-president.

COGGESHALL (0376)

Antique Metals, 9a East Street, CO6 1SH TEL: 562252 PARKING: Easy OPEN: Mon-Sat 9-6, Sun 11-5 MIN: £10 MAX: £1,000 PERIOD: 18th-19th century SPECIALIST: Period & Victorian brass, copper, steel.

Coggeshall Antiques, 1 Doubleday Corner TEL: 562646 PARKING: Own carpark OPEN: 10-5 MIN: £5 MAX: £4,000 PERIOD: 17th-20th century GENERAL: Decorative furniture, paintings OTHER INFO: Good hotel opposite.

Lindsell Chairs, 11 Market Hill, CO6 1TS TEL: 562766, home (0371) 820222 PARKING: Easy Open Mon-Sat 10.30-6 MIN: £40 MAX: £4,000 SPECIALIST: Most kinds of seating 1780-1914 GENERAL: Dining & occasional tables. Full traditional restoration (chairs, settees etc).

Joan Jobson's Antiques, 5a Church Street, CO6 1TV TEL: 561717 (home) PARKING: Easy Open: Mon-Sat 10-1, 2-5 closed Wed PM MIN: £1 MAX: £200-300 PERIOD: 19th-20th century GENERAL: Quality furniture, small collectables, bric-a-brac etc.

Mark Marchant Antiques, Market Square, CO6 1TS TEL: 561188 PARKING: Easy OPEN: Mon-Sat 10.30-5, Sun 2-5 MIN: £5 MAX: £15,000 PERIOD: 17th-20th century SPECIALIST: Clocks GENERAL: Decorative items OTHER INFO: Market day Thursdays.

Elkin Mathews Bookshop, 16 Stoneham Street TEL: 561730 PARKING: Own carpark OPEN: 9.30-1, 2-4.30 closed Weds MIN: £1 MAX: £3,000 PERIOD: 17th-20th century SPECIALIST: Childrens' books GENERAL: All subjects.

FELSTED (0371)

Argyll House Antiques, CM6 3DG TEL: 820682 PARKING: Easy OPEN: Mon, Tues, Thurs-Sat 10-

5 & by appt (resident) MIN: 5p MAX: £1,000 PERIOD: 18th-20th century SPECIALIST: Ephemera, postcards GENERAL: General antiques OTHER INFO: Many 12th century houses and large public school is associated with Cromwell & Lord Riche.

GREAT BARDFIELD (0371)

Golden Sovereign, Old Police House, High Street, CM7 4SP TEL: 810507 PARKING: Easy OPEN: Mon, Tues, Thurs 10-6, Wed, Fri-Sun 2-6 MIN: £5 MAX: £500+ PERIOD: 18th-20th century GENERAL: Mainly smalls of any material with some furniture OTHER INFO: Café, small Cottage Museum & lockup open Sat-Sun.

SIBLE HEDINGHAM (0787)

Hedingham Antiques, 100 Swan Street, CO9 3HP TEL: 460360 PARKING: Easy OPEN: Mon-Sat 10-12.30, 1.30-5 MIN: £5 MAX: £2,000 PERIOD: 18th-20th century SPECIALIST: Victorian, Edwardian silver plate GENERAL: Furniture c.1800, Art Deco, secondhand showroom OTHER INFO: B&B available here.

W.A. Pinn & Sons, 124 Swan Street, CO9 3HP TEL: 461127 ASSNS: BADA, LAPADA PARKING: Easy OPEN: 9.30-6 MIN: £40 MAX: £10,000 PERIOD: 17th-19th century SPECIALIST: Real antiques GENERAL: Furniture & accessories OTHER INFO: Castle Hedingham.

HALSTED (0787)

Antique Bed Shop, Napier House, Head Street, CO9 2BT TEL: 477346 FAX: 478757 PARKING: Own carpark OPEN: Wed-Sat 9-6 & by appt MIN: £995 MAX: £3,500 PERIOD: 19th century SPECIALIST: Most comprehensive range of antique wooden beds complete with new base & mattress. Delivery worldwide OTHER INFO: Top Indian food for miles only a stone's throw away.

WHITE COLNE (0787)

Fox & Pheasant Pine, Colchester Road, CO6 2PS TEL: 223297 FAX: 224497 PARKING: Own carpark OPEN: 8-6 PERIOD: 19th century GENERAL: Antique pine OTHER INFO: In attractive complex with restaurant.

COLCHESTER (0206)

Elizabeth Cannon Antiques, 85 Crouch Street, CO3 3EZ TEL: 575817 PARKING: Easy OPEN: Mon-Sat 9-5.30 MIN: £10 MAX: £3,000 PERIOD: 18th-20th century SPECIALIST: General antiques OTHER INFO: The oldest recorded town in England. Large castle.

Richard Iles Gallery, 10 Northgate Street, CO1 1HA TEL: 577877 PARKING: Own carpark OPEN: Mon-Sat 9.30-4.30 MIN: £3 MAX: £1,000 PERIOD: 19th century SPECIALIST: Watercolours, framing & ready-made frames GENERAL: Posters & prints & restoration.

Partner & Puxon , 7 North Hill, CO1 1DZ TEL: 573317 PARKING: Medium OPEN: Mon-Sat 9-1, 2.15-5.30, Thurs AM only MIN: £5 Max: £25,000 PERIOD: 17th-19th century GENERAL: English furniture, ceramics, needlework.

Trinity Antiques Centre, 7 Trinity Street TEL: 577775 PARKING: Medium OPEN: 9.30-5 MIN: £1 MAX: £350 PERIOD: 18th-20th century GENERAL: China, silver, jewellery, treen, brass & copper, small furniture etc. OTHER INFO: We are in 16th century building.

FRINTON-ON-SEA (0255)

Dickens Curios, 151 Connaught Avenue TEL: 674134 PARKING: Easy OPEN: MIN: 25p MAX: £200+ PERIOD: 19th-20th century GENERAL: General antiques.

GREAT BROMLEY (0206)

J. Dean Antiques, Mill Farm, Harwich Road, CO7 7JQ TEL: 250485 FAX: 252040 PARKING: Own carpark OPEN: Seven days 9.30-5.30 MIN: £5 MAX: £1,600 PERIOD: 19th century SPECIALIST: Original pine & country furniture GENERAL: Victorian furniture OTHER INFO: Constable Country's Dedham Vale 5 miles, Harwich port 12 miles.

MANNINGTREE (0206)

Antiques, 49 High Street, CO11 1AH TEL: 346170 PARKING: Usually easy OPEN: Mon-Sat 10-1, 2-5 MIN: £5 MAX: £3,500 PERIOD: Sometime 17th,

18-20th century GENERAL: 5 rooms of furniture, porcelain, silver, linens, glass OTHER INFO: Stour Estuary.

HADLEIGH (0473)

Gordon Sutcliffe, 105 High Street TEL: 823464 ASSNS: BADA PARKING: Own carpark OPEN: Mon-Sat 9.30-5 MIN: £250 MAX: £20,000 SPECIALIST: 18th century furniture OTHER INFO: Many medieval towns & villages, timbered buildings & old churches. Hindlesham Hall Hotel & restaurant.

Tara's Hall Antiques, Victoria House, Market Hall, IP7 5DL TEL: 824031 PARKING: Own carpark OPEN: 10-1, 2-5, not Weds MIN: £1 MAX: £1,000 PERIOD: 19th century SPECIALIST: Textiles, jewellery GENERAL: Small silver, glass, decorative antiques OTHER INFO: Near lovely river walk.

IPSWICH (0473)

A. Abbott Antiques, 757 Woodbridge Road, IP4 4NE TEL: 728900 FAX: 728900 PARKING: Easy OPEN: Mon, Tues, Thurs-Sat 10-5 MIN: £5 MAX: £2,000 PERIOD: 18th-20th century SPECIALIST: Clocks, conversation pieces GENERAL: General antiques. Reproduction OTHER INFO: You get nothing for nothing but a lot for a little in Ipswich. Try us. Near Felixstowe container-port.

Tony Adams, Wireless & Bygones, 175 Spring Road, IP4 5NQ TEL: 714362 PARKING: Medium OPEN: Mon, Tues, Thurs-Sat 10-12.30, 2.30-5 PERIOD: 19th-early 20th century SPECIALIST: Period wireless sets, cameras, trains.

Ashley Antiques, 20a Fore Street, IP4 IJU TEL: 251696 Fax 233974 PARKING: Medium OPEN: Mon-Fri 9-1 & 2-5, Sats 10-4 MIN: £50 MAX: £5,000 PERIOD: 18th-19th century SPECIALIST: Furniture, barometers GENERAL: Clocks, Victorian glass OTHER INFO: Christchurch Mansion Houses, some good works of art.

Country Bygones & Antiques, 13 St Peter's Street, IP1 1XF TEL: 253683 PARKING: Easy OPEN: Mon-Sat 10-5 MIN: £2 MAX: £500 PERIOD: 18-19th + some early 20th century SPECIALIST: Kitchenalia, country porcelain & silver GENERAL: Decorative antiques & the unusual OTHER INFO: In Old Ipwsich near Docks, 16th/17th century buildings.

Croydons, 50-56 Tavern Street, IP1 3AL TEL: 256514 FAX: 231565 PARKING: Medium OPEN: Mon-Sat 9-5.30 MIN: £1 MAX: £ thousands

PERIOD: 17th-20th century SPECIALIST: Diamonds GENERAL: Jewellery, giftware etc OTHER INFO: Kersey (place of interest), Ancient House, restaurants, Huntlesham Hall, Seckford Hall.

The Edwardian Shop, 556 Spring Road TEL: 716576, home 712890 PARKING: Own carpark OPEN: Mon-Sat 9.45-5 MIN £20 MAX: £1,000 PERIOD: 19th-20th century SPECIALIST: Quality 20's, 30's shipping goods, furniture OTHER INFO: Sited caravan sleeping 6 available.

Hyland House Antiques, 45 Felixstowe Road, IP4 5HP TEL: 210055 PARKING: Easy OPEN: Mon-Tues, Fri-Sat 9.30-5 MIN: £1 MAX: £1,250 PERIOD: 20th century SPECIALIST: 1900-1930's oak furniture GENERAL: China, copper, kitchenalia in 6 showrooms.

Spring Antiques, 436 Spring Road TEL: 725606 PARKING: Medium OPEN: 9.30-1, not Thurs MIN: £2 MAX: £700 PERIOD: 18th-20th century GENERAL: General antiques.

Thompson's Furniture, 418 Norwich Road, IP1 5DX TEL: 747793 FAX: 255570 PARKING: Own carpark OPEN: Mon-Sat 9-5 MIN: £5 MAX: £2,000 PERIOD: 19th-20th century GENERAL: Victorian & shipping goods OTHER INFO: 1 mile from town centre on main Norwich road.

MARTLESHAM (0394)

Martlesham Antiques, The Thatched Roadhouse, The Street, IP12 4RJ TEL: 386732 FAX: 382959 PARKING: Own carpark OPEN: Mon-Sat 10-5 MIN: £50 MAX: £20,000 PERIOD: 18th-20th century GENERAL: Mahogany, walnut, oak.

John Read, 29 Lark Rise, The Heath, IP5 7SA TEL: (0473) 624897 FAX: 382896 PARKING: Own carpark OPEN: Anytime but phone first MIN: £100 MAX: £4,000 PERIOD: 18th-early 19th century SPECIALIST: Staffordshire figures and animals, porcelain, pottery.

WOODBRIDGE (0394)

Bagatelle, 40 Market Hill TEL: 380204 PARKING: Easy OPEN: 10.30-5 MIN: £20 MAX: £3,000 PERIOD: 18th-19th century SPECIALIST: Oriental ceramics GENERAL: English period furniture, Victorian paintings, jewellery, objets d'art.

Simon Carter Gallery, 23 Market Hill, IP12 4LX TEL: 382242 FAX: 388146 PARKING: Easy OPEN: Mon-Sat 9-5.30 MIN: £1 MAX: £10,000 PERIOD: 17th-20th century SPECIALIST: English oils & watercolours 1700-1950 GENERAL: Unusual furniture from all periods, decorative objects, prints, posters OTHER INFO: Cleaning, restoration & relining of oil paintings, all on premises. Valuations. Private house atmosphere at Bassett's hotel with excellent gardens etc. Woodbridge Winebar.

David Gibbins, 21 Market Hill, IP12 4LX TEL: 383531 FAX: 388146 ASSNS: BADA PARKING: Own carpark OPEN: Mon-Sat 9.30-5 MIN: £100 MAX: £60,000 PERIOD: 17th-18th century SPECIALIST: 18th century English furniture, English porcelain and objects OTHER INFO: Old town of narrow streets, with tide mill. Seckford Hall Hotel, Melton Grange Hotel.

Hamilton Antiques, 5 Church Street TEL: 387222 PARKING: Medium but public nearby OPEN: 9.30-1, 2-5.30 MIN: £60 MAX: £10,000 PERIOD: 18th-19th century OTHER INFO: Bloxsomes Restaurant, The Captain's Table (seafood).

Anthony Hurst Antiques, (estd 1955), 13 Church Street TEL: 382500 ASSNS: LAPADA PARKING: Own carpark OPEN: 9.30-1, 2-5.30 MIN: £60 MAX: £10,000 GENERAL: Wide range oak, mahogany, walnut furniture (1700-1900).

Jenny Jackson Antiques, 30 Market Hill TEL: 380667 PARKING: Easy OPEN: Mon-Wed, Sat 10.30-5 MIN: £20 PERIOD: 18th-19th century SPECIALIST: Jewellery, paintings GENERAL: Anything early, i.e. 17th-18th century & decorative OTHER INFO: Thirtlesham Hall Hotel.

Edward Manson (Clocks), 8 Market Hill, IP12 4LU TEL: 380235 PARKING: Easy OPEN: 10-1, 2-5 PERIOD: 17th-19th century SPECIALIST: Clocks, barometers GENERAL: Scientific instruments.

Melton Antiques, Melton TEL: 386232 PARKING: Easy OPEN: Mon-Sat 9.30-5.30 MIN: £15 MAX: £600 PERIOD: 18th-20th century SPECIALIST: Decorative items, collectables, small silver GENERAL: All stock antique, sewing items, small furniture OTHER INFO: 20 miles from Constable Country, 12 miles Snape Maltings, Aldeburgh Festival.

Sarah Meysey-Thompson, 10 Church Street, IP12 1DH TEL: 382144, (071) 727 3609 PARKING: Medium OPEN: 9.45-5, Wed AM only MIN: £15 MAX: £4,000 PERIOD: 18th-20th century SPECIALIST: Curtains, textiles GENERAL: Pretty period furniture, decorative items, antique & 20th

century curtains OTHER INFO: Riverside restaurant. Great day out.

WICKHAM MARKET (0728)

Crafers Antiques, The Hill, IP13 0QS TEL: 747347 PARKING: Own carpark OPEN: Summer 9.30-6, Winter closed Sun. (closed lunch Tues & Thurs) MIN: £1 MAX: £1,500 PERIOD: 18th-early 20th century SPECIALIST: English ceramics & glass GENERAL: General antiques OTHER INFO: Beautiful Heritage coast 7 miles. Sutton Hoo, Minsmere bird sanctuary, NT heathland, Orford & Framlingham castles, plenty of rivers and boat trips.

HACHESTON (0728)

Joyce Hardy Pine & Country Furniture, The Street, IP13 0DS TEL: 746485 PARKING: Own carpark OPEN: Mon-Sat Mon-Sat 9.30-6, Sun 10-12.30 MIN: £65 MAX: £1,000 PERIOD: 18th-20th century SPECIALIST: Furniture OTHER INFO: B&B's available in our large Tudor house.

FRAMLINGHAM (0728)

Bed Bazaar, 29 Double Street, IP13 9BN. TEL: 723756 FAX: 724626 ASSNS: Guild of Master Bed Restorers (founder member) PARKING: Own carpark OPEN: 24 hours, 7 days by appt MIN: £45 MAX: £5,000 PERIOD: 18th-19th century SPECIALIST: Antique brass, brass & iron, & all iron bedsteads OTHER INFO: Mattresses & bed bases in all standard & any odd sizes. Castle, church, classic motorcycle dealer.

DEBENHAM (0728)

Gil Adams Antiques, The Foresters Hall, 52 High Street, IP14 6QW TEL: 860777 FAX: 860142 PARKING: Easy OPEN: 9.30-5 PERIOD: 17th-19th century SPECIALIST: Dining tables GENERAL: Oak & mahogany furniture OTHER INFO: Ex *Lovejoy* auction house. Ancient village which won Architectural Heritage Year 1983.

NEEDHAM MARKET (0449)

Roy Arnold, 77 High Street, IP6 8AN TEL: 720110 PARKING: Easy OPEN: Mon-Sat 9.30-5.30 & by appt PERIOD: 17th-19th century SPECIALIST: Tools of trades and scientific instruments GENERAL: Books (antiquarian, s/hand & new) about trades and tools OTHER INFO: Englands finest example of 15th century carpentry in church roof.

Needham Market Antiques Centre, Old Town Hall, High Street, IP6 8AL TEL: 720773 PARKING: Easy OPEN: Mon-Sat 10-5 MIN: £1 MAX:

£1,500 PERIOD: 19th-20th century SPECIALIST: Jewellery GENERAL: 22+ dealers with vast range of furniture, porcelain, glass, bric-a-brac, collectables & antiques.

WOOLPIT (0359)

John Heather Antiques, (estd 1946), The Old Crown, Woolpit, IP30 9SA TEL: 40297 PARKING: Easy OPEN: All reasonable times seven days MAX: £20,000 PERIOD: 17th-19th century SPECIALIST: English 18th-19th century furniture OTHER INFO: Bespoke reproduction & decorative items.

IXWORTH (0359)

Ixworth Antiques, 17 High Street, IP31 2HH TEL: 31691, (0860)902562 PARKING: Easy OPEN: Mon, Tues, Thurs-Sat 10-5 & by appt MIN: £5 MAX: £2,000 PERIOD: 19th-20th century SPECIALIST: Silver plate, pine GENERAL: General antiques OTHER INFO: Good food at 17th century coaching inn opposite.

BRADFIELD ST GEORGE (0449)

Denzil Grant (Suffolk Fine Arts), Hubbards Corner, IP30 0AQ Tel: 736576 FAX: 737679 ASSNS: BADA PARKING: Own carpark OPEN: Anytime though appt advisable (resident) PERIOD: 17th-19th century SPECIALIST: Oak, walnut farm tables GENERAL: English country & French provincial furniture 16th-19th century.

BURY ST EDMUNDS (0284)

Corner Shop Antiques, 1 Guildhall Street TEL: 701007 PARKING: Medium OPEN: 10-5, closed Thurs MIN: £1 MAX: £200 PERIOD: 19th-20th century SPECIALIST: Victoriana GENERAL: Collectables OTHER INFO: Historic hub of East Anglia, ancient ruins & houses. Class winner *Britain in Bloom*,

Peppers Period Pieces, 23 Churchgate Street TEL: 768786 FAX: 768786 PARKING: Medium OPEN: Mon-Sat 10-5.15 MIN: £2+ MAX: £10,000 PERIOD: 16th-19th century SPECIALIST: Copper, brass, iron, tin, pewter GENERAL: Furniture. No reproductions OTHER INFO: Historic town, good restaurants within 100 yards of shop in centre of town, also many hotels and guest houses only short walk.

RISBY (0284)

Risby Barn Antique Centre, TEL: 811126 FAX: 811126 PARKING: Own carpark OPEN: Seven days 9-5.30 MIN: £1 MAX: £1,500 PERIOD: 19th-20th century SPECIALIST: Clocks, porcelain

GENERAL: Furniture, particularly oak & pine country OTHER INFO: Shared site with Garden Centre. Good local facilities.

LAVENHAM (0787)

J & J Baker, 12-14 Water Street (& 3a High Street), CO10 9RW TEL: 247610 PARKING: Easy OPEN: Mon-Sat 9-5.30 MIN: £20 MAX: £12,000 PERIOD: 17th-19th century SPECIALIST: English antiques OTHER INFO: 16th century Swan Inn (100 yds) in remarkable medieval village. Fine church & Guildhall.

HAWKEDON (0284)

Freya Antiques, The Old Forge, IP29 4NN TEL: 89267 PARKING: Own carpark OPEN: Flexible or by appt MIN: £1 MAX: £1,000 PERIOD: 19th century SPECIALIST: Antique pine furniture, upholstery GENERAL: Some glass, ceramics, kitchenalia.

LONG MELFORD (0787)

Antique Clocks by Simon Charles, St Mary's Court, Hall Street TEL: 880040 ASSNS: BWCMG PARKING: Own carpark OPEN: 10-5.30 MIN: £5 MAX: £8,000 PERIOD: 18th-19th century SPECIALIST: Quality period English clocks GENERAL: Always some 15 longcase, 3 lantern clocks, also wall, carriage & bracket.

Ashley Gallery, Belmont House, Hall Street, CO10 9JF TEL: 375434 PARKING: Easy OPEN: Mon-Sat 10-5 MIN: £100 MAX: £4,000 PERIOD: 17th-20th century SPECIALIST: Paintings & watercolours GENERAL: Some china OTHER INFO: We run Alexander Lyall Antiques in same building.

The Chater House Gallery, Foundry House, Hall Street TEL: 379831 PARKING: Easy OPEN: Mon-Sat 10-5 MIN: £2+ MAX: £3,000 PERIOD: 17th-20th century SPECIALIST: Pianos GENERAL: General antiques. At barn (2 miles away) lesser quality antiques & 2nd hand furniture etc OTHER INFO: Melford Hall, Kentwell Hall, Gainsborough's house, Sudbury. Bull Hotel, Black Lion Hotel & restaurants: Chimney, Canes.

Sandy Cooke Antiques, Hall Street TEL: 378265 FAX: (0284) 830935 PARKING: Own carpark OPEN: Mon, Fri-Sat 9-1, 2-5.30 MIN: £100 MAX: £30,000 PERIOD: 17th-19th century SPECIALIST: 18th century English furniture GENERAL: Furniture and smalls.

Bruno Cooper Antiques, Little St.Marys, CO10

9LQ TEL: 312613 PARKING: Own carpark OPEN: Mon-Sat 10-5.30 MIN: £1,000 MAX: £25,000 PERIOD: 17th-18th century SPECIALIST: Fine period furniture, paintings, sculpture.

Court Antiques, Little St Mary's Court, CO10 9LQ TEL: 312613 FAX: (0206) 271678 PARKING: Easy OPEN: 10-5 MIN: £10 MAX: £4,000 PERIOD: 18th-19th century SPECIALIST: Georgian & 19th century furniture GENERAL: General antiques.

The Enchanted Aviary, 63 Hall Street, CO10 9JR TEL: 378814 PARKING: Easy OPEN: Mon-Sat 10-5, appt advisable MIN: £10 MAX: £2,000 PERIOD: Late 19th-early 20th century SPECIALIST: Victorian taxidermy: birds, mammals, fish, butterflies. GENERAL: Natural history items only.

Alexander Lyall Antiques, Belmont House, Hall Street, CO10 9JF. Tel 375434 PARKING: Easy OPEN: Mon-Sat 10-5 MIN: £100 MAX: £5,000 SPECIALIST: Desks GENERAL: Furniture 1750-1850.

Long Melford Antiques Centre, Chapel Maltings TEL: 379287 PARKING: Own carpark OPEN: 9.30-5.30 MIN: £10 MAX: £10,000 PERIOD: 17th-20th century GENERAL: Period & 19th century furniture, pictures, silver, objets d'art, clocks, china, glass, lamps & accessories.

Magpie Antiques, Hall Street, CO10 9JT TEL: 310581 PARKING: Easy OPEN: 10.30-5 not Wed or Sat MIN: £5 MAX: £300 PERIOD: 19th-20th century. SPECIALIST: Country pine GENERAL: China, country items

Patrick Marney, The Gate House, Melford Hall, CO10 9AA TEL: 880533 PARKING: Easy OPEN: By appt MIN: £100 MAX: £10,000 PERIOD: 19th century SPECIALIST: Mercury barometers GENERAL: Aneroid & pocket aneroid barometers, scientific instruments.

Noel Mercer Antiques, Aurora House, Hall Street, CO10 9RJ TEL: 311882 PARKING: Easy OPEN: 10-5.30 MIN: £250 MAX: £15,000 PERIOD: 17th-18th century SPECIALIST: Oak, walnut, country furniture & complementary works of art. Sometimes medieval & 16th century.

Neptune Antiques, Hall Street, CO10 9JF TEL: 375787 FAX: 375242 ASSNS: LAPADA PARKING: Easy OPEN: Mon-Sat 10-5.30 MIN: £20 MAX: £20,000 PERIOD: 17th-18th century SPECIALIST: Early English oak.

Seabrook Antiques/Old Maltings Antique Co, Hall Street, CO10 9JB TEL: 379638 PARKING: Easy OPEN: 9.30-5.30 MIN: £50 MAX: £5,000 PERIOD: 17th-20th century GENERAL: Oak, mahogany, walnut furniture. Decorative items.

Oswald Simpson Antiques, Hall Street, CO10 9JL TEL: 377523 ASSNS: BADA PARKING: Easy OPEN: Mon-Sat 10-5.30 MIN: £25 MAX: £25,000 PERIOD: 17th-19th century GENERAL: Country furniture, metalware, Staffordshire pottery.

Suthburgh Antiques, Red House, Hall Street, CO10 9JQ TEL: 374818 ASSNS: GMC PARKING: Own carpark OPEN: 10-5.30 but anytime by appt (resident) MIN: £20 MAX: £20,000 PERIOD: 17th-18th century SPECIALIST: 17th century oak furniture, longcase & bracket clocks & barometers. 18th century mahogany furniture GENERAL: Maps, prints, brass candlesticks, pewter, oak carved panels OTHER INFO: Sudbury is birthplace of 18th century painter, Thomas Gainsborough.

Tudor Antiques, Little St Mary's CO10 9HY TEL: 375950 PARKING: Easy OPEN: Mon-Sat 9-5 MIN: £2 MAX: £2,000 PERIOD: 18th-19th century SPECIALIST: Silver + plate (trading as Melford Antiques) GENERAL: General antiques. Large range, large stock.

SUDBURY (0787)

Napier House Antiques, Church Street, CO10 6BJ TEL: 477346 FAX: 478757 PARKING: Easy OPEN: 9-5.30 MIN: £100 MAX: £3,500 PERIOD: 18th-19th century SPECIALIST: Furniture.

CLARE (0787)

Clare Antique Warehouse, The Mill, Malting Lane, CO10 8NW TEL: 278449 PARKING: Easy OPEN: Mon-Sat 9.30-5.30, Sun 1-5, most bank hols MIN: £1 MAX: £5,000 PERIOD: 17th-20th century GENERAL: 50 dealers, 10,000+ sq ft. Period to shipping furniture, decorative, glass, linen, pictures, upholstered, etc.

The Clare Collector, 1 Nethergate Street, CO10 8NP TEL: 277909 ASSNS: LAPADA PARKING: Easy OPEN: Mon, Tues, Thurs-Sat 10-1, 2-5.30 PERIOD: 17th-19th century SPECIALIST: When possible, French provincial from Normandy. Decorative items & the unusual GENERAL: Furniture, porcelain, prints, embroideries & Oriental rugs.

J. De Haan & Son, Market Hill, CO10 8NN TEL: 278870 FAX: 278713 PARKING: Easy OPEN:

Essex and Suffolk

Tues, Thurs-Sat 10-5 & by appt MIN: £200 MAX: £5,000 PERIOD: 18th-19th century SPECIALIST: English 18th century furniture, barometers GENERAL: Gilt mirrors OTHER INFO: Clare Country Park & castle ruins.

F.D. Salter Antiques, 1-2 Church Street, CO10 8NN TEL: 277693 PARKING: Medium OPEN: Mon-Sat 9-5, Weds AM only MIN: £1 MAX: £2,500 PERIOD: 18th-early 19th century GENERAL: English furniture, porcelain, glass OTHER INFO: This & several other shops used filming TV's *Lovejoy*. Ancient East Anglian wool town, with castle ruins, priory and various parget work buildings. B&B's arranged.

HEMPSTEAD (0440)

Michael Beaumont Antiques, Hempstead Hall, CB10 2PR TEL: 730234 PARKING: Own carpark OPEN: 10.30-5 MIN: £75 MAX: £4,500 PERIOD: 17th-20th century SPECIALIST: Furniture & rugs GENERAL: Antique furniture 17th-19th century, handmade reproduction furniture copies, Oriental rugs OTHER INFO: One of largest furniture outlets in East Anglia all in large country house. Excellent food at Blue Bell Pub (Dick Turpin's birthplace).

SAFFRON WALDEN (0799)

Bush Antiques, 26-28 Church Street TEL: 523277 PARKING: Medium OPEN: Mon-Wed, Fri-Sat 11-4.30 MIN: £15 MAX: £1,000 PERIOD: 19th century SPECIALIST: Early 19th century Blue & White pottery, pink & copper lustre GENERAL: General antiques OTHER INFO: In this medieval market town full of old buildings, Bush Antiques is opposite the plasterworked Sun Inn which Cromwell used as his HQ during Civil War.

Lankester Antiques and Books, The Old Sun Inn, Church Street, Market Hill, CB10 1HQ TEL: 522685 PARKING: Medium OPEN: Mon-Sat 9.30-1, 2-5.30 MIN: £1 MAX: £1,000 PERIOD: 18th-20th century GENERAL: Wide range general antiques, reproductions & 30,000 secondhand books OTHER INFO: Situated in the 14th century Old

Sun Inn, famous for its pargetting and association with Oliver Cromwell.

Littlebury Antiques, 58-60 Fairycroft Road, CB10 1LZ TEL: 527961 FAX: 527961 PARKING: Easy OPEN: 8.45-5.15 MIN: £100 MAX: £40,000 PERIOD: 19th century SPECIALIST: Barometers, ship models, marine antiques.

GREAT CHESTERFORD (0799)

Charles & Joan Mortimer & Son, School Street, CB10 1NN TEL: 530261 PARKING: Own carpark OPEN: Thurs, Sat 2.30-5, viewing Suns & by appt MIN: £400 MAX: £23,000 PERIOD: 16th-18th century SPECIALIST: Early oak & portraits.

ICKLETON (0799)

Abbey Antiques, 18 Abbey Street, CB10 1SS TEL: 530637 PARKING: Easy OPEN: Mon-Sat 10-5, Sun 2-5 MIN: £35 MAX: £2,500 PERIOD: 18th-19th century SPECIALIST: 3 showrooms of furniture OTHER INFO: Good food at Red Lion.

LITTLE ABINGTON (0223)

Abington Books, 29 Church Lane TEL: 891645 FAX: 893724 PARKING: Easy OPEN: By appt MIN: £1 MAX: £5,000+ PERIOD: 19th-20th century SPECIALIST: Books on Oriental rugs & classical tapestries.

LITTLE SHELFORD (0223)

Cambridge Fine Art, Priesthouse, 33 Church Street, CB2 5HG TEL: 842866 ASSNS: LAPADA PARKING: Own carpark OPEN: Mon-Sat 10-6 or by appt MIN: £10 MAX: £30,000 PERIOD: 18th-20th century SPECIALIST: British & Continental oils 1780-1940 plus large selection of Victorian colour prints. Baxter licensees (1850-60). English watercolours OTHER INFO: Large galleries in country house setting. A natural beginning or end to your tour being just off M11, 4 miles south of Cambridge.

DUXFORD (0223)

Riro D. Mooney, Mill Lane, CB2 4PS TEL: 832252 PARKING: Easy OPEN: Mon-Sat 9-7 MIN: £100 MAX: £1,000 PERIOD: 19th-20th century GENERAL: Wide attractive range of quality stock.

East Anglia

The Old Bridge at Queen's College, Cambridge

The East Anglian tour passes through some of the lowest lying and flattest land in England. It is also some of the richest, agriculturally. In this area there has been a continual battle against the sea with land reclamation on the one side and coastal erosion on the other. The region's ports have had much trade with Holland through the centuries and many of the towns and villages show a pronounced Dutch influence in their architecture. There is also a rich cultural heritage demonstrated particularly in Cambridge, Norwich and Ely.

  After first calling on the village of Harston, the route reaches Cambridge, one of the most beautiful town's in England and world famous for its University. The largest of the University Colleges is Trinity, founded by Henry VIII, and its Great Court is claimed to be the largest university court in the world. The library was built by Christopher Wren between 1679 and 1695. It contains bookcases carved by Grinling Gibbons and possesses original manuscripts by Milton, Thackeray, Tennyson, Newton and Byron.

  The earlier King's College, founded in 1441 by Henry VI, is famous for its

East Anglia

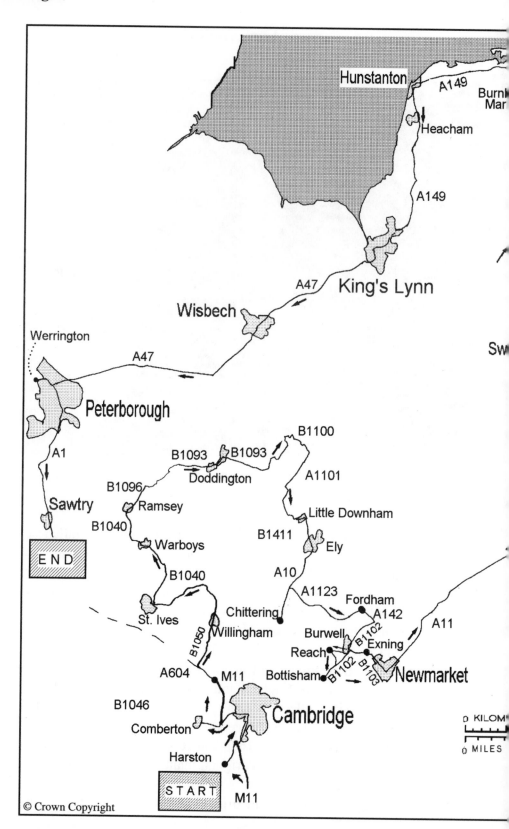

EAST ANGLIA

chapel and its beautiful choral singing. Started in 1446, work on the chapel was halted by the Wars of the Roses and only finished in 1515. Even then it took a further quarter of a century for Flemish craftsmen to install the immensely beautiful stained glass windows. The Adoration of the Magi by Rubens, the altar piece, was donated to the chapel in 1959.

Christopher Wren was involved in another of the Colleges. Pembroke College's new chapel of 1663 was built with a donation from Bishop Wren of Ely, uncle of Christopher whose design of the chapel was his first commission. This college is even earlier than King's having been founded in 1346 by the Countess of Pembroke.

This is only a small taste of the University. The other Colleges are just as fascinating with wonderful stories attached and whole books written about them.

Turning to the town, this is as steeped in history as its University. There is evidence of a settlement here from prehistoric times. This is hardly surprising standing as it does upon a navigable river where a number of roads met at a natural ford.

There are several fine museums. The Fitzwilliam Museum in Trumpington Street has a picture gallery and an exhibition of antiquities, ceramics, drawings, prints and historical and medieval manuscripts. Cambridge & County Folk Museum, Castle Street, housed in the former White Horse Inn, covers the ordinary lives of the people of Cambridgeshire over the last three hundred years. The Sedgwick Museum of Geology, Downing Street, is, as its name suggests, a collection of rocks, ornamental marbles, etc and it includes one million fossils. A collection of historic scientific instruments from the 16th to 19th century can be seen at the Whipple Museum of the History of Science in Free School Lane.

This is not an exhaustive list of the museums either. Cambridge is another town where it is essential for visitors to go to the Tourist Information Centre.

Leaving Cambridge, the next stop is at Comberton and then Willingham, whose restored church has an interesting tower and spire. The tour moves on to St Ives, a market town on the River Ouse with strong associations with Oliver Cromwell who was churchwarden here. A statue of Cromwell can be seen on Market Hill. There is a 15th century bridge with a rare restored chapel on it. A fine collection of local items can be seen in the Norris Museum.

Onwards to Warboys, another village with an interesting church which has a good 13th century tower and broach spire, a Norman chancel arch, and a rare lion door knocker. Then to Ramsey where there are the remains of a Benedictine Abbey founded in AD969 by St Oswald, Archbishop of York, and Ailwyn, foster-brother to King Edgar. Little remains of the abbey, only parts of the gatehouse and a small room with a mid 13th century marble tomb.

Passing through the villages of Doddington and Little Downham we next arrive at the city of Ely. According to the Venerable Bede, it acquired its name because of the large numbers of eels caught in the fens. Its magnificent cathedral dominates the surrounding Fenland and was begun, as part of a monastery, in 1083 when Ely was an island. Notable features are the octagonal lantern tower and choir stalls, both designed by Alan de Walsingham. The west front and tower, the lady chapel, the prior's door, and the chantry chapels are also of interest. There is a 15th century Bishop's Palace and across the green is the Chantry, a late 17th century house. The ancient grammar school incorporates a gateway house known as Ely Porta, and the beautiful Prior Crauden's Chapel is now the school chapel.

Ely Cathedral

Ely has historical connections. The surrounding area, at that time treacherous marshland, gave sanctuary to Hereward the Wake and his followers who provided the last Saxon resistance to the Norman invasion. He held out against the Normans until 1071 and was only defeated when a road was built across the marshes. His defeat signalled the end of Saxon hopes.

Also in Ely is the old vicarage, once a tithe house, home of Oliver Cromwell and his family for ten years.

South of Ely lies Wicken Fen, in the care of the National Trust and one of the most important wetland reserves in Europe. The Fens once covered 2500 acres and Wicken is all that remains undrained making it a refuge for many rare species of plants, birds, butterflies and moths. The Fens have gradually been drained to provide rich agricultural land and much of this lies well below sea level because, once drained, the peat contracts. As Wicken has never been drained it now stands above the surrounding land and so water has to be pumped up to it while the boundary banks have been sealed to prevent leakage to the surrounding area.

From Ely and Wicken Fen, we go on to Fordham with its famous abbey, and then to Burwell where there is a sad memorial to a major tragedy in the village. A tombstone, carved with a flaming heart, marks the grave of 82 people who died on the 8th September 1727. A travelling puppet showman had set up his theatre in a barn and people came from far and wide to see him. Although the audience was larger than the barn could comfortably hold the doors were closed. A few moments later a fire started which quickly engulfed the audience who could not escape because it was found that the doors had been nailed shut. Later a man was accused of arson but he was acquitted at Cambridge Assizes. Nearly fifty years later, however, a Fordham man confessed on his deathbed to starting the fire because he wanted to spite the showman.

After leaving Burwell we arrive at the tiny village of Reach, once the Roman river port for Cambridge. It was fed by a canal from the River Cam at Upware and its quays were in use through medieval times.

Pausing only in Bottisham next is Newmarket, closely associated with horseracing since the 17th century. The headquarters of the Jockey Club are here as is the National Stud. There is also a National Horseracing Museum containing paintings by Stubbs and Munnings. Racing is omnipresent in and around Newmarket, whether it is the obviously horsey types in the streets and pubs or the gallops and stables around the town. There was a disastrous fire in 1683 that virtually destroyed the town and the only surviving building is a house in Palace Street that is said to have belonged to Nell Gwynne, mistress of Charles II.

The tour now enters Norfolk, a very rural county with the built-up area comprising only 5 per cent of the land. The farming in this area is a tribute to mechanisation and the agrochemical industry. Hedges, a valuable wildlife resource, have mostly gone, as have mixed woodlands, wetlands and pastures. As a consequence much of the agricultural land resembles a prairie and waterways have been polluted by fertilisers and weedkillers. Not all is negative, however, Norfolk has some excellent nature reserves: on the Broads, on the coast and in Breckland in the south-west of the county.

The following stop is in Attleborough, once famous for its turkeys and cider. We then proceed through the villages of Garboldisham, Brockdish and Stradbroke again back in Suffolk. The latter has a decorated and perpendicular church with a lovely carved niche on the chancel wall. The route calls first at Laxfield, whose church has a Seven Sacraments font, before moving on to Peasenhall, Yoxford and Leiston where there are remains of a 14th century abbey.

Still in Suffolk, we reach Snape, famous as an international centre for music. Benjamin Britten and Peter Pears started the Aldeburgh Festival in 1948 which moved to the purpose built complex at The Maltings in Snape in 1967. Our next stop, Aldeburgh, on the coast, is a quiet holiday resort with pebble beach. There are some Georgian houses in the main road and the Moot Hall is 16th century.

Following the B1125, parallel to the coast, we turn northwards to Blythburgh, a busy port in the 15th century. The church has some fine carvings including a portrayal of the Seven Deadly Sins on the benches. Parliamentary troops, during the Civil War, used the church as a stable and marks on the pillars, where the horses were tethered, still may be seen.

Back at the coast, the village of Southwold, on the mouth of the River Blyth, has been settled since at least Saxon times but nowadays it is the Dutch influence on the local architecture that is such a feature. Following the A12, we continue northwards, via Wrentham, to Kessingland, a holiday resort with a Wildlife and Rare Breed Centre, before turning inland again to Beccles. This riverside town has some good Georgian houses and lovely gardens. St Michael's Church has a separate 14th century bell tower with a peal of ten bells.

Our next stop is the village of Bungay, dominated by the remains of its 12th century castle. We then return to the coast to visit Great Yarmouth. Throughout the Middle Ages this was a busy port and there are many remains of its medieval past including parts of the town walls, the narrow lanes called Rows and the 13th century Tollhouse which contains a local history museum and brass rubbing centre. The Elizabethan House Museum on South Quay is housed in a 16th century merchant's house and has displays of Victorian domestic life.

South Walsham, inland, has two churches in one churchyard. St Lawrence's was burnt down in 1827 and only the ruined tower and restored chancel remain. The other, St Mary's, is in the decorated and perpendicular style, and displays a nice two-storeyed porch. There is also a seven mile waymarked path from the village to Upton and the nearby nature reserve there.

Heading north we come to Stalham Green and then North Walsham, a market town, where the fine decorated church features a painted screen, a 15th century font cover and a 17th century monument to Sir William Paston who founded the grammar school here in 1606 where later Nelson was a pupil.

The road now goes south towards Norwich but there are a number of picturesque towns and villages to visit on the way. Next is Coltishall, a shooting and angling centre, situated on the River Bure and the edge of the Norfolk Broads. Next we come to Buxton and then Wroxham known as the capital of the Broads and a noted yachting centre. The river bridge of 1614 was later widened, and Hoveton Little and Great Broads lie nearby. The church has a very fine late-Norman doorway and the old manor house has stepped gables.

And so Norwich. Again a visit to the Tourist Information Centre at the Guildhall in Gaol Hill is essential especially as there are guided tours from here. Norwich has a thousand listed buildings, thirty three medieval churches and many fine modern buildings. It is the only English city on the list of European Community cities which preserve their social amenities in spite of commercial and industrial success.

At the centre of the city lies the cathedral which is basically Norman and built in the

Norwich Cathedral. By courtesy of Norwich Area Tourism Agency

12th century. The two-storeyed cloister is unique and the prior's door from the cloister to the church is particularly beautiful. One treasure discovered in the 1840s is a painting of five scenes of the suffering of Christ and was probably meant for the high altar. It was the underside of a table when it was found and has been damaged in places. Norwich Cathedral was fortunate that much of its beautiful carving was out of reach of the 17th century Puritans who damaged so many lovely churches.

As one might expect, Norwich is rich in museums. There is the Norwich Castle Museum with displays of natural and social history. The Royal Norfolk Regimental Museum in Castle Meadow chronicles the history of this regiment and the Norfolk Yeomanry since 1685. The Sainsbury Centre for the Visual Arts, University of East Anglia, Watton Road, has many important paintings and sculptures on display including works by Picasso, Henry Moore, Giacometti and Francis Bacon. There is also the Anderson Collection of Art Nouveau on exhibition here. Then there is Strangers' Hall in Charing Cross. This 14th century building was a merchant's house but now it displays urban domestic life from 16th to 19th centuries.

After Norwich the route detours to Long Stratton before arriving in Wymondham (pronounced Win-dam) which has a particularly fine heritage of buildings most built after a fire in 1615. The streets radiate from the Market Place which has an octagonal, timber market building, one of only three surviving in the country. Evidence of the devastating fire can be seen on the 15th century Green Dragon, one of the few buildings to survive, whose timbers show signs of charring. One of the most distinctive sights in the town is the church with its twin towers. This was once part of a Benedictine Priory, another casualty of the Dissolution of the Monasteries, although the church survives.

The villages of Bawdeswell and Reepham are next before the route turns west to Swaffham standing at 210 feet above sea level. There is a story about a 15th century pedlar called John Chapman. He dreamt that if he went to London and stood on London Bridge he would meet a man who would make him rich, so off he went to London. After waiting on the bridge for several days a shopkeeper asked him what he was doing and when John told him the shopkeeper recounted a dream of his own. He had dreamt that a pedlar in Swaffham had found treasure beneath a tree in his garden. John hastened home and, sure enough, he did find treasure. He gave much of the money to the church to rebuild the north aisle and his generosity is recorded in the town's parish records.

In the centre of Swaffham is the Market Place with its Market Cross, given to the town by the Earl of Oxford, nephew of the writer Horace Walpole, in 1783. The cross is actually a dome held

Bridewell Alley, Norwich. By courtesy of Norwich Area Tourism Agency

up by eight pillars with a statue on top of the cross of Ceres, Roman goddess of agriculture. A market is still held here every Saturday.

Turning back along the A1065 we come to Fakenham, an attractive market town on the River Wensum with an unusual museum: the Fakenham Museum of Gas and Local History in Hempton Road, housed in a mid 19th century gasworks. It is the only surviving example in England of the small horizontal-retort hand-fired gasworks. The works were closed in 1965 but have since been restored. The next village, Melton Constable, also has rare industrial interest with its locomotive works that belonged to the Midland and Great Northern Railway.

Now the route comes to Holt which was destroyed by fire in 1708 but rebuilt to the medieval street plan. Of interest is Gresham's School, founded in 1555 by Sir William Gresham, Lord Mayor of London and also founder of the Royal Exchange. The original Tudor school building stands in the town square, though the school itself is now half a mile outside the town along the Cromer road.

On the coast again, Cromer has lofty cliffs with good bathing beaches and all the attractions of a popular holiday resort. A speciality of the town is the locally caught crabs. It also has two interesting museums. The Cromer Museum, Tucker Street, is in a terrace of five Victorian fishermen's cottages. One of the cottages has been furnished as it would have been before the First World War. The museum also has exhibitions of the natural history, geology and history, including photographs of the town in Victorian and Edwardian times. The other one is the Old Boathouse Lifeboat Museum on The Slipway which tells the story of the local lifeboats and the men who manned them.

At West Runton, between Sheringham and Cromer, Norfolk reaches it highest point, 340 feet (102 metres) above sea level, and the chalk that underlies most of the county comes to the surface on the beach here.

Sheringham, also on the seaside, was once an important fishing port with over two hundred boats operating from it. Fishing has declined in importance, although there are still a few fishing boats left. There is a good bathing beach, golf links and a carnival in August. Of note is the National Trust property of Sheringham Park, designated as a Site of Special Scientific Interest for the fulmars which nest on the cliff face. In the park are woodlands with brilliant displays of rhododendrons and azaleas and also a section of the North Norfolk coastal path.

Continuing along the coast we come to Cley-next-the-Sea. Unfortunately this once busy port suffered a decline when the sea retreated leaving half a mile of marshes between it and the North Sea. However, our next stop, Wells-next-the-Sea is still appropriately named. A typical seaside resort, there are amusement arcades and souvenir shops along the seafront although some old buildings still exist including the Old Customs House in East Street. There is a good, sandy, beach and a light railway operates in summer to Walsingham. Little Walsingham, on the way to Fakenham, was a place of pilgrimage as one of Europe's great shrines where the Virgin Mary is said to have appeared.

The tour proceeds to Burnham Market, one of seven villages in the area with Burnham in the name. In Burnham Market, the most prosperous of the seven, there is an important craft market in August. Nearby Burnham Thorpe was Lord Nelson's birthplace and the local pub, named after the naval hero, is full of his memorabilia.

From there the tour returns to the sea at the Victorian resort of Hunstanton on the Wash with its famous striped cliffs. Following the A149, via Heacham, we arrive at Snettisham. It is worth noting that there is a nature reserve comprising over 3000 acres of intertidal sand and mudflats, a haven for birds including the pink-footed goose, ringed plover, oystercatcher and tern, all of which breed here. The village also has a windmill built in 1800. This was restored to working condition and now it is open to the public with demonstrations and an exhibition.

Still on the A149, we come to King's Lynn, near the southern corner of the Wash. Standing on the Great Ouse river, its position has brought prosperity to this thriving port and market town since the Middle Ages. Called Bishop's Lynn until the king seized it in 1536, it has many features of historic interest. The 15th century Hanseatic Warehouse, a reminder of King's Lynn's past, is a tall, brick and timber-framed building with an overhanging upper storey and belonged to the Hanseatic League of north European merchants until the mid 18th century. Downriver the ornate Customs House, built in 1683, has a statue of Charles I over its door - King's Lynn was a Royalist town during the Civil War. Between these is the Saturday Market Place, the centre of the town in the Middle Ages, with its mostly 13th century St Margaret's Church. Closeby stands the Guildhall, built in 1421, with its striking chequered front. This is now the town hall and Tourist Information Centre. It also houses a museum which displays the King John Sword and a wonderful silver-gilt and enamel cup, called the King John Cup. Unfortunately, they are not King John's lost treasure as they are dated about 100 years after his death.

The town has a another guildhall, St George's, which was built in the early 15th century and is the largest surviving guildhall in England. Its size and grandeur testify to the wealth of the trade Guild of St George that built it. This building also has a chequered front and, inside, an open timber roof. Now the great hall has been converted into a theatre and stages the annual King's Lynn Festival in July.

Apart from the museum already mentioned, King's Lynn also has the Bridewell Museum of Local Industries and the Colman's Mustard Museum, both in Bridewell Alley. The Colman's Museum traces the history of the Colman family and the story of mustard. It is attached to the Mustard Shop where many varieties unique to the shop can be bought.

Next is Wisbech. It is incredible to think, looking at the town now, that this was once a thriving port. 250 years ago the River Nene, on which the town stands, was navigable right into the heart of Wisbech and so trade with Holland was of considerable importance to the town. Unfortunately, the shifting coastline of the Wash has meant that the town is now 12 miles from the coast and not accessible to ships. A legacy of its former prosperity can be found in the many fine Georgian merchants' houses situated facing the quays and river. The Dutch influence is seen in some of the architecture with Dutch gables and hipped roofs.

On the north bank of the River Nene in Wisbech stands Peckover House owned by one of the leading Quaker merchants of the town, Jonathan Peckover. He bought the house in 1777 and five years later set up a bank in partnership with two others in a wing of the house. The bank, Gurney, Birkbeck and Peckover merged with Barclays a century later. Although the house itself has some interesting features it is the garden that is truly delightful. It has survived as a Victorian garden in which each of the plants is as important as the overall effect. It has some superb specimens: a tulip tree, redwoods, a ginkgo, a Chusan palm and a monkey puzzle tree. There is also an orangery, with three orange trees that bear fruit, and a fern house. Of interest to animal lovers is the cats' cemetery which commemorates the owners' pets.

East Anglia

We now come to Peterborough also on the Nene. This city grew up around a medieval monastery but today few historic buildings survive. Those that do include the Knight's Gateway, the Bishop's Palace, and the west gateway which is of Norman and 14th century origin. St John's Church dates back to the 15th century and houses a painting of Charles I. The museum in Priestgate contains Roman remains and also has a costume gallery, a Victorian nursery and a period shop.

However, Peterborough's high point is the cathedral, started in 1118 and completed by the end of that century. Although some authorities do not rate the outside highly, it is agreed that inside is a wonderful example of Norman architecture. Particularly interesting are the west front, the painted nave ceiling, the nave arcades, and the fan tracery in the 15th century retrochoir. Both Catherine of Aragon, Henry VIII's first wife, and Mary, Queen of Scots were buried in the cathedral, although Mary was later moved to Westminster Abbey. There is also an 18th century picture of Robert Scarlett, the verger who buried both queens.

The village of Sawtry, our last stop on this tour, is associated with the martyr, William Sawtry, who was burnt at the stake for his beliefs in 1401.

From there we carry on down the A604 to join the M11 and the journey home.

ANTIQUE DEALERS
HARSTON (0223)
Antique Clocks, 1 High Street, CB2 5PX TEL: 870264 PARKING Own carpark OPEN: Daily PERIOD: 17th-19th century SPECIALIST: All types of clocks.
CAMBRIDGE (0223)
20th Century, 169 Histon Road, CB4 3JD TEL: 359482 PARKING Own carpark OPEN: Tues-Fri 12-6, Sat 10-5 MIN: £5 MAX: £2,000 PERIOD: 20th century SPECIALIST: Arts & Crafts, Art Nouveau, Art Deco, furniture, ceramics, lighting, jewellery, smalls.

Jess Applin Antiques, 8 Lensfield, CB2 1EG TEL: 315168 PARKING: Easy OPEN: Mon-Sat 9.0-5.30 MIN: £20 MAX: £10,000 PERIOD: 17th-19th century SPECIALIST: Furniture & works of art OTHER INFO: Near other antique shops & Fitzwilliam Museum, colleges etc.

John Beazor & Sons Ltd, 78-80 Regent Street, CB2 1DP TEL: 355178 ASSNS: BADA PARKING Medium OPEN: Mon-Sat 9-5 MIN: £300 MAX: £20,000. PERIOD 18th-19th century SPECIALIST: Furniture GENERAL: Clocks, barometers, decorative items OTHER: Good hotels, 1 hour from London.

Benet Gallery, 19 King's Parade TEL: 353783 PARKING: Difficult OPEN: Mon-Sat 9-5 MIN: £1 MAX: £1,100 PERIOD: 16th-20th century SPECIALIST: Mostly related to Cambridge and its colleges 1575-1993 OTHER INFO: In shadow of King's College Chapel.

The Bookroom, 13a St Eligius Street, CB2 1HS TEL: 69694 PARKING Easy OPEN: Mon-Fri 9.30-5 or by appt MIN: £2 MAX: £250 PERIOD: 18th-20th century SPECIALIST: Folio Society books GENERAL: Natural history, medicine, science, literature, travel/exploration, topography OTHER INFO: 400 yds rail station.

Buckies Jewellers, Silversmiths & Valuers, 31 Trinity Street, CB2 1TB TEL: 357910 ASSNS: NAG, LAPADA, GA PARKING Multi-storey nearby OPEN: Tues-Sat 9.45-5 MIN: £15 MAX: £15,000 PERIOD: 19th-20th century SPECIALIST: Antique, secondhand jewellery & silverware GENERAL: Distinctive new jewellery, silverware & giftware. Antique coloured glassware.

Collector's Market, Unit 3, Dales Brewery, Gwydir Street (off Mill Street) CB1 2LJ PARKING Easy OPEN: Mon-Sat 10-5 MIN: £1 MAX: £700 c. PERIOD: 19th-20th century SPECIALIST: Fireplaces, kitchenalia GENERAL: Sofa, mirrors, pictures, easy chairs etc OTHER INFO: One of 4 markets in this brewery. ° mile from colleges & universities. Garden House Hotel. Good food at The Plough pub. Excellent Midsummer House restaurant. Another 2 antique shops just outside Collectors' Market.

Gabor Cossa Antiques, 34 Trumpington Street, CB2 1QY TEL: 356049 PARKING: Medium OPEN: Mon-Sat 10-5.30 MIN: £5 MAX: £2,000 PERIOD: 17th-19th century SPECIALIST: English & Continental Delft, early & Chinese ceramics, English glass.

Cottage Antiques, 16-18 Lensfield Road, CB2 1EG TEL: 316698 PARKING Medium OPEN: Mon-Sat 10-5.30 MIN: £2 MAX: £2,000 PERIOD: 18th-19th century SPECIALIST: Ceramics GENERAL: Glass, copper, brass, country furniture, antiquities - Roman, British, Etruscan etc OTHER: We run a B&B 6 miles NW at Oakington.

G. David Bookseller, 3, 4, & 16 St.Edward's Passage, CB2 3PJ TEL: 354619 FAX: 354619 ASSNS: PBFA PARKING Difficult OPEN: Nos.3 & 4; Mon-Wed, Fri-Sat 9.30-5, No. 16; Mon-Wed, Fri-Sat 9-5 MIN: £1 MAX: around £2,000 PERIOD: 17th-20th century SPECIALIST: Fine antiquarian books at Nos. 3 & 4 plus academic remainders GENERAL: Secondhand books on most subject (excluding sciences), publishers' remainders OTHER: Shops are in a quiet passageway opposite King's College. Numerous bookshops in walking distance.

Gwydir Street Antiques Centre, Units 1 & 2, Dales Brewery, Gwydir Street (off Mill Road), CB1 2LJ TEL: 300269 PARKING: Easy OPEN: Mon-Sat 10-5 MIN: £1 MAX: £500+ PERIOD: 19th-20th century GENERAL: Secondary antiques, collectors items, furniture, bric-a-brac, OTHER INFO: 200 yards to accommodation from £3.

Hyde Park Corner Antiques, 12 Lensfield Road, CB2 1EG TEL: 353654 PARKING Medium OPEN:Mon-Sat 10-5 MIN: £5 MAX: £1,000 PERIOD: 18th-19th century GENERAL: General antiques OTHER INFO: Three antiques shops in a row & 5 more within easy walking distance. Garden House Hotel, famous Brown's restaurant.

Sebastian Pearson, 3 Free School Lane, Benet Street, CB2 3QA TEL: 323999 PARKING Medium

OPEN: Tues-Sat 10-5.30 MIN: £30 MAX: £4,000 PERIOD: 18th -20th century SPECIALIST: 20th century British etchings GENERAL:19th-20th century oils and watercolours, 19th century prints, sporting & topographical.

Barry Strover, 55 Sturton Street, CB1 2QG TEL: 66302 PARKING: Easy OPEN: Chance or by appt MIN: £50 MAX: £5,000 PERIOD: 18th-19th century SPECIALIST: Exclusively original painted pine, particularly dressers. Trading from warehouse for trade & public.

S.J. Webster-Speakman, 79 Regent Street, CB2 1AW TEL: 315048 ASSNS: BADA PARKING: Medium OPEN: Mon-Sat 10-5.30 MIN: £20 MAX: £15,000 PERIOD:17th-19th century SPECIALIST: Animal Staffordshire GENERAL: Period furniture up to 1830 OTHER INFO: Seven other antique shops nearby, four BADA.

COMBERTON (0223)

Comberton Antiques, 5a West Street, CB3 7DS TEL: 262674 PARKING Own carpark OPEN: Fri, Sat, Mon 10-5, Sun 2-5 MIN: £5 MAX: £2,000 PERIOD: 18th-19th century SPECIALIST: Victorian furniture GENERAL: Good furniture & general antiques OTHER INFO: Wimpole Hall (NT), good B&B's in village

WILLINGHAM (0954)

Willingham Antiques, 27 Green Street, CB4 5JA TEL: 60283 PARKING Easy OPEN: Mon-Wed, Fri-Sun 10-5 MIN: £5 MAX: £1,000 PERIOD: 18th-19th century GENERAL: General antiques OTHER INFO: Good food, pubs, good parking outside.

ST IVES (0480)

Broadway Antiques, 31 The Broadway TEL: 461061 PARKING: Easy OPEN: Mon-Wed, Fri, Sat 9.30-4.30 MIN: £1 MAX: £2,500 PERIOD: 18th-19th century SPECIALIST: Treen, Vestas, early lighting, metalware, medical GENERAL: Victorian & Edwardian furniture.

B.R. Knight & Sons, Quay Court, Bull Lane off Bridge Street, PE17 4AR TEL: 468295, 300042 PARKING Easy OPEN: Mon, Fri-Sat 10.30-1, 2.30-4.30, MIN: £1 MAX: £250 PERIOD: 18th-20th century SPECIALIST: Art, pottery, pictures by Huntingdonshire artists GENERAL: Pottery, porcelain, pictures, prints, costume & Victorian jewellery OTHER INFO: Historic town in Cromwell country, the 15th century bridge with a chapel in the middle, is one of only three in England. Light meals at Lizzy's on riverside quay.

WARBOYS (0487)

Warboys' Antiques, Old Church School, High Street, PE17 4DG TEL: 823686 FAX: (0480)496296 PARKING Own carpark OPEN: Tues-Sat 11-5 MIN: £1 MAX: £2,500 PERIOD: 19th-20th century SPECIALIST: Biscuit tins, advertising, sporting items GENERAL: 2,000 sq ft of best selection of collectables in Cambs. OTHER INFO: Warboys is one of historic centres of English witchcraft.

RAMSEY (0487)

Abbey Antiques, 63 Great Whyte, PE17 1HL TEL: 814753 PARKING Easy OPEN: Tues-Sun 10-5 MIN: £3 MAX: £1,500 PERIOD: 19th-20th century SPECIALIST: Collectables: Doulton, Beswick, Carlton, Goss, Victoriana, Wade, Shelley. Small furniture OTHER INFO: Enesco, Mabel Lucie Attwell, figurines. we have formed special club: 'Memories UK' for collectors of Memories of Yesterday Mabel Lucie Attwell figurines. Abbey Gatehouse (NT), Abbey School & Church, Rural Museum. Cromwell country.

DODDINGTON (0354)

Doddington House Antiques, 2 Benwick Road, PE15 0TG TEL: 740755 PARKING Own carpark OPEN: Mon-Sat 10-5.30 MIN: £10 MAX: £3,000 PERIOD: 18th-19th century SPECIALIST: Clocks, barometers, furniture.

LITTLE DOWNHAM (0353)

The Old Bishops Palace Antique Centre, Tower Farm, Tower Road, CB6 2TD TEL: 699177 PARKING: Own carpark OPEN: Fri-Sun +bank hols 10-5.30 MIN: £5 MAX: £4,100 PERIOD: 17th-20th century SPECIALIST: Picture gallery, originals & prints, guns, fishing tackle, golf clubs, lace, linens. Kelims SE Asian artifacts, bronzes, swords GENERAL: Quality furniture well displayed, extensive range of smalls OTHER INFO: Very competitive prices. In medieval Bishop of Ely's Summer Palace, a beautiful, historic building in grounds of Tower Farm complete with horses, riding stables and pastures. Excellent B&B's, 200 yds from country pub: The Plough.

ELY (0353)

Mrs Mills Antiques, CB7 4ER TEL: 1a St Mary's Street PARKING: Easy OPEN: Mon, Wed-Sat 10-1, 2-5 MIN: £5 MAX: £1,000 PERIOD: 19th-20th century GENERAL: Porcelain, silver, jewellery OTHER INFO: River and cathedral. Thursday is market day.

Waterside Antiques, The Wharf, CB7 4AU TEL: 667066 PARKING Own carpark OPEN: Mon-Sat 9.30-5.30, Sun 1-5.30 MIN: £1 MAX: £5,000 PERIOD: 17th-20th century GENERAL: Antique centre with 70 dealers offering a complete range of antiques & collectables. Some specialists OTHER INFO: Historic cathedral, we are by the waterside with cafeterias & restaurants close by.

CHITTERING (0223)

Simon & Penny Rumble, The Old School, CB5 9PW TEL: 861831 PARKING: Easy OPEN: Generally open but appt advisable PERIOD: 17th-18th century SPECIALIST: Oak & country furniture OTHER INFO: Next to good food pub.

FORDHAM (0638)

Phoenix Antiques, 1 Carter Street, CB7 5NG TEL: 720363 PARKING Own carpark OPEN: Increasingly by appt MIN: £5 MAX: £10,000 PERIOD: 16th-18th century SPECIALIST: Pre 1750 interiors GENERAL: General antiques OTHER INFO: Close to 2 antiques centres & several dealers. Anglesea Abbey & Newmarket Racing Museum. Limited B&B on premises (16th century 4 poster bed).

BURWELL (0638)

Peter Norman Antiques, 55 North Street, CB5 0BA TEL: 742197 ASSNS: Guild of Master Craftsmen PARKING Own carpark OPEN: Mon-Sat 9-5.30 MIN: £200 MAX: £3,000 PERIOD: 17th-19th century GENERAL: Furniture, clocks, arms and Oriental rugs.

REACH (0638)

Reach Antiques, Vine House (Antiques Warehouse) TEL: 741989 FAX: 743239 ASSNS: Guild of Master Craftsmen, Assn. of Master Upholsters PARKING Own carpark OPEN: Mon-Fri 7.30-6, Sat 8-12 & anytime by appt MIN: £20 MAX: £3,000 PERIOD: 19th century GENERAL: Furniture for restoration. OTHER INFO: Personal collection of bygones on display. All restoration services. Good village pub & food.

BOTTISHAM (0223)

Cambridge Pine & Oak, Hall Farm, Lode Road, CB5 9DN TEL: 811208 PARKING Own carpark OPEN:: Mon-Sat 10-5 MIN: £50 MAX: £1,200 PERIOD: 18th-20th century SPECIALIST: Pine

furniture OTHER INFO: Half mile from Anglesey Abbey.

EXNING (0638)

Derby Cottage Antiques & Collectables, Derby Cottage, Fordham Road, CB8 7LG TEL: 578422 PARKING: Own carpark OPEN: 9-7 MIN: £1 MAX: £1,500 PERIOD: 19th-20th century SPECIALIST: Derby porcelain GENERAL: Furniture, collectables, bygones, porcelain.

NEWMARKET (0638)

Equus Art Gallery, Sun Lane TEL: 560445 ASSNS: FATG PARKING: Easy OPEN: 9.30-5.30, Wed closes 1pm MIN: £200 MAX: £4,000 PERIOD: 19th-20th century SPECIALIST: Equestrian art GENERAL: Paintings, bronzes, prints.

Jemima Godfrey, 5 Rous Road, CB8 8DH TEL: 663584 PARKING: Medium OPEN: Thurs-Fri 10-1, 2-4.30 & by appt MIN: £1 MAX: £500 PERIOD: 19th-20th century SPECIALIST: Linen GENERAL: Jewellery, collectables, silverplate, postcards, bric-a-brac OTHER INFO: Racing museum, Jockey Club, Tattersalls racehorse sales, 2 courses & extensive training grounds.

ATTLEBOROUGH (0953)

A.E. Bush & Partners, Vineyard Antique Gallery, Leys Lane, NR17 1NE TEL: 452175 FAX: 456481 PARKING: Own carpark OPEN: Seven days 9-6 MIN: £100 MAX: £5,000 PERIOD: 17th-20th century SPECIALIST: Case furniture GENERAL: Bureau desks, writing tables etc OTHER INFO: Clients collected from airports & train & bus stations.

GARBOLDISHAM (0953)

Swan House Country Crafts & Tea Rooms, Hopton Road, IP22 2RQ TEL: 818221 PARKING: Own carpark OPEN: Easter-end Sept Thurs-Sun 11-5 MIN: £1 MAX: £500 PERIOD: 20th century GENERAL: Country crafts, furniture, bric-a-brac OTHER INFO: All in 17th century characterful coaching inn.

DISS (0379)

Diss Antiques, 2-3 Market Place TEL: 642213 FAX: 642213 ASSNS: LAPADA, GMC PARKING: Easy OPEN: 9-5 MIN: £5 MAX: £6,000 PERIOD: 17th-19th century SPECIALIST: Furniture, barometers GENERAL: Porcelain, silver, copper, clocks OTHER INFO: Bressingham Gardens & Steam Museum, many oak-beamed pubs.

Raymond Norman Antiques, 12 Market Hill TEL:

650360 PARKING: Easy OPEN: Mon-Sat 10-5 & by appt (resident) MIN: £100 MAX: £10,000 PERIOD: 18th-19th century SPECIALIST: Longcase clocks, mechanical music GENERAL: Georgian, Victorian furniture OTHER INFO: Excellent holiday town, winebar opposite. Fridays large auction.

BROCKDISH (0379)

Brockdish Antiques, Commerce House, IP21 4JL TEL: 75498 PARKING: Easy OPEN: 9-5, not Wed MIN: £10 PERIOD: 19th-20th century SPECIALIST: Upholstered chairs GENERAL: Georgian, Victorian, Edwardian furniture.

STRADBROKE (0379)

Mary Palmer Antiques, Cottage Farm, New Street (B1117), IP21 5JG TEL: 388100 PARKING: Easy OPEN: Seven day (resident) MIN: £1 MAX: £1,000 PERIOD: 18th-19th century SPECIALIST: Glass GENERAL: Small furniture, collectables. Valuations.

Stubcroft Period Furnishings & Restorations, Cottage Farm, New Street (B1117), IP21 5JG TEL: 388100 PARKING: Own carpark OPEN: Seven days (resident) MIN: £50 MAX: £2,500 PERIOD: 18th-19th century SPECIALIST: Oak, mahogany & country made furnishing pieces etc OTHER INFO: In 1840 Stradbroke sent 200 pauper emigrants to America.

LAXFIELD (0986)

Mangate Gallery, Old Vicarage, IP13 8DT TEL: 798524 FAX: 798524 ASSNS: LAPADA PARKING: Own carpark OPEN: By appt MIN: £100 MAX: £3,000 PERIOD: 19th-20th century GENERAL: Watercolours & conservation, prints, some oils. Valuations OTHER INFO: Framlingham Castle, Birds of Prey Centre, Laxfield Museum.

PEASENHALL (0728)

Peasenhall Art & Antiques Gallery, IP17 2HJ TEL: 79224 PARKING: Easy OPEN: Seven days 9-6 MIN: £20 MAX: £2,000 PERIOD: some 18th, 19th-early 20th century SPECIALIST: Walking sticks GENERAL: Oils, watercolours, (with full restoration service). Oak, mahogany & fruitwood furniture OTHER INFO: Sea and freshwater fishing all year nearby.

YOXFORD (0728)

Suffolk House Antiques, High Street, IP17 3EP TEL: 778122 FAX: 778122 PARKING: Easy OPEN: Mon-Tues, Thurs-Sat 10-1, 2.15-5.15 MIN:

£20 MAX: £20,000 PERIOD: 17th-18th century SPECIALIST: Early oak & country furniture, Delft, metalware, rugs etc.

LEISTON (0728)

Leiston Trading Post, 13a High Street, IP16 4EL TEL: 830081 PARKING: Easy OPEN: Mon-Sat 9.30-5, Weds AM only MIN: £1 MAX: £1,000 PERIOD: 19th century SPECIALIST: Quality collectables GENERAL: Georgian-1930's furniture, loads of china, glass & bric-a-brac OTHER INFO: On Heritage Coast, near Sizewell Power Station.

Warren's Antiques, High Street, IP16 4EL TEL: 831414 PARKING: Own carpark OPEN: 9-1, 2-5 (closed Weds, Sat) but anytime by appt MIN: £5 MAX: £2,000 PERIOD: 18th-20th century SPECIALIST: Chests of drawers, antique restorations GENERAL: Mahogany, oak, walnut & shipping furniture 1920's china & glass OTHER INFO: Orford & Framlingham Castles.

SNAPE MALTINGS (0728)

Snape Antique & Collectors Centre, IP17 1SR TEL: 688038 PARKING: Own carpark OPEN: Summer 10-6, Winter 10-4.30 MIN: £1 PERIOD: 19th-20th century 40+ dealers GENERAL: Good smalls, country & decorative textiles, linens, silver + plate, china, antique maps, prints, pictures, jewellery, costume jewellery OTHER INFO: Next to world famous concert hall within riverside centre. All facilities & beautiful scenery.

ALDEBURGH (0728)

Aldeburgh Galleries, 132 High Street, IP15 5AQ TEL: 453963 PARKING: Easy OPEN: Mon-Sat 10-5, Sun 2-4.30 MIN: £5 MAX: £450 PERIOD: 19th-20th century SPECIALIST: Contemporary studio ceramics GENERAL: General antiques OTHER INFO: Benjamin Britten country, Snape concert halls.

BLYTHBURGH (0502)

E.T. Webster Preservation in Action, Westwood Lodge TEL: 70539 PARKING: Own carpark OPEN: 8-8 MIN: £5 MAX: £32,000 PERIOD: 15th-17th century SPECIALIST: Period oak panelling, doors, floors, fireplaces & fittings GENERAL: Complete medieval house & rooms, 30 in stock ready for reconstruction OTHER INFO: Restoration experts on staff. 16th to 17th century manor house sleeping 10 for short or long lets.

SOUTHWOLD (0502)

Emporium Antiques &Collectors Centre, 70 High Street, IP18 6DN TEL: 723909 PARKING: Easy OPEN: Mon-Sat 10-5, Sun 12-5 MIN: £1 MAX: £3,000 PERIOD: 19th-20th century Selling on behalf of 40 dealers GENERAL: Silver, china, porcelain, collectables, glass, books, prints & pictures, furniture, Art Deco, jewellery, metals, Arts & Crafts.

WRENTHAM (0502)

Wrentham Antiques Centre, 7 High Street TEL: 75323 PARKING: Own carpark OPEN: 10-5 MIN: £1 MAX: £3,000 PERIOD: 18th-20th century SPECIALIST: Art Deco, period mahogany GENERAL: Collectables OTHER INFO: Beautiful Heritage Coast, Southwold, Walberswick. Cold easterly wind.

KESSINGLAND (0502)

Kessingland Antiques, 36a High Street, NR33 7QQ TEL: 740562 PARKING: Own carpark OPEN: Seven days 10-5.30 MIN: £1 MAX: £1,500 PERIOD: 18th-20th century SPECIALIST: Clocks & watches GENERAL: Everything you can think of, I stock it.

BECCLES (0502)

Saltgate Antiques, 11 Saltgate, NR34 9AN TEL: 712776 PARKING: Easy OPEN: Mon-Sat 9-5, Weds AM only MIN: £50 MAX: £3,800 PERIOD: 18th-20th century GENERAL: Furniture, copper, brass, oils, etchings OTHER INFO: Riverside Hotel 1 min, Good B&B & restaurant next door.

BUNGAY (0986)

Country House Antiques, 30 Earsham Street TEL: 892875 PARKING: Easy OPEN: 9.30-4.30 & anytime by appt MIN: £1 MAX: £3-5,000 PERIOD: 17th-20th century SPECIALIST: Georgian mahogany furniture GENERAL: Victorian, Edwardian furniture, porcelain, china & collectables.

Black Dog Antiques, 51 Earsham Street, NR35 1AF TEL: 895554 PARKING: Easy OPEN: 10-5 MIN: £1 MAX: £1,000 PERIOD: 17th-20th century SPECIALIST: Roman pots, coins to 20th century clothes. Shop shared by 10 dealers OTHER INFO: Green Dragon with own brewery. Good walks & bike rides shown on town map.

Earsham Hall Pine, Earsham Hall, NR35 2AN TEL: 894423 FAX: 895656 ASSNS: GMC PARKING: Own carpark OPEN: Mon-Fri 8-5, Sat-Sun 10-4 MIN: £1 MAX: £3,000 PERIOD: 19th-20th century GENERAL: Pine furniture made from old wood, new wood, originally restored pine, lighting, fireplaces, soft furnishings, gifts OTHER INFO: Unique location in country mansion under restoration. Largest pine range in East Anglia.

GREAT YARMOUTH (0493)

The Ferrow Family, 6-7 Hal Quay TEL: 855391 ASSNS: LAPADA PARKING: Medium OPEN: 9-5, Thurs AM only MIN: £10 MAX: £5,000 PERIOD: 18th-20th century GENERAL: General antiques.

Haven Gallery, 6-7 Hall Quay TEL: 855391 PARKING: Medium OPEN: 9-5, Thurs AM only MIN: £20 MAX: £5,000 PERIOD: 19th-20th century GENERAL: Oils, watercolours, etchings, prints.

SOUTH WALSHAM (0605)

Leo Pratt & Son, Old Curiosity Shop, NR13 6EA TEL: 49204 FAX: 49204 PARKING: Own carpark OPEN: 9.30-1, 2-5.30 MIN: £2 MAX: £8,000+ PERIOD: 17th-20th century SPECIALIST: English furniture GENERAL: Lots of china & glass, brassware, clocks, etc, stocked in 5 warehouses OTHER INFO: South Walsham Broad (part of Norfolk Broads), excellent country club.

STALHAM (0692)

Stalham Antiques Gallery, 29 High Street, NR12 9AH TEL: 580636 FAX: 580636 PARKING: Own carpark OPEN: Mon-Fri 9-1, 2-5, Sat 9-1 MIN: £50 MAX: £10,000 PERIOD: 17th-19th century SPECIALIST: Period furniture GENERAL: Brass, copper, paintings, country furniture. No repro OTHER INFO: In heart of Norfolk Broads yet 20 mins from Norwich.

NORTH WALSHAM (0692)

Anglia Antique Exporters, Station Yard, Norwich Road, NR28 0DS TEL: 406266 FAX: 406266 PARKING: Own carpark OPEN: Mon-Fri 9-5, Sat 9-1 MIN: £25 MAX: £2,000 PERIOD: 19th-20th century SPECIALIST: Japanese, Australian, German markets OTHER INFO: Full packing & container facilities.

Eric Bates & Sons, Melbourne House, Bacton Road, NR28 0RA TEL: 403221 FAX: 404388 ASSNS: GMC PARKING: Own car park OPEN: Mon-Sat 8-5 MIN: £1 MAX: £10,000 PERIOD: 19th century SPECIALIST: Sets of chairs & dining tables GENERAL: Victorian furniture, 17,000 sq ft stock. Close to Norfolk Broads. Owner is known to

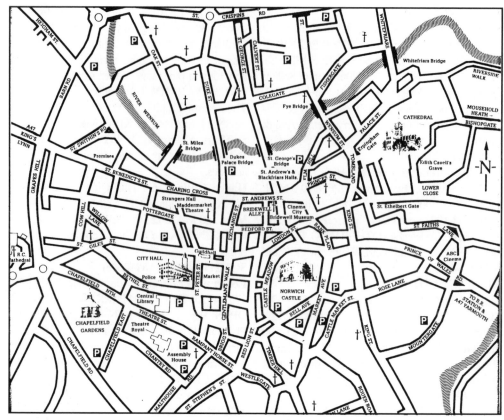

Street Map of Norwich
By courtesy of Norwich City Council

trade as The Chairman.

COLTISHALL (0603)

Liz Allport-Lomax, TEL: 737631 ASSNS: Retired member LAPADA PARKING: Own carpark OPEN: By appt MIN: £5 MAX: £10,000 PERIOD: 19th century SPECIALIST: English porcelain, small collectables GENERAL: Silver, glass, small furniture OTHER INFO: Antique Centre + 3 shops.

Eric Bates & Sons, High Street, NR12 7AA TEL: 738716 FAX: 738966 ASSNS: GMC PARKING: Own carpark OPEN: Mon-Sat 8-5 MIN: £1 MAX: £10,000+ PERIOD: 18th-20th century SPECIALIST: Sets of chairs & dining tables GENERAL: Victorian furniture OTHER INFO: Owner is known in the trade as The Chairman. On Norfolk Broads, good facilities.

Gwendoline Golder, Point House, High Street TEL: 738099 PARKING: Own carpark OPEN: Mon-Sat 10-5 MIN: £5 MAX: £500 PERIOD: 19th-20th century GENERAL: Furniture, porcelain, small

silver collectors items.

BUXTON (0603)

As Time Goes By, Buxton Mill TEL: 278080 FAX: 278080 PARKING: Easy OPEN: Tues-Fri 9.30-5, Sat-Sun 10-4 MIN: £10 MAX: £5,000 PERIOD: 17th-20th century SPECIALIST: Antique clocks including repair & restoration.

WROXHAM (0603)

T.C.S. Brooke, The Grange, Norwich Road TEL: 782644 ASSNS: BADA PARKING: Own carpark OPEN: 9.15-5.30 MIN: £25 MAX: £10,000 PERIOD: 18th-19th century SPECIALIST: 18th century English porcelain GENERAL: General antiques. Valuations OTHER INFO: Centre of Norfolk Broads.

NORWICH (0603)

Allbrow & Sons, 10 All Saints Green, NR1 3NA TEL: 622569 ASSNS: NAG PARKING: Easy OPEN: 9.30-4.30 MIN: £5 MAX: £4,000 PERIOD: 19th century SPECIALIST: Antique jewellery &

silver GENERAL: Mixed new, s/h & antique.

William Allchin, 22-24 St. Benedicts Street, NR2 4AQ TEL: 660046 FAX: 660046 PARKING: Medium OPEN: Mon-Sat 10.30-5 MIN: £10 MAX: £2,500 PERIOD: 19th-20th century SPECIALIST: Lighting, fireplaces, mantels GENERAL: Brass & iron bedsteads, furniture, soft furnishings OTHER INFO: 2 other antique shops in street, 3 restaurants within 5 mins. Adlards (Michelin star) 8 mins walk.

Antiques Centre, St. Michael at Plea, Bank Plain (nr top Elm Hill), TEL: 619129 PARKING: Medium OPEN: Mon-Sat 9.30-5 MIN: £1 MAX: £1,000 PERIOD: 19th-20th century (mostly pre 1940) SPECIALIST: Clocks, Oriental china, lighting, linen & lace GENERAL: General antiques OTHER INFO: St. Michael at Plea is a medieval church (now deconsecrated). Norwich city has a church for every Sunday in the year & a public house for every day.

The Bank House Gallery, 71 Newmarket Road, NR2 2HW TEL: 633380 FAX: 633387 ASSNS: LAPADA PARKING: Own carpark OPEN: By appt MIN: £500 MAX: £50,000 PERIOD: 18th-19th century SPECIALIST: Norwich & Suffolk Schools GENERAL: Oils OTHER INFO: Norwich Castle Museum fine art collection.

Arthur Brett & Sons Ltd, 42 St. Giles Street TEL: 628171 FAX: 630245 ASSNS: BADA PARKING: Easy OPEN: Mon-Fri 9.30-1, 2.15-5 & by appt MIN: £200 MAX: £15,000 PERIOD: 17th-19th century SPECIALIST: English 18th century furniture GENERAL: Furniture OTHER INFO: Medieval city with fine Norman cathedral.

Cloisters Antique Fair, St. Andrews Hall, St. Andrews Plain, NR3 1AW TEL: 425158 PARKING: Easy OPEN: Weds 8-3.30 MIN: £1 MAX: £500 PERIOD: 19th-20th century GENERAL: Jewellery, Oriental, watches, silver, ceramics, antiquarian books, postcards, ephemera, collectables OTHER INFO: Crypt café adjoins. Norwich Castle Museum & Cathedral, mediæval cobbled streets (Elm Hill). 2 antique centres within easy walk, Norfolk Broads nearby.

Fairhurst Gallery, Websdales Court, Bedford Street, NR2 1AS TEL: 614214 PARKING: Medium OPEN: 10-5.30 MIN: £5 MAX: £4,500 PERIOD: 18th-20th century SPECIALIST: Leaning towards nautical OTHER INFO: In centre of Norwich, restaurant next door.

Gallery 45, 45 St. Benedicts Street, NR2 4PG TEL: 763771 PARKING: Easy OPEN: Tues-Fri 11-3, Sat 11-4 MIN: £50 MAX: £1,500 PERIOD: 20th century SPECIALIST: Modern British & Continental paintings incl. original prints & etchings & engravings OTHER INFO: Telephone home for appt 742977. Further stock available at The Coach House, Townhouse Road, Old Costessy, Norwich.

Michael Hallam Antiques, at St Michael at Plea Antique Centre, Redwell Street (nr London Street) TEL: 413692 PARKING: Medium OPEN: 9.30-5 MIN: £10 MAX: £1,000+ PERIOD: 19th century SPECIALIST: Oriental porcelain, pottery etc GENERAL: Mainly smalls OTHER INFO: A dealer's dealer

John Howkins Antiques, 1 Dereham Road TEL: 627832 PARKING: Own carpark OPEN: Mon-Sat 10-5 MIN: £10 MAX: £15,000 PERIOD: 18th-20th century SPECIALIST: 18th & 19th century furniture GENERAL: Quality furniture for American, Italian, Australian, Japanese markets OTHER INFO: Packing & shipping service available. Restoration.

Leona Levine Silver Specialist, at Zelley The Jewellers, 35 St Giles Street, NR2 1JP TEL: 628709 ASSNS: BADA PARKING: Medium OPEN: Mon-Wed, Fri-Sat 9.15-5 MIN: £8 MAX: £1,000+ PERIOD: 18th-20th century SPECIALIST: Dining table silver GENERAL: Range of silver cutlery (antique & s/h), some Sheffield plate OTHER INFO: 200 yds from Town Hall & Tourist Office which exhibits free the Norwich City Silver Regalia + important early silver collection. Good facilities closeby.

Mandell's Gallery, Elm Hill, NR3 1HN TEL: 626892, 629180 FAX: 767471 ASSNS: FATG PARKING: Own carpark OPEN: Mon-Sat 9-5.30 MIN: £500 MAX: £50,000 PERIOD: 19th-20th century SPECIALIST: Norwich School GENERAL: English & Continental paintings & watercolours, large stock.

Queen of Hungary Antiques, 49 St.Benedicts Street, NR2 4TG TEL: 625082 PARKING: Easy OPEN: Mon-Wed, Fri, Sat 10.30-5.30 MIN: £15 MAX: £1,000 PERIOD: 18th-20th century SPECIALIST: Early pine, good mahogany, brass & iron beds, ° testers GENERAL: Old pine, furniture, misc farm tools OTHER INFO: 14th century museum. St. Benedicts Street is quite short & only 5 mins from centre.

Tooltique, 54 Waterloo Road, NR3 1EW TEL: 414289 PARKING: Easy OPEN: Mon-Sat 9-5.30 MIN: £1 MAX: £1,000 PERIOD: 18th-20th century SPECIALIST: Antique woodworking tools GENERAL: Used woodworking tools.

LONG STRATTON (0508)

Old Coach House Antiques, Ipswich Road, NR15 2TA TEL: 30942 PARKING: Easy OPEN: Tues-Sat 10-5 MIN: £5 MAX: £500 PERIOD: 19th-20th century GENERAL: Late Victorian & later mahogany, pine, oak furniture.

WYMONDHAM (0953)

Margaret King, 16 Market Place, NR18 0AX TEL: 604758 PARKING: Easy OPEN: Mon-Sat 9-4.30 MIN: £20 MAX: £3,000 PERIOD: 18th-19th century SPECIALIST: Victorian figures & cranberry glass, furniture GENERAL: General antiques OTHER INFO: Historic town with ancient Abbey & Market Cross.

Turret House, 27 Middleton Street, NR18 0AB TEL: 603462 ASSNS: PBFA PARKING: Easy OPEN: Normally 9-6 but appt advised (resident) MIN: £1 MAX: £2,000 PERIOD: Mostly late 18th-early 20th century SPECIALIST: Antiquarian books, especially science & medicine, also antique scientific instruments GENERAL: 2nd hand & antiquarian books OTHER INFO: Attractive market town with fine Norman abbey.

BAWDESWELL (0362)

Norfolk Polyphon Centre, Wood Farm, NR20 4RX TEL: 88230 FAX: 88669 PARKING: Own carpark OPEN: Anytime by appt MIN: £1,000 MAX: Considerable PERIOD: 19th-early 20th century SPECIALIST: Musical boxes, mechanical organs, orchestrions etc, automata OTHER INFO: Country farmhouse near coast & Broads

REEPHAM (0603)

The Chimes, Market Place, NR10 4JJ TEL: 870480 PARKING: Easy OPEN: 9-5.30 MIN: £20 MAX: £1,500 PERIOD: 18th-19th century GENERAL: Furniture, writing slopes, boxes, objets d'art OTHER INFO: Perfect Georgian square in conservation area. Tearoom with homemade cakes.

SWAFFHAM (0760)

Cranglegate (Antiques), Cranglegate, Market Place, PE37 7LE TEL: 721052 ASSNS: Antique Traders Assn PARKING: Easy OPEN: Tues, Thurs, Sat 10-5.30 (resident) MIN: £20 MAX: £500ish PERIOD: 17th-20th century SPECIALIST:

Religious items, Oriental GENERAL: Small furniture, pottery & china, bronzes & sculpture.

Swaffham Antiques, Cranbury Place, Theatre Street TEL: 721697 PARKING: Own carpark OPEN: By appt MIN: £20 MAX: £7,000+ PERIOD: 18th-20th century GENERAL: Selection of quality antiques OTHER INFO: Horse & Groom restaurant & hotel, Swaffham poultry market. Traditional open auction market on Sats.

FAKENHAM (0328)

Fakenham Antique Centre, Old Congregational Chapel, 14 Norwich Road, NR21 8AZ TEL: 862941 PARKING: Easy OPEN: Mon-Sat 10-4.30 MIN: £10 MAX: £2,000 PERIOD: 18th-19th century SPECIALIST: French furniture GENERAL: General antiques.

Market Place Antiques, 28 Upper Market TEL: 862962 PARKING: Easy OPEN: Mon-Sat 10-4.30 PERIOD: 19th-20th century SPECIALIST: Victorian jewellery GENERAL: General antiques OTHER INFO: Flea market every Thursday. Sandringham House, Congham Hall.

MELTON CONSTABLE (0263)

Sharrington Antiques, NR24 2PQ TEL: 861411 PARKING: Own carpark OPEN: Mon-Sat 9.30-5.30 MIN: £1 PERIOD: 18th-19th century SPECIALIST: Snuff boxes, treen, lace bobbins etc GENERAL: All small interesting & strange objects OTHER INFO: Holiday homes in grounds. Good pubs in Holt (4 miles). Don't go to Melton Constable - we are 4 miles west of Holt!

HOLT (0263)

Collector's Cabin, 7 Cromer Road TEL: 712241 PARKING: Easy OPEN: Mon-Wed, Fri, Sat 10-1, 2-4.30, Thurs 10-1 MIN: £1 MAX: £50 PERIOD: 19th-20th century GENERAL: Bric-a-brac, clothes, toys, jewellery etc

R.L. Cook Antiquarian & Secondhand Books, 10 Heathfield Road, High Kelling, NR25 6RG TEL: 711163 ASSNS: ABA PARKING: Own carpark OPEN: Anytime by appt MIN: £5 MAX: £500 PERIOD: 17th-20th century GENERAL: Many subjects, small stock.

Richard Scott Antiques, 30 High Street TEL: 712479 PARKING: Medium OPEN: Mon-Wed, Fri, Sat 11-5 MIN: £5 MAX: £500 PERIOD: 18th-20th century SPECIALIST: Large stock porcelain, pottery & glass OTHER INFO: Good Georgian town close to 4 fine country house: Holkham,

Houghton, Felbrigg & Blickling. 5 miles from famous beautiful coastline.

CROMER (0263)

Bond Street Antiques, 6 Bond Street, NR27 9DA TEL: 513134 ASSNS: NAG, FGA PARKING: Medium OPEN: Mon-Sat 9-1, 2-5.30 MIN: £10 MAX: £10,000 PERIOD: 18th-20th century SPECIALIST: Silver, gold & jewellery GENERAL: Georgian, Victorian & Edwardian jewellery, silver, porcelain OTHER INFO: End-of-Pier show, swimming complex, The Broads, Yarmouth, Norwich all near. Lifeboat station.

SHERINGHAM (0263)

Dorothy's Antiques, 23 Waterbank Road, NR26 8RB TEL: 822319 PARKING: Own carpark OPEN: Daily 11.15-4 PERIOD: 19th-20th century GENERAL: Small furniture, cranberry glass, Royal Worcester & other porcelain, commemoratives, collectables.

J.H. Parriss, 20 Station Road, NR26 8RE TEL: 822661 ASSNS: NAG PARKING: Easy OPEN: Mon, Tues, Thurs-Sat 9.15-1, 2.15-5 MIN: £100 MAX: £5,000 PERIOD: 18th-20th century GENERAL: Clocks, silver, jewellery.

Westcliffe Gallery, 2-8 Augusta Street, NR26 8LA TEL: 824320 PARKING: Medium OPEN: Mon, Tues, Thurs-Sat 9.30-1, 2-5.30 MIN: £90 MAX: £12,000 PERIOD: 18th-20th century SPECIALIST: Ornithological paintings (period) GENERAL: Oils, watercolours, drawings & period furniture (over 250 pictures always on display) OTHER INFO: Links Country Park Hotel (West Runton), Felbrigg Hall, Blickling Hall (NT).

CLEY-NEXT-THE-SEA (0263)

B. & J. Kerridge Antiques, Rocket House, High Street TEL: 741154 FAX: 741154 PARKING: Medium OPEN: 10-5 MIN: £5 MAX: £2,000 PERIOD: 17th-19th century SPECIALIST: Country house items GENERAL: Period furniture OTHER INFO: Area of outstanding natural beauty. Good teashop next door.

WELLS-NEXT-THE-SEA (0328)

Church Street Antiques, 2 Church Street, NR23 1JA TEL: 711698 PARKING: Easy OPEN: Tues-Sat 10-4 & by appt MIN: £1 MAX: £500 PERIOD: 19th-20th century SPECIALIST: Costume jewellery, hat pins, linen & lace, textiles GENERAL: Small furniture, collectables, china, glass etc OTHER INFO: Quaint pretty seaside town &

Jane Maufe

MARKET HOUSE
BURNHAM MARKET, NORFOLK
(0328) 738475
Some of the finest antique furniture & works of art in East Anglia

35 miles from Norwich & 22 from King's Lynn

harbour, 2 miles Holkham Hall, Potteries & Bygones, Walsingham. Along coast: Heacham's Norfolk Lavender Fields, and inland: Sandringham House at Dersingham.

BURNHAM MARKET (0328)

M. & A. Cringle, The Old Black Horse, PE31 8HD TEL: 738456 PARKING: Easy OPEN: Mon-Tues, Thurs-Sat 9-1, 2-5 MIN: £50 MAX: £3,000 PERIOD: 18th-19th century SPECIALIST: Furniture GENERAL: Glass, decorative prints, some porcelain OTHER INFO: Listed preserved Georgian village square, good restaurants & hotels. 4 antique shops.

Anne Hamilton Antiques, North Street TEL: 738187 PARKING: Easy OPEN: Mon-Sat 10-1, 2-5 MIN: £5 MAX: £4,000 PERIOD: 18th-19th century SPECIALIST: English porcelain GENERAL: Small decorative items, glass, silver & furniture.

Market House, PE31 8HF TEL: 738475 PARKING: Very easy OPEN: Mon-Sat 9-6 MAX: £25,000 PERIOD: 18th century SPECIALIST: Period English furniture & works of art OTHER INFO: Norfolk's loveliest village & Nelson's birthplace. Excellent hotel adjacent: The Captain Sir William Hoste. Fishes restaurant.

HUNSTANTON (0485)

Delawood Antiques, 10 Westgate, PE36 5AL TEL: 532903 PARKING: Easy OPEN: Mon, Wed, Fri, Sat usually 10-5 & by appt MIN: £1 MAX: £1,000 PERIOD: 19th-20th century SPECIALIST: Jewellery, books GENERAL: Furniture & collectables, clocks, barometers OTHER INFO: Porcelain high quality restoration. Pretty Victorian seaside town famous for its red & white cliffs.

R.C. Woodhouse (Antiquarian Horologist), 10 Westgate, PE36 5AL TEL: 532903 ASSNS: BHF,

BWCMG, UKICHAW PARKING: Easy OPEN: Mon, Wed, Fri, Sat usually 10-5 & by appt MIN: £1 MAX: £1,000 PERIOD: 19th-20th century SPECIALIST: Clocks GENERAL: Barometers, books, general antiques & collectors items OTHER INFO: Restoration of antique clocks, barometers & porcelain. Sea Life Centre in town, good birdwatching along coast

HEACHAM (0485)

Peter Robinson, Pear Tree House, 7 Lynn Road TEL: 70228 PARKING: Easy OPEN: Mon-Sat 9-5 MIN: £1 MAX: £5,000 PERIOD: 17th-19th century SPECIALIST: English furniture GENERAL: Wide variety interesting antiques.

KING'S LYNN (0553)

Norfolk Galleries, 1 Stanley Street, Railway Road, PE30 1PF TEL: 765060 PARKING: Medium OPEN: 8.30-1, 1.30-5.30 MIN: £5,000 MAX: £20,000 PERIOD: 19th century SPECIALIST: Victorian & reconstructed period style furniture.

Old Curiosity Shop, 25 St. James Street, PE30 5AD TEL: 766591 PARKING: Easy OPEN: Mon, Tues, Thurs-Sat 11-5 MIN: £1 MAX: £600 PERIOD: 18th-20th century GENERAL: Antiques & collectables OTHER INFO: Ancient port, small market town, historic buildings. East Anglia's northern gateway, 2 museums, 15 miles to seaside resort.

The Old Granary Antiques Centre, King's Staithe Lane, (off Queen Street), PE30 1LZ TEL: 775509 PARKING: Easy OPEN: Mon-Sat 10-5, most Suns June-Sept. MIN: £1 MAX: £1,000 PERIOD: 19th-20th century GENERAL: General antiques OTHER INFO: An Aladdin's Cave in a 16th century granary in the historic part of town, near the Old Customs House & Hanseatic Warehouse.

Tower Gallery, Middleton Tower, PE32 1EE TEL: 840203, 840581 PARKING: Own carpark OPEN: Seven days MIN: £5 MAX: £2,000 PERIOD: 18th-20th century GENERAL: Everything.

WISBECH (0945)

Peter A. Crofts, 117 High Road, Elm, PE14 0DN TEL: 584616 ASSNS: BADA, CINOA PARKING Own carpark OPEN: Mon-Fri 8-5 (pls telephone) MIN: £5 MAX: £5,000 PERIOD: 18th-20th century SPECIALIST: Pottery & porcelain, silver GENERAL: Furniture, glass, Victorian jewellery OTHER INFO: We have a large warehouse beside a bungalow - NO SIGN. Good pub on corner.

PETERBOROUGH (0733)

Fitzwilliam Antiques Centres Ltd., Fitzwilliam Street TEL: 65415 PARKING Own carpark OPEN: Mon-Sat 10-5, Sun 12-5 MIN: £5 MAX: £5,000+ GENERAL: 40+ dealers showing quality stock including porcelain, furniture, pine, jewellery, glass, maps, books, toys, silver, commemorative coins OTHER INFO: Peterborough is a development city with an 11th century cathedral, 5 miles from the M1. Many good hotels, leisure park, Queensgate Shopping Centre.

Old Soke Books, 68 Burghley Road, PE1 2QE TEL: 64147 PARKING: Medium OPEN: Tues-Sat 10.30-5.30 MIN: £1 MAX: £300 PERIOD: 19th century GENERAL: Mostly secondhand and old books, good selection of prints, some paintings & small antiques.

SAWTRY (0487)

A Barn Full of Brass Beds, Manor Farm, St Judiths Lane, PE17 5XE TEL: 832664 PARKING: Own carpark OPEN: By appt MIN: £250 MAX: £1,000 PERIOD: 19th century SPECIALIST: 200 antique brass & iron beds.

East Midlands

Stratford-upon-Avon

This tour covers the rural heart of England passing through Warwickshire, Leicestershire and Northamptonshire with their historic market towns and charming villages. We also visit three major cities: Coventry, Leicester and Northampton.

Travelling up the M40, we leave at Junction 12 to visit the village of Kineton before moving onwards to Stratford-upon-Avon, home of the Royal Shakespeare Company. The town has many fine buildings but, above all, it is William Shakespeare that brings visitors here. Stratford has five principal properties associated with Shakespeare and in the summer months visitors must be prepared to queue. Anne Hathaway's Cottage is a delightful thatched house and was her home before her marriage to Shakespeare. Another of the properties is Shakespeare's Birthplace, displaying many rare items as well as the BBC Television Costume Exhibition. Hall's Croft was the home of the Bard's daughter and her husband. Then there is New Place, Shakespeare's last home, with its lovely Elizabethan knot garden. Finally, the Shakespeare Countryside Museum at Mary Arden's House, Wilmcote about three and a half miles from Stratford, is a Tudor farmhouse and the home of Shakespeare's mother.

Crossing the motorway we visit the village of Hatton before arriving in Warwick, the next stop on this tour. This town possesses the finest medieval castle in England. It is possible that this was the site of a Saxon defensive mound against the Danes, standing as it does on the River Avon. In 1068 William the Conqueror gave the site and borough to Henry de Newburgh who started the castle by building a motte and shell keep. It was during the 14th century that Thomas Beauchamp, Earl of Warwick, built the castle that largely survives today. The best known Earl of Warwick was nicknamed "Kingmaker" for his role in the Wars of the Roses, meeting his death at the Battle of Barnet in 1471. Right at the end of the 15th century, another Earl of Warwick was executed for his part in the Perkin Warbeck plot (it was claimed that Perkin Warbeck was the son of Edward IV and rightful heir to the throne). Another Earl, John Dudley, was executed in 1554 after being

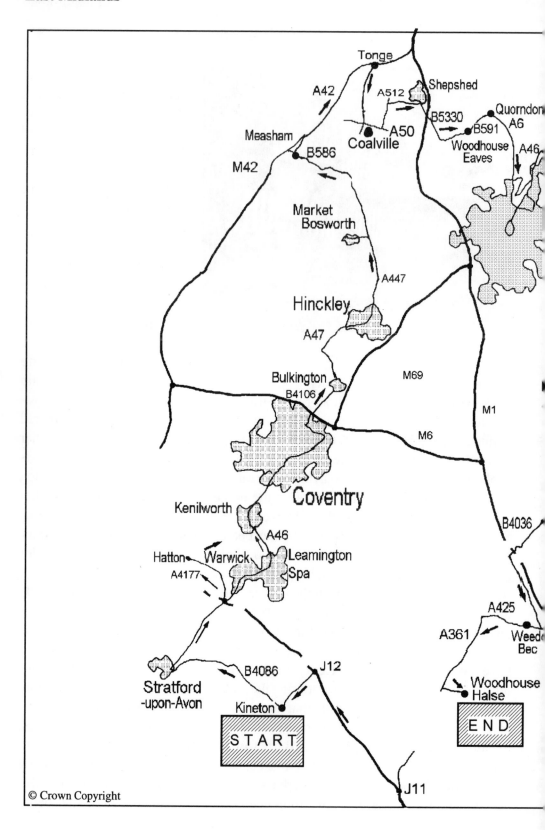

© Crown Copyright

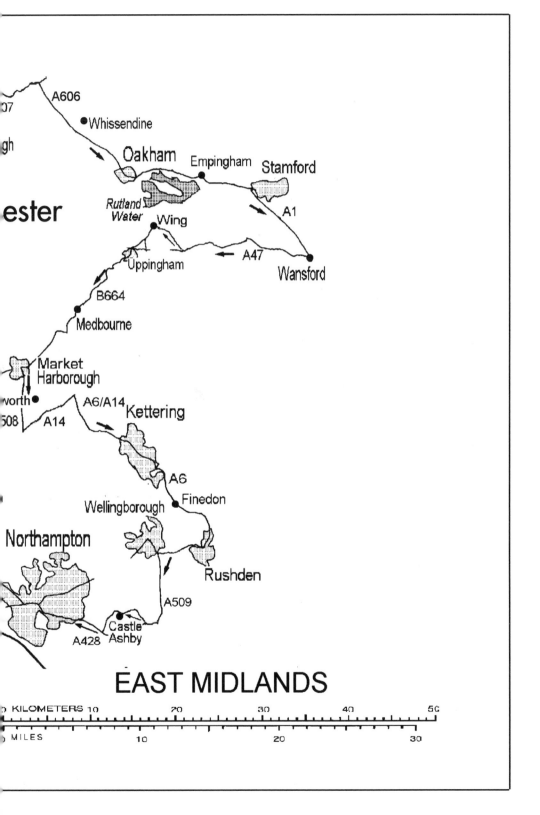

EAST MIDLANDS

The Lord Leycester Hospital, Warwick

involved in the attempt to put Lady Jane Grey on the throne. Owners of Warwick Castle seemed to have an unfortunate record of choosing the wrong side.

Now the Castle has much to offer the visitor. There are battlements and towers, a dungeon, a torture chamber and state apartments with a wonderful collection of pictures by Rubens, Van Dyck, etc. Owned by a subsidiary of Madame Tussauds, there is also an award winning exhibition titled "A Royal Weekend Party 1898".

Other interesting buildings in the town include the 15th century Beauchamp Chapel in St Mary's Church containing the Purbeck marble tomb of Richard Beauchamp, Earl of Warwick, who died in 1439 and the Lord Leycester Hospital, built in 1571 by Robert Dudley, Earl of Leicester.

These are just a few of the attractions of this historic town and visitors are strongly recommended to visit the Tourist Information Centre for a more complete list and details.

We go next to the adjoining town of Leamington Spa standing on the River Leam and the Grand Union Canal. With its natural spring waters, it has baths, many Regency terraces and the Royal Pump Room. More properly the town's name is Royal Leamington Spa, an honour granted by Queen Victoria after a visit in 1838.

Kenilworth, another town with a famous castle, is our next stop. This castle, unlike Warwick, is a ruin. It was started in the early 12th century and in the 13th century it was held by Simon de Montfort who rebelled against Henry III. Simon de Montfort was killed in the Battle of Evesham in 1265 although his followers held the castle against all attacks for another six months. It was only illness and starvation that caused them to surrender. It was later given to John of Gaunt and in the 16th century, Elizabeth I gave it to her favourite, Robert Dudley, Earl of Leicester. In the 17th century Parliamentary forces, who controlled it, demolished part of the keep, walls and towers to prevent its further military use.

Our next stop, the city of Coventry has developed from a small Saxon settlement and its prosperity came, over the centuries, from the wool trade. It is said that Leofric, Earl of Mercia, began this prosperous business in the 11th century when he started a monastery and gave the monks land for sheep. It was this same Leofric whose wife pleaded with him to cut taxes but he told her she could ride through the streets naked before he did so. The story goes that Godiva took him at his word after first instructing the residents of the town to stay indoors with their shutters closed. As a result of Godiva's ride, her husband cut taxes. Peeping Tom, who broke the ban on watching Godiva and was struck blind as a consequence, was an 18th century addition to the story. However, figures portraying Godiva and Tom re-enact the scene every hour on a clock over Hertford Street.

During the Civil War Coventry was held for Parliament and captured Royalists were imprisoned there. On the Restoration of the monarchy the city was ordered to knock down its city walls which was done but the twelve gates were left standing, two of which may still be seen today in Lady Herbert's Garden.

The city's prosperity continued and clock making and silk weaving also became important until the 19th century when Coventry could no longer compete with imports. However, engineering was established and Coventry became a manufacturing base for the motor car. During the Second World War the city's factories became a major target for German bombing and the raid suffered on the 14th November 1940 is said to have been the worst inflicted on any British town. About 40 acres of the city were flattened and out of approximately 1000 buildings in the city centre only 30 were left undamaged. That night the cathedral of St Michael was almost completely destroyed; only the spire and outer walls were left standing. These are linked to the new cathedral, completed in 1962, by a canopied porch.

In spite of the bombing many medieval buildings have survived. There is the 14th century Guildhall of St Mary, the Tudor almshouses of Ford's Hospital and Cheylesmore Manor House dating originally from 1230.

The tour now moves on to the village of Bulkington whose church has a font made from a Roman marble column. Then we stop in Hinckley, a centre for the hosiery industry, before moving on to Market Bosworth where Dr Johnson was once an usher at the school. Bosworth Field, two miles south of the town, was the site of the battle where Richard III was defeated and the Tudors were established on the throne of England.

East Midlands

From there we continue through the villages of Measham, Tonge, Shepshed, Woodhouse Eaves and Quorndon to arrive in Leicester. This city has been in existence since Roman times. It contains many historic buildings and also a number of good museums. However, like many English towns and cities, it was the Industrial Revolution and the coming of the railways that really brought prosperity and caused an enormous expansion from quiet market town to busy city.

Jewry Wall, the city's only visible relic of the Romans, was part of the public baths. Overlooking the excavated site stands the Jewry Wall Museum with exhibitions covering the city's history from earlist times to the 16th century.

Leicester Castle dates from the 11th century and stands on the site of an earlier Saxon fortification. Newarke was a 14th century addition to the castle and once enclosed a church which has since disappeared. Newarke now houses a museum covering social history from the 16th century to the present day. It also has a fine collection of clocks.

The church of St Nicholas is of Saxon origin and may have been built as early as the 7th century. Stone from Roman buildings was used in its construction and, although Saxon in style, it does incorporate a Norman doorway. The 14th century St Martin's Church was upgraded to a cathedral in 1927. Unfortunately, by the 19th century, the fabric of the church was so decayed that it was extensively restored so reflecting Victorian design rather than that of its origins.

Moving on, we come to the villages of Queniborough, Hoby and then Whissendine with its beautiful early-English to perpendicular church which has some quite fine window tracery. Our next stop is the quiet country town of Oakham, once the capital of Rutland, England's smallest county until the boundary changes of 1974 when it was merged with Leicestershire. Its 12th century castle contains a unique collection of horseshoes. There was a tradition that any peer of the realm passing through Rutland should present an inscribed horseshoe to the lord of the manor. The Rutland County Museum, housed in an 18th century cavalry riding school, tells the story of life in the county with exhibits of agricultural implements, wagons, local crafts and domestic items.

The route continues along the A606 through the village of Empingham to Stamford, a beautiful stone-built town with many fine Georgian buildings. It has prospered over the centuries. In Norman times it was a centre for great religious houses and their schools, then later, from the 12th century, the wool trade became important. Standing on the Great North Road it was also a great coaching town as can be seen from its many fine inns. One of the old buildings, Browne's Hospital founded in 1483, now houses a museum which includes a good collection of medieval stained glass.

A most memorable mansion, Burghley House, stands about a mile east Stamford. Built by William Cecil, the first Lord Burghley, he designed much of the house himself. He envisaged it as being a house fit for Queen Elizabeth I to visit, as indeed she did. William Cecil was farsighted, or perhaps just lucky, because he supported Elizabeth when her half-sister, Mary, was on the throne which could have been dangerous if not actually fatal. When Elizabeth became Queen, William Cecil's fortunes rose correspondingly as he was made Lord High Treasurer.

The state rooms of this mansion are breathtaking in their splendour with painted figures appearing to leap from walls and ceilings. In contrast, there is the opportunity to see below-stairs in the Old Kitchen - a vast room containing more than 260 copper cooking utensils. Burghley House is not just the creation of William Cecil but also of his descendents who all brought something to the mansion. The walls and ceilings were painted in the 18th century to such marvellous effect, Grinling Gibbons carvings are in evidence and the park was landscaped by Capability Brown. A house not to be missed.

Moving on through Wansford and Wing we come to Uppingham, a small market town probably best known for its public school. Then, taking the B664, we arrive in Market Harborough. Standing beside the River Welland, the town has held markets since 1204. The attractive 14th century church of St Dionysius overlooking the market place is said to have been founded by John of Gaunt.

Going via the village of Artingworth, the next stop is Kettering, on the banks of the River Ise and best known for the manufacture of footwear. The remains of a Roman settlement have been found near the town and some of these may be seen in the local museum. Three miles to the north of Kettering stands Boughton House. It was built in the grand manner, on the site of an earlier monastery, by Ralph Montagu, one-time ambassador to the Court of Louis XIV. The French influence is strongly reflected in the building and the magnificent treasures inside which include works by El Greco, Murillo, Caracci and 40 Van Dyck sketches.

Continuing along the A6 the tour reaches Finedon where The Old Bell is one of the earliest inns in the country. The town's church has a spire which rises to 133 feet and an unusual carved strainer-arch in the nave. Two miles north east of the town there is a Wellington Tower built in commemoration of the Duke of Wellington's visit to the town.

Taking the A45 we reach Rushden, which also has an interesting and beautiful church, before arriving in Wellingborough, another Northamptonshire town associated with footwear. Standing on the River Nene, its church dates from the 14th and 15th centuries and All Hallows church hall is a 17th century stone built house. Our next stop, Castle Ashby, is so-called because a castle has stood here since the 11th century. The original had disappeared by the 16th century and then in 1574 Lord Compton started construction of the present building which is more grand house than castle.

Now we come to the county town of Northampton, also well known for the making of shoes. It has one of the largest market squares in England as a result of the rebuilding of the town after a disastrous fire in 1675 which destroyed most of the existing buildings. There are also a number of fine country houses nearby. For example, Holdenby House stands seven miles to the north west. This was once the largest Elizabethan house in England and was used as a prison for Charles I during the Civil War. Another fine house is Cottesbrooke Hall, a magnificent Queen Anne building with a fine collection of sporting and equestrian pictures, furniture and porcelain. Then, of course, there is Althorp, childhood home of the Princess of Wales. Standing 6 miles north west of Northampton it has been the home of the Spenser family since 1508. This too has a wonderful collection of pictures including Reynolds, Gainsboroughs, Rubens, Van Dycks, etc. together with fine French furniture and rare porcelain.

The tour finishes with calls on the villages of West Haddon, Weedon Bec and Woodhouse Halse.

ANTIQUE DEALERS
KINETON (0926)
The Old Mill Antique Furniture Exporters, Mill Lane TEL: 640971 PARKING: Own carpark OPEN: Mon-Fri 8.30-5.30, Sat 9.30-1 MIN: £50 MAX: £5,000 PERIOD: 18th-20th century SPECIALIST: 10,000 sq ft warehouse of furniture for all export markets OTHER INFO: Excellent Walton Hall Hotel 4 miles.

STRATFORD-ON-AVON (0789)
Arbour Antiques Ltd, Poets Arbour, Sheep Street, CV37 6EF TEL: 293453 PARKING: Difficult OPEN: Mon-Fri 9-5.30 MIN: £100 MAX: £20,000 PERIOD: 16th-19th century SPECIALIST: Arms & armour.

Art Deco Ceramics, Unit 4, The Courtyard, Stratford Antique Arcade, Ely Street, CV37 6LN TEL: 297496, home 299524 PARKING: Medium OPEN: Mon, Wed, Fri, 10-5, some Suns 2-5 MIN: £10 MAX: £1,500 PERIOD: 20th century SPECIALIST: Art Deco ceramics OTHER INFO: We are authors of *Collecting Clarice Cliff, The Colourful World of Clarice Cliff* & *Collecting Art Deco Ceramics* (worldwide postal service).

Bow Cottage Antiques, Dolls & Toys Museum, 30 Henley Street TEL: 297485 shop but best on private-205883 PARKING: Medium OPEN: 10-5 MIN: £20 MAX: £200 PERIOD: 18th-20th century SPECIALIST: English pottery, porcelain, glass, books GENERAL: Objets d'art, silver, jewellery etc, topographical & sporting pictures.

Howards Jewellers, 44a Wood Street, CV37 6JG TEL: 205404 FAX: 293652 ASSNS: NAG PARKING: Medium OPEN: 9.30-5.30 MIN: £18 MAX: £60,000 PERIOD: 18th-20th century SPECIALIST: Fine antique & period jewellery and silver.

Jazz, Civic Hall, Rother Street, CV37 6LU TEL: 298362 PARKING: Good OPEN: Tues-Sat 10-6 MIN: £10 MAX: £1,000 PERIOD: 19th-20th century SPECIALIST: Art Nouveau, Arts & Crafts, Art Deco GENERAL: Ceramics, metalware, furniture, lighting etc OTHER INFO: Owner, Susan Hill, is the author of Shelley ceramics reference book: *Shelley Style*

The Loquens Gallery, The Minories, Rother Street TEL: 297706 PARKING: Own carpark OPEN: Mon-Sat 9.15-5 or by appt PERIOD: 18th-20th century SPECIALIST: Fine Victorian watercolours, oils GENERAL: Prints, etchings.

Robert Vaughan Antiquarian Booksellers, 20 Chapel Street, CV37 6EP TEL: 205312 ASSNS: ABA PARKING: Easy OPEN: Mon-Sat 9.30-6 MIN: £5 MAX: £25,000 PERIOD: 17th-19th century SPECIALIST: Shakespeare, Elizabethan, Jacobean literature & drama GENERAL: Fine & rare books OTHER INFO: Shakespeare's birthplace & burial place (Holy Trinity church), both 5 mins walk.

HATTON (0926)
Antiques Corner, Unit 42, Hatton Country World TEL: 499731 PARKING: Own carpark OPEN: 10-5 MIN: £2 MAX: £1,000 PERIOD: 19th-20th century GENERAL: China, glass, furniture, clocks, linen, jewellery, old phones, prints OTHER INFO: 8 dealers. Free valuations.

Summersons Antique Restoration, 15 Carthorse Walk, CV35 8XA TEL: 843443 ASSNS: BHI PARKING: Own carpark OPEN: Six days MIN: £100 MAX: £5,000 PERIOD: 18th-19th century SPECIALIST: Clocks & barometers OTHER INFO: Part of Hatton Country World complex.

WARWICK (0926)
John Goodwin & Sons, Units F & M, Budbrooke Industrial Estate, Budbrooke Road, CV34 5XH TEL: 491191 FAX: 491191 PARKING: Own carpark OPEN: Mon-Fri 9-5.30, Sat 10-4 MIN: £5 MAX: £5,000 PERIOD: 18th-20th century SPECIALIST: 19th, early 20th century furniture.

Patrick & Gillian Morley Antiques, 62 West Street, CV34 6AN TEL: 494464 FAX: 400531 ASSNS: LAPADA PARKING: Own carpark OPEN: Mon-Fri 9-5.30 MIN: £50 MAX: £25,000 PERIOD: 17th-20th century SPECIALIST: Quality period furniture GENERAL: Unusual items OTHER INFO: Close to Warwick Castle, Kenilworth Castle.

Don Spencer Antiques, 36a Market Place, CV34 4SH TEL: 407989 PARKING: Easy OPEN: 10-5 MIN: £600 MAX: £3,000 PERIOD: 19th century SPECIALIST: Antique desks GENERAL: Victorian furniture.

Martin Payne Antiques, 30 Brook Street, CV34 4BL TEL: 494948 ASSNS: LAPADA PARKING: Easy OPEN: Mon-Sat 10-5.30 MIN: £10 MAX: £9,000 PERIOD: 18th-20th century

SPECIALIST: Antique & collectable silver.

Smith Street Antique Centre, 7 Smith Street TEL: 497864, 400554 PARKING: Medium OPEN: Mon-Sat 10-5 MIN: £1 MAX: £15,000 PERIOD: 18th-20th century SPECIALIST: Military, Oriental, taxidermy GENERAL: Silver, glass, silverplate, cigarette cards, porcelain, golfing memorabilia, furniture OTHER INFO: St. Johns Museum, Dolls Museum.

Vintage Antiques Centre, 36 Market Place TEL: 491527 ASSNS: WADA PARKING: Easy OPEN: Six days 10-5 MIN: £1 MAX: £500 PERIOD: 19th-20th century SPECIALIST: Glass, ceramics, Art Deco, small furniture GENERAL: Collectables.

Warwick Antiques, 16-18 High Street, CV34 4AP TEL: 492482 FAX: 493867 PARKING: Own carpark OPEN: 9-5 MIN: £1 MAX: £5,000 PERIOD: 19th-20th century SPECIALIST: General antiques.

Warwick Antique Centre, 20 High Street, CV34 4AP TEL: 495704 PARKING: Own carpark OPEN: 10-5 PERIOD: 18th-20th century GENERAL: Silver, jewellery, porcelain, glass, furniture, toys, coins, books, militaria, teddy bears, pens, Derby OTHER INFO: Good trade call. Warwick Races, St Mary's Church.

Westgate Antiques, 28 West Street, CV34 6AN TEL: 494106 FAX: 494106 ASSNS: LAPADA PARKING: Easy OPEN: Mon-Fri 10-5.30, Sat 9.30-1 MIN: £20 MAX: £5,000 PERIOD: 18th-20th century SPECIALIST: Silver, silverplate GENERAL: Furniture, decoratives, glass, boxes.

LEAMINGTON SPA (0926)

Olive Green Ltd, 12 Station Approach, Avenue Road, CV31 5NN TEL: (0860) 613610 PARKING: Easy OPEN: Thurs-Sat 10-5 & by appt MIN: £5 MAX: £2,000 PERIOD: 18th-20th century SPECIALIST: 19th century furniture, decorative arts GENERAL: Furniture & allied arts OTHER INFO: Art Gallery, Manor House hotel.

The Incandescent Lighting Company, 36 Regent Street, CV32 5EG TEL: 422421 PARKING: Easy OPEN: 9.30-5.30 MIN: £20 MAX: £2,500 SPECIALIST: 19th-20th century electric lighting OTHER INFO: Charming Regency town a few hundred yards from neighbouring Warwick and its castle & wealth of antique shops.

Kings Cottage Antiques, 4 Windsor Street TEL:

422927 PARKING: Medium OPEN: 9.30-5.30 MIN: £50 MAX: £4,500 PERIOD: 17th-18th century SPECIALIST: Oak & country furniture GENERAL: Furniture for restoration.

Leamington Antique Centre, 20 Regent Street TEL: 429679 PARKING: Easy OPEN: Mon-Sat 9-6 MIN: £1 MAX: £2,000 PERIOD: 19th-20th century GENERAL: Antiques, pine, shipping items & bric-a-brac.

Yesterdays, 21 Portland Street, CV32 5EZ TEL: 450238 PARKING: Easy OPEN: Mon-Sat 10-5 MIN: £5 MAX: £3,000 PERIOD: 18th-20th century GENERAL: 19th century decorative mahogany furniture, pretty china & framed prints.

KENILWORTH (0926)

Castle Gallery, 32 Castle Hill, CV8 1NB TEL: 58727 PARKING: Easy OPEN: Tues, Fri-Sun 11-5 MIN: £50 MAX: £3,000 PERIOD: 18th-20th century GENERAL: British watercolours & drawings, also contemporary OTHER INFO: Picturesque old town, close to the dramatically ruined Kenilworth Castle.

Janice Paull, Beehive House, 125 Warwick Road, CV8 1HY TEL: 55253, (0831) 619254 ASSNS: LAPADA PARKING: Own carpark OPEN: By appt PERIOD: 19th century SPECIALIST: Mason's & other ironstone ware GENERAL: Pottery, porcelain.

COVENTRY (0203)

Memories Antiques, 400a Stoney Stanton Road TEL: 687994 PARKING: Own carpark OPEN: Mon, Tues, Thurs-Sat 10-5, Sun 10-2 PERIOD: 19th-20th century SPECIALIST: China GENERAL: Antiques & collectables, Royal Doulton.

BULKINGTON (0203)

Sport & Country Gallery, Northwood House, 121 Weston Lane, CV12 9RX TEL: 314335 ASSNS: LAPADA PARKING: Own carpark OPEN: Anytime by appt MIN: £100 MAX: £6,000 PERIOD: 19th-20th century SPECIALIST: Sporting paintings, bronzes GENERAL: Oils & watercolours, small furniture OTHER INFO: Opposite Weston Hall Hotel, food & live music.

HINKLEY (0455)

House Things Antiques, Trinity Lane, 44 Mansion Street, LE10 0AU TEL: 618518 PARKING: Easy OPEN: Mon-Sat 10-6 MIN: £1 MAX: £500 PERIOD: 19th-20th century GENERAL: Brass

& iron beds, fireplaces, furniture, clocks, general artifacts. Many unusual items OTHER INFO: Renown for hansom cab (original on show), Axe & Compass, canals. Kings Hotel.

MARKET BOSWORTH (0455)
Corner Cottage Antiques, 5 Market Place, The Square, CV13 0LF TEL: 290344 PARKING: Easy OPEN: Mon-Sat 10-5 MIN: £5 MAX: £5,000 PERIOD: 18th-20th century GENERAL: General antiques OTHER INFO: Historic Battle of Bosworth site, Water Sports Centre, Sharkestone Steam Railway (summer only).

COALVILLE (0530)
Keystone Antiques, 9 Ashby Road, LE67 3LF TEL: 835966 ASSNS: LAPADA, NAG, Fellow Gemmological Assn PARKING: Own carpark OPEN: Mon-Tues, Thur-Fri 10-5, Sat 10-4.30 MIN: £20 MAX: £2,500 PERIOD: 18th-20th century SPECIALIST: Victorian, Edwardian jewellery & silver GENERAL: Glass, prints, collectables OTHER INFO: Snibston Discovery Park & Industrial Museum.

MEASHAM (0530)
Ashley House Antiques, 61 High Street, DE12 7HR TEL: 273568,PARKING: Easy OPEN: Thurs, Fri, Sat 11-5 MIN: £5 MAX: £2,000 PERIOD: 19th century SPECIALIST: General antiques, always a large stock, no reproductions. OTHER INFO: Several olde worlde pubs with good meals. Village setting, B&Bs.

TONGE (0332)
C. Reynolds Antiques, The Spindles, DE7 1BD TEL: 862609 FAX: 862609 PARKING: Own carpark OPEN: By appt MIN: £100 upwards SPECIALIST: Unusual clocks & watches OTHER INFO: 3 miles from East Midlands Airport and the Motor Museum.

SHEPSHED (0509)
G.K. & J.V. Hadfield, Blackbrook Hill House, Ticklow Lane, LE12 9EY TEL: 503014 FAX: 600136 PARKING: Own carpark OPEN: Thurs-Sat 9-5 MIN: £2 MAX: £10,000 PERIOD: 17th-19th century SPECIALIST: Longcase & dial clocks, horological books GENERAL: French, German, USA & other really unusual clocks.

WOODHOUSE EAVES (0509)
Paddock Antiques, The Old Smithy, Brand Hill, LE12 8SS TEL: 890264 PARKING: Easy OPEN: Thurs-Sat 10-5.30 MIN: £20 MAX:

£5,000 PERIOD: 18th-20th century SPECIALIST: Fine English & Continental china GENERAL: Glass & small furniture.

QUORNDON (0509)
Quorn Pine & Decoratives, The Mills, Leicester Road TEL: 416031 ASSNS: GMC PARKING: Own carpark OPEN: Mon-Sat 9-6, Sun 2-5 MIN: £5 MAX: £2,000 PERIOD: 19th-20th century SPECIALIST: Pine furniture GENERAL: Reproduction pine, kitchenalia, new & old decorative items OTHER INFO: Home of Quorn Hunt, favourite of Prince Charles.

LEICESTER (0533)
Boulevard Antiques, Old Dairy, Western Boulevard, LE2 7BU TEL: 541201 FAX: 854315 PARKING: Own carpark OPEN: Mon-Sat 9-6, Sun 12-5 MIN: £1 MAX: £2,500 PERIOD: 19th-20th century GENERAL: Furniture, a few smalls.

Britains Heritage, Shaftesbury Hall, 3 Holy Bones TEL: 519592 FAX: 419371 PARKING: Medium OPEN: Mon-Fri 9.30-5.30, Sat 9.30-5, Sun 2-5 MIN: £5 MAX: £10,000 PERIOD: 18th-20th century SPECIALIST: Fully restored English & French fireplaces GENERAL: Fireside accessories OTHER INFO: UK delivery/fitting. Next to historic Roman Jewry Wall & old part of city.

Corrys Antiques, 24-26 Francis Street Stoneygate, LE2 2BD TEL: 703794 FAX: 703794 ASSNS: LAPADA PARKING: Own carpark OPEN: Mon-Sat 9-5.30 MIN: £10 MAX: £15,000 PERIOD: 18th-19th century GENERAL: Furniture, paintings, silver, porcelain, jewellery OTHER INFO: City's southside exclusive shopping area. Quality shops.

Letty's Antiques, 6 Rutland Street, LE1 1RA TEL: 626435 PARKING: Medium OPEN: Mon-Wed, Fri, Sat 9.30-5 MIN: £1 MAX: £3,500 PERIOD: 19th-20th century SPECIALIST: Jewellery, silverware GENERAL: Small secondhand antique items.

Montague Antiques, 60 Montague Road (off Queen's Road nr university), LE2 1TH TEL: 706485 PARKING: Easy OPEN: Mon, Thurs-Sat 10-6, Sun 12-5 MIN: £1 MAX: £800 PERIOD: 18th-20th century GENERAL: Furniture, collectables, glass, china (no jewellery).

Walter Moores & Son, 89 Wellington Street,

ST. MARTINS
antiques &crafts
CENTRE

23a High Street,
St. Martins, Stamford,
Lincolnshire
PE9 2LF

Open every day
10.00 am – 5.00 pm
Car Park at rear of building

● Period furniture ● Porcelain & china
● Pictures & prints ● Clocks & Watches ● Silver & jewellery
● Rugs ● Books & toys ● Textiles & clothes ● Military books
● Coffee shop ● Shipping ● Dolls ● Militaria

Telephone: (0780) 481158
Fax: (0780) 50210

LE1 6HJ TEL: 551402 PARKING: Own carpark OPEN: Tues-Fri 8.30-5.30, Sat 9.30-12.30 & by appt MIN: £10 MAX: £10,000 PERIOD: 17th-19th century GENERAL: Furniture OTHER INFO: 5 mins walk from station.

The Rug Gallery, 50 Montague Road, Clarendon Park, LE2 1TH TEL: 700085 (24 hrs) PARKING: Easy OPEN: Sat only 10-4 or by appt MIN: £10 MAX: £5,000 PERIOD: 19th-20th century SPECIALIST: Oriental rugs & kilims old & new GENERAL: Furniture, textiles, jewellery from Central Asia.

QUENIBOROUGH (0533)

J. Green & Son, 1 Coppice Lane, LE7 3DR TEL: 606682 FAX: 606882 PARKING: Own carpark OPEN: By appt MIN: £200 MAX: £30,000 PERIOD: 17th-19th century GENERAL: 18th & early 19th century furniture, clocks & pictures.

HOBY (0664)

Withers of Leicester, The Old Rutland, 6 Regent Road TEL: 434803 PARKING: Own carpark OPEN: Seven days 9-6 MIN: £100 MAX: £5,000 PERIOD: 17th-19th century GENERAL: Furniture and decorative objects OTHER INFO: Famous Ragdale Hall Health Hydro in next village, convenient for dealers who feel they have over-expanded.

WHISSENDINE (0664)

Old Bakehouse Fine Furniture, 11 Main Street, LE15 7ES TEL: 79691 PARKING: Own carpark OPEN: Erratic MIN: £25 MAX: £500 PERIOD: 19th-20th century GENERAL: Mainly antique pine furniture OTHER INFO: B&B available.

OAKHAM (0572)

Grafton Country Pictures, TEL: 757266 PARK-ING: Easy OPEN: By appt MIN: £5 MAX: £500 PERIOD: 18th-19th century SPECIALIST: Agricultural & farming prints GENERAL: Prints OTHER INFO: Rutland Water, Eyebrook Reservoir for fishing & birdwatching, Lake Isle Hotel excellent local watering hole.

Old House Gallery, 13-15 Market Place TEL: 755538 PARKING: Easy OPEN: 10-1, 2-5 MIN: £5 MAX: £5,000 PERIOD: 17th-20th century SPECIALIST: Paintings, prints, antique maps GENERAL: Studio ceramics, sculpture OTHER INFO: Small interesting gallery with easy friendly relaxed atmosphere.

EMPINGHAM (0780)

Churchgate Antiques, 13 Church Street, LE15 8PN TEL: 86528 PARKING: Easy OPEN: Afternoons or by appt MIN: £5 MAX: £3,000 PERIOD: 19th-20th century GENERAL: General antiques OTHER INFO: 1 min from Rutland Water & good range of water pursuits.

Old Bakery Antiques, Church Street, LE15 8PN TEL: 460243 PARKING: Easy OPEN: Mostly seven days 10-6 but check for midweek MIN: £15 MAX: £3,500 PERIOD: 17th-20th century SPECIALIST: Dining tables & chairs GENERAL: Oak furniture, some brass, copper, prints, porcelain OTHER INFO: At Dam end of Rutland Water. Rutland is the county expected to be reborn.

STAMFORD (0780)

St George's Antiques, 1 St.George's Square, PE9, 2BN TEL: 54117 PARKING: Easy OPEN: Mon-Fri 9-1, 2-4.30 MIN: £1 MAX: £10,000 PERIOD: 18th-19th century GENERAL: Mainly furniture, some smalls, silver + plate OTHER INFO: Burghley House.

St Martins Antiques & Crafts Centre, 23a High Street, St Martins, PE9 2LF TEL: 481158 FAX: 56210 PARKING: Own carpark OPEN: 10-5 (or 5.30) MIN: £3 MAX: £10,000 PERIOD: 18th-20th century SPECIALIST: Military history books GENERAL: General antiques, militaria, nauticalia OTHER INFO: Coffee shop. One of finest stone towns in Europe.

St Mary's Galleries, 5 St Mary's Hill, PE9 2DP TEL: 64159 PARKING: Own carpark OPEN: 9-5 MIN: £10 MAX: £8,000 PERIOD: 17th-19th century GENERAL: Jewellery, pictures, furniture & unusual items.

Staniland (Booksellers), 4-5 St. George's Street, PE9 2BJ TEL: 55800 ASSNS: PBFA PARKING: Medium OPEN: Mon-Sat 10-5 MIN: £1 MAX: £1,000 PERIOD: 17th-20th century SPECIALIST: Local topography & architecture GENERAL: About 25,000 books in 8 rooms. All subjects. Some 16th century incunabula OTHER INFO: George Hotel, famous coaching inn, 5 churches. Stamford is famous for its well-preserved stone architecture dating from 16th-18th century.

Andrew Thomas Antiques, 10 North Street, PE9 2YN TEL: 62236 FAX: 62236 PARKING: Easy OPEN: Mon-Sat 9-6 with variable lunchbreak MIN: £5 MAX: £2,500 PERIOD: 18th-20th century SPECIALIST: Painted, pine & country furniture GENERAL: Early metalware & decorative items. We buy from Holland, Germany, Poland, Yugoslavia & most of Eastern Block.

WANSFORD-IN-ENGLAND (0780)

Old House Antiques, 16 London Road, PE8 6JB TEL: 783462, 783999 FAX: 783452 PARKING: Easy OPEN: Tues-Sat 9.30-6 & by appt PERIOD: 19th-20th century SPECIALIST: Period lighting 1850's-1950's GENERAL: Glass, lighting, candles OTHER INFO: Opposite excellent 18th century coaching hotel: The Haycock (with business facilities)

WING (0572)

Robert Bingley Antiques, Church Street TEL: 85725 FAX: 85284 PARKING: Own carpark OPEN: Mon-Sat 9-5, Sun 11-4 MIN: £20 MAX: £5,000 PERIOD: 18th-19th century GENERAL: Huge shop (4,000 sq ft/10 rooms) mainly of furniture. Some smalls OTHER INFO: Beautiful countryside around Rutland Water.

UPPINGHAM (0572)

Bay House Antiques, 33 High Street East, LE15 9PY TEL: 821045 PARKING: Easy OPEN: Mon-Sat 10-5 MIN: £5 MAX: £1,500 PERIOD: 19th century GENERAL: Pottery, porcelain, metalware, Victorian, Edwardian furniture, small agricultural items OTHER INFO: Small historic market town with excellent facilities.

John Garner Fine Art & Antiques, 51-53 High Street East, LE15 9PY TEL: 823607 FAX: 821654 ASSNS: FATG, GMC PARKING: Medium OPEN: 9-5.30 MIN: £1 MAX: £10,000+ PERIOD: 18th-20th century SPECIALIST: 19th century oils & furniture GENERAL: Dining suites, sporting pictures, prints OTHER INFO: The Old Vicarage, Laxton B&B £13.

T.J. Roberts Antiques, 39-41 High Street, LE15 9PY TEL: 821493 PARKING: Easy OPEN: Mon-Sat 9.30-5.30 MIN: £25 MAX: £5,000 PERIOD: 17th-19th century GENERAL: Furniture, general antiques OTHER INFO: Historic market town with famous public school.

E. & C. Royall, 3 Printers Yard TEL: (0858) 83744 PARKING: Medium OPEN: 10-5 closed Thurs MIN: £10 MAX: £1,000 PERIOD: 18th-20th century SPECIALIST: Oriental ivories & bronzes GENERAL: Jewellery, furniture, pictures, objets d'art.

Tattersall's, 14 Orange Street, LE15 9SQ TEL: 821171 PARKING: Easy OPEN: 9.30-5 not Thurs MIN: £45 MAX: £4,500 PERIOD: 19th-20th century SPECIALIST: Persian rugs, antiques, old & new rugs, upholstery, some mirrors.

MEDBOURNE (0858)

E. & C. Royall, 10 Waterfall Way TEL: 83744 PARKING: Easy OPEN: 8.30-5 MIN: £10 MAX: £500 PERIOD: 18th-20th century SPECIALIST: Ivories, Oriental bronzes, restoration GENERAL: European furniture, jewellery, pictures OTHER INFO: All forms of restoration undertaken.

MARKET HARBOROUGH (0858)

Abbey Antiques, 17 Abbey Street, LE16 9AA TEL: 462282 PARKING: Easy OPEN: 10.30-5 MIN: £1 MAX: £2,000 PERIOD: 19th century GENERAL: Smalls of all kinds, furniture, old pine OTHER INFO: Good trade call.

Richard Kimbell Ltd, Riverside Industrial Estate, LE16 7PT TEL: 433444 FAX: 467627 PARKING: Own carpark OPEN: Mon-Fri 9-6, Sat 9-5, Sun 1-4 MIN: £1 MAX: £3,000 PERIOD: 19th century SPECIALIST: Antique & reproduction pine GENERAL: Country furniture & crafts.

J. Stamp & Sons, The Chestnuts, 15 Kettering Road TEL: 462524 FAX: 465643 PARKING: Own carpark OPEN: Mon-Fri 8-5, Sat 9-12.30 & by appt MIN: £50 MAX: £5,000 PERIOD: 18th-19th century SPECIALIST: Mahogany, oak, walnut furniture OTHER INFO: Restorers.

Duncan Watts Oriental Rugs, 61 Northampton Road TEL: 462620 ASSNS: LAPADA PARK-

Dales Of Finedon

For a wide selection of furniture, ceramics, glass, silver, copper, brassware, etc. Georgian, Victorian, Edwardian, Deco.

Situated between Wellingborough & Kettering, just off the A6, 5 mins from the A45, 20 mins from the M1 (J15).

Open 7 days/week (Sunday pm only). 1 High St., Finedon, Northants. 0933 680973

ING: Own carpark OPEN: Mon, Tues, Thurs-Sat 10-5 MIN: £25 MAX: £2,500 PERIOD: 19th-20th century SPECIALIST: Oriental rugs.

LUBENHAM (0858)

Leicester Sporting Gallery & Brown Jack Bookshop, (estd 1954), The Old Granary, 62 Main Street TEL: 465787 ASSNS: Racecourse BPA PARKING: Own carpark OPEN: 10-5 intending buyers only MIN: £1 MAX: £500+ PERIOD: 18th-20th century SPECIALIST: Original Vanity Fair cartoons, sporting books, prints & oils, horse brasses, Furniture, old maps, medals, militaria.

ARTHINGWORTH (0858)

Coughton Galleries Ltd, The Old Manor, LE16 8JT TEL: 86436 FAX: 86535 PARKING: Own carpark OPEN: Wed-Thur, Sat-Sun 10.30-5 MIN: £150 MAX: £5,000 PERIOD: 20th century GENERAL: Modern British & Irish oils & watercolours.

KETTERING (0536)

Albion Antiques, 36 Duke Street, NN16 9DY TEL: 516220 PARKING: Easy OPEN: Tues 10-5, Fri 10-6, Sat 10-1 MIN: £2 PERIOD 20th century SPECIALIST: Cane, rushing & upholstery, high quality restoration arranged GENERAL: Bric-a-brac, furniture.

Antiques Warehouse, 53 Havelock Street, NN16 9PZ TEL: 510522 PARKING: Own carpark OPEN: Mon-Sat 9-5.30 MIN: £2 MAX: £3,000 PERIOD 18th-19th century SPECIALIST: Pine furniture, oak, fireplaces & stoves, also reproduction.

Alexis Brook, 74 Lower Street, NN16 8DL TEL: 513854 PARKING: Own carpark OPEN: Lucky chance or by appt MIN: £1 MAX: £1,000 PERIOD 19th century GENERAL: Mainly tôle, glass, pottery, porcelain, small furniture, bygones.

C.W. Ward Antiques, Deene House, 40 Lower Street TEL: 513537 PARKING: Own carpark OPEN: Mon-Sat 10-4 MIN: £10 MAX: £3,500 PERIOD 18th-20th century GENERAL: Furniture, general antiques OTHER INFO: Rockingham Castle, Wickstead Park (for those with children), Royal Hotel, Sir Alfred East Art Gallery.

FINEDON (0933)

Simon Banks Antiques, Quaker Lodge, Church Street, NN9 5NA TEL: 680371 PARKING: Easy MIN: £1 MAX: £3,500 PERIOD: 19th-20th century SPECIALIST: Edwardian inlaid furniture GENERAL: Mahogany & oak, shipping furniture OTHER INFO: Near Bell Inn reputedly one of the oldest in England.

Jean Burnett Antiques, 31 High Street, NN9 5JN TEL: 680430 PARKING: Easy OPEN: Mon-Sat 10-1, 2.30-5 MIN: £5 MAX: £1,500 PERIOD 18th-19th century SPECIALIST: Needlework tools & accessories, samplers, embroidered pictures GENERAL: Some country furniture, general antiques OTHER INFO: Tudor Gate Hotel next door, we can even boast of the oldest licensed premises in England, The Bell, snacks & meals. 2 antique centres, 2 warehouses & 3 shops in Finedon.

M.C. Chapman Antiques, 12-20 Regent Street TEL: 681688 FAX: 681688 PARKING: Own carpark OPEN: Mon-Fri 9-5 PERIOD 18th-19th century SPECIALIST: Furniture GENERAL: Furnishings & decorative items.

Dales of Finedon, 1 High Street TEL: 680973 PARKING: Easy OPEN: Mon-Sat 10-5, Sun 2-5 MIN: £1 MAX: £5,000 PERIOD: 18th-20th century GENERAL: Furniture, ceramics, silver, glassware OTHER INFO: 5 other antique shops, Tudor Gate Hotel & pubs within 400 yds.

Finedon Antiques, 1-3 Church Street TEL: 681260 FAX: 681688 PARKING: Own carpark OPEN: Mon-Sat 9.30-5.30, Sun 2-5 PERIOD 18th-20th century SPECIALIST: Furniture GENERAL: Covering whole spectrum of the antiques & collectables trade OTHER INFO: 6 shops & 2 large warehouses, good Tudor Gate Hotel & The Bell, oldest inn in England.

Thorpe Antiques, 12-20 Regent Street TEL: 680196, 681688 FAX: 681688 PARKING: Own carpark OPEN: Mon-Fri 8.30-5.30 MIN: £50

MAX: £5,000 PERIOD 18th-20th century SPECIALIST: Chests of drawers GENERAL: Mahogany furniture OTHER INFO: Very good restaurant/hotel in town: The Tudor Gate, oldest recorded pub, goes back to 12th century. We will also provided local area courier service & make appts to trade only warehouses.

RUSHDEN (0933)

Sherwood Antiques, 59 Little Street TEL: 53265 PARKING: Easy OPEN: Tues, Wed, Fri, Sat 12-5 PERIOD: 19th century.

Shire Antiques, 111 High Street South, NN10 1OL TEL: 315567 PARKING: Easy OPEN: Mon-Sat 9.30-6 MIN: £5 MAX: £1,000 PERIOD 19th-20th century GENERAL: Clocks, porcelain, pine, mahogany, oak, sewing machines, typewriters, gramophones.

WELLINGBOROUGH (0933)

Park Book Shop, 12 Park Road, NN8 4PG TEL: 222592 PARKING: Easy OPEN: Mon-Wed, Fri, Sat 10-5 MIN: £1 MAX: £250 PERIOD 19th-20th century GENERAL: Topography, art, antiques, history, hobbies.

Park Gallery, 16 Cannon Street, NN8 5DJ TEL: 222592 PARKING: Easy OPEN: Mon-Wed, Fri, Sat 10-5 MIN: £2 MAX: £500 PERIOD: 18th-20th century SPECIALIST: Local maps & topography GENERAL: Prints, picture framing.

Bryan Perkins Antiques, 52 Cannon Street, NN8 4DJ TEL: 228812 PARKING: Own carpark OPEN: Mon-Fri 9-5.30, Sat 9-12.30 MIN: £1 MAX: £10,000 PERIOD: 18th-19th century SPECIALIST: Victorian dining tables, chests of drawers GENERAL: Mahogany furniture OTHER INFO: Near Althorp House, Boughton, Burghley etc. Our own good B&B.

CASTLE ASHBY (0604)

Geoffrey S. Wright (Fine Paintings), Castle Ashby Gallery, The Old Farmyard, NN7 1LF TEL: 696787 PARKING: Own carpark OPEN: Tues-Sun 10.30-5.30 MIN: £650 MAX: £20,000 PERIOD: 19th-20th century SPECIALIST: British oils, Victorian & modern British & contemporary works by Rodney J.K. Charman & Lawrie Williamson FRSA, limited edition prints OTHER INFO: Castle Ashby House & grounds, restaurant & other shops.

NORTHAMPTON (0604)

Buley Antiques, 164 Kettering Road TEL: 31588, 491577 PARKING: Medium OPEN: Mon-Sat 10.30-4 MIN: £5 MAX: £200 PERIOD 19th-20th century GENERAL: Antiques & bric-a-brac OTHER INFO: Museums, parks, hotels.

F. & C.H. Cave, 111 Kettering Road TEL: 38278 PARKING: Easy OPEN: Mon-Wed, Fri, Sat 9-5.30 MIN: £200 MAX: £8,000 PERIOD 17th-19th century SPECIALIST: Antique & decorative furniture OTHER INFO: Large basement devoted to antiques only (ground floor & windows display new furniture), Swallow Hotel 5 Star, excellent meals & rooms, St. Matthews Church contains Henry Moore's Madonna & Graham Sutherland paintings. One of only 3 surviving Queen Eleanor's Crosses (the one at Charing Cross is a replica).

Nostalgia Antiques, 190 Kettering Road TEL: 33823 PARKING: Easy OPEN: Mon-Sat 10-5 MIN: £1 MAX: £400 PERIOD 19th-20th century SPECIALIST: Clocks, watches GENERAL: Militaria, tin plate, model cars, general antiques OTHER INFO: ° mile from town centre.

Occultique, 73 Kettering Road, NN1 4AW TEL: 27727 ASSNS: ABA PARKING: Medium OPEN: Mon-Sat 10-5 MIN: £1 MAX: £750 PERIOD 20th century SPECIALIST: Unusual, bizarre, occult & Oriental books & artifacts OTHER INFO: Holy Sepulchre Church, Regent Square, St. Peter's Church, Hunsbury Hill, French Partridge, Houghton. Tourist info: Mr Grant's House, 10 St Giles Square.

The Old Brigade, 10a Harborough Road, Kingsthorpe, NN2 7AZ TEL: 719389 ASSNS: Arms & Militaria Society PARKING: Easy OPEN: Mon-Sat 10.30-5 MIN: £5 MAX: £5,000 PERIOD 19th-20th century SPECIALIST: Antique arms & militaria, Third Reich items OTHER INFO: Trains from Euston (London) 1 hour, good restaurants & plenty of hotels.

Pennys Antiques, 83 Kettering Road, NN1 4AW TEL: 32429 ASSNS: IACF PARKING: Easy OPEN: Mon-Wed 11-4, Fri 11-3.30, Sat 10-5 MIN: £1 MAX: £250 PERIOD 19th-20th century SPECIALIST: Chairs & pictures GENERAL: General antiques OTHER INFO: 200 year old shop, close to town centre, 2 other antique shops close & large furniture store Plough, Grand, Angel, Langham & Moathouse hotels in or near town centre.

Regent House Antiques, Royal Terrace, NN1 3RF TEL: 37992 PARKING: Own carpark OPEN: Mon-Fri 10.30-5 MIN: £150 MAX: £15,000 PERIOD 17th-19th century SPECIALIST: Georgian furniture OTHER INFO: This detached Georgian house is furnished with antiques that are for sale. Near Regent Square, St. Sepulchre's Church (one of England's 4 remaining round churches) 5 mins walk, Lime Trees Hotel (2 star), nearby at 8 Langham Place.

Talent Pastimes Ltd, 85 Kettering Road, NN1 4AW TEL: 36396 PARKING: Medium OPEN: Mon-Sat 9-5 PERIOD: 18th-20th century SPECIALIST: UK stamps & postal history GENERAL: Postcards, cigarette cards OTHER INFO: 10 mins from town centre.

WEST HADDON (0788)

Antiques, 9 West End, NN6 7AY TEL: 510773 PARKING: Easy OPEN: Tues-Sat 10-5 MIN: £30 MAX: £4,500 PERIOD: 17th-19th century SPECIALIST: Copper, brass & ironwork GENERAL: Country furniture, metalwork & domestic items.

WEEDON (0327)

Rococo Antiques, 5 New Street, Lower Weedon, NN7 4QS TEL: 41288 PARKING: Easy OPEN: Mon-Sat 10-5.30 MIN: £5 MAX: £3,000 PERIOD: 18th-20th century SPECIALIST: Brass & iron bedsteads, fireplaces GENERAL: Ironwork, pine furniture, doors OTHER INFO: Prettiest & best stocked shop in Weedon.

The Village Antique Market, 62 High Street, NN7 4QD TEL: 42015 PARKING: Own carpark OPEN: Mon-Fri 9.30-5.30, Sat 10-5.15, Suns & Bank Hols 10.30-5.15 PERIOD 17th-20th century OTHER INFO: On Grand Union Canal at A45/A5 junction. 40 dealers.

WOODFORD HALSE (0327)

The Corner Cupboard, 14-18 Station Road, NN11 6RB TEL: 60725 PARKING: Easy OPEN: Wed-Sun 9-7 MIN: £10 MAX: £800 PERIOD: 19th-20th century SPECIALIST: Stripped pine antique furniture GENERAL: Victorian brass & iron bedsteads, armchairs.

The Cotswolds

Bourton-on-the-Water near Stow-on-the-Wold

The Cotswolds countryside typifies for many the quintessential English rural scene with its sheep pastures, wooded valleys, dry stone walls and weathered Cotswold stone buildings. In the villages it is still possible to imagine life in the Middle Ages, so timeless do they seem. This is probably, also, the area outside London that is best known for its antique shops.

Our Cotwold tour starts with the small village of Bladon where, in 1965, Sir Winston was buried in the churchyard of St Martin's Church, beside the grave of his father Sir Randolph. Also buried there are his wife, Clementine, his son and two of his daughters.

Woodstock, next, is a small town with royal connections going back to the Saxons. Henry I, at the beginning of the 12th century, built a residence and kept an exotic menagerie here. His grandson, Henry II, enlarged the royal manor and visited it with his mistress, the Fair Rosamund. The legendary Black Prince, eldest son of Edward III, was born at Woodstock Palace in 1330. Woodstock continued as a royal residence until the Civil War when it was beseiged and badly damaged. At the beginning of the 18th century Queen Anne gave the manor and estate to John Churchill, first Duke of Marlborough, in gratitude for the victories he had won, particularly at Blenheim against the French and Bavarian armies. Not only was he given this estate, Queen Anne also promised to pay for the

The Cotswolds

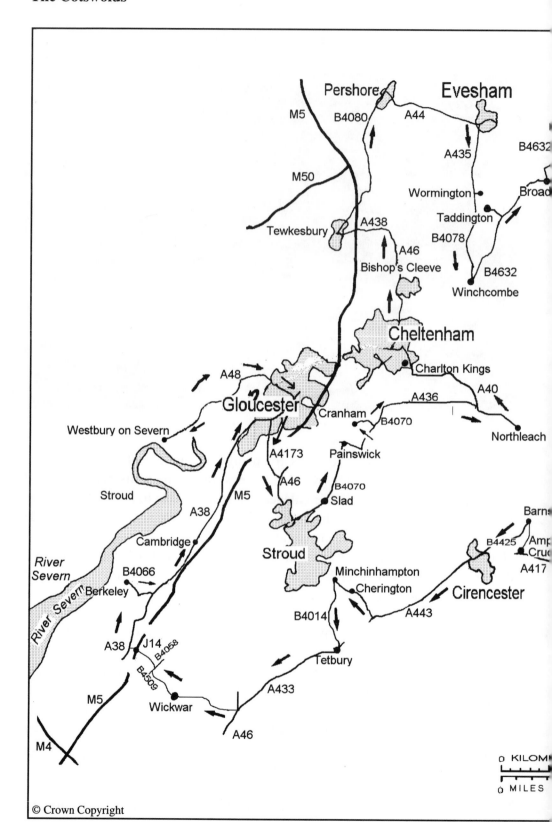

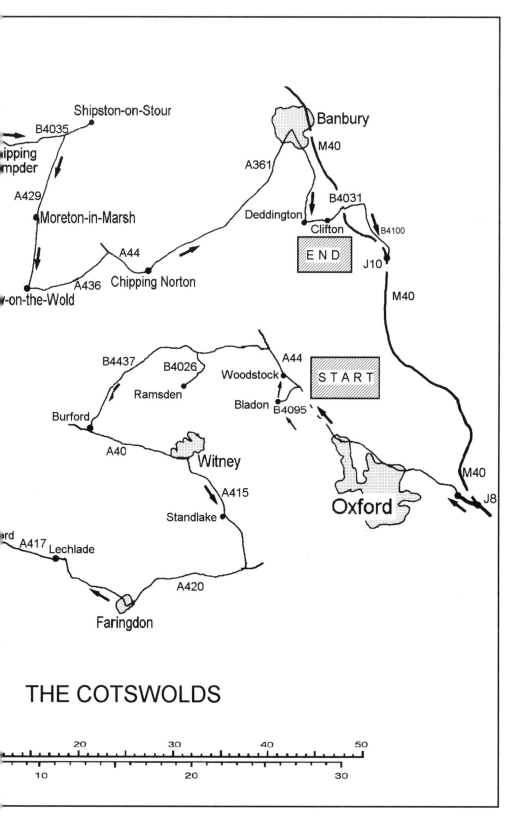

THE COTSWOLDS

Burford

building of a house on the site.

The house, designed by Sir John Vanbrugh, was started in 1705. There was a series of difficulties in completing the work. Sarah, Duchess of Marlborough was the Queen's lady-in-waiting and Keeper of the Privy Purse, and these posts enabled her to keep the Queen to her promise to pay for the house. However, in 1710 she fell from favour and payments for the building work stopped and in 1712 all work on the house also ceased. By all accounts, Sarah Churchill was an extremely difficult character, albeit devoted to her husband, and she had numerous arguments with Vanbrugh who finally resigned at the end of 1716 although building had restarted some two years earlier. The Duke of Marlborough died in 1722 but Sarah continued with the work on Blenheim Palace for the remaining twenty two years of her life, seeing it as a tribute to her husband and refusing several offers of marriage.

Blenheim Palace, set in its 2500 acre park redesigned later in the 18th century by Capability Brown, has been described as a masterpiece of Vanbrugh's work with its magnificent rooms, the most celebrated of which is the Long Library, originally designed as a picture gallery. The battle of Blenheim is commemorated in a ceiling painting in the Great Hall and again in the Green Writing Room. There are also portraits of the forceful Sarah Churchill, possibly without whose indomitable will this glorious palace would never have been completed.

Blenheim's more recent claim to fame is that it was the birthplace of Sir Winston Churchill and it was beside the lake, in the Temple of Diana, that he proposed to his future wife, Clementine. Today there is a Churchillian exhibition and the room where he was born is also open to the public.

The next town on this Cotswold tour is the lovely Burford, on the River Windrush, which still retains its medieval bridge. On one of the great coaching roads and prospering accordingly, Burford thrived through the Middle Ages as a centre for cloth, wool, saddlery and stone from quarries around the town; stone from these was used in building Blenheim Palace. When the railways came, Burford did not get a line so it went into something of a decline; however, the boom in tourism has again brought prosperity to the town. There are many places of interest in the town: amongst these are the Great Almshouses founded in 1457 and partly rebuilt in the 19th century, the 15th century Lamb Inn, the mostly 15th century Parish Church and Burford Grammar School, founded in 1577.

Now the tour proceeds, via the village of Ramsden, to Witney on the River Windrush and famous for its blankets, made in the town since the days of Edward III and still important today. The Cotswolds as a whole was once an important woollen textile area but after the Industrial Revolution it declined. Witney, however, had such a reputation for its blankets, with its name a guarantee of quality, that the weaving of blankets has continued to prosper. One of the town's notable buildings is the Blanket Hall, built in 1721. Another is the 13th century church which retains its early architecture outside but inside the Victorian restoration was not sympathetic. In the Market Place there is a 17th century Butter Cross with a clock turret beneath a cupola.

The tour continues to Standlake then to the market town of Faringdon, noted for its dairy produce and bacon. Its church is of interest showing architecture ranging from trans-Norman to early English and containing historic monuments and brasses. During the Civil War it lost its spire. Faringdon has numerous interesting buildings and inns including the 18th century Market Hall.

On the A417 between Faringdon and our next stop in Lechlade stands the 18th century, 55 acre, Buscot Park. The house and estate, now a National Trust property, belonged, amongst others to two very different and interesting characters. The first was an Australian, Robert Tertius Campbell, who, in the mid 19th century, made the estate into the most progressive farming enterprise of the time, growing mostly sugar beet. Amongst his projects was a distillery for turning the beet into alcohol and a narrow gauge railway for transporting the crop. Unfortunately, these ventures were not successful and he lost the fortune he had made before buying Buscot. The second remarkable owner was Alexander Henderson, later the first Lord Faringdon, who bought Buscot Park in the late 19th century, and put together a remarkable art collection to which his grandson later added more treasures.

Further along the A417, Lechlade is the limit of navigation upstream for large boats on the River Thames. The town has a fine perpendicular church with a beautiful carved door to the vestry. It has a striking slender spire and strange figures on its tower buttresses. It was in this churchyard that the poet, Shelley, was inspired to write *Summer Evening Meditation*. Lechlade has two bridges spanning the Thames: Ha'penny Bridge, dating from the 18th century, still with its tollhouse, and the early 13th century St John's Bridge lying where the Rivers Thames and Leach meet. There is also a wealth of 17th and 18th century buildings in the rest of the town.

From Lechlade we continue on the A417 to Fairford on the River Coln. An Anglo-Saxon cemetary was found in the 19th century just to the west of the town indicating that there has been a settlement here for a considerable period of time.

The Cotswolds

In the Middle Ages it was the home of one of the region's most prosperous familys of wool merchants, the Tames. It was this family that built the very fine perpendicular chuch with its great tower, glorious carvings, oak beamed roof and wonderful stained glass windows possibly done by the same craftsmen who did those in the Lady Chapel in Westminster Abbey. Fairford was once on the coach road between London and Gloucester and there are reminders of this in the historic inns. A more recent development is the American Airforce base, R.A.F. Fairford, to the south of the town which has a long runway and was also used for testing the British prototype of Concorde.

After visiting the small village of Ampney Crucis, the largest of three Ampney villages and the site of a beautiful church and a gabled inn, detours to another village, Barnsley, before reaching the city of Cirencester, situated on the junction of three Roman roads: Ermin Way, Fosse Way and Akeman Street. At one time it was also the second largest Roman town in Britain. There is little to be seen of the Roman town now but the Corinium Museum in Park Street displays a very fine collection of Roman antiquities from the local area. After the Roman withdrawal from Britain, Cirencester declined in importance although it prospered again in the Middle Ages. Nowadays there are many fine and historic buildings to be seen in the town.

The renewed prosperity of the Middle Ages is reflected in the magnificent parish church of St John, the building of which was largely financed by wealthy local wool merchants. Built in the 15th century as part of an abbey, it escaped the ravages of the Dissolution by being turned into the town hall. It was only in the 18th century that it was returned to the Church. The fine interior contains a painted wineglass pulpit and beautiful stained glass windows as well as brasses and monuments in the Trinity Chapel. The church's unusual three storeyed porch was built by local guilds at the beginning of the 16th century.

Three miles to the south west of Cirencester stands Thames Head Bridge, once part of the Fosse Way crossing the Thames. It is close to the true source of the river at Trewsbury Mead which can be reached by footpath from the Thames Head Inn, although there is little to see apart from a stone slab inscribed with the information that this is the source of the River Thames.

We then proceed to the small village of Cherington and next to the country town of Minchinhampton which has a a a restored church with a 14th century tower, a 17th century market hall on pillars and a famous golf course.

Now the tour comes to the pleasant, unspoilt, market town of Tetbury on the River Avon. As the wool collecting centre for the surrounding region, it has had a prosperous history reflected in the fine 17th and 18th century houses. It has an unusual 17th century Market House, mounted on stumpy pillars. Every Spring Bank Holiday the Tetbury Festival takes place. As part of this, young men and women form two teams in the Woolsack Race where they have to race down and then up the 1-in-4 Gumstool Hill with a 65lb sack of wool. There are also Morris dancers, a jester and stall holders dressed in medieval costume.

We now cross the M5 motorway and out of the Cotswolds proper to visit Berkeley. This is the site of a 12th century castle which has been in the hands of the Berkeley family for almost 850 years. The deposed king, Edward II, was kept here as a prisoner and then murdered in an undetectable but particularly grisly manner. Later, during the Civil War, the castle was held for the king and withstood a siege by Parliamentary troops. Today it contains fine collections of pictures, tapestries, furniture, silver and porcelain. The dungeons, including Edward II's cell, medieval kitchen, the Great Hall and State Apartments are also on show.

Our next call is on Stroud, a centre of the Cotswolds cloth industry. Stoud's advantage was that, situated on the River Frome, it had a plentiful supply of clean water for washing the wool and also minerals for dyeing it. At the height of its prosperity as a wool town, there were more than 150 cloth mills around Stroud. Indeed, one mile south east is an area known as the Golden Valley, between Chalford and Brimscombe, apparently because of the wealth brought to it by the weaving industry during the Middle Ages. With the coming of the Industrial Revolution and then foreign competition this industry declined and now there are only two companies left. However, the town has succeeded in attracting other light industry so it remains relatively prosperous. There are a number of interesting buildings including the Tudor Town Hall and the Shambles, formerly a meat market but today a twice weekly general market. There are also several typical Cotswolds cottages preserved in Church Street.

The following stop, Painswick, also benefited from the availability of fresh, clean water and grew prosperous as a centre for woollen and dyed cloth, reaching its peak in the 18th century. The most popular attraction in the town is the churchyard with its mass of yew trees, mostly planted at the end of the 18th century, clipped in all imaginable shapes and forms. Some have grown and intertwined together to form arches. There is a legend, difficult to check now because of the intertwining, that only ninety nine yew trees will grow here at any one time because the Devil always kills the hundredth. On the first Sunday after 18th September each year, a clipping ceremony is held in the churchyard. In this open air service children of the village, wearing flowers in their hair, hold hands to encircle the church singing a hymn. Afterwards each receives a traditional Painswick Bun and a silver coin. The churchyard holds further attractions in the form of superbly carved stone tombs.

Painswick's prosperity has left a pleasing legacy of houses, shops and inns, all built in the cream coloured stone quarried from Painswick Hill, just outside the town. A less peaceful reminder of the past is found in the 19th century stocks put in St Mary's Street for "the punishment of those who carry on carousels to the annoyance of neighbours." Perhaps an idea that might find favour today.

The Cotswolds

Half a mile from the village, on the Gloucester road, is a beautiful garden, the Painswick Rococo Garden. It is an 18th century six acre garden which has been restored to its original appearance.

We continue through the villages of Cranham and Ullenwood to Northleach. Standing on the Roman Fosse Way has brought prosperity to this town as its fine coaching inns show. It was also a wool town and the church was endowed by wool merchants in the 15th century who are commemorated by brasses inside. The town's museum, situated in its former House of Correction, tells the story of rural Cotswold life and social history.

Our next stop is Cheltenham, a once fashionable spa. Mineral springs were discovered in 1716 but it was the visit of George III in 1788 that transformed Cheltenham into a major spa town. Throughout the 19th century the town thrived and even today, as a centre for tourism, it is still prosperous.

It is a beautiful Regency town and it is well worth spending some time here. Amongst the finest of the buildings are the Montpellier Rotunda, the restored Pittville Pump Room and the two storeyed Regency Arcade of shops. The Cheltenham Music Festival, started in 1944, is another of the town's attractions. Here works by Benjamin Britten, Sir Arthur Bliss, Malcolm Arnold and many other British composers were performed for the first time. A less exalted feature of the town is the steeplechase course where the Cheltenham Gold Cup race is run annually in March.

Turning west, the route come to Gloucester, another Roman town and, for a number of years, the base for the Second Legion before it went to subdue the Welsh tribes. Along with Lincoln, York and Colchester, Gloucester was one of the great Roman colonies, i.e. a place where veteran Roman soldiers were given grants of land to settle on when they retired. After the Roman withdrawal, like so many other towns, it experienced a decline. However, by the 7th century a monastery was built here, a royal palace by the 9th century and a priory, St Oswards, by the early 10th century. The town was a royal court under Edward the Confessor and William the Conqueror and it was here that the decision was taken which led to the Domesday Book. It was about this time that the building on the abbey church of St Peter was started, later to become the cathedral.

It was the grisly murder of Edward II in 1327, however, that greatly benefited St Peters Church. He was was buried here and, surprisingly perhaps because he appears to have been a fairly unpleasant character, his tomb became a shrine. The benefits were that, as today, pilgrims mean an income for the place of pilgrimage. This money was poured into glorifying and extending the church which is now an elegant mixture of Norman and perpendicular styles, but done superbly to give a feeling of unity. Points of particular note in this beautiful cathedral are the east window, which, when it was made, was the largest in the world, the slender columns and the cloister where fan vaulting was used, a new idea at that time.

At the Dissolution, the abbey church became a cathedral but during the reign of the Roman Catholic Mary Tudor, "Bloody Mary" as she was called, the Bishop of Gloucester was burnt at the stake in the city. Elizabeth I granted the city the right to have docks which, although never rivalling the nearby Bristol, were reasonably busy until the 18th century.

As might be expected in a city with such a long history, there are many places to see and a visit to the Tourist Information Centre in St Michael's Tower is advisable. Amongst the museums in Gloucester are the City East Gate in Eastgate Street, the Folk Museum, Westgate Street, the National Waterways Museum and the Regiments of Gloucestershire Museum, both on the Docks.

Westbury-on-Severn, our most westerly stop, contains the lovely Westbury Court with its formal Dutch water-gardens and canals, all laid out in the 17th century, the earliest examples still remaining in the country.

Now returning eastwards, the tour visits Bishop's Cleeve with its 14th century church containing an early 17th century carved oak musicians' gallery. We now continue to Tewkesbury, a town of half-timbered houses and narrow alleys. It was the site of the decisive battle in the Wars of the Roses when the Lancastrian Prince of Wales was killed and the Yorkist Edward consolidated his claim to the throne. At the Dissolution of the Monasteries the town's magnificent abbey was saved by the townspeople. They collected enough money to buy it for the parish from the king. Its altar, dated 1239 and made from Purbeck marble, is one of the oldest in the country.

Next we arrive in Pershore on the River Avon and famous for Pershore plums, before reaching Evesham, centre of the famous Vale of Evesham noted for the growing of fruit and vegetables. A cross stands in the town to the memory of Simon de Montfort killed at the Battle of Evesham in 1265, an event which signalled the end of the barons' revolt against Henry III. The town also has a number of fine old buildings: the 14th century Almonry with later additions, the Tudor Round House and Walker Hall from the 15th century.

The tour continues through Berry Wormington and then on to the unspoilt town of Winchcombe. The town has numerous historic and interesting buildings including the medieval, galleried George Inn which is all that is left of the great abbey and was once its pilgrims' hostel. The abbey church, happily, survived the Dissolution and has many notable features, amongst which are grotesque gargoyles and a magnificent altar cloth. Some remnants of the abbey survive, however, in Hailes Abbey Museum. On display are fragments of architecture from the ruins, 13th century roof bosses and medieval floor tiles.

To the south east of Winchcombe stands Sudeley Castle, a place with an eventful history. It was largely built by Admiral Ralph Botelar in the time of Henry V. He obtained the money to build the castle by holding a French admiral to ransom,

Broadway

a common practice at the time. Unfortunately Botelar fell from favour and the King claimed the castle. It passed through several owners until the time of Elizabeth I when it came to Thomas Seymour, Lord High Admiral of England and fourth husband of Catherine Parr, the wife who survived Henry VIII. She found her new husband was unfaithful so retired from London to Sudeley Castle where she gave birth to a daughter. Within a week of the birth, Catherine Parr, at the age of 36, died of puerperal fever and is buried in the castle chapel. During the Civil War, the castle was held for the King by Prince Rupert of the Rhine when it was put under siege by Parliamentary troops. Later it was slighted (damaged so that it could no longer be used as a fortification) and left to decay. It was only in the 19th century that it was bought by a wealthy family and restored. Today, it is a popular tourist attraction with an award winning Tudor rose garden, craft workshops, and a wonderful collection of art.

Next is the charming village of Broadway, perhaps one of the most visited in the Cotswolds. It became prosperous in the 18th century as a staging post on the coach road from London to Worcester and suffered some decline after the advent of the railways. However, it was discovered by people like William Morris and his friends and very soon it was again thriving with the new tourist trade and has continued to do so since.

It is indeed a picturesque village with buildings made from mellow Cotswold stone. The 17th century Lygon Arms, in the centre of the High Street, is a reminder of Broadway's past as it was a coaching inn. One and a half miles south east stands the late 18th century, Gothic folly of Broadway Tower in Broadway Tower Country Park. At 1024 feet above sea level, this is the second highest point in the Cotswolds and a wonderful viewpoint where, on a clear day, twelve counties may be seen.

Moving onwards, via the delightful Ebrington, we arrive in Chipping Campden, another largely unspoilt town. This was an important wool centre as early as the mid 13th century with a weekly market and three annual fairs. Over the next two centuries its importance increased with trade in wool between here and Europe. Like many of the the other Cotswold wool towns, Chipping Campden's impor-

Stow-on-the-Wold

tance declined with the coming of the Industrial Revolution. However, its prosperous past has left it with a heritage of lovely buildings. Amongst these are the 14th century Grevel's House, the Woolstapler's Hall of the same period which is now used as a museum and Tourist Information Centre, the Market Hall, built in 1627 and a row of 17th century almshouses.

We now go to Shipston-on-Stour, lying in the Vale of the Red Horse at the edge of the Cotswolds. Once the site of a thriving sheep market, it has remained prosperous over the centuries. First of all it was on a coaching road, as its inns testify, then it had a branch line of the tramway linking Stratford-on-Avon to Moreton-in-Marsh and finally part of this tramway was converted into a railway line. The town's continued prosperity has left it with a legacy of many fine 17th, 18th and 19th century houses.

Now the route turns south down the A429 to Moreton-in-Marsh which sits astride the Roman Fosse Way forming the town's High Street. The buildings in the High Street are typical of the charming stone houses and shops one expects in this area. A building of special distinction is the White Hart Royal Hotel where Charles I slept in July 1644, five years before his execution.

Continuing south, Stow-on-the-Wold is a mecca for lovers of antiques. This is an ancient town with evidence of settlement going back to the Iron Age. It stands on a hill some 700 feet above sea level and is the junction of eight roads including the Roman Fosse Way. The twice weekly markets and two annual fairs, formerly for the sale of sheep and wool, have been held here since 1107. It has a number of buildings constructed in the traditional Cotswold stone.

Chipping Norton, next, has one of the largest parish churches in Oxfordshire built by wealthy wool merchants who are commemorated by the brasses inside. The town is over a thousand years old and since medieval times its prosperity was founded on the wool industry, particularly tweed. Nowadays, though, it is an important tourist centre for the Cotswolds. It contains some ancient buildings including the Town Hall, whose windows betray Tudor origins, and almshouses in Church Street dating from 1640. A Bronze Age stone circle, the Rollright Stones, stand just three miles north of Chipping Norton.

We go now to Banbury, a town that dates back to Saxon times although little remains from before the 17th century. In the past the residents of the town have not had much respect for ancient buildings. For example, in the 18th century the local church was blown up because nobody wanted to pay for restoring it. Puritans destroyed the original cross made famous by the nursery rhyme, the one seen today is a replica erected in 1859. The cake shop that made Banbury synonymous with tarts was demolished as recently as 1967 although the original shop front now hangs in the museum. There was also a 12th century castle, at one time covering three acres, but this was demolished after holding out for the King during the Civil War.

We now finish the tour, first with the market town of Deddington where it is said that Charles I spent the night at the local Castle Farm and then finally ending in the village of Clifton lying closeby the M40, along which we may return home.

ANTIQUE DEALERS
BLADON (0993)
Mark Carter Antiques, 25 Park Street, OX20 1RW TEL: 811841 ASSNS: TVADA PARKING: Easy OPEN: Mon-Fri 9.30-5.30 or by appt MIN: £100 MAX: £5,000 PERIOD: 17th-19th century GENERAL: Oak, fruitwood, mahogany furniture.

Park House Antiques, 26 Park Street TEL: 812817 PARKING: Own carpark OPEN: Mon-Sat 9-6 MIN: £150 MAX: £10,000 GENERAL: Walnut, mahogany, satinwood, rosewood furniture 1690-1830 OTHER INFO: Sir Winston churchills grave in churchyard opposite.

WOODSTOCK (0993)
Thistle House Antiques, 14 Market Place, OX20 1TA TEL: 811736 PARKING: Own carpark OPEN: Mon-Sat 10-6 MAX: £4,000 PERIOD: 17th-19th century SPECIALIST: High class brass, desks, bureaux, chest on chests, lowboys. Mahogany & walnut OTHER INFO: The Bear & Feathers hotels have international reputation.

Woodstock Antiques, 11 Market Street, OX20 1SU TEL: 811494 ASSNS: LAPADA, TVADA PARKING: Easy OPEN: Tues-Sat 9.30-5.30 MIN: £50 MAX: £15,000 PERIOD: 18th-19th century SPECIALIST: Staffordshire pottery, animals GENERAL: Traditional & decorative furniture, interesting objects OTHER INFO: Author of *The A to Z of Staffordshire Dogs*.

BURFORD (0993)
Ashton Gower Antiques, 6-7 Cotswold Gateway Antiques Centre, Cheltenham Road, OX8 4JA TEL: 822450 ASSNS: LAPADA PARKING: Own carpark OPEN: Mon-Sat 10-5.30 MIN: £50 MAX: £5,000 PERIOD: 18th-19th century SPECIALIST: English & Continental painted furniture & mirrors GENERAL: Dining tables, chairs, paintings, English oak, decorative items OTHER INFO: Next to Gateway Hotel.

The Burford Gallery, High Street, OX18 4QA TEL: 822305 PARKING: Easy OPEN: Mon-Sat 9.30-5.30 MIN: £5 MAX: £7,000 PERIOD: 18th-20th century SPECIALIST: Watercolours.

Jonathan Fyson Antiques, 50 High Street TEL: 823204 ASSNS: CADA PARKING: Medium OPEN: Mon-Sat 9.30-5.30 MIN: £5 MAX: £5,000 PERIOD: 17th-19th century GENERAL: Furniture, porcelain, glass, metalware.

Gateway Antiques, Cheltenham Road, Burford Roundabout, OX18 4JA TEL: 823678 FAX: 823600 ASSNS: CADA PARKING: Own carpark OPEN: Mon-Sat 10-5.30, Sun 2-5 MIN: £5 MAX: £10,000 PERIOD: 17th-20th century GENERAL: Large stock (8,000sq ft covering 8 showrooms). Mainly English furniture, English pottery & metalware, arts & crafts, Victoriana & Edwardiana & prints.

Howards of Burford, Clement House, 51 High Street, OX18 4QA TEL: 823172 ASSNS: NAG PARKING: Medium OPEN: Mon-Sat 9.30-5.30 MIN: £5 MAX: £35,000 PERIOD: 18th-20th century SPECIALIST: 19th century jewellery & silverware GENERAL: Antique, period & modern jewellery, silver & objets de vertu with emphasis on the more unusual & interesting collectors items.

Anthony Nielsen Antiques, 80 High Street, OX18 4QF TEL: 822014 PARKING: Easy OPEN: Mon-Sat 9.30-5.30 MIN: £50 MAX: £25,000 PERIOD: 17th-19th century SPECIALIST: Good English furniture, especially walnut & mahogany. Brass & copper.

Richard Purdon Antiques Carpets, 158 High Street, OX18 4QY TEL: 823777 FAX: 823719 ASSNS: BADA, CADA PARKING: Medium OPEN: Mon-Sat 9.30-5.30 MIN: £50 MAX: £25,000 PERIOD: 18th-19th century SPECIALIST: Antique Eastern carpets OTHER INFO: Angel & Lamb hotels.

Robin Shield, 134 High Street, OX8 4QV TEL: 822462 ASSNS: BADA, LAPADA, CADA PARKING: Medium OPEN: Mon-Sat 9.30-5.30 MIN: £20 MAX: £10,000 PERIOD: 18th-19th century SPECIALIST: English furniture, works of art, decorative items OTHER INFO: With Stow-on-the-Wold, Burford is the prime antiques centre of the Cotswolds.

Brian Sinfield Gallery, 128 High Street, OX18 4QV TEL: 822603 PARKING: Easy OPEN: Tues-Sun 10-1, 2-5.30 MIN: £300 MAX: £45,000 PERIOD: 19th-20th century SPECIALIST: Contemporary NEAC & RA painters GENERAL: Contemporary Edwardian, Victorian paintings & watercolours OTHER INFO: Also early watercolours. Best hotels: The Lamb, The Baytree. Nearby is The Cotswold Wooling Weavers & The Cotswold Wildlife Park.

Swan Gallery, High Street, OX18 4RE TEL: 822244 PARKING: Easy OPEN: Mon-Sat 9.30-5.30 MIN: £100 MAX: £10,000 PERIOD: 17th-19th century GENERAL: Fine country furniture, Staffordshire figures, decorative & unusual items.

Wren Gallery, 4 Bear Court, High Street, OX18 4RR TEL: 823495 PARKING: Easy OPEN: Mon-Sat 10-1, 2-5.30 MIN: £150 MAX: £10,000 PERIOD: 19th-20th century SPECIALIST: Watercolours & drawings.

WITNEY (0993)

Country Pine Antiques, 14a West End, OX8 6NE TEL: 778584 PARKING: Easy OPEN: Normal MIN: £48 MAX: £1,800 PERIOD: 19th-20th century SPECIALIST: Antique pine GENERAL: Furniture.

Colin Greenway Antiques, 90 Corn Street, OX8 7BU TEL: 705026 PARKING: Easy OPEN: Mon-Sat 9-6 or by appt/chance PERIOD: 17th-20th century GENERAL: General antiques OTHER INFO: Working farm museum, excellent sport facilities. Interesting town.

Ian Pout Antiques, 99 High Street, OX8 6LY TEL: 702616 FAX: 702334 ASSNS: CADA PARKING: Medium OPEN: Mon-Sat 9.30-5.30 MIN: £10 MAX: £1,000 PERIOD: 19th century SPECIALIST: Vintage teddy bears GENERAL: Country & decorative furniture & bygones

Anthony Scaramanga Antiques, 108 Newland, OX8 6JA TEL: 703472 ASSNS: BADA PARKING: Easy OPEN: Mon-Thurs, Sat 10-5, Fri 2.15-5 MIN: £100 MAX: £3,000 PERIOD: 17th-19th century SPECIALIST: Samplers & needlework, pictures GENERAL: Small furniture, blue & white pottery, Staffordshire figures.

Windrush Antiques, 107 High Street TEL: 772536 PARKING: Own carpark OPEN: Mon-Sat 10-5.30 MIN: £100 MAX: £4,000 PERIOD: 17th-18th century SPECIALIST: Country furniture, some Georgian mahogany GENERAL: Some metalware & smalls.

Witney Antiques, 96-100 Corn Street, OX8 7BU TEL: 703902 FAX: 779852 ASSNS: BADA, CINOA, CADA PARKING: Own carpark OPEN: Mon-Sat 9.30-5 or by appt MIN: £200 MAX: £80,000 PERIOD: 17th-19th century SPECIALIST: Fine English & Continental furniture, clocks, pewter, needlework One of the finest stocks of antique furniture & associated

Witney Antiques

96-100 CORN STREET
WITNEY, OXFORDSHIRE
OX8 7BU
TELEPHONE: WITNEY (0993) 703902
FAX: WITNEY (0993) 779852

L.S.A. Jarrett.   C.J. Jarrett.   R. Jarrett Scott.

An outstanding collection of antique furniture, clocks and works of art including one gallery devoted to 17th - 19th century needlworks.

items in the country. Large stock & all items in fine condition OTHER INFO: Witney is the first stop out of London (1-1° hrs) just off A40 & at the beginning of Cotswolds, plenty of good hotels & restaurants locally. Cogges Farm Museum

STANDLAKE (0865)

Manor Farm Antiques, Manor Farm, OX8 7RL TEL: 300303 PARKING: Own carpark OPEN: Mon-Sat 10-6 MIN: £275 MAX: £1,500 PERIOD: 19th-20th century SPECIALIST: Victorian brass & iron bedsteads OTHER INFO: Rose Revived hotel & restaurant, New Bridge, Standlake, Harcourt Arms restaurant, Stanton Harcourt.

FARINGDON (0367)

La Chaise Antique, 30 London Street. SN7 7AA TEL: 240427 & mobile (0831) 205002 PARKING: Easy at rear OPEN: Mon-Sat 9.30-5.30 or by appt MIN: £50 MAX: £5,000 PERIOD: Late 18th-mid 19th century SPECIALIST: Leather & fabric upholstery GENERAL: Good upholstered furniture, mahogany & rosewood items OTHER INFO: Good base to visit the Cotswolds & Vale of the White Horse.

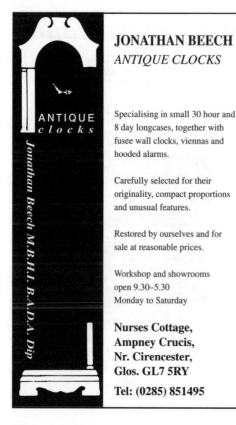

JONATHAN BEECH
ANTIQUE CLOCKS

Specialising in small 30 hour and 8 day longcases, together with fusee wall clocks, viennas and hooded alarms.

Carefully selected for their originality, compact proportions and unusual features.

Restored by ourselves and for sale at reasonable prices.

Workshop and showrooms open 9.30–5.30 Monday to Saturday

**Nurses Cottage,
Ampney Crucis,
Nr. Cirencester,
Glos. GL7 5RY**

Tel: (0285) 851495

Jonathan Beech M.B.H.I. B.A.D.A. Dip

Faringdon Gallery, 21 London Street , SN7 7AG. TEL: 242030 PARKING: Easy OPEN: Mon-Sat 9.30-5.30 MIN: £75 MAX: £5,000 PERIOD: 19th-20th century GENERAL: Quality watercolours & oils, also work by leading contemporary artists OTHER INFO: 2 excellent coaching inns, good hotels & restaurant in the Market Square.

LECHLADE-ON-THAMES (0367)

Antiques Etcetera, High Street, GL7 3AD TEL: 52567 PARKING: Medium OPEN: Mon-Wed, Fri, Sat 10-5 MIN: £5 MAX: £1,500 PERIOD: 18th-19th century SPECIALIST: Good smalls GENERAL: Country effects & furniture OTHER INFO: Lechlade is last navigable point on R. Thames, and as such, is a small & busy place.

Gerard Campbell, Maple House, Market Place, GL7 3AB TEL: 252267 PARKING: Easy OPEN: By appt only PERIOD: 18th-19th century. SPECIALIST: Biedermeier period Viennese regulators GENERAL: Clocks & paintings OTHER INFO: Lechlade is the first point of navigation on R. Thames, 50+ miles upstream from the capital.

D'Arcy Antiques, High Street, GL7 3AE TEL: 252471 PARKING: Easy OPEN: Mon-Sat 10.30-5 MIN: £1 MAX: £1,800 PERIOD: 19th-20th century GENERAL: 1,000 sq ft of furniture, glass, brass, china & furniture OTHER INFO: Good tourist facilities, restaurants, pubs, church, main routes north & south.

Lechlade Antiques Arcade, 5-7 High Street, TEL: 52832 PARKING: Easy OPEN: seven days 10-6 MIN: £1 MAX: £1,000 PERIOD: 17th-20th century GENERAL: Mixed OTHER INFO: Good restaurants, plenty of B&B, riverside walks, hotels & moorings, Cotswold cottages.

Little Barrow Antiques, High Street, GL7 3AE TEL: 253140 PARKING: Medium OPEN: Seven days 9.30-5.30 MIN: £5 MAX: £1,000 PERIOD: 19th-20th century GENERAL: General antiques OTHER INFO: William Morris's Kelmscot Manor, New Inn Hotel.

Mark A. Serle Antiques & Restoration, 6 Burford Street, GL7 3AP TEL: 253145 PARKING: Easy OPEN: Mon-Fri 9.30-5 MIN: £1 MAX: £1,000 PERIOD: 19th-20th century SPECIALIST: Old woodworking tools GENERAL: Militaria, brass door furniture, collectables.

Swan Antiques Centre, Burford Street, GL7 3AP TEL: 252944 PARKING: Own carpark OPEN: Mon-Sat 10.30-4.30 MIN: £2 MAX: £1,000 PERIOD: 19th-20th century SPECIALIST: Doulton, Wedgwood, Staffordshire figures GENERAL: Ceramics, glass, jewellery, books, furniture, collectables OTHER INFO: Coaching Inn, The Swan, next door.

FAIRFORD (0285)

Blenheim Antiques, Market Place, GL7 4AB TEL: 712094 ASSNS: CADA PARKING: Easy OPEN: Mon-Sat 9-6 MIN: £30 MAX: £3,000 PERIOD: 17th-19th century GENERAL: Town & country furniture OTHER INFO: Opposite Bull Hotel (coaching inn with trout fishing). 15th century church with medieval glass & early choir stalls.

Cirencester Antiques, High Street, GL7 4AB TEL: 713774 FAX: 713324 ASSNS: CADA PARKING: Own carpark OPEN: Mon-Sat 9-5.30 MIN: £2 MAX: £35,000 PERIOD: 17th-19th century SPECIALIST: Fine furniture, works of art OTHER INFO: Our sister shop, Gloucester House Antiques, close by for country antiques.

Gloucester House Antiques Ltd, Market Place, GL7 4AB TEL: 712790 FAX: 713324 ASSNS: CADA PARKING: Own carpark OPEN: Mon-Sat 9-5.30 MIN: £2 MAX: £16,000 PERIOD: 18th-19th century SPECIALIST: French & English country furniture GENERAL: Pottery, faïence, decorative pieces.

AMPNEY CRUCIS (0285)
Jonathan Beech Antique Clocks, Nurses Cottage, GL7 5RY TEL: 851495 ASSNS: BHI PARKING: Own carpark OPEN: Mon-Sat 9.30-5.30 & by appt MIN: £300 MAX: £5,000 PERIOD: 17th-19th century SPECIALIST: Antique clocks especially pretty country longcase clocks, 30 hour & 8 day. Also bracket, Vienna and wall clocks OTHER INFO: We also sell at Tetbury Antiques Emporium. Nurses Cottage is set in a beautiful Cotswold village with 2 good pubs offering food & accom.

BARNSLEY (0285)
Denzil Verey Antiques, Barnsley House, GL7 5EE TEL: 740402 ASSNS: CADA PARKING: Own carpark OPEN: Mon-Fri 9.30-5.30, Sat 10.30-5.30 MIN: £5 MAX: £1,500 PERIOD: 18th-19th century GENERAL: Country furniture, pine, kitchenalia, unusual & decorative items OTHER INFO: Barnsley House range of teak garden furniture & associated pieces. Award winning Barnsley House Gardens open Mon, Wed, Thurs Sat 10-6.

CIRENCESTER (0285)
At the Sign of the Herald Angel, 19 Park Street, GL7 2BX TEL: 652972 PARKING: Medium OPEN: Mon-Sat 9-5.30 MIN: £20 MAX: £3,000 PERIOD: 17th-19th century SPECIALIST: Glass, old Sheffield, needlework tools & workboxes GENERAL: Small works of art OTHER INFO: Corinium Museum (mainly Roman). Town was largest Roman settlement after London. Corinium Court Hotel, Gloucester Street, several good private hotels & boarding houses, also B&B.

Walter Bull & Son Ltd, 10 Dyer Street TEL: 653875 ASSNS: NAG PARKING: Medium OPEN: Mon-Sat 9-5 MIN: £50 MAX: £5,000 PERIOD: 19th-20th century SPECIALIST: Antique silver.

Forum Antiques, 20 West Way, The Forum, GL7 1JA TEL: 658406 PARKING: Easy OPEN: Mon-Fri 9-5, Sat 10-5 MIN: £20 MAX: £10,000 PERIOD: 17th-19th century SPECIALIST: Oak furniture GENERAL: Oak, mahogany, walnut etc, furniture 1600-1850, some decorative items.

Jay Gray Antiques, Syrena House, 1 Cheltenham Road, GL7 2HS TEL: 652755 PARKING: Easy OPEN: Mon-Sat 9-6, or ring doorbell anytime MIN: £100 MAX: £10,000 PERIOD: 18th-19th century SPECIALIST: English, Sevres & Meissen porcelain GENERAL: French & Regency furniture, bronzes, French ormolu & porcelain mantel clocks, oils & watercolours, glass OTHER INFO: Wool town in heart of Cotswolds with beautiful parish church. Excellent hotels & restaurants.

Hares Antiques, 17-19 Gosditch Street, GL7 2AG TEL: 640077 FAX: 653513 ASSNS: LAPADA, CADA PARKING: Easy OPEN: Mon-Sat 9.30-5.30 or by appt MIN: £100 MAX: £30,000 PERIOD: 18th-19th century SPECIALIST: Dining furniture, upholstery GENERAL: Good all round selection restoration & upholstery service OTHER INFO: Cathedral-sized church in lovely Cotswold market town. Excellent facilities, restaurants, hotels, museums.

A.J. Ponsford Antiques, 51-53 Dollar Street, GL7 2AS TEL: 652355 PARKING: Medium OPEN: Mon-Fri 8-5.30 MIN: £50 MAX: £10,000 PERIOD: 18th-20th century GENERAL: Oak, walnut, mahogany, rosewood furniture, producers of false books etc OTHER INFO: Restorations in own workshops. All furniture in good condition.

Rankine Taylor Antiques, 34 Dollar Street, GL7 2AN TEL: 652529 ASSNS: LAPADA CADA PARKING: Own carpark OPEN: Mon-Sat 9-5.30 MIN: £15 MAX: £25,000 PERIOD: 17th-19th century SPECIALIST: Furniture & associated objects GENERAL: Silver, glass, rare objects OTHER INFO: Cirencester was a Roman corinium. Good museum. Nearly all 7 antique shops in one street, north of the 13th century church. Stratton House Hotel, ° mile from market place on Gloucester Road, several hotels around town centre. Harry Hare's Brasserie, open all day for meals, opposite side of church.

William H. Stokes, The Cloisters, 6-8 Dollar Street, GL7 2AJ TEL: 653907 FAX: 640214 ASSNS: BADA PARKING: Easy OPEN: Mon-

Fri 9.30-5.30, Sat 9.30-4.30 MIN: £100 MAX: £20,000 PERIOD: 17th-18th century SPECIALIST: Early oak furniture, brass, textiles OTHER INFO: Parish church, Roman museum, Harry Hare's & Tatyan Chinese restaurant, Stratton House & The Fleece hotels.

Waterloo Antiques, 20 The Waterloo, GL7 2PZ TEL: 644887 PARKING: Easy OPEN: Seven days 10-5 MIN: £3 MAX: £3,000 PERIOD: 17th-20th century GENERAL: English & Continental pine. Mahogany, elm, oak, walnut country furniture, silver, porcelain & decorative pieces OTHER INFO: Our warehouse 5 min drive where further unrestored stock may be seen.

Bernhard Weaver, 28 Gloucester St, GL7 2DH TEL: 652055 ASSNS: CADA PARKING: Easy OPEN: Mon-Fri 9-6, Sat 9-1, MIN: £25 MAX: £20,000 PERIOD: 18th-20th century SPECIALIST: Oak & mahogany furniture GENERAL: Metamorphic/dual-purpose furniture OTHER INFO: Shipping arrangements co-ordinated.

MINCHINHAMPTON (0453)

Mick & Fanny Wright Antiques, The Trumpet, West End, GL7 9JA TEL: 883027 PARKING: Medium OPEN: Wed-Sat 10.30-5.30 MIN: £1 MAX: £1,500 PERIOD: 17th-20th century SPECIALIST: Pocket watches, pine GENERAL: Silver + plated ware, Jewellery, pottery, porcelain, furniture, clocks OTHER INFO: Medium stock so not all periods all the time. Weighbridge Inn (2 in 1 pies-yum yum) close. 2 other antique/bric-a-brac shops.

TETBURY (0666)

Antique Interiors, 35 Long Street, GL8 8AA TEL: 504043 PARKING: Easy OPEN: Mon-Sat 9-6 MIN: £50 MAX: £3,000 PERIOD: 18th-early 19th century SPECIALIST: Papier maché & tôle tray tables GENERAL: English & French decorative furniture and accessories, mainly from the Empire & Regency periods OTHER INFO: 20+ antique shops in Tetbury, Highgrove House (home of HRH Prince of Wales), Westonbirt Arboretum. Many good hotels & B&B's in town.

The Antiques Emporium, The Old Chapel, Long Street, GL8 8AA TEL: 505281 PARKING: Medium OPEN: Mon-Sat 10-5, Sun 1-5 MIN: £1 MAX: £15,000 PERIOD: 17th-20th century SPECIALIST: Clocks, Staffordshire, country furniture, jewellery GENERAL: 30 dealers with ecletic & varied stock OTHER INFO: Charming 17th century wool town in the Royal Triangle, 20 more antique shops.

Balmuir House Antiques Ltd, 14 Long Street, GL8 8AQ TEL: 503822 FAX: 505285 PARKING: Easy OPEN: Mon-Fri 9.30-5.30, Sat 10.30-5.30 MIN: £25 MAX: £8,000 PERIOD: 19th century SPECIALIST: The best Edwardian & Victorian furniture GENERAL: Mirrors, paintings & decorative items OTHER INFO: Close & Calcott Manor hotels.

Breakspeare Antiques, 36 & 57 Long Street, GL8 5AQ TEL: 503122 ASSNS: LAPADA CADA PARKING: Easy OPEN: Mon-Sat 9.30-5.30 but closed Thurs pm MIN: £350 MAX: £12,500 GENERAL: Early walnut 1690-1740, Georgian mahogany furniture OTHER INFO: Close Hotel owned by Richard Branson.

J & M Bristow Antiques, 28 Long Street, GL8 8AQ TEL: 502222 PARKING: Easy OPEN: Mon-Wed, Fri, Sat 9.30-1, 2-5.30 MIN: £85 MAX: £10,000 PERIOD: 17th-18th century SPECIALIST: Long case, bracket & lantern clocks, barometers, furniture, metalware GENERAL: Occasional oak pieces.

The Chest of Drawers Antiques, 24 Long Street, GL8 8AQ TEL: 502105 PARKING: Easy OPEN: Mon-Sat 9.30-6 MIN: £10 MAX: £5,000 PERIOD: 17th-19th century GENERAL: Good furniture, pictures, brass & other smalls.

Country Homes, 61 Long Street, GL8 8AA TEL: 502342 PARKING: Medium OPEN: Mon-Sat 9-5.30, Sun 1-5.30 MIN: £10 MAX: £2,300 PERIOD: 19th century GENERAL: Beautiful original Irish, English & German old pine furniture, restored on the premises, treen.

Day Antiques, 5 New Church Street, GL8 8DS TEL: Mon-Sat 9-5.30 PARKING: Easy OPEN: Mon-Sat 9-5.30 PERIOD: 17th-19th century SPECIALIST: Oak & country furniture, pottery, metalware & treen.

Dolphin Antiques, 48 Long Street, GL8 8AQ TEL: 504242 PARKING: Easy OPEN: Mon-Wed, Fri-Sat 10-5.30 MIN: £20 MAX: £2,000 PERIOD: 19th century SPECIALIST: Decorative porcelain GENERAL: Mainly European porcelain & small general antiques.

Elgin House Antiques, 1 New Church Street, GL8 8DT TEL: 504068 FAX: 503401 PARK-

ING: Easy OPEN: Seven days 9-5.30 PERIOD: 18th-19th century SPECIALIST: Beds GENERAL: Furniture.

Hampton Gallery, 10 New Church Street, GL8 8DT TEL: 502971 PARKING: Medium OPEN: By appt MIN: £50 MAX: £5,000 PERIOD: 17th-20th century SPECIALIST: Arms & armour.

Old George Antiques & Interiors, 3a The Chipping, GL8 8EU TEL: 503405 PARKING: Easy OPEN: Mon-Sat 10-5.30 MIN: £50 MAX: £8,000 PERIOD: 17th-18th century GENERAL: Pre 1830 & decorative items OTHER INFO: We can find anything at a competitive price. Good decorative furniture & items from any period.

Porch House Antiques, 42 Long Street, GL8 8AQ TEL: 502687 PARKING: Medium OPEN: Mon-Sat 10-5 MIN: £2 MAX: £2,000 PERIOD: 17th-20th century GENERAL: General antiques OTHER INFO: About 20 antique shops here.

Upton Lodge Galleries, 6 Long Street, GL8 8AQ TEL: 503416 PARKING: Medium OPEN: Mon-Fri 10-6, Sat 10.30-5.30 MIN: £75 MAX: £5,000 PERIOD: 20th century SPECIALIST: Early 20th century British paintings GENERAL: Contemporary paintings OTHER INFO: 18th century church & covered market.

WICKWAR (0454)

Bell Passage Antiques, 36-38 High Street, GL12 8NP TEL: 294251 FAX: 294251 ASSNS: LAPADA PARKING: Own carpark OPEN: Tues, Wed, Fri, Sat 9-5 MIN: £5 MAX: £10,000 PERIOD: 16th-20th century SPECIALIST: Glass & quality antiques GENERAL: English mahogany, oak, pictures, clocks. French OTHER INFO: On American Heritage Trail. Wickwar family of Dewares gave name to Delaware.

BERKELEY (0453)

Keith Gardner Antiques, The Market Place, GL13 9PB TEL: 511032 PARKING: Own carpark OPEN: Tues-Sat 9.30-1, 2-5 MIN: £1 MAX: £1,000 PERIOD: 18th-20th century GENERAL: Brass, furniture, general OTHER INFO: Berkeley Castle. 3 other antique shops here.

CAMBRIDGE (0453)

Bell House Antiques, GL2 7BD TEL: 890463 PARKING: Own carpark OPEN: Mon-Sat 10-1, 2-5 MIN: £1 MAX: £1,000 PERIOD: 19th-20th century OTHER INFO: George Inn in village. Slimbridge Wildfowl Trust 2 miles.

STROUD (0453)

Gnome Cottage Antique & Modern, 55 Middle Street, GL5 1DZ TEL: 763669 PARKING: Own carpark OPEN: Mon-Sat 9.30-6 MIN: £1 MAX: £1,000 PERIOD: 19th-20th century GENERAL: Victorian dining furniture GENERAL: Furnishing antiques OTHER INFO: Modern and secondhand furniture. London Road & The Imperial hotels.

Shabby Tiger Antiques, 18 Nelson Street, GL5 2HN TEL: 759175 PARKING: Easy OPEN: Mon-Sat 10.30-5.30 MIN: £5 MAX: £1,000 PERIOD: 18th-19th century GENERAL: Furniture and general antiques OTHER INFO: On good trade route between Bath & Cheltenham (A46). Painswick (Queen of the Cotswold villages) only 3 miles, Princess Anne's residence near Minchinhampton, 3 miles away. Prince Charles's (Tetbury) 12 miles.

SLAD (0453)

Ian Hodgkins & Co Ltd, Upper Vatch Mill, The Vatch, GL6 7JY TEL: 764270 FAX: 766716 ASSNS: ABA PARKING: Own carpark OPEN: By appt PERIOD: 19th century SPECIALIST: Pre-Raphaelites: 19th Century Literary Ladies, 1860's Illustrated Books, The 1890's, 19th Century Royalty, Victorian Lady Travellers OTHER INFO: Slad is the home of Laurie Lee.

PAINSWICK (0452)

Country Living, Cardynham House, The Cross, GL6 6XA TEL: 814006 PARKING: Medium OPEN: Mon-Sat 10.30-5 PERIOD: 19th-20th century SPECIALIST: Pine, painted furniture, china, prints GENERAL: Dummy boards, quilts, bric-a-brac OTHER INFO: Cardynham House, a Grade II listed building dating from 1489, is in centre of unspoilt village. Prinknash Abbey nearby.

Craig Carrington Antiques, Brook House, GL6 6SE TEL: 813248 FAX: 813539 PARKING: Own carpark OPEN: By appt MIN: £200 MAX: £50,000 PERIOD: 17th-19th century SPECIALIST: English & Continental furniture GENERAL: Fine objects, needlework, marble sculpture OTHER INFO: Painswick Hotel in village comfortable country house hotel, Oakes Restaurant 2 miles, good food.

Painswick Antique & Craft Centre, New Street, GL6 6XH TEL: 812431 PARKING: Medium/difficult OPEN: Mon-Fri 10-5, Sat 9.30-5.30, Sun 11-5.30 MIN: £2 MAX: £3,000 PERIOD: 18th-19th century GENERAL: Porcelain, jewellery, small furniture, silver, books OTHER INFO: The whole village is of interest.

Regent Antiques, Dynevor House, New Street TEL:812543 PARKING: Medium OPEN: Resident, anytime MIN: £100 MAX: £5,000 PERIOD: 17th-19th century SPECIALIST: 17th & 18th century oak & walnut furniture GENERAL: Some mahogany & decorative items OTHER INFO: Painswick Hotel - excellent, Country Elephant restaurant.

CRANHAM (0452)

Heather Newman Gallery, Milidduwa, Mill Lane, GL6 6TX TEL: 812230 PARKING: Own carpark OPEN: By appt MIN: £100 MAX: £10,000 PERIOD: 18th-early 20th century SPECIALIST: Quality British watercolours & drawings.

NORTHLEACH (0451)

Keith Harding's World of Mechanical Music, High Street, GL54 3EU TEL: 860181 FAX: 861133 ASSNS: BHI (Fellow) PARKING: Own carpark OPEN: Seven days 10-6 PERIOD: 18th-20th century SPECIALIST: Clocks & musical boxes including restoration OTHER INFO: Continuous tours of our award-winning museum of clocks & mechanical music.

CHARLTON KINGS (0242)

Art & Antique Centre, 268 London Road, GL52 6EH TEL: 522939 ASSNS: LAPADA PARKING: Own carpark OPEN: Mon-Sat 10-5.30 MIN: £5 MAX: £3,000 PERIOD: 18th-19th century GENERAL: Interesting varied reasonable stock. Only high quality OTHER INFO: Also sell on commission.

Charlton Kings Antique & Craft Centre, 199 London Road TEL: 510672 PARKING: Easy OPEN: Mon-Sat 9.30-5.30 MIN: £5 MAX: £1,500 PERIOD: 19th-20th century GENERAL: Furniture, china, glass, silver plate, prints, mirrors, watercolours & crafts.

CHELTENHAM SPA (0242)

Bailey's Quality Antique Lighting, 16 Suffolk Road, GL50 2AQ TEL: 255897 ASSNS: GMC PARKING: Own carpark OPEN: Mon-Sat 10-6 but appt advisable weekdays MIN: £10 MAX: £30,000 PERIOD: 19th-20th century SPECIALIST: High quality antique & pre-1940 gas, oil & early electric lighting fixtures & fittings. Spare parts, restoration, re-wiring. Some period advertising OTHER INFO: Near all antique shops.

David Bannister FRGS, 26 Kings Road, GL52 6BG TEL: 514287 FAX: 513890 ASSNS: AMPF PARKING: Own carpark OPEN: By appt only MIN: £25 PERIOD: 16th-17th century SPECIALIST: Antique maps & views only.

Bed of Roses, 12 Prestbury Road, GL52 2PW TEL: 231918 (24 hrs) PARKING: Medium OPEN: Tues-Sat 10-1, 2-5 PERIOD: 19th century SPECIALIST: Fine stripped pine OTHER INFO: 50+ antique shops. Pittville Park & Pump Rooms, Holst Birthplace Museum (free).

Butler & Co, 111 Promenade, GL50 1NW PARKING: Medium OPEN: Sat 10-4 PERIOD: 17th-20th century SPECIALIST: Coins & medals of all countries.

Cameo Antiques, 31 Suffolk Parade TEL: 233164 PARKING: Easy OPEN: Mon-Sat 10-1 & 2-5 or by appt MIN: £100 MAX: £6,500 PERIOD: 19th-20th century GENERAL: Edwardian inlaid, decorative, Victorian walnut, paintings (occasional).

Cheltenham Antique Market, 54 Suffolk Road, GL50 2AQ TEL: 529812 PARKING: Medium OPEN: Mon-Sat 9.30-5.30 MIN: £1 MAX: £1,000 PERIOD: 19th-20th century GENERAL: Furniture, pictures, mirrors, pine, fireplaces OTHER INFO: 25 dealers

Cocoa, 7 Queens Circus, Montpellier, GL50 1RX TEL: 233585 PARKING: Medium OPEN: Mon-Sat 10-5 MIN: £1 MAX: £2,000 PERIOD: 18-20th century SPECIALIST: Antique lace, wedding dresses GENERAL STOCK: Costume jewellery, antique linens, christening gowns etc OTHER INFO: Very near Queens Hotel. Fine selection of restaurants. We are set in heart of Montpellier, which is full of interesting & quality shops. Close to Cheltenham Antique Centre.

Greens of Montpellier, 15 Montpellier Walk TEL: 512088 FAX: 512088 PARKING: Medium OPEN: Mon, Tues, Thurs-Sat 9-1 & 2-5 MIN: £100 MAX: £10,000 PERIOD: 18th-19th century SPECIALIST: Antique & Art Deco jewellery, silver, Oriental porcelain, glass, furniture.

Heydens Antiques & Militaria, 420 High Street, GL50 3JA TEL: 582466 PARKING: Medium OPEN: Mon-Sat 10-5.30 MIN: £1 MAX: £1,500 PERIOD: 19th-20th century SPECIALIST: Antique weapons GENERAL: Militaria & collectables.

David Howard 20th Century Paintings, 42 Moorend Crescent, GL53 0EL TEL: 243379 PARKING: Easy OPEN: By appt MIN: £200 MAX: £2,000 PERIOD: 19th-20th century SPECIALIST: Only fine paintings & drawings.

Kyoto House Antiques, 14 Suffolk Road, GL50 2AQ TEL: 262549 FAX: 262549 ASSNS: BADA, Cert.in Furniture Restoring PARKING: Difficult OPEN: Mon-Sat 10-6 MIN: £5 MAX: £8,000 PERIOD: 19th century SPECIALIST: Japanese GENERAL: Japanese furniture & small items, English furniture (trade) OTHER INFO: All stock bought in Japan personally.

Latchfords, 215 London Road TEL: 226263 PARKING: Easy OPEN: Mon-Sat 10-5.30 MIN: £1 MAX: £1,000 PERIOD: 19th-20th century GENERAL: Stripped pine, Victorian & Edwardian furniture, giftware.

Montpellier Clocks, 13 Rotunda Terrace, Montpellier Street, GL50 1SW TEL: 242178 ASSNS: BADA PARKING: Easy OPEN: Mon-Sat 8.30-5.30 MIN: £100 MAX: £20,000 PERIOD: 17th-19th century SPECIALIST: Clocks & barometers only OTHER INFO: Full restoration & conservation on premises.

Eric Pride Oriental Rugs, 44 Suffolk Road, GL50 2AQ TEL: 580822 FAX: 522946 ASSNS: GMC PARKING: Medium OPEN: Tues-Fri 10-6 or by appt MIN: £100 MAX: £10,000 PERIOD: 19th-20th century SPECIALIST: Caucasian tribal rugs & kilims GENERAL: Old & new Persian, Caucasian & Central Asian rugs, carpets & kilims.

Michael Rayner Bookseller, 11 St Luke's Road, GL53 7JQ TEL: 512806 PARKING: Own carpark for one MIN: £1 MAX: £500 PERIOD: 19th-20th century GENERAL: Wide variety of books incl topography, transport, modern firsts etc OTHER INFO: Close town centre.

Scott-Cooper Ltd, 52 The Promenade, GL50 1LY TEL: 522580 ASSNS: BADA NAG PARKING: difficult OPEN: Mon-Fri 0930-1 & 2.15-5, Sat 0930-12 MIN: £35 PERIOD: 17th-20th century GENERAL: Jewellery, silver & objets d'art.

Tapestry Antiques, 33 Suffolk Parade TEL: 512191 PARKING: Medium OPEN: Mon-Sat 9.30-5.30 MIN: £5 MAX: £2,000 PERIOD: 19th century SPECIALIST: Decorative items, brass & iron beds GENERAL: Mirrors, textiles, dining furniture, lamps, china OTHER INFO: Attractive Spa town with many restaurants, shopping centre, parks, gardens.

The Triton Gallery, 27 Suffolk Parade, GL50 2AE TEL: 510477 PARKING: Difficult OPEN: Mon-Sat 9-5.30 & by appt (resident) MIN: £5 MAX: £5,000 PERIOD: 19th-20th century SPECIALIST: Antique mirrors, furniture, paintings GENERAL: Decorative furniture OTHER INFO: Commendation Award of Civic Society for design of garden at rear of showroom.

GLOUCESTER (0452)

Gloucester Antique Centre, 1 Severn Road TEL: 529716 FAX: 507161 PARKING: Own carpark OPEN: Mon-Sat 9.30-5, Sun 1-5 MIN: £1 MAX: £10,000 PERIOD: 18th-19th century SPECIALIST: Furniture GENERAL: Silver & print jewellery OTHER INFO: 67 dealers under one roof, licenced restaurant. Full restoration & delivery service & exports.

HQ84 Military Curiosity Shop, At the Southgate, GL1 2DX TEL: 527716 PARKING: Medium OPEN: Seven days 10-5.30 MIN: £1 MAX: £275 PERIOD: 19th-20th century SPECIALIST: Militaria of the World GENERAL: Supplier to retail, trade & film industry of reproduction uniforms, badges & medals (5000 items, lists available £1). Small antiques, brass etc OTHER INFO: Antique Market (48 stalls) 500 yds, plenty of eating places close. Historical docks 100 yds. 3 museums adjacent, also Gloucester Cathedral. Large indoor market close.

Paul Medcalf, Unit 29 Gloucester Antique Centre, 1 Severn Road TEL: 415186 PARKING: Own carpark OPEN: Mon-Sat 9-5, Sun 1-5 MIN: £5 MAX: £2,500 PERIOD: 19th-20th century GENERAL: Oils, watercolours, etchings, Japanese prints. Works by Birmingham artists. OTHER INFO: We are in historic docks.

WESTBURY ON SEVERN (0452)

Pine & Country Furniture, Landeck, Rodley TEL: 760315 PARKING: Own carpark OPEN: Seven days 9-6 MIN: £20 MAX: £1,000 PERIOD: 18th-20th century GENERAL: Stripped pine & country pieces incl. kitchens from reclaimed timber OTHER INFO: Forest of Dean, Wye Valley.

BISHOPS CLEEVE (0242)

Cleeve Picture Framing, Church Road TEL: 673532 ASSNS: FATG, FPPF PARKING:

Medium OPEN: Mon-Fri 9-1, 2-5.30, Sat 9-1 MIN: £10 MAX: £500 PERIOD: 17th-20th century SPECIALIST: Antique prints & maps, topographical and sporting GENERAL: Original oils & watercolours, limited edition prints.

TEWKESBURY (0684)

F.W. Taylor, 71 Church Street TEL: 295990 PARKING: Easy OPEN: Mon-Sat 9-5 MIN: £10 MAX: £3,000 PERIOD: 18th-19th century GENERAL: General antiques OTHER INFO: Historic medieval town with Abbey as the centrepiece.

PERSHORE (0386)

Hansen Chard Antiques, 126 High Street, WR10 1EA TEL: 553423 ASSNS: BHI PARKING: Easy OPEN: Tues-Wed, Fri-Sat 10-5 & by appt MIN: £5 MAX: around £3,000 PERIOD: 18th-19th century SPECIALIST: Clocks & barometers.

Look-In Antiques, 134b High Street (main A44) TEL: 556776 PARKING: Medium OPEN: Mon-Sat 10.15-5.15 MIN: £1-4 MAX: £550 PERIOD: 19th-20th century GENERAL: Furniture all types, except the very large, and general antiques OTHER INFO: 6 antique shops on A44 plus 1 other. The town is of great historical interest having celebrated the millenium of its Royal Charter. There are 5 Georgian houses in Bridge Street which continues from High Street. Fine Abbey in town centre occupied by Cistercian monks until early this century.

Penoyre Antiques, 9 Bridge Street, WR10 1AJ TEL: 553522 FAX: (0905) 754129 PARKING: Easy OPEN: Mon-Wed, Fri-Sat 9.30-1, 2-5.30 MIN: £500 MAX: £25,000 PERIOD: 18th-19th century GENERAL: Georgian mahogany dining room furniture OTHER INFO: 10th century Pershore Abbey, The Angel is an old coaching inn and was the original model for J.M.Barrie's *Quality Street*.

Swantiques, Abbey Showrooms, Newlands, WR10 1BP TEL: 555580 FAX: 556205 PARKING: Own carpark OPEN: Mon-Sat 9-5, Sun 2-4.30 MIN: £100 MAX: £3,000 PERIOD: 18th-20th century SPECIALIST: Victorian & Edwardian bedroom furniture.

BERRY WORMINGTON (0242)

Hay Loft Gallery, WR12 7NH TEL: 621202 PARKING: Own carpark OPEN: Any reasonable time by appt MIN: £400 MAX: £20,000 PERIOD: 19th century SPECIALIST: Victorian oils, landscapes, animal, genre GENERAL: Some watercolours.

WINCHCOMBE (0242)

Muriel Lindsay, Queen Anne House, High Street, GL54 5LJ TEL: 602319 PARKING: Medium OPEN: Mon-Sat 9.30-1, 2.15-5.30, or by appt, resident MIN: £4 MAX: £700 PERIOD: 18th-19th century SPECIALIST: Metalwork, glass, Staffordshire GENERAL: Small furniture, silver, a little porcelain OTHER INFO: We are well-known for our constantly changing stock of small goods at keen price. 15 years experience posting to USA. Glass suited to Japanese trade.

Pritchard Antiques, 16 High Street, GL54 5LJ TEL: 603566 ASSNS: CADA PARKING: Easy OPEN: Mon-Sat 9-5.30 & by appt PERIOD: 17th-19th century GENERAL: Period furniture & accessories, boxes, brassware, etc OTHER INFO: Sudeley Castle (castle gardens & garden centre-especially roses). Railway Museum.

TADDINGTON (0386)

Architectural Heritage, Taddington Manor TEL: 73414 FAX: 73236 ASSNS: CADA PARKING: Own carpark OPEN: Mon-Fri 9.30-5.30, Sat 10.30-4.30 MIN: £250 PERIOD: 17th-20th century GENERAL: Garden statuary, fire surrounds, panelling, stained glass, bizarre items OTHER INFO: Statuary made to order.

BROADWAY (0386)

Broadway Old Books, The Long Room, 45 High Street, WR12 7DP TEL: 853668 ASSNS: FATG PARKING: Own carpark OPEN: Mon-Sat 9.30-5.30, Sun 11-5 MIN: £1 MAX: £5,000 PERIOD: 19th century SPECIALIST: Early literature, fine bindings GENERAL: Books & engravings from 16th century, childrens' books & prints.

Gavina Ewart, 58 High Street, WR12 7DT TEL: 853371 FAX: 858948 ASSNS: BADA PARKING: Easy OPEN: Mon-Sat 9.30-1, 2-5.30 PERIOD: 18th-20th century SPECIALIST: English table silver & cutlery GENERAL: Porcelain incl Royal Worcester, pot lids & Prattware OTHER INFO: Lygon Arms Hotel, Buckland Manor Hotel.

Fenwick & Fisher Antiques, 88-90 High Street, WR12 7AJ TEL: 853227, home 858502 FAX: 858504 ASSNS: CADA PARKING: Own carpark

OPEN: Mon-Sat 10-6 & by appt MIN: £2 MAX: £ 7,000 PERIOD: 17th-early 19th century SPECIALIST: Treen, pewter, samplers, boxes, lace bobbins GENERAL: Pre-Victorian furniture & accessories up to 1850 OTHER INFO: England's prettiest village, convenient for theatre at Stratford & other Cotswold antiques centres. Lygon Arms, Luigi's Backyard, Hunters Lodge etc.

Richard Hagen Ltd, Yew Tree House, WR12 7DT TEL: 853624, 858561 FAX: 852172 ASSNS: BADA PARKING: Easy OPEN: Mon-Sat 9.30-5.30 MIN: £550 MAX: £45,000 PERIOD: Late 19th-20th century SPECIALIST: Bronzes by James Butler R.A. GENERAL: British oil paintings & watercolours including contemporary artists.

High Park Antiques Ltd, 62 High Street, WR12 7DT TEL: 853130 PARKING: Easy OPEN: Tues-Sat 10.30-5 MIN: £50 MAX: £12,500 PERIOD: 18th-19th century GENERAL: Furniture, silver, porcelain.

H.W. Keil Ltd, Tudor House, WR12 7DP TEL: 852408 PARKING: Own small carpark OPEN: Mon-Sat 9.15-12.45, 2.15-5.30 PERIOD: 17th-early 19th century SPECIALIST: Large furniture in oak, walnut & mahogany OTHER INFO: Early metalwork, brass & copper etc, Sheffield plate. Near Lygon Arms, Buckland Manor, Dormy House hotels. Hunter's Lodge excellent retaurant. NT house to visit.

John Noott Fine Art, 14 Cotswold Court, WR12 7AA TEL: 858969 FAX: 858348 ASSNS: BADA, LAPADA, CADA PARKING: Own carpark OPEN: 9.30-1, 2-5 MIN: £20 MAX: £20,000 GENERAL: Fine original paintings 17th century to contemporary OTHER INFO: Famous & very pretty Cotswold village, lots of art & antiques, restaurants, hotels & gift shops.

Olive Branch Antiques, 80 High Street, WR12 7AJ TEL: 853831 FAX: 853440 PARKING: Own carpark front/rear OPEN: Seven days 9-5.30 MIN: £1 MAX: £3,000 PERIOD: 19th-20th century SPECIALIST: Clocks OTHER INFO: Well supplied with hotels & guest houses. In fact Olive Branch Guest House right next door (10 bedrooms ensuite, parking etc tel: 853440).

Withington Fine Art, 62 High Street, WR12 7DT TEL: 853130 FAX: (0432) 851267 PARKING: Medium OPEN: Mon-Sat 9.30-5.30 MIN: £50 MAX: £10,000 PERIOD: 18th-20th century GENERAL: Paintings, furniture, antique & modern jewellery.

EBRINGTON (0386)

Natural Craft Taxidermy, 21 Main Street, GL55 6NL TEL: 78231 PARKING: Easy OPEN: Anytime by appt MIN: £20 MAX: £4,000 PERIOD: 19th-20th century SPECIALIST: Over 250 pieces Victorian & Edwardian furniture GENERAL: Antique & modern OTHER INFO: Middle of pretty N.Cotswolds village.

CHIPPING CAMPDEN (0386)

Campden Country Pine, High Street, GL55 6HN TEL: 840315 PARKING: Easy OPEN: Mon-Sat 10-5 MIN: £50 MAX: £1,500 PERIOD: 18th-19th century SPECIALIST: Stripped Victorian & earlier pine GENERAL: English & Continental furniture OTHER INFO: Most beautiful high street in Britain, fine Cotswold restaurants, shops & hotels.

Swan Antiques, High Street, GL55 6HB TEL: 840759 ASSNS: NAG, holder of Anderson Medal for Gemmology PARKING: Medium OPEN: Mon-Wed, Fri, Sat 9.30-5 MIN: £15 MAX: £15,000 PERIOD: 18th-19th century SPECIALIST: Silver & jewellery GENERAL: Porcelain, pictures, furniture OTHER INFO: Woolstaplers Museum, several good restaurants.

SHIPSTON-ON-STOUR (0608)

Fine-Lines Fine Art, The Old Rectory Lodge, West Street, CV36 4HD TEL: 662323 PARKING: Easy OPEN: Anytime by appt MIN: £300-800 MAX: £12-20,000 SPECIALIST: Quality watercolours & selected oils from 1850 to present GENERAL: 1850-1940 Accent on the fine condition & presentation of stock, which includes still life, landscapes, good figure studies, garden subjects, marines, still life etc OTHER INFO: Few contemporary works

Time in Hand, 11 Church Street TEL: 662578 FAX: 662578 PARKING: Medium OPEN: Mon-Sat 9-1, 2-5.30 MIN: £50 MAX: £4,500 PERIOD: 18th-19th century SPECIALIST: Wide range of clocks & barometers OTHER INFO: Small rural town on edge of the Cotswolds, 2 good clock shops, friendly accommodation arranged

MORETON-IN-MARSH (0608)

Astley House-Fine Art, Astley House, High Street, GL56 0LL TEL: 650601 FAX: 651777 ASSNS: CADA PARKING: Easy OPEN: Mon,

Tues, Thurs-Sat 9-5.30 MIN: £300 MAX: £20,000 PERIOD: 19th-20th century SPECIALIST: Portraits & large decorative paintings GENERAL: Oils OTHER INFO: We have two other galleries. Specialist framing of paintings & porcelain. Restaurants: Annies, Oxford Street & The Marsh Goose, High Street.

Avon Gallery, High Street TEL: 650614 PARKING: Easy OPEN: Mon, Tues Thurs-Sat 9.30-1 & 2-5, Weds 9.30-1 PERIOD: 19th-20th century SPECIALIST: Hunting, racing, dogs GENERAL: Prints-some limited editions.

Chandlers Antiques, Chandlers Cottage, High Street, GL56 0AD TEL: 651347 PARKING: Easy OPEN: Mon-Sat 9.30-1, 2-5.30 MIN: £1 MAX: £750 PERIOD: 18th-20th century SPECIALIST: English porcelain & glass GENERAL: Jewellery, treen, faïence (Quimper & Rouen, etc), early Chinese pottery, smalls OTHER INFO: Good food at Marsh Goose, Black Bear. Large market Tues.

Grimes House Antiques & Fine Art, Grimes House, High Street, GL56 0AT TEL: 651029 PARKING: Easy OPEN: Mon-Sat 9.30-1 & 2-5, Weds 9.30-1 PERIOD: 19th century SPECIALIST: Probably the largest selection for sale anywhere of Victorian cranberry glass, collectable boxes GENERAL: Victorian furniture, glass. Accent on decorative pieces OTHER INFO: A spacious Cotswold town with a good range of antiques available at sensible prices. Many good restaurants & hotels plus plentiful parking.

Lemington House Antiques, Oxford Street, GL56 0LA TEL: 651443 PARKING: Own carpark OPEN: Mon-Sat 10-5.30 MIN: £10 MAX: £40,000 PERIOD: 17th-19th century SPECIALIST: Period walnut & mahogany furniture GENERAL: Porcelain, pewter, silver & works of art OTHER INFO: We are town's largest historic building (1430).

A.K. Nielsen, Seaford House, High Street, GL56 0AD TEL: 650448 ASSNS: LAPADA PARKING: Easy OPEN: Thurs-Sat 9.30-1, 2-5 MIN: £85 MAX: £7,500 PERIOD: 19th-20th century SPECIALIST: English porcelain GENERAL: Quality English furniture, porcelain.

Elizabeth Parker Antiques, High Street, GL56 0LL TEL: 650917 PARKING: Easy OPEN: Mon-Sat 9-6 MIN: £100 MAX: £8,000 PERIOD: 18th-19th century GENERAL: Quality furniture, some porcelain, copper & brass.

Anthony Sampson Antiques, Dale House, High Street, GL56 0AD TEL: 650763 ASSNS: BADA PARKING: Easy OPEN: Mon-Sat 9-5.30 or by appt (Resident) MIN: £50 MAX: £20,000 PERIOD: 17th-19th century SPECIALIST: Period furniture to 1830 GENERAL: Occasional silver, paintings, porcelain, pottery, garden ornaments, decorative items.

Southgate Gallery, Fosse Manor Farm, GL56 9NQ TEL: 650051 PARKING: Own carpark OPEN: By appt only MIN: £500 MAX: £5,000 PERIOD: 20th century GENERAL: Modern British paintings from 1920 to present day OTHER INFO: Several good restaurants & hotels. Very central to other buying areas, Stow-on-the-Wold, Broadway etc

Windsor House Antiques Centre, High Street TEL: 650993 PARKING: Very easy OPEN: Seven days 10.30-5.30 MIN: £25 MAX: £3,500 PERIOD: 17th-19th century GENERAL: Quality antiques of all kinds in one elegant building OTHER INFO: 30+ antique shops.

STOW-ON-THE-WOLD (0451)

Acorn Antiques, Sheep Street, GL54 1AA TEL: 831519 PARKING: Easy OPEN: Mon-Sat 10-1 & 2.15-5, MIN: £5 MAX: £2,000 PERIOD: 19th-20th century SPECIALIST: Staffordshire figures & animals GENERAL: Glass, pottery, small furniture OTHER INFO: Tourist heaven incl some 30 antique shops.

Baggott Church Street Ltd, Church Street, GL54 1BB TEL: 830370 FAX: 832174 ASSNS: BADA CADA PARKING: Easy OPEN: Mon-Sat 9.30-5.30 MIN: £50 MAX: £50,000 PERIOD: 17th-19th century SPECIALIST: English furniture GENERAL: All manner of pieces appertaining to the comforts & necessities of gentlefolk for sale & in good order OTHER INFO: Numerous hotels & inns offering reliable meals & accommodation. Unicorn & Grapevine hotels, also Queen's Head Inn.

Duncan J. Baggott, Woolcomber House, Sheep Street, GL54 1AA TEL:830662 FAX: 832174 ASSNS: CADA PARKING: Easy OPEN: Mon-Sat 9.30-5.30 MIN: £50 MAX: £50,000 PERIOD: 17th-19th century SPECIALIST: Fine old English furniture & paintings GENERAL:

Domestic metalware, fireplace accoutrements, collectables & some garden statuary & ornaments OTHER INFO: Wyck Hill House & Fosse Manor hotels, Marsh Goose restaurant.

Bow Cottage Antiques, Park Street TEL: 832311 PARKING: Easy OPEN: Mon-Sat 10-5 MIN: £5 MAX: £100 PERIOD: 18th-20th century SPECIALIST: English pottery & porcelain, topographical engravings & maps & small furniture.

J & J Caspall Antiques, Sheep Street TEL: 831160 PARKING: Easy OPEN: Mon-Sat 9.30-5.30 MIN: £150 MAX: £10,000 PERIOD: 16th-18th century (to 1750) SPECIALIST: Early English oak furniture, lighting devices, medieval carvings, metalware, early & rare domestic & decorative.

Annarella Clark Antiques, 11 Park Street, GL54 1AQ TEL: 830535 PARKING: Easy OPEN: Anytime by appt MIN: £5 MAX: £2,000 PERIOD: 19th century SPECIALIST: Decorative country painted furniture, needlework, quilts, textiles & acessories, conservatory & garden antique baskets OTHER INFO: Best B&B at 14 Park Street.

Cotswold Antiques Centre, The Square, GL54 1BQ TEL: 831585 PARKING: Easy OPEN: Mon-Sat 10-5 MIN: £2 MAX: £2,000 PERIOD: 17th-19th century SPECIALIST: Silver, pictures, furniture, porcelain & earthenware, ironstone.

Cotswold Galleries, The Square, GL54 1AB TEL: 830586 FAX: 870678 ASSNS: CADA PARKING: Easy OPEN: Mon-Sat 9-1, 2-5.30 MIN: £20 MAX: £5,000 PERIOD: 19th-20th century GENERAL: Original British landscape oils (easy to live with types), also village scenes etc.

Country Life Antiques, Grey House, The Square, GL54 1AF TEL: 831564 FAX: 870048 PARKING: Easy OPEN: Mon-Sat 10-5.30 & by appt MIN: £15 MAX: £5,000 PERIOD: 17th-20th century SPECIALIST: Scientific intruments, pewter, brass GENERAL: Good quality mahogany, oak & pine furniture & large stock of decorative accessories.

Fosse Way Antiques, Ross House, The Square, GL54 1AF TEL: 830776 ASSNS: CADA PARKING: Easy OPEN: Mon-Sat 10-5 MIN: £50 MAX: £7,000 PERIOD: 18th-19th century SPECIALIST: Lots of dining chairs GENERAL: Furniture, oils & decorative accessories, bronzes, Sheffield plate, mirrors, writing boxes & caddies.

Keith Hockin 'Antiques' Ltd, The Square TEL: 831058 ASSNS: BADA, CADA PARKING:

Medium OPEN: Mon-Sat 10-6 MIN: £50 MAX: £15,000 PERIOD: 17th-18th century SPECIALIST: Early English oak & furniture GENERAL: Brass, pewter, copper, ironwork, period objects.

Huntington Antiques Ltd, Church Street, GL54 1BE TEL: 830842 FAX: 832211 ASSNS: LAPADA, CADA, European Fine Art Foundation PARKING: Own carpark OPEN: Mon-Sat 9.30-5.30 MIN: £500 MAX: £100,000 PERIOD: 17th-18th century SPECIALIST: Early period furniture, works of art, tapestries GENERAL: Fine country furniture, metalware, treen, textiles OTHER INFO: Hotels and restaurants arranged locally.

Little Elms Antiques, The Square, GL54 1AF TEL: 870089 PARKING: Easy OPEN: Mon-Sat 10-5 MIN: £300 MAX: £8,000 PERIOD: 17th-18th century SPECIALIST: Oak country furniture GENERAL: Dressers, tables, chairs.

Peter Norden Antiques, The Little House, Sheep Street, GL54 1AA TEL: 830455 PARKING: Medium OPEN: Mon-Sat 9.30-5.30 MIN: £5 MAX: £10,000 PERIOD: 17th-19th century SPECIALIST: Oak & country furniture GENERAL: Metalware, treen, arms & armour, walnut and mahogany furniture.

No. 2 Park Street Antiques, 2-3 Park Street, GL54 1AQ TEL: 832311 PARKING: Easy OPEN: Mon-Sat 10-5 MIN: £5 MAX: £1,500 PERIOD: 19th-20th century GENERAL: 15-20 dealers. An antique centre with 10 open stands & 10 cabinets. Wide range of porcelain, pottery, glass, furniture etc.

Park House Antiques, Park Street TEL: 30159 PARKING: Easy OPEN: Mon-Sat 10-5 MIN: £1 MAX: £6,000 PERIOD: 18th-20th century SPECIALIST: Dolls, teddies, Victorian linen & lace GENERAL: 6 showrooms. Porcelain, pottery, glass, metalware, collectables, Georgian-Victorian furniture.

Antony Preston Antiques Ltd., The Square, GL54 1AB TEL: 831586 FAX: (071) 581 5076 ASSNS: BADA, CINOA, LAPADA, CADA PARKING: Easy OPEN: Mon-Sat 9.30- 6 MIN: £200 MAX: £30,000 PERIOD: 17th-19th century SPECIALIST: Fine tôle-ware, ormolu, barometers GENERAL: Good English furniture & upholstery OTHER INFO: Fox Inn, Lower Oddington.

PRIESTS
Antiques and Fine Arts

"The Malt House", Digbeth Street,
Stow-on-the-Wold, Gloucestershire
Telephone: 0451 830592

An 18th century fruitwood cupboard settle.

Priests Antiques, The Malt House, Digbeth
Street, GL54 1BN TEL: 830592 FAX: 830592
PARKING: Easy OPEN: Mon-Fri 10-5, Sat
10.30-5 MIN: £250 MAX: £15,000 PERIOD:
17th-19th century SPECIALIST: English oak,
walnut, mahogany & fruitwood furniture.
Queen's Parade Antiques Ltd, The Square,
GL54 1AB TEL: 831586 FAX: (071) 581 5076
ASSNS: BADA, CINOA PARKING: Easy
OPEN: Mon-Sat 9.30-6 MIN: £200 MAX:
£15,000 PERIOD: 18th-19th century SPECIAL-
IST: Papier maché, tôle-ware GENERAL: Period
lighting, needlework, pictures, English & Con-
tinental furniture OTHER INFO: Buckland
Manor Hotel, Lygon Arms (Broadway).
Ruskin Antiques, 5 Talbot Court, GL54 1DP
TEL: 832254 PARKING: Easy OPEN: Mon-Sat
10-5.30, Sun 11-4 MIN: £12 MAX: £1,500
PERIOD: 19th-20th century SPECIALIST: Art
Deco, Art Nouveau, Arts & Crafts GENERAL:
Items from any period OTHER INFO: Some 40
antique shops. Unspoilt Cotswold village square.
St Breock Gallery, Digbeth Street TEL: 830424

FAX: (07) 243 8300 PARKING: Easy OPEN:
Mon-Sat 10-5 MIN: £50 MAX: £2,500 PERIOD:
19th-20th century SPECIALIST: Watercolours.
Samarkand Galleries, 2 Brewery Yard, Sheep
Street, GL54 1AA TEL: 832322 FAX: 832322
ASSNS: LAPADA, CADA PARKING: Own
carpark OPEN: Mon-Sat 10-5.30 MIN: £50
MAX: £10,000 PERIOD: 19th-20th century
SPECIALIST: Antique tribal rugs & trappings
GENERAL: Antique, old & contemporary natu-
ral and dyed eastern rugs, carpets & kilims.
Stow Antiques, The Square, GL54 1AF TEL:
830377 FAX: 870018 ASSNS: LAPADA,
CADA PARKING: Easy OPEN: Mon-Sat Af-
ternoons MIN: £200 MAX: £24,000 PERIOD:
18th-19th century SPECIALIST: Georgian ma-
hogany furniture GENERAL: Fine mahogany,
rosewood, satinwood furniture, gilded mirrors.
Talbot Court Galleries, 7 Talbot Court, GL54
1BQ TEL: 832169 ASSNS: FATG PARKING:
Easy OPEN: Mon-Sat 9.30-5.30, Sun 11-5 MIN:
£10 MAX: £1,000 PERIOD: 17th-19th century
SPECIALIST: Antiquarian engravings & maps
GENERAL: Very large stock English topography, botanical & sporting prints.
Vanbrugh House Antiques, Park Street, GL54
1AQ TEL: 830797 PARKING: Easy OPEN:
Mon-Sat 10-6 MIN: £25 MAX: £10,000
PERIOD: 17th-19th century SPECIALIST:
Music boxes, antique maps GENERAL: Fine
furniture (pre 1830) & associated items, inc.
clocks & barometers OTHER INFO: This is the
antiques "capital" of the beautiful Cotswolds,
some 40 antiques shops & numerous good hotels & restaurants.

CHIPPING NORTON (0608)
Bugle Antiques, 9 Horse Fair, OX7 5AL TEL:
643322 FAX: 643322 ASSNS: LAPADA PARK-
ING: Easy OPEN: Mon-Sat 9-6.30 PERIOD:
18th-19th century SPECIALIST: Sets of Windsor
chairs GENERAL: Dressers, tables & other
country furniture.
Chipping Norton Antiques Centre, Ivy House,
1 Middle Row, Market Square, OX7 5NH TEL:
644212 PARKING: Easy OPEN: Seven days 10-
5.30 MIN: £1 MAX: £5,000 PERIOD: 18th-20th
century GENERAL: Brass, treen, kitchenalia,
clocks, copper, country furniture, oak & pine.
The Emporium, 26 High Street, OX7 5AD TEL:

643103 PARKING: Medium OPEN: Mon-Sat 10-1, 2-5.30 MIN: £1 MAX: £100 PERIOD: 19th-20th century SPECIALIST: Postcards GENERAL: General antiques & collectables.

Georgian House Antiques, 21 West Street TEL: 641369 PARKING: Medium OPEN: Mon-Sat 10-5 PERIOD: 18th-19th century GENERAL: Wide variety of general antiques.

The Old Bakery Antiques, 50 West Street TEL: 643441 PARKING: Medium OPEN: Mon-Sat 9-6 MIN: £5 MAX: £2,000 PERIOD: 18th-19th century GENERAL: Country furniture.

Peter Stroud Antiques, 35 New Street TEL: 642571 FAX: 644529 ASSNS: CADA PARKING: Own carpark OPEN: Mon-Sat 9-5.30 MIN: £50 MAX: £10,000 PERIOD: 18th-19th century GENERAL: Furniture.

Trada, 21 High Street, OX7 5AD TEL: 644325 PARKING: Easy OPEN: Mon-Wed, Fri-Sat 9-5.30 MIN: £3 MAX: £500 PERIOD: 17th-18th century maps otherwise 18th-19th century SPECIALIST: Maps of English counties GENERAL: Natural history, childrens illustrations, cartoons, English topography. All steel/copper or stone engravings OTHER INFO: Small old theatre known throughout for a friendly lively performance.

BANBURY (0295)

Judy Vedmore - Furniture & Antiques, 42 Parson's Street, OX16 8NA TEL: 269626 PARKING: Medium OPEN: Tues-Sat 10-5 MIN: £2 MAX: £4,000 PERIOD: 18th-20th century GENERAL: Silver, unusual books, general antiques & collectables OTHER INFO: Right item at right price, right present, right investment. Early & late swim at Leisure Centre.

DEDDINGTON (0869)

Deddington Antiques Centre, Market Place, OX5 0TT TEL: 38968 PARKING: Easy OPEN: Mon-Sat 10-5 MIN: £1 MAX: £1,000 PERIOD: 19th-20th century GENERAL: Furniture & general antiques.

CLIFTON (0869)

Castle Antiques Ltd, Manor Farm, OX15 0PA TEL: 38688 ASSNS: LAPADA PARKING: Own carpark OPEN: Mon-Sat 10-5 MIN: £1 MAX: £4,500 PERIOD: 18th-20th century GENERAL: Furniture, metalware, silver, china & glass. Large showroom, 6 miles from exit 10 M40.

Central England

Aston Hall. By courtesy of Birmingham City Council

This tour moves from rural Shropshire to Birmingham, England's second largest city, to the Welsh border. We can see reminders of the Industrial Revolution in the towns and cities of the West Midlands and Staffordshire and then see, in Shropshire, the sites of border wars between the English and the Welsh.

Our first stop is at Solihull, on the outskirts of Birmingham, which has the Tudor timber framed houses of Solihull Hall and Old Berry Hall. Now on to Birmingham, second only in size to London: to get round this city successfully it is essential to get a detailed street map and details of things to see and do from the Tourist Information Centre.

There are many relics of Birmingham's medieval past. Aston Hall, two and a half miles from the city centre, is a fine house built between 1615 and 1635 with splendid Jacobean plaster work and many rooms furnished in period style. It also has good collections of tapestries, paintings, furniture, glass and ceramics. Three miles from the city centre stands Blakesley Hall, a timber framed yeoman's cottage from the late 16th century furnished in the style of the period. In Edgbaston, two miles west of the city centre, is what has been described as "Birmingham's most eccentric building", Perrott's Folly built in 1758, a 96 foot high tower with seven floors.

The city has a number of fascinating museums. The largest is the Birmingham Museum and Art Gallery in Chamberlain Square with several large departments ranging from Fine Art to Natural History. For lovers of cars there is Autoworld at the Patrick Collection in Lifford Lane and the Museum of Science and Industry, Newhall Street, also has transport exhibits as well as other industrial and scientific items.

We continue on to Sutton Coldfield with its 16th century church and grammar school before arriving in the industrial town of Walsall. The birthplace of Jerome K. Jerome, author of *Three Men in a Boat*, this town still has traces of its past be-

Chamberlain Square, Birmingham
By courtesy of Birmingham City Council

fore the Industrial Revolution. There are a few remnants of the 14th century castle demolished in 1646 and involved in the Civil War. The Museum and Art Gallery in Lichfield Street also has a local history gallery. The Walsall Leather Centre Museum, housed in a Victorian factory in Wisemore, gives a fascinating glimpse of the past with displays showing leather production from tanning to finishing. There are also demonstrations in authentic period workshops.

Taking the A461 via Pelsall and Whittington, the route arrives in Lichfield, with its famous cathedral which developed around the tomb of St. Chad. In the 12th century work was started on the cathedral although little of that is now in evidence. The present building dates from the 14th and 15th centuries and is unique in having three spires. Although marked by pollution, it is a delightful building, with much stone carving and decoration on the outside. The cathedral has seen some violence. During the Civil War the cathedral and close formed a Royalist enclave and consequently came under siege in 1643 and 1646. In the attacks the central spire was shot down, medieval windows broken, tombs were smashed, lead was stripped off the roof and books and records were burnt. However, one precious item was saved: a copy of the Gospels made by the monks of Lindisfarne in 730AD and now kept in the Chapter House. Much of the damage was repaired in the reign of Charles II and there is a statue of him on the West Front. More

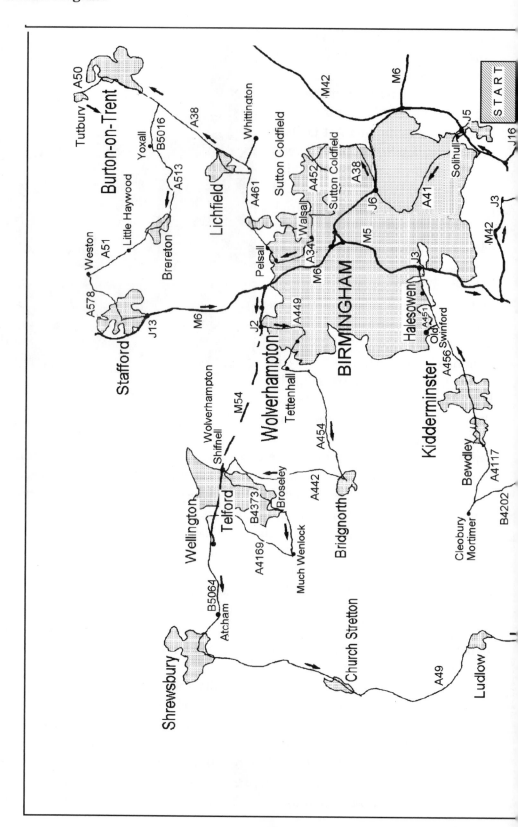

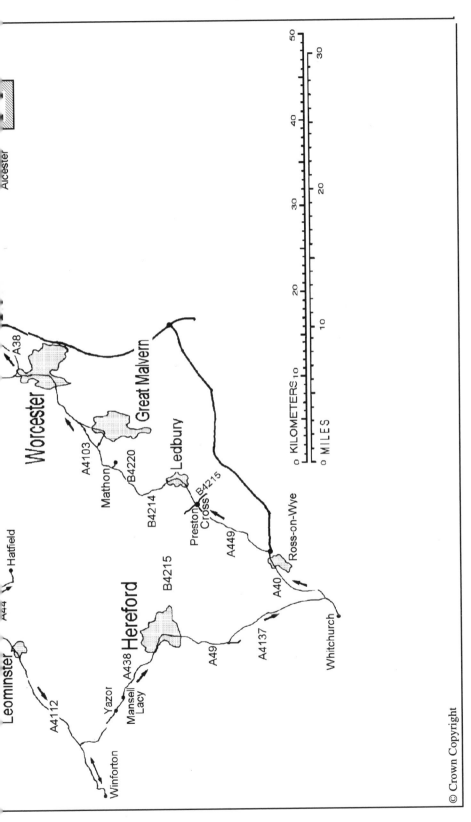

© Crown Copyright

309

restoration work was carried out from 1790 through to Victorian times because the sandstone, from which the cathedral was built, was crumbling badly and at one time it appeared that the nave might collapse.

The town is a charming place with many 18th century houses standing in old narrow streets. It was the birthplace of Samuel Johnson and David Garrick amongst others and Johnson's parents are buried here. There is also the Samuel Johnson Birthplace Museum in Breadmarket Street. Another museum is the Lichfield Heritage Exhibition, Treasury and Munument Room in the Market Square covering the city's history as well as displaying regimental plate, mace, state sword, Ashmole Cup, etc.

We go next to the beer-making town of Burton-on-Trent, then to Tutbury whose castle has strong royal associations. It once belonged to John of Gaunt and later Mary, Queen of Scots was imprisoned here for a while. Now only ruins remain. Our next calls are on the villages of Yoxall, Brereton, Little Haywood and Weston before reaching Stafford. Although Stafford retains much of its original medieval street layout, it has lost many of its black and white, half-timbered houses. Of those that survive, High House is perhaps the most interesting. It is the largest timber-framed house in England and was built in 1595. It is said that Charles I and Prince Rupert sheltered in this house in 1642. It has collections of furniture, costume, paintings, ceramics and rare 18th and 19th century wallpapers.

Stafford was the home and birthplace of Izaak Walton, author of *The Compleat Angler*. Born in 1593 and baptised in the local church, his home at Shallowfield is now a memorial to his work and life. The fine neo-classical Shugborough Hall stands six miles east of the town on the A513. Completed in 1693 and the seat of the Earls of Lichfield, the hall is set in beautiful gardens and parkland containing a working rare breeds farm.

The route now follows the M6 and then the M54 motorways to reach the industrial town of Wolverhampton. Here Bantock House in Bradmore is famous for its collection of English painted enamels and Jappaned ware from the West Midlands. Painted enamels are also the subject of the Bilsom Museum and Art Gallery in Mount Pleasant although the museum includes displays on the social and industrial history of the area. Wightwick Manor, three miles west of the town on the A454, is a 19th century house whose interior shows the strong influence of William Morris and the Pre-Raphaelites.

Moving onwards via Tettenhall we now come to the quiet market town of Bridgnorth in Shropshire. Divided in half by the River Severn, this town was once a busy river port and also a producer of iron and carpets. Features of note include a fine 16th century half timbered house, elegant Georgian houses in East Castle Street, several timber framed buildings including the Swan Inn, and the last remnant of a castle and a tower which leans at an angle three times greater than the Leaning Tower of Pisa. The town stands on a sandstone bluff and it has the Cliff Railway built in 1892 and still working. It now uses electricity but originally the cars were powered by running water in and out of tanks beneath them. The feat of engineering can only be appreciated when it is realised that the gradient on the cliff is two in three, making it the steepest railway in England.

Following the A442, the tour arrives in Shifnal. The future King Charles II hid here in Boscobel House after the battle of Worcester in 1651. In the 19th century the house was restored and furnished in the style of the mid 17th century.

The route now enters the new town of Telford and then Broseley before reaching Much Wenlock which is set on the extreme north eastern side of Wenlock Edge. This old market town contains picturesque black and white buildings in narrow streets. The town was sacked by the Danes and then rebuilt by Lady Godiva's husband, Leofric. Raynald's Mansion from 1682 and the timbered guildhall resting on wooden pillars are of particular interest.

Tudor House, Shrewsbury

Wellington is our next stop. This now forms part of Telford but still has half timbered houses standing in narrow streets. Close by is the Wrekin, a hill rising sharply to 1335 feet and giving dramatic views over the surrounding countryside. Excavations have revealed that this was the site of a major Iron Age fort, possbily the base for the Cornovii tribe.

From Wellington we proceed westward along the A5 via the village of Atcham which is sited on a river of the same name. This pleasant village has a seven arch bridge, built in 1768, spanning the river. Its Norman church was built with Roman stones taken from Wroxeter and contains roof timbers that are at least 500 years old.

Next we reach Shrewsbury on the River Severn. Shrewsbury Castle stands on a bend of the River Severn giving it a natural moat. The site of a Saxon fort, it was built in the 11th century by Roger de Montgomery and partly rebuilt in the 13th century. In the Middle Ages the castle was used as a base for attacking the Welsh and saw action again during the Civil War as a Royalist stronghold but was captured by Parliamentary forces in 1644. After Charles II came to the throne it passed into private hands and was eventually remodelled by Thomas Telford in the 18th century.

The town itself has many buildings of interest. Its centre is a jumble of narrow, crooked streets lined with many timbered and half timbered shops and houses including the house in Wyle Cop where Henry Vll stayed prior to the Battle of Bosworth in 1485. A more recent building is the town's fine railway station built in Tudor style. There are several good museums. The Georgian Clive House in College Hill has an outstanding collection of Shropshire porcelain and art and the

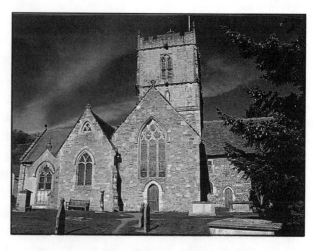

St Laurence's Church, Church Stretton

Radbrook Culinary Museum in Radbrook Road has a unique exhibition of domestic and household items. There is also the Coleham Pumping Station at Old Coleham with a preserved beam engine and Rowley's House Museum, in a 17th century mansion in Barker Street, displays a range of exhibits including archaeology, geology, costume and local history.

The route now turns south to the market town of Church Stretton, given its charter by King John in 1214. An unexpected feature of St Laurence's Church is the female fertility figure, a Sheila-na-gig, built into the wall above the disused North Door. Continuing on, we arrive at our next stop, Ludlow, most famous for its 11th century castle. This was one of the thirtytwo castles built in the Welsh Marches. Situated on a cliff overlooking the Rivers Teme and Corve, the castle has seen much action over the centuries. It is also the place where Richard III's nephews, the two princes, lived before they were moved to the Tower of London and to their deaths.

The Feathers Hotel, Ludlow

The town has many things to offer the visitor including the 18th century Hosyer's almshouses, the 14th century grammar school, the 15th century Guildhall and the butter cross from 1744. Also of note is St Laurence's

Church, a "wool" church, so called because it was built from the prosperity brought by wool in the Middle Ages. It has some particularly fine stained glass windows.

Via the village of Hatfield, the route now reaches Leominster (pronounced Lemster), another town which prospered through the medieval wool trade. The town contains many fine black and white houses including Grange Court, a supreme example of this type of architecture. There is also the fine 12th century priory church of St Peter and St Paul built on the site of a 9th century nunnery. Unfortunately a fire at the end of the 17th century largely destroyed the building and it was only in the 19th century that it was fully restored.

From Leominster the route detours to the small village of Winforton before turning back, via Yazor and Mansell Lacy, to Hereford, once the capital of West Mercia. Standing on the River Wye, this city has been the seat of the bishop since the 7th century. The Saxon church was replaced by the present cathedral in the 11th century but it has had many later alterations and additions. It has the largest chained library in the world with almost 1450 books including a copy of the Anglo-Saxon Chronicle dating from the 9th century.

The town has several interesting museums including Hereford City Museum and Art Gallery in Broad Street, the Cider Museum and King Offa Cider Brandy Distillery in Pomona Place, the Jacobean period museum of The Old House in High Town and the Churchill Gardens Museum in Venn's Lane with an extensive collection of costume and also fine furniture and watercolours.

The tour proceeds to its most southerly point, the town of Ross-on-Wye, an excellent base for exploring the beautiful Forest of Dean and the Wye Valley. This is an historic town going back at least to Saxon times. It has several buildings of note including the 17th century Market Hall and John Kyrle's house opposite. John Kyrle was responsible for giving Ross a public water supply and he laid out the public gardens in 1693.

After passing through the village of Preston Court, we reach Ledbury, birthplace of Poet Laureate, John Masefield, in 1878. Again we see the black and white houses that are such a feature of this area. Great Malvern, next on the tour, is one of several towns with Malvern in the name. It is dominated by the Worcestershire Beacon which rises to 1395 feet. The spring that brought prosperity to the town as a spa starts on its slopes and also provides the world famous Malvern Water. The Beacon is designated as an area of outstanding natural beauty. The town is also well-known for its public school, Malvern College.

Worcester, on the River Severn, is our next stop and is another cathedral city. Standing at a natural ford on the river, the city has been of strategic importance and was the site of a Norman castle of which little remains. It was the scene of battles in the war between King Stephen and the Empress Matilda in the 12th century and was also subjected to raids by the Danes sweeping up the river.

The cathedral was built of the local sandstone in the 11th and 12th centuries

Worcester

with some later additions. However, the softness of the stone has meant that it has had to undergo considerable restoration and rebuilding in the mid 19th century and so little remains of the original stone carvings. The cathedral contains the tomb and a Purbeck marble effigy of King John dating from 1232, the earliest royal effigy in the country.

One of the many notable buildings in the city is The Greyfriars, a fine 15th century town house built by a wealthy local brewer. Another building of considerable interest is the magnificent Guildhall. During the Civil War Worcester was solidly Royalist and the Guildhall illustrates this with statues of Charles I and Charles II on the facade together with a model of Oliver Cromwell's head nailed by the ears above a doorway. The city's museums include the Dyson Perrins Museum of Worcester Porcelain in Severn Street, the 15th century timber framed Commandery in Sidbury and The Elgar Birthplace in Crown East Lane.

The tour now moves on to the spa town of Droitwich before continuing to Ombersley and Cleobury Mortimer. We now reach the Severn side town of Bewdley where there are several fine 18th century buildings. From there the tour continues to Kidderminster and then Alcester (pronounced Olster) in Warwickshire. Our final stop is Henley-in-Arden, lying in the ancient Forest of Arden although little remains of the forest today. The town has several buildings dating from the 15th century onwards including the timbered Guildhall from 1448.

ANTIQUE DEALERS
SOLIHULL (021)

Renaissance Antiques, 18 Marshall Lake Road, Shirley, B90 4PL TEL: 745 5140 PARKING: Medium OPEN: Mon-Sat 9-5 PERIOD: 18th-20th century GENERAL: Wide range. Restoration & re-upholstering.

SUTTON COLDFIELD (021)

M. Allen Watchmaker, 76a Walsall Road, Four Oaks, B74 4QY TEL: 308 6117 PARKING: Easy OPEN: Mon-Sat 9-5.30 MIN: £75 MAX: £4,000 PERIOD: 18th-20th century SPECIALIST: Vintage gold wristwatches GENERAL: Constantly changing stock of clocks, watches from U.S., Germany, France. Fascinating showroom. All repairs.

Thomas Coulborn & Sons, Vesey Manor, 64 Birmingham Road, B72 1QP TEL: 354 3974/3139 FAX: 354 4614 ASSNS: BADA PARKING: Own carpark OPEN: Mon-Sat 9.15-1, 2-5.30 MIN: £500+ PERIOD: 18th-19th century SPECIALIST: English & French furniture, giltwood mirrors. Finest furniture outside London OTHER INFO: Close to NEC, International Convention Centre, Belfrey International Golf Centre & hotel, New Hall Hotel.

Driffold Gallery, The Smithy, 78 Birmingham Road TEL: 355 5433 PARKING: Own carpark OPEN: Mon-Sat 10-5.30 MIN: £100 MAX: £10,000 PERIOD: 19th-20th century GENERAL: Oil paintings & watercolours + original illustrations OTHER INFO: Part of our premises date back to 14th century. Henry VIII is believed to have visited The Smithy whilst hunting in park.

Osbornes Antiques, 91 Chester Road, New Oscott, B73 5BA TEL: 355 6667 FAX: 355 0666 PARKING: Easy OPEN: Mon 9-1, 2-4, Tues-Fri 9-1, 2-5, Sat 9.15-12.15 MIN: £95+ MAX: £5,500 SPECIALIST: Barometers, clocks, barographs. OTHER INFO: Scientific glass blowers (thermometers & tubes), & restorers on premises.

Robert & Mary Taylor, Windy Ridge, Worcester Lane, Four Oaks, B75 5QS TEL: 308 4209 FAX: 323 3473 PARKING: Own carpark OPEN: By appt MIN: £5 PERIOD: 20th century SPECIALIST: Corgi & Dinky Toys GENERAL: All collectable toys & diecast models.

BIRMINGHAM (021)

Always Antiques, 285 Vicarage Road, Kings Heath, B14 7NE. TEL: 444 8701 PARKING: Easy OPEN: Thurs-Sat 9.30-6 MIN: £10 MAX: £1,000 PERIOD:

19th-20th century SPECIALIST: Ceramics GENERAL: 1930's furniture OTHER INFO: Weekly markets. 3 miles city centre, ICC centre.

Ashleigh House Antiques, 5 Westbourne Road, Edgbaston, B15 3TH TEL: 454 6283 FAX: 454 6283 PARKING: Own carpark OPEN: By appt MIN: £200 MAX: £10,000 PERIOD: 18th-19th century SPECIALIST: Regency furniture, French clocks, paintings GENERAL: Antique furniture, clocks, Oriental & Continental works of art, ivories, bronzes OTHER INFO: We are large listed mansion, accommodation overnight for bona fide buyers by prior appt.

Barnt Green Antiques, 93 Hewell Road, Barnt Green, B45 8NL TEL: 445 4942 ASSNS: BAFRA PARKING: Easy OPEN: Mon-Fri 9-5.30, Sat 9-1 MIN: £50 MAX: £ 50,000+ PERIOD: 18th-19th century SPECIALIST: Furniture, some 17th century stock OTHER INFO: Close to Lickey Hills.

Birmingham Bookshop, 567 Bristol Road, B29 6AF TEL: 472 8556 PARKING: Easy OPEN: Tues-Sat 11-4 PERIOD: 20th century SPECIALIST: Books & prints.

Garratt Antiques Ltd, 35 Stephenson Street, B2 4BH TEL: 643 9507 FAX: (0283) 791725 ASSNS: GMC, BJA, NAG PARKING: Medium OPEN: 10-5 MIN: £2 MAX: £10,000+ PERIOD: 19th-20th century SPECIALIST: Jewellery, Birmingham silver, British paintings, crystal GENERAL: General antiques OTHER INFO: Come and join us for tea or coffee. Enjoy browsing in our friendly, helpful little antique shop.

The Graves Gallery, (estd 1752), 3 The Spencers, Augusta Street, Hockley TEL: 212 1635 ASSNS: FATG PARKING: Own carpark OPEN: 10.30-4.30 MIN: £65 MAX: £4,000 PERIOD: 19th-20th century SPECIALIST: Silverplate, studio pottery GENERAL: Oils & watercolours OTHER INFO: Restoration, framing, valuations. In heart of jewellery quarter with the best restaurants.

Bob Harris & Sons, 2071 Coventry Road, Sheldon, B26 3DY TEL: 743 2259 FAX: 743 2259 ASSNS: LAPADA PARKING: Own carpark OPEN: 9-6 MIN: £5 MAX: £ 8,500 PERIOD: 18th-20th century SPECIALIST: Furniture, Staffordshire figures, GENERAL: Metalware, shipping goods OTHER INFO: 3 miles from NEC.

Holliday Wharf Antique Centre, 164-166 Holliday Street TEL: 643 9900 ASSNS: LAPADA PARKING: Own carpark OPEN: 9-5.30 MIN: £10 MAX: £50,000 PERIOD: 18th-20th century SPECIALIST: Early oak & metalware, Georgian mahogany GENERAL: Decorative items, walnut, inlaid furniture, good shipping stock, porcelain, silver, paintings OTHER INFO: Rear of Hyatt Hotel.

John Hubbard Antiques, 224-226 Court Oak Road, Harbourne, B32 2EG TEL: 426 1694 FAX: 428 1214 ASSNS: LAPADA PARKING: Own carpark OPEN: Mon-Sat 9-6 MIN: £20 MAX: £15,000 PERIOD: 18th-19th century SPECIALIST: Furniture GENERAL: Paintings, watercolours, clocks, lighting & decorative items OTHER INFO: 2 mins from world famous award-winning Egon Ronay-recommended Jonathan restaurant & hotel, all furnished with antiques.

Huddington International Trade Warehouse, 73 Western Road, Hockley, B18 7QD TEL: 523 8862 FAX: 554 1741 PARKING: Medium OPEN: 9-4.30 MIN: £5 PERIOD: 17th-20th century SPECIALIST: Furniture & mahogany replica furniture OTHER INFO: On A4157 next to Dudley Road Hospital.

Kestrel House, 72 Gravelly Hill, North Erdington, B23 6BB TEL: 373 2375 ASSNS: ATD, FIBD PARKING: Own carpark OPEN: Mon-Sat 10-7 MIN: £5 MAX: £500 PERIOD: 19th-20th century SPECIALIST: Oils & watercolours GENERAL: Mainly antiques & general goods. Regular auction.

March Medals, 113 Gravely Hill North, B23 6BJ TEL: 384 4901 PARKING: Own carpark OPEN: 10-5 MIN: £5 MAX: £5,000 PERIOD: 19th-20th century SPECIALIST: Orders, decorations & medals GENERAL: Militaria.

Moseley Pianos, Unit L, 68 Wyreley Road, Witton, B6 7BN TEL: 327 2701, (0831) 560518 PARKING: Easy OPEN: Mon-Thurs 10-2 or anytime by appt MIN: £100 MAX: £5,000 PERIOD: 19th-20th century SPECIALIST: Secondhand upright & grand pianos some with ornate cabinets. Specialising in the export trade OTHER INFO: Facilities for loading & packing containers. Stock suitable for immediate retail or for dealer restorer.

Piccadilly Jewellers, 10 Piccadilly Arcade, New Street, B2 4HD TEL: 643 5791 FAX: 631 2167 ASSNS: NAG PARKING: Medium OPEN: Mon-Sat 9.30-5 MIN: £15 MAX: £10,000 PERIOD: 19th-20th century SPECIALIST: Antique jewellery & silverware.

Treasure Chest Antique & Bric-a-Brac Centre, 1407 Pershore Road, Stirchley, B30 2JR TEL: 459 4587 FAX: 458 3705 PARKING: Own carpark OPEN: Mon-Sat 9-5.45, Sun 10-5 PERIOD: 20th century GENERAL: Antiques & bric-a-brac.
Warley Antique Centre, 146 Pottery Road, Oldbury, B68 9HD TEL: 434 3813 PARKING: Easy OPEN: Mon-Sat 9-6, Sun 10-3 PERIOD: 19th-20th century SPECIALIST: Ruskin pottery, antique dolls GENERAL: 50 dealers showing radios, china, glass, furniture, pottery, clocks, pictures OTHER INFO: Excellent restaurant. Close to M5 jct 3.
WALSALL 0922)
Cobwebs Antiques, 639 Bloxwich Road, Leamore TEL: 493670 PARKING: Easy OPEN: Easy MIN: £5 MAX: £400 PERIOD: 19th-20th century GENERAL: General antiques OTHER INFO: Coffee & gossip always at the ready.
Nicholls Jewellers, 57 George Street TEL: 641081 PARKING: Easy OPEN: Mon-Sat 9-5 PERIOD: 20th century SPECIALIST: Antique rings, pendants etc GENERAL: New & secondhand jewellery.
Past and Present, 66 George Street, WS1 1RS TEL: 611151 PARKING: Easy OPEN: Mon-Sat 9.30-5.30 MIN: £4 MAX: £3,000 PERIOD: 18th & 20th century SPECIALIST: General antiques, a veritable pot pourri, all reasonably priced.
Walsall Antiques Centre, 7a The Digbeth Arcade, WS1 1RE TEL: 725163/5 PARKING: Easy OPEN: Mon-Sat 10-6 MIN: £2 MAX: £5,000 PERIOD: 18th-20th century SPECIALIST: Royal, military & political commerative pottery & porcelain GENERAL: General antiques OTHER INFO: Close to NEC, National Convention Centre.
PELSALL (0543)
L.P. Furniture (Midlands) Ltd, Lime Lane Industrial Estate, Lime Lane, WS3 5AP TEL: 370256, (0860) 249097 FAX: 370256 PARKING: Own carpark OPEN: 9-5 MIN: £50 MAX: £5,000 PERIOD: 19th-20th century SPECIALIST: Major importer of French shipping & country GENERAL: English Art Deco, painted furniture, walnut, pine.
WHITTINGTON (0543)
Milestone Antiques, 5 Main Street, WS14 9JU TEL: 432248 PARKING: Easy OPEN: Thur, Fri, Sat 10-6, Sun 10-3 MIN: £10 MAX: £5000 PERIOD: 18th & 19th century SPECIALIST: Coalport GENERAL: English furniture and decorative items, no reproduction.

LICHFIELD (0543)
Mike Abrahams Books, Cranmere Court, Walsall Road, WS13 6RF TEL: 256200 ASSNS: PBFA PARKING: Easy OPEN: Seven days 10-6 by appt private premises. MIN: £1 MAX: £1,000 PERIOD: 19th-20th century SPECIALIST: Books: antiquarian, childrens, topographical, transport, collecting, military, illustrated, magic, gypsies, witchcraft OTHER INFO: Stock of 20,000. Historic cathedral city, birthplace of Samuel Johnson & David Garrick. Plenty of restaurants & accommodation.
The Antique Shop, 31 Tamworth Street. WS13 6JP TEL:268324 PARKING: Easy OPEN: Mon-Sat 9.30-5.30, occasionally closed 1.30-2.30 MIN: £3 MAX: £1,000 PERIOD: 19th century GENERAL: General antiques OTHER INFO: Heritage Exhibition. Hotels: The George, Little Barrow, Swinfen Hall. Thrales restaurant.
Cordelia & Perdy's Antique Junk Shop, 53 Tamworth Street, WS13 6JW TEL: 263223 PARKING: Medium OPEN: Mon-Sat 10-4 MIN: £1 MAX: £350 PERIOD: 19th & 20th century GENERAL: Wide range, buying only from house clearances OTHER INFO: Excellent B&Bs, good restaurants & pubs in the street.
Images at the Staffs Bookshop, 4-6 Dam Street, WS13 6AA TEL: 264093 PARKING: Easy OPEN: Mon-Sat 9.30-5.30 MIN: £5 PERIOD: 17th-20th century SPECIALIST: Childhood, objects and books. Antiquarian books of all kinds. Printed ephemera.
The Tudor of Lichfield Antique Centre, Bore Street, WS13 6LL TEL: 263951 PARKING: Difficult OPEN: Mon-Sat 10-5 MIN: £1 MAX: £1000 PERIOD: 17th-19th century GENERAL: General antiques OTHER INFO: The Antiques Centre is situated above an old-established restaurant in a black and white timbered building.
BURTON-ON-TRENT (0283)
Derby Street Antique Emporium, 138 Derby Street, DE14 2LF TEL: 515202 PARKING: Own carpark OPEN: Mon-Sat 9.30-5.30 MIN: £5 MAX: £5000 PERIOD: 19th century GENERAL: Good cross section OTHER INFO: Also monthly auction last Thursday of every month.
C. & R. Scattergood, 132 Branston Road, DE14 3DQ TEL: 46695 PARKING: Own carpark OPEN: Mon-Sat 9-6 MIN: £100 MAX: £10,000 PERIOD: 17th-20th century SPECIALIST:

Wemyss pottery GENERAL: English & Continental ceramics & glass.

TUTBURY (0283)

Town & Country Antiques, 40 Monk Street, DE13 9NA TEL: 520556 PARKING: Easy OPEN: 7 days a week 10-5.30 MIN: £1 MAX: £1,000 PERIOD: 19th century GENERAL: Pine furniture, linen & lace, porcelain.

Tutbury Mill Antiques, 6 Lower High Street, DE13 9LU TEL: 815999 PARKING: Own carpark OPEN: 9-5 MIN: £1 MAX: £3500 PERIOD: 18th-20th century SPECIALIST: Country furniture, Victoriana GENERAL: Shipping, smalls OTHER INFO: Large converted mill with 12 other country shops inc restaurant and B&B. Off High Street with 15th century inn and 2 glassworks open to public and 12th century castle.

YOXALL (0543)

Armson's of Yoxall Antiques, The Hollies, DE13 8NH TEL: 472352 ASSNS: LAPADA PARKING: Own carpark OPEN: Mon-Fri 9-5 MIN: £20 MAX: £5,000 PERIOD: 17th-19th century SPECIALIST: Practical antique furniture GENERAL: Furniture OTHER INFO: Many useful trade calls in area, also plenty of hotels. 30 mins from Birmingham Airport, NEC, M1, M6 & M42.

H.W. Heron & Son Ltd, 1 King Street, DE13 8NF TEL: 472266 ASSNS: LAPADA PARKING: Mon-Fri 9-6 OPEN: Mon-Fri 9-6, Sat 10.30-5.30, Sun 2-6 MIN: £20 MAX: £5000 PERIOD: 18th & 19th century SPECIALIST: Early 19th century porcelain GENERAL: English ceramics and small items.

BRERETON (0889)

Rugeley Antique Centre, 161-163 Main Road, WS15 1DX TEL: 577166 PARKING: Own carpark OPEN: Mon-Sat 9-5 MIN: £1 MAX: No limit PERIOD: 19th & 20th century GENERAL: 26 dealers with varying stock of furniture and smalls OTHER INFO: Also B&B in self-contained unit.

LITTLE HAYWOOD (0889)

Jalna Antiques, Jalna Coley Lane, ST18 0UP TEL: 881381 PARKING: Own carpark OPEN: Resident on premises MIN: £20 MAX: £3,000 PERIOD: 18th-19th century SPECIALIST: Chairs & chaise longues GENERAL: Furniture.

WESTON-UPON-TRENT (0889)

Weston Antique Gallery, Boat Lane, ST18 0HV TEL: 270450 PARKING: Own OPEN: Wed-Sat 10-5.30 MIN: £10 MAX: £750 PERIOD: 17th-early

20th century century SPECIALIST: Antique maps, prints of Staffordshire GENERAL: General antiques OTHER INFO: We are located between Wedgwood Visitor Centre & Shugborough Hall.

STAFFORD (0785)

Windmill Antiques, 9 Castle Hill, Broadeye TEL: 228505 PARKING: Easy OPEN: Mon-Sat 10-5 MIN: £1 MAX: £2000 PERIOD: 18th-20th century SPECIALIST: Tools, Staffordshire figures, glass GENERAL: Very wide range OTHER INFO: The shop is situated next to an ancient windmill currently being restored.

WOLVERHAMPTON (0902)

Martin Quick Antiques Ltd, 323 Tettenhall Road, WV6 0JZ TEL: 754703 FAX: 756889 ASSNS: LAPADA PARKING: Easy OPEN: Mon-Fri 9-5.30, Sat 9-4 MIN: £10 MAX: £5,000 PERIOD: 18th-20th century SPECIALIST: Large stock of antique beds GENERAL: Furniture from all periods OTHER INFO: Large premises with large turnover, wholesale & retail. Close to M5, M6 & M54.

Wakeman & Taylor Antiques, 140b Tettenhall Road, WV6 0BQ TEL: 751166 PARKING: FAX: 746502 ASSNS: LAPADA OPEN: Mon-Fri 8.30-5.30 & by appt MIN: £50 MAX: £5,000+ PERIOD: 18th-19th century SPECIALIST: Italian, Spanish, French & German good quality 19th century walnut, marquetry inlaid OTHER INFO: 20 years established trade call.

BRIDGNORTH (0746)

English Heritage of Bridgnorth, 2 Whitburn Street, WV16 4QN TEL: 762097 PARKING: Medium OPEN: Mon-Sat 9.30-5 MIN: £1 MAX: £1,500 PERIOD: 19th-20th century SPECIALIST: Jewellery, militaria GENERAL: General antiques OTHER INFO: Near Ironbridge Gorge Museum, numerous pubs, Severn Valley Railway.

Micawber Antiques, 64 St Mary's Street TEL: 763254 PARKING: Easy OPEN: 10-5 MIN: £5 MAX: £1,000 PERIOD: 19th century SPECIALIST: Early 19th century English porcelain GENERAL: General antiques OTHER INFO: Situated in mainly 16th century-timbered St Mary's Street. Best B&B at delightful Mary Champion's.

Parmenter Antiques, 5 Central Court, High Street. WV16 4DQ TEL: 765599 FAX: 767480 PARKING: Easy OPEN: 10-5 MIN: £5 MAX: £2,000 PERIOD: 17th-20th century SPECIALIST: Furniture GENERAL: Objects, pictures, jewellery

OTHER INFO: Town Hall is medieval barn on piers straddling High Street. The remaining stump of our castle leans at alarming angle (worse than Leaning Tower of Pisa), England's only funicular railway.

SHIFNAL (0902)

Doveridge House of Neachley, Neach Hill, Long Lane, TF11 8PJ TEL: 373131-2 ASSNS: BADA, CINOA, LAPADA PARKING: Own carpark OPEN: Seven days 9-5 MIN: £30 MAX: £15,000 PERIOD: 17th-19th century SPECIALIST: Furniture GENERAL: General antiques.

TELFORD (0952)

Granny's Attic, 33 Market Street, Oakengates TEL: 610330 PARKING: Medium OPEN: 10-5 not Thurs PERIOD: 17th-20th century GENERAL: Exciting wide range, bit of everything.

BROSELEY (0952)

Gallery 6, 6 Church Street, TF12 5DG TEL: 882860 PARKING: Own carpark OPEN: 11-6 (resident) MIN: £100 MAX: £2,000 SPECIALIST: 20th century oils, watercolours, etchings GENERAL: 19th-20th century same inc contemporary OTHER INFO: Broseley has many houses associated with the Industrial Revolution, Ironbridge and its earliest iron bridge in the world.

MUCH WENLOCK (0952)

Cruck House Antiques, 23 Barrow Street, TF13 6EN TEL: 727165 PARKING: Easy OPEN: 10-5 MIN: £2 MAX: £1,000 PERIOD: 18th-20th century SPECIALIST: Silver, watercolours GENERAL: Small furniture, pictures, small items.

Wenlock Fine Art, 3 The Square, TF13 6LX TEL: 728232 PARKING: Easy OPEN: 10-5 MIN: £100 MAX: £10,000 SPECIALIST: Some 19th but mainly 20th century British paintings OTHER INFO: Ceramics & sculpture.

WELLINGTON (0952)

Bernie Pugh Antiques, 120 High Street, TF1 1JU TEL: 256184 Mobile: 0860 219944 PARKING: Medium OPEN: Mon, Tues Thurs-Sat 10-12, 1-5.30, Weds 10-12 PERIOD: 19th-20th, some 18th century SPECIALIST: We try to deal in the unusual OTHER INFO: Good B&B 5 mins, Birtley house, Holyhead Rd.

ATCHAM (0952)

Mytton Antiques, 2-3 Norton Cottages, Norton Crossroads, SY4 4UM TEL: 86229 FAX: 461154 PARKING: Own carpark OPEN: Mon-Sat 10-5, Sun 2-5 MIN: £5 MAX: £5,000 PERIOD: 18th-19th century SPECIALIST: Country oak furniture, longcase clocks GENERAL: Mahogany, oak 1700-1900, general antiques.

SHREWSBURY (0743)

Candle Lane Books, 28-31 Princess Street, SY1 1LW TEL: 365301 PARKING: Medium OPEN: Mon-Sat 9.30-5 PERIOD: 19th-20th century SPECIALIST: Large stock of antiquarian & secondhand books.

Hutton Antiques, 18 Princess Street, SY1 1LP TEL: 245810 PARKING: Easy OPEN: 9.30-5 MIN: £5 MAX: £1,500 PERIOD: 19th-20th century SPECIALIST: Silver & porcelain GENERAL: General antiques OTHER INFO: Clive House Museum (Coalport porcelain), Military Museum.

F.C. Manser & Son Ltd, 53-54 Wyle Cop, SY1 1XJ TEL: 351120 FAX: 271047 ASSNS: LAPADA PARKING: Own carpark OPEN: 9-5 MIN: £5 MAX: £12,000 PERIOD: 18th-20th century GENERAL: General antiques OTHER INFO: Right in medieval town centre. Hotels: Lion, Prince Rupert, Albrighton. Country Friends restaurant.

Raleigh Antiques, 23 Bellevue Road, SY5 7LN TEL: 359552 ASSNS: Founder Guild of Antique Dealers & Restorers PARKING: Medium OPEN: Mon-Sat 9.30-5 MIN: £2 MAX: £10,000 PERIOD: 18th-20th century GENERAL: General antiques OTHER INFO: Excellent hotels: The Prince Rupert (need to book) & The Lion.

Shrewsbury Antique Market, Frankwell Quay Warehouse, SY3 8LG TEL: 350916 PARKING: Easy OPEN: Mon-Sat 9.30-5 MIN: £1 MAX: £1,000 PERIOD: 19th-20th century GENERAL: General antiques.

Tiffany Antiques, Unit 1, Princess Antique Centre, 14a The Square TEL: 247704, home (0270) 257425 PARKING: Medium OPEN: 9.30-5.30 MIN: £5 MAX: £500 PERIOD: 19th-20th century SPECIALIST: Glass GENERAL: Collectables.

Wyle Cop Antiques, The Old School (off Wyle Cop), SY1 1UT TEL: 231180 PARKING: Medium OPEN: Mon-Sat 9.30-5.30 PERIOD: 19th-20th century GENERAL: Mainly furniture.

CHURCH STRETTON (0694)

Antiques On The Square, 2 Sandford Court, Sandford Avenue, SY6 6DA TEL: 724111, 723072, Mobile (0831) 336052 ASSNS: Art Deco Dealers Assn PARKING: Own carpark OPEN: Mon-Tues, Thurs-Sat 9.30-5, Wed 9-1 MIN: £10 MAX: £5,000

PERIOD: 20th century SPECIALIST: Clarice Cliff, Susie Cooper, pottery, 1930's Art Deco, etc OTHER INFO: Opposite large antique centre, Thursday market, Longmynde Hotel, Stretton House Hotel, Spa water.

Old Barn Antiques, High Street, SY6 6BX. TEL: 722294, 722294 ASSNS: LAPADA PARKING: Own carpark OPEN: By appt MIN: £150 MAX: £12,000 PERIOD: 18th-19th century SPECIAL-IST: Furniture & furnishings.

Stretton Antiques Market, 36 Sandford Avenue, SY6 6BH TEL: 723718 FAX: 781502 PARKING: Easy OPEN: Mon-Sat 9.30-5.30, Sun 10.30-4.30 MIN: £1 MAX: £3,000 PERIOD: 19th-20th century GENERAL: Variety of antique & reproduction furniture & collectables.

LUDLOW (0584)

R.G. Cave & Sons Ltd, Walcote House, 17 Broad Street, SY8 1NG TEL: 873568 ASSNS: BADA, LAPADA PARKING: Easy OPEN: Mon-Sat 9.30-5.30 MIN: £20 MAX: £8,000 PERIOD: 17th-19th century SPECIALIST: 18th century English furniture GENERAL: General antiques OTHER INFO: Probate & insurance valuations.

Curiosity Shop, 127 Old Street, SY8 1NU TEL: 875927 PARKING: Easy OPEN: Mon-Sat 9-5.30 & by appt MIN: £20 MAX: £20,000 PERIOD: 17th-19th century SPECIALIST: Clocks, weapons & early oak GENERAL: Militaria, music boxes, country furniture.

The Corve Gallery, 12 Corve Street, SY8 1DA TEL: 873420 FAX: 825249 PARKING: Easy OPEN: Mon-Sat 10-5.30 MIN: £10 MAX: £15,000 PERIOD: 18th-early 20th century SPECIALIST: 19th century paintings, marines, Newlyn School etc GENERAL: General antiques. Furniture/paintings

restoration available OTHER INFO: Ludlow Castle, The Dinham Arms Hotel & restaurant.

Dickinson's Architectural Antiques & Interiors, 140 Corve Street, SY8 2PG TEL: 876207 PARKING: Easy OPEN: Mon-Sat 10-1, 2-5 MIN: £2 MAX: £3,000 PERIOD: 19th century SPECIAL-IST: Period bathrooms GENERAL: Fireplaces, lighting, doors, interior fittings etc.

G. & D. Ginger, 5 Corve Street, SY8 1DA TEL: 876939 PARKING: Easy OPEN: Mon-Sat 8.30-5.30 & by appt MIN: £100 MAX: £10,000 PERIOD: 18th century SPECIALIST: Country furniture GENERAL: All types of antique furniture.

Pepper Lane Antique Centre, Pepper Lane, SY8 1PX TEL: 876494 PARKING: Medium OPEN: Mon-Sat 10-5 MIN: £1 MAX: £1,500 PERIOD: 19th-20th century GENERAL: General antiques OTHER INFO: Feathers Hotel, Black & White houses. Button Cross Market on Mon, Fri, Sat.

M. & R. Taylor Antiques, 53 Broad Street, SY8 1NM TEL: 874169 PARKING: Easy OPEN: Mon-Sat 9-6 & by appt MIN: £25 MAX: £4,000 PERIOD: 17th-late 19th century GENERAL: Furniture, brass, treen etc OTHER INFO: Unicorn Inn.

Teme Valley Antiques, 1 The Bull Ring, SY8 1AD TEL: 874686 ASSNS: NAG PARKING: Easy OPEN: 10-5 MIN: £5 MAX: £2,500 PERIOD: 17th-20th century SPECIALIST: Portrait miniatures GENERAL: General antiques.

HATFIELD (0568)

Coltsfoot Gallery, HR6 0SF TEL: 82277 ASSNS: Paper Conservation Institute PARKING: Own carpark OPEN: 9-5 & by appt PERIOD: 19th-20th century SPECIALIST: 19th century sporting prints GENERAL: Watercolours, prints, landscape, sporting & wildlife OTHER INFO: Restoration/conservation of works of art on paper & oils.

LEOMINSTER (0568)

The Barometer Shop, New Street, HR6 8BT TEL: 610200, 613652 PARKING: Own carpark OPEN: 9-5.30 closed Wed MIN: £45 MAX: £8,500 PERIOD: 18th-20th century SPECIALIST: Clocks & barometers GENERAL: Period furniture OTHER INFO: The Banfield Collection of barometers at Churchill Gardens Museum, Hereford.

Chapman Antiques, 2 Bridge Street, HR6 8DX TEL: 615803, mobile 0836 566146 ASSNS: LAPADA PARKING: Easy OPEN: Mon-Sat 9.30-5.30 MIN: £200 GENERAL: Fine quality 17th to early 19th century furniture OTHER INFO: In an antique area, we already specialise in U.S. market.

Farmers Gallery, 28 Broad Street, HR6 8BS TEL: 611413 FAX: 611492 PARKING: Easy OPEN: Wed-Sat 11-4 & by appt MIN: £10 MAX: £1,000 PERIOD: 18th-20th century SPECIALIST: Oils, watercolours, miniatures, prints 1750-1950 frames, silver, porcelain, glass OTHER INFO: Talbot Hotel, Royal Oak Hotel & Marsh Country House.

Jeffrey Hammond Antiques, Shaftesbury House, 38 Broad Street, HR6 8BS. TEL: 614876 ASSNS: LAPADA PARKING: Own carpark OPEN: Mon-Sat 9-6 ring bell out of hours MIN: £500 MAX: £20,000 PERIOD: 17th-early 19th century SPECIALIST: Furniture, some clocks & pictures OTHER INFO: The town is set where the English plains meet the Welsh mountains. Its turbulent past has witnessed the battles of Celt, Roman, Saxon, Dane, Norman, Plantagenet, Tudor, Roundhead & Royalist. All have left their mark.

Hubbard Antiques, Bridge Street, HR6 8DU TEL: 614362 ASSNS: BADA PARKING: Own carpark OPEN: Mon-Sat 9-5 & by appt (resident) MIN: £25 MAX: £10,000 PERIOD: 17th-19th century SPECIALIST: Country furniture, brass & copper, horse brasses OTHER INFO: Hope End Hotel, Marsh Country Hotel.

Jennings of Leominster, 30 Bridge Street, HR6 8DX TEL: 612946 PARKING: Medium OPEN: Mon-Sat 9.30-6 MIN: £20 MAX: £10,000 PERIOD: 17th-19th century SPECIALIST: Period furniture & clocks.

Leominster Antiques Market, 14 Broad Street TEL: 612189 PARKING: Easy OPEN: Mon-Sat 10-5 PERIOD: 18-20th century GENERAL: 10 dealers on offering a wide range of quality antiques.

WINFORTON (05446)

Gerald & Vera Taylor, Winforton Court, HR3 6FA TEL: 226 PARKING: Own carpark OPEN: Anytime by appt MIN: £500 MAX: £10,000 PERIOD: 18th-19th century SPECIALIST: Longcase clocks GENERAL: Furniture.

YAZOR (0981)

M.P. & O.J. Russell Antiques, The Old Vicarage TEL: 22674 PARKING: Easy OPEN: Anytime but appt usual MIN: £50 MAX: £50,000 PERIOD: 17th-19th century SPECIALIST: Period oak & country furniture GENERAL: Other period furniture (not pine).

MANSELL LACEY (0981)

Bernard & Catherine Gay Pictures & Antiques, The Old School House, HR4 7HQ TEL: 22269 PARKING: Own carpark OPEN: 9-6 MIN: £10 MAX: £5,000 PERIOD: 17th-20th century SPECIALIST: Paintings & prints GENERAL: Smalls, ceramics, glass, furniture etc OTHER INFO: A Victoran Gothic pile in lovely countryside, travel rated as like *Pilgrim's Progress*. We also offer B&B's ensuite including coach parties by appt.

HEREFORD (0432)

Antiques & Bygones, 47 St Owen Street TEL: 276241 PARKING: Easy OPEN: Seven days 8-6 PERIOD: 18th-20th century GENERAL: Antiques & bygones OTHER INFO: Large restaurant next door.

I. & J.L. Brown Ltd, 58 Commercial Road, HR1 2BP TEL: 358895 FAX: 275338 PARKING: Easy OPEN: Mon-Sat 9-5.30 MIN: £10 MAX: £10,000 PERIOD: 18th-19th century SPECIALIST: UK's largest source (56,000 sq ft) of English country & French provincial furniture.

G.E. Richards & Son (Antiques), 57 Blueschool Street, HR1 2AR TEL: 267840 PARKING: Own carpark OPEN: Mon-Sat 9-5 MIN: £5 MAX: £5,000 PERIOD: 18th-20th century SPECIALIST: Antiques GENERAL: Mixed antiques & reproductions

WHITCHURCH (0600)

Olivers of Whitchurch, The Square, HR9 6DJ TEL: 890662 PARKING: Own carpark OPEN: Mon-Sat 10-5.30 MIN: £100 MAX: £950 PERIOD: 19th-20th century SPECIALIST: Victorian & Edwardian brass & iron bedsteads, mattresses & bases GENERAL: Pine furniture, scales, metalware OTHER INFO: ° mile from beautiful Symonds Yat, boating on River Wye, stunning views.

ROSS-ON-WYE (0989)

Baileys Architectural Antiques, The Engine Shed, Ashburton Industrial Estate, HR9 7BW TEL: 63015 FAX: 768172 PARKING: Own carpark OPEN: Mon-Fri 9-5, Sat 10-5 MIN: £2 MAX: £3,000 PERIOD: 19th-20th century SPECIALIST: Original fireplaces & bathrooms GENERAL: Original & traditional design garden furniture, mirrors, kitchenalia, shop fittings.

Fritz Fryer Decorative Antique Lighting, 12 Brookend Street, HR9 7EG TEL: 67416 FAX: 66742 ASSNS: LAPADA PARKING: Easy OPEN: Mon-Sat 10-5.30 MIN: £30 MAX: £3,000 SPECIALIST: Decorative lighting 1830-1930 OTHER INFO: No traffic jams!

Robert Green Antiques, 46 High Street, HR9 5HG TEL: 67504 PARKING: Medium OPEN: 10-5 MIN: £1 MAX: £5,000 PERIOD: 18th-20th century SPECIALIST: Dining tables & soft furnishings GENERAL: Mahogany furniture, silver, jewellery, glass, china OTHER INFO: Lovely market town overlooking famous Horseshoe Bend.

Robin Lloyd Antiques, 23-24 Brookend Street,

HR9 7EE TEL: 62123 FAX: 768145 PARKING: Easy OPEN: Mon-Sat 10-5 MIN: £5 MAX: £5,000 PERIOD: 17th-19th century SPECIALIST: Oak, country furniture, brass candlesticks GENERAL: Anything decorative or unusual good trade call OTHER INFO: Museum of Advertising, Button Museum. The Pheasants in Eddycross Street, best restaurant in W.Midlands.

Old Pine Shop, 27 Gloucester Road TEL: 64738, 768278 FAX: 66331 PARKING: Easy OPEN: Mon-Sat 9.30-1, 2-5 MIN: £15 MAX: £2,000 PERIOD: 18th-20th century SPECIALIST: Victorian brass, iron & wooden bedsteads, stained glass & period glazing GENERAL: Furniture OTHER INFO: Good hotel next door.

Relics, 19 High Street, HR9 5BZ TEL: 64539 PARKING: Medium OPEN: Mon-Sat 10-5, Wed 10-1 MIN: £1 MAX: £1,000 PERIOD: 19th-20th century SPECIALIST: Silver, jewellery GENERAL: General antiques.

Ross Old Book & Print Shop, 51-52 High Street, HR9 5HH ASSNS: PBFA PARKING: Medium OPEN: Mon-Sat 10-5 MIN: £1 MAX: probably £1,000 PERIOD: 17th-20th century SPECIALIST: Topographical maps & prints GENERAL: Antiquarian & secondhand books.

Trecilla Antiques, 36 High Street, HR9 5HD TEL: 63010 PARKING: Own carpark OPEN: Mon-Sat 9.30-5, but Wed am only MIN: £5 MAX: £3,000 PERIOD: 17th-20th century SPECIALIST: Arms & period furniture GENERAL: 6 showrooms of something for all OTHER INFO: In centre next to Old Market House in beautiful 'Jewel of the Wye'. Tintern Abbey, Goodrich, Raglan & Monmouth castles etc. Ross is the gateway to the Wye Valley, a beautiful little market town (markets Thurs & Sats). Royal hotel, Pengethley Hotel + many good restaurants, good small hotels & B&B.

PRESTON COURT (0531)

Serendipity, The Tythings, HR8 2LL TEL: 660380 FAX: 660421 PARKING: Own carpark OPEN: Mon-Sat 9-5 or anytime by appt MIN: £5 MAX: £15,000+ PERIOD: 17th-20th century SPECIALIST: Traditional oak & mahogany furniture, large selection OTHER INFO: In courtyard of our Elizabethan manor & church. On B4215 just down from Preston Cross.

LEDBURY (0531)

York House of Ledbury, 155 The Homend TEL:

634687 PARKING: Easy OPEN: Mon, Tues, Thurs-Sat 9.30-1, 2-5.30 MIN: £10 MAX: £5,000 PERIOD: 18th-19th century GENERAL: Furniture, glass, silver plate, decoratives OTHER INFO: very attractive small market town, exceptional half-timbered stilted market house.

MATHON (0684)

Phipps & Company Ltd, Mathon Court, WR13 5NZ TEL: 892242 FAX: 575226 PARKING: Own carpark OPEN: By appt MIN: £100 MAX: £50,000+ PERIOD: 20th century SPECIALIST: Modern British paintings & sculpture OTHER INFO: The British Camp on the Malvern Hills is UK's highest Iron Age hill fort.

MALVERN (0684)

Joan Coates of Malvern, 26 St Ann's Road, WR14 4RG TEL: 575509 PARKING: Medium OPEN: Thurs-Fri 10-1, 2.30-5.30, Sat 10-1 MIN: £8 MAX: £450 PERIOD: 18th-20th century SPECIALIST: Small silver & old English ware GENERAL: Decoratives & small furniture, brass & copper. OTHER INFO: Hotels: Cottage-in-the-Wood, Old Vicarage, Mount Pleasant.

Great Malvern Antiques, Salisbury House, 6 Abbey Road, WR14 3AG TEL: 575490 PARKING: Own carpark OPEN: Mon-Fri 9.30-5.30 or by appt MIN: £50 MAX: £5,000+ PERIOD: 18th-20th century SPECIALIST: Unusual furniture & objects GENERAL: Very varied - furnishings, pictures etc (no arms or jewellery) OTHER INFO: Close to Croque en Bouche restaurant & Abbey Hotel.

Kimber & Son Antiques, 6 Lower Howsell Road, Malvern Link, WR14 1EF TEL: 574339 PARKING: Own carpark OPEN: Mon-Fri 9-1, 2-5, Sat 9-12.30 MIN: £20 MAX: £20,000 PERIOD: 18th-19th century GENERAL: General furnishings & decorative smalls.

Gandolfi House, 211-213 Wells Road, Malvern Wells, WR14 4HF TEL: 569747 PARKING: Easy OPEN: Tues-Sat 10-5.30 MIN: £10 MAX: £5,000 SPECIALIST: 19th, 20th century watercolours, oils, original prints, Art Deco pottery GENERAL: 18th, 19th century furniture, glass, fire irons OTHER INFO: Next to the Croque en Bouche restaurant (Michelin rosette).

Malvern Studios, 56 Cowleigh Road TEL: 574913 ASSNS: BAFRA, UKIC, Museum & Galleries Commission listed PARKING: Own carpark OPEN: Mon-Thurs 9-5.15, Fri-Sat 9.4.45 PERIOD: 17th-20th century SPECIALIST: Satinwood & painted furniture when possible GENERAL: Period furniture from single chair to D-end dining tables. Restoration workshops for any furniture but specialising in boule & gilt, hand polishing.

St James Antiques, De Lys, Wells Road, WR14 4JL TEL: 563404 PARKING: Own carpark OPEN: 9-5 & by appt MIN: £50 MAX: £1,000 PERIOD: 19th-20th century SPECIALIST: Continental pine GENERAL: Importers.

WORCESTER (0905)

Antique Warehouse, rear 74 Droitwich Road TEL: 27493 PARKING: Own carpark OPEN: Mon-Fri 8-6, Sat 10-4.30 MAX: £2,000 PERIOD: 19th century GENERAL: Victorian pine.

Andrew Boyle (Booksellers) Ltd, 21 Friar Street, WR1 2NA TEL: 611700 ASSNS: ABA, PBFA PARKING: Medium OPEN: Mon-Wed, Fri 9.30-4 MIN: £6 MAX: £1,000 PERIOD: 17th-20th century GENERAL: Most subjects.

Bygones by the Cathedral, 32 College Street TEL: 25388 ASSNS: LAPADA, Fellow Gemmological Assn of GB PARKING: Medium OPEN: Mon-Sat 9.30-1, 2-5.30 MIN: £10+ MAX: £20,000 PERIOD: 17th-20th century SPECIALIST: Jewellery, Worcester china GENERAL: General antiques OTHER INFO: Anything that makes us smile.

Bygones of Worcester, 55 Sidbury, WR1 2HN TEL: 23132 ASSNS: LAPADA, Fellow Gemmological Assn of GB PARKING: Medium OPEN: Mon-Sat 9.30-1, 2-5.30 MIN: £10+ MAX: £20,000 PERIOD: 17th-20th century SPECIALIST: Worcester porcelain, Georgian/Victorian arts & crafts, furniture GENERAL: General antiques, eccentricities, the odd dinosaur's egg & narwals horn

Jean Hodge Antiques, Peachley Manor, Hallows Lane, Lower Broadheath WR2 6QL TEL: 640255 PARKING: Own carpark OPEN: Seven days from 9am MIN: £5 MAX: £2,500 PERIOD: 18th-19th century SPECIALIST: Period furniture, old pine, kitchenalia.

Sarah Hodge Antiques, Peachley Manor, Hallows Lane, Lower Broadheath WR2 6QL TEL: 640255 PARKING: Own carpark OPEN: Seven days from 9am MIN: £5 MAX: £2,500 PERIOD: 18th-19th century SPECIALIST: Period furniture, kitchenalia, old pine.

The Original Choice Ltd, 56 The Tything TEL: 613330 PARKING: Medium OPEN: Mon-Sat 10-

6, Sun 1-5.30 MIN: £2 MAX: £20,000 PERIOD: 18th-20th century SPECIALIST: Fireplaces, stained glass.

The Tything Antique Market, 49 The Tything TEL: 610597 PARKING: Medium OPEN: Mon-Sat 10-5 PERIOD: 17th-20th century GENERAL: Wide range of quality items.

Worcester Antiques Centre, Reindeer Court, WR1 4DF TEL: 610593 FAX: 610593 PARKING: Easy OPEN: Mon-Sat 10-5 MIN: £5 MAX: £3,000 PERIOD: 19th century SPECIALIST: Royal commemorative, English & Continental pottery & porcelain GENERAL: Metalware, silver, jewellery, glass, prints OTHER INFO: Cathedral city, Malvern close by beauty spot, Elgar country, on River Severn.

DROITWICH (0905)

Grant Books/Grant Fine Art, 9a Victoria Square TEL: 778155 FAX: 794507 ASSNS: PBFA, U.S. & British Golf Collectors Societies PARKING: Easy OPEN: 9-5 & by appt MIN: £5 MAX: £2,000 PERIOD: 19th-20th century SPECIALIST: Golf books, prints, clubs, ephemera OTHER INFO: Perhaps world's largest selection of golf books,

golfiana. Publishers of limited edition golf books. Relaxing brine baths.

H. & B. Wolf Antiques Ltd, 128 Worcester Road, WR9 8AN TEL: 772320 PARKING: Own carpark OPEN: Fri, Sat 9.30-5.30 or by appt MIN: £20 MAX: £1,500 PERIOD: 18th-19th century SPECIALIST: China, pottery, glass GENERAL: Some collables & furniture.

OMBERSLEY (0905)

Stable Antiques, The Forge, Chatley, WR9 0AP TEL: 620353 PARKING: Own carpark OPEN: Sat & anytime by appt MIN: £50 MAX: £3,000 PERIOD: 17th-19th century GENERAL: Quality period furniture & smalls OTHER INFO: Cheerful courier service.

CLEOBURY MORTIMER (0299)

Antique Centre, Childe Road, DY14 9XR TEL: 270513 PARKING: Own carpark OPEN: 10-6 MAX: £35,000 PERIOD: 17th-20th century GENERAL: Antique beds, Georgian, Victorian, Edwardian furniture, smalls, bric-a-brac, architectural items OTHER INFO: Village ambience, Clee Hills, old church/buildings.

BEWDLEY (0299)
Ma's Antiques, 89 Welch Gate, DY12 2JY TEL:
403845 PARKING: Easy OPEN: Thurs-Sat 10-5
or by appt MIN: £10 MAX: £500 PERIOD: 19th
century SPECIALIST: Souvenirware GENERAL:
Small collectables, i.e. sewing implements, snuff
boxes, button hooks, Mauchlinware OTHER
INFO: Small Georgian town on River Severn, steam
railway, Wyre forest.

KIDDERMINSTER (0562)
BBM Jewellery, Coins & Antiques, 8-9 Lion
Street, DY10 1PT TEL: 744118 FAX: 825954
ASSNS: BJA PARKING: Easy OPEN: 10-5 closed
Tues MIN: £1 MAX: £8,500 PERIOD: 19th-20th
century SPECIALIST: Antique jewellery GEN-
ERAL: secondhand quality jewellery for all ages,
diamonds OTHER INFO: Truly an Aladdin's Cave.

OLD SWINFORD (0384)
Old Swinford Gallery, 106 Hagley Road, DY8
1QV TEL: 395577 PARKING: Easy OPEN: Tues-
Fri 9.30-5, Sat 9.30-1 MIN: £50 MAX: £5,000
PERIOD: Some 18th, but mainly 19th-early 20th
century SPECIALIST: Oils, watercolours, maps,
antiquarian prints.

HALESOWEN (021)
Clent Books, 52 Summer Hill, B63 3BU TEL: 550
0309, home (0299) 401090 PARKING: Easy
OPEN: Mon-Sat 10-4 MIN: £4 MAX: £250
PERIOD: 17th-20th century SPECIALIST: Topog-
raphy, history, local history OTHER INFO:
Organisers of Waverley Antiques & Book Fair.

ALCESTER (0789)
Malthouse Antiques Centre, 4 Market Place
TEL: 764032 PARKING: Easy OPEN: Mon-
Sat 10-5, Sun 2-5 MIN: £5 MAX: £2,000
PERIOD: 19th-20th century GENERAL:
General antiques.

HENLEY-IN-ARDEN (0564)
The Chadwick Gallery, 2 Doctors Lane (off

Cleobury Mortimer Antiques Centre
Helen & Peter Rust
Childe Road, Cleobury Mortimer,
Nr. Kidderminster, Worcestershire
3,000 sq.ft. of Antiques, Bric-a-Brac, Old Pine,
Edwardian, Victorian & Period Furniture, Old Beds,
Architectural Antiques
OPEN:
10am–5pm Monday to Saturday
11am–5pm Sunday
Telephone: 0299 270513

High Street), B95 5AW TEL: 794820 ASSNS:
LAPADA PARKING: Own carpark OPEN:
Tues-Wed, Fri-Sat 10-5 MIN: £50 MAX:
£5,000 PERIOD: 19th-20th century GEN-
ERAL: Watercolours, etchings.
Colmore Galleries Ltd, 52 High Street, B95
5AN TEL: 792938 ASSNS: LAPADA PARK-
ING: Easy OPEN: Mon-Fri 11-5.30, Sat 11-
4.30 MIN: £100 PERIOD: 19th-20th century
SPECIALIST: Victorian oils & watercolours
GENERAL: Modern paintings & signed lim-
ited editions.
G.B. Horton - The Arden Gallery, 54 High
Street, B95 5AN TEL: 792520 PARKING:
Medium OPEN: Mon-Fri 1-6 MIN: £1 MAX:
£2,000 PERIOD: 19th-20th century GEN-
ERAL: Watercolours and oils, miniatures.
Lacy Gallery, 56 High Street, TEL: 793073 PARK-
ING: Easy OPEN: Tues, Weds, Thurs 10-1
SPECIALIST: Oils, watercolours & prints, art
reference books.
Jasper Marsh, 3 High Street TEL: 792088
ASSNS: BADA PARKING: Medium OPEN:
Mon-Sat 10-5.30 MIN: £100 MAX: £5,000
PERIOD: 18th-19th century GENERAL: Ma-
hogany & oak furniture.

Nottinghamshire and South Yorkshire

This relatively short tour starts in historic Nottingham and passes through lovely countryside to the east of the city before moving into some of the industrial towns of South Yorkshire. It continues through the eastern side of the Peak Disrict and rejoins the motorway for the homeward journey just east of Derby.

Leaving the M1 from London at Junction 24, south of Nottingham, the first stop is at Long Eaton, an industrial town owing its development to lace making, although many new industries are now more important. From Long Eaton we proceed into Nottingham, most famous for Robin Hood and his long-running battle with the Sheriff. Unfortunately, there is no proof that Robin Hood ever existed and there are many theories

Robin Hood, by courtesy of Nottingham City Council

about the source of the legend. Some think it is a composite of different men and others that it harks back to the pagan myths of the green man, a fertility symbol.

Nottingham Castle is the most outstanding feature in the city. William the Conqueror built a castle here soon after he took power. This castle saw much action during the centuries. John captured it in 1191 and it was recaptured by his brother, King Richard I, three years later. Richard III stationed himself here while awaiting news of Henry Tudor's landing in the country. He left the castle to go to the Battle of Bosworth where he was killed and the Tudor line established on the throne of England. Another king, Charles I, used Nottingham Castle as his headquarters. After he had fled from London he came here and gathered his army before moving on eventually to win the Battle of Edgehill. Later the Parliamentary Forces took the castle and after the Civil War much of it was demolished. It was rebuilt in an Italian style in 1679 but burnt down by a Luddite mob in 1831 although later restored. Now it houses a museum with displays of pictures, decorative arts, militaria and a History of Nottingham Exhibition.

As might be expected in such an historic town, there is much to see including several Georgian houses in Castle Street, St. Peter's Church with some 13th century features and the Cathedral built by Pugin. There is also a racecourse and the

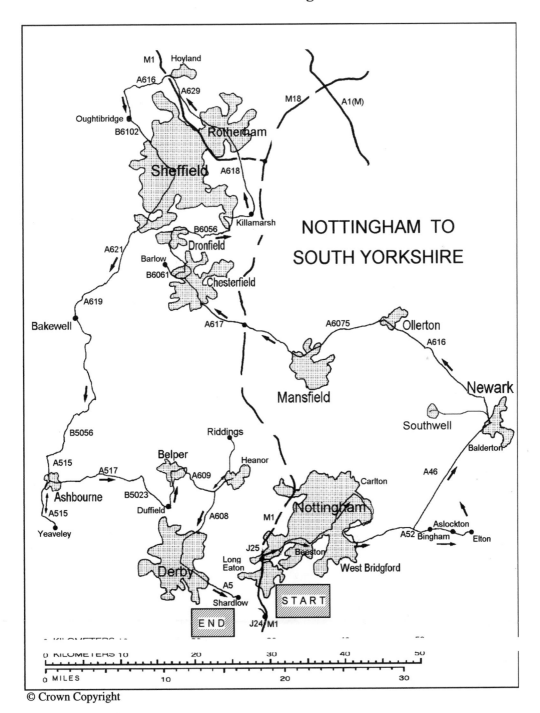

famous cricket ground at Trent Bridge.

The city contains several good museums, amongst which are The Lace Centre in Castle Road, Museum of Costumes and Textiles, Castlegate, the Canal Museum in Canal Street and Brewhouse Yard Museum at the foot of Castle Rock.

From Nottingham we continue our journey, stopping first at Carlton and West Bridgford, then the villages of Bingham and Aslockton, before reaching Elton with the fine romantic style Elton Hall, dating from the 15th century but with many later additions and alterations. It has belonged to the Proby family for three hundred years and visitors may see their remarkable collections of furniture, paintings, including Gainsboroughs, Reynolds, Constables, and books, including Henry VIII's prayer book.

The tour now turns north, via Balderton, to the ancient town of Newark standing on the River Trent and close to a junction of the Great North Road and the Roman Fosse Way. A major feature of the town is the ruins of Newark Castle. Although there had been several fortifications built on the site before, the main castle was constructed in 1123 by the Bishop of Lincoln. King John died here in October 1216 after travelling from Wisbech. During the Civil War Newark was a Royalist stronghold which led to the castle being besieged three times. On the

Newstead Abbey, about 5 miles north of Nottingham.
By courtesy of Nottingham City Council

last occasion in 1645, King Charles I was on his way to relieve it when he encountered Parliamentary troops and fought the Battle of Naseby where he suffered his final defeat. The King and other survivors escaped to Newark but left later for Oxford. The following year the King was taken and Newark Castle surrendered. The castle was slighted (damaged so that it could no longer be used as a stronghold) and was never rebuilt.

Another striking feature of the town is Newark Town Hall, said to be one of the best Georgian town halls in the country. It has a fine collection of civic plate dating mostly from the 17th and 18th centuries, also paintings and historical records. An interesting collection of dolls and juvenalia can be found at the Vina Cooke Museum in Millgate. In the same street there is a Folk Museum and at Winfield Airfield there is the Newark Air Museum.

We detour now to the lovely small town of Southwell, the cathedral city for the diocese of Nottinghamshire. Its parish church attained cathedral status in 1884. In Saxon times a church was built on the site of a Roman villa and then that was replaced by a Norman church which is what we see today. The cathedral has some wonderful stone carving in the chapter house where the 13th century stone-carvers sculpted leaves that appear unbelievably lifelike.

Following the A616, the tour calls first at Ollerton and then Mansfield. The town now stands on the eastern edge of Sherwood Forest but the centre oak of the forest stood in the town's Westgate until the 1940s when it had to be felled. A plaque marks the spot where it stood.

Next stop is Chesterfield in Derbyshire, an ancient market town mentioned in the Domesday Book. George Stephenson, the famous railway engineer, lived at Tapton House, north east of the town, and he supervised the building of the railway through Chesterfield. His grave may be found in Trinity Church. The town is most famous for it 14th century church, All Saints, with the twisted spire. The Peacock Heritage Centre is an interesting museum housed in a 16th century timber framed building, restored in 1981.

Nearby Dronfield contains a number of 18th century houses and the church dates back, in parts, to the 14th century. Inside the church there is a good example of a Jacobean pulpit and a brass of two priests dating back to about 1390.

Now moving into the South Yorkshire conurbation via Killamarsh, the next stop is Rotherham, an industrial town on the River Don. It has a bridge with a restored 15th century chapel on it and there is also a fine perpendicular church. The Clifton Park Museum is also of interest. Housed in a late 18th century mansion its rooms are furnished in period style. There are also displays of Victoriana, Roman antiquities, local history, glass-making, etc.

The tour continues through Hoyland and Oughtibridge before it reaches the industrial and university city of Sheffield, also on the River Don and famous for steel and cutlery. The city has a Roman Catholic cathedral of partly 14th to 15th century origin which was originally the parish church. On the outskirts are the remains of the 12th century Beauchief Abbey and there are several Georgian houses in Paradise Square.

Continuing southwards we enter the town of Bakewell in the centre of the Peak District and a mecca for visitors. In the space available here it is just not possible to detail all the wonderful scenery and places to go in the Peak District. However, it would be a real pity for visitors not explore one of the most beautiful parts of England. For more information there are Tourist Information Centres in the Old Market Hall in Bakewell and at 13 Market Place, Ashbourne.

Bakewell is probably most famous for its pudding which was created by accident when a cook at the Rutland Hotel misunderstood instructions. Much of the town is Victorian but the church is 12th-14th century and has a Saxon cross in the churchyard. The Old House Museum is an early Tudor house with wattle and daub interior walls. On display are a Victorian kitchen, costumes, lace, craftsmen's tools, and toys.

Nearby Chatsworth is one of the most famous houses in England. This magnificent mansion, owned by the Dukes of Devonshire, was started in 1687 and is a treasure house of priceless pictures, books, furniture and works of art. The house is set in beautiful gardens with a maze and the Emperor Fountain, the highest gravity fed fountain in the world, able to rise to a height of 260 feet. This house is not to be missed and needs at least a day to see it.

Another house that must be visited is Haddon Hall, two miles south east of Bakewell on the A6. It is a perfectly preserved 12th century manor house owned by the Duke of Rutland who also owns Belvoir Castle. It was preserved because in the 18th century the family inherited Belvoir and so left Haddon Hall uninhabited. At the beginning of this century the ninth Duke decided to restore the house. Time had stopped at Haddon, no alterations or changes had been made for two hundred years. Now it gives a window into life from the 12th to 18th centuries. It also contains a fascinating museum of things people had lost over the years that workmen found under floorboards and in various nooks and crannies.

The tour proceeds to Ashbourne, on the edge of the Peak District. This market town has many buildings of interest including the 15th century timber framed Gingerbread Shop, the Green Man and Black's Head Royal Hotel claiming to have the longest inn name in the country and the many Georgian houses in Church Street. The town's church is also of interest with the oldest parts dating from the 13th century. Strangers visiting the town on Shrove Tuesday or Ash Wednesday get a big surprise because the traditional game of football is played then. However, it is quite unlike the usual form of the game. The goals are three miles apart and the two teams consist of hundreds of men. The town's shops board up their windows which is probably wise as there are very few rules.

From Ashbourne we stop in the village of Yeaveley before arriving at Duffield

Ashbourne

where there are foundations of a Norman castle with a keep almost as big as the White Tower in the Tower of London.

The tour continues onwards via Belper and Heanor, before reaching the county town of Derby on the River Derwent. An ancient town, it was the site of a Roman camp and by the time of the Norman Conquest it had a population of 2000. In the early 18th century silk mills were opened and the town's industrial base expanded even more with the coming of the railways when it was the site of a big locomotive and coach works. It also has a Rolls-Royce factory and a statue of Sir Henry Royce may be found in the Arboretum Park. Royal Crown Derby Porcelain is still producing fine bone china here. There is also a cathedral built in 1727 incorporating a tower built 200 years earlier. The city has several interesting buildings. Amongst them are St Peter's Church, mentioned in the Domesday Book, the former 16th century Derby School and the County Hall's facade is mid 17th century. Amongst the city's museums are the Derby Industrial Museum in the Silk Mill off Full Street, Pickford's House Museum, Friar Gate which is a Georgian Town house exhibiting items of social history and the Royal Crown Derby Museum in Osmaston Road.

Our very last call is on the village of Shardlow before rejoining the M1 motorway for the journey home.

ANTIQUE DEALERS

BEESTON (0602)

Elizabeth Bailey, 33 Chilwell Road TEL: 255685 PARKING: Easy OPEN: Mon 2-5.30, Tues, Wed, Fri, Sat 10-1, 2-5.30 GENERAL: Antiques, Victoriana & decorative items.

NOTTINGHAM (0602)

Breck Antiques, 726 Mansfield Road, Woodthorpe, NG5 3FW TEL: 605263, 621197 ASSNS: NADA PARKING: Own carpark OPEN: Tues, Fri, Sat 9.30-5.30 & by appt MIN: £50 MAX: £8,000 PERIOD: 18th-19th century SPECIALIST: English porcelain GENERAL: Porcelain, glass fairings, pot lids small furniture items OTHER INFO: 15 miles to Robin Hood's Sherwood Forest.

N.J. Doris, 170 Derby Road, NG7 1LR TEL: 781194 PARKING: Medium OPEN: Mon-Wed, Fri-Sat 10-5 MIN: £1 MAX: £1,000 PERIOD: 18th-20th century GENERAL: Antiquarian & secondhand books: military, theology, English Literature, natural history, huntings OTHER INFO: Derby road is city's antique centre. Close to castle, Trent Bridge, Robin Hood Centre.

Golden Cage, 99 Derby Road, Canning Circus TEL: 411600 PARKING: Medium OPEN: Mon-Sat 10-5 MIN: £30 MAX: £300 PERIOD: 20th century SPECIALIST: Period clothes GENERAL: Mens/womens 20's, 30's & 40's clothes for hire or buy. All good condition OTHER INFO: Excellent catering facilities at restaurant next door.

Hockley Coins, 170 Derby Road, NG7 1LR TEL: 790667 PARKING: Easy OPEN: 10-5 MIN: £1 MAX: £100 PERIOD: Roman, medieval-milled SPECIALIST: English & foreign coins GENERAL: Cigarette cards, medals, army badges.

Melville Kemp Ltd, 79-81 Derby Road, NG1 5BA TEL: 417055 FAX: 417055 ASSNS: NAG, LAPADA, NADA PARKING: Easy OPEN: Mon-Wed, Fri-Sat 9-5.30 MIN: £30 MAX: £25,000 PERIOD: 19th-20th century SPECIALIST: Probably the finest & most unusual selection of antique jewellery, silver, fob & pocket watches GENERAL: Porcelain & glass.

Lustre Metal Antiques Nottingham Ltd, Units 10-12, The Cattle Market, Meadow Lane, NG2 3GY TEL: 863523 PARKING: Own carpark OPEN: Mon-Sat 9-4.30 & by appt MIN: £2 MAX: £3,000+ PERIOD: 18th-20th century SPECIALIST: Victorian brass & iron beds, fireplaces, mantels

GENERAL: Brass, cast iron, fenders, fire irons, hanging lights, garden vases etc.

Pegasus Antiques, 62 Derby Road, NG1 5FD TEL: 474220 ASSNS: NAG, NADA PARKING: Easy OPEN: Mon-Sat 9.30-5 MIN: £5 MAX: £5,000 PERIOD: 17th-late 19th century GENERAL: Quality furniture, also copper, small silver & jewellery, some 19th century brass & porcelain.

David & Carole Potter, 76 Derby Road, NG1 5FD TEL: 417911 ASSNS: LAPADA PARKING: Easy OPEN: Mon-Sat 10-5 MIN: £50 MAX: £15,000 PERIOD: 18th-19th century GENERAL: General antiques.

Val Smith Coins Books & Collectors Centre, 170 Derby Road, NG7 1LR TEL: 781194 ASSNS: IPM, Notts Numismatic Society PARKING: Easy OPEN: 10-5 MIN: £1 MAX: £500 PERIOD: 18th-20th century SPECIALIST: Postcards, banknotes, bullion GENERAL: Coins, medals, jewellery.

Top Hat Antique Centre, 66-72 Derby Road, NG1 5FD TEL: 419143 ASSNS: NADA PARKING: Easy OPEN: Mon-Sat 9.30-5 MIN: £1 MAX: £5,000 PERIOD: 18th-20th century GENERAL: Victorian, Edwardian furniture, general antiques OTHER INFO: Good tourist town, major attractions 5 mins.

Trident Arms, 74 Derby Road, NG1 5FD TEL: 413307 FAX: 414199 ASSNS: NADA PARKING: Easy OPEN: Mon-Fri 9.30-5, Sat 10-4 PERIOD: 17th-20th century SPECIALIST: Antique & modern weapons & militaria OTHER INFO: One of the largest stocks of weapons in UK.

CARLTON-ON-TRENT (0636)

Tudor Rose Antiques, Yew Tree Farm, NG23 6NL TEL: 821841 PARKING: Own carpark OPEN: MIN: £10 MAX: £3,000 PERIOD: 18th-19th century SPECIALIST: Furniture GENERAL: Treen, copper, brass, metalware.

WEST BRIDGFORD (0602)

Bridgford Antiques, 2a Rushworth Avenue, NG2 7LF TEL: 821835 PARKING: Easy OPEN: Mon-Sat 10-5 MIN: £1 MAX: £500 PERIOD: 19th-20th century GENERAL: Shipping goods, bric-a-brac, postcards OTHER INFO: Close Notts cricket & football grounds. Good trade call with realistic prices, Lithuanian spoken (honest).

Joan Cotton Antiques, 5 Davies Road TEL: 813043 PARKING: Own carpark OPEN: 9-5 except Wed MIN: £20 MAX: £80 PERIOD: 20th cen-

Street Map of Nottingham

By courtesy of Nottingham City Countcil

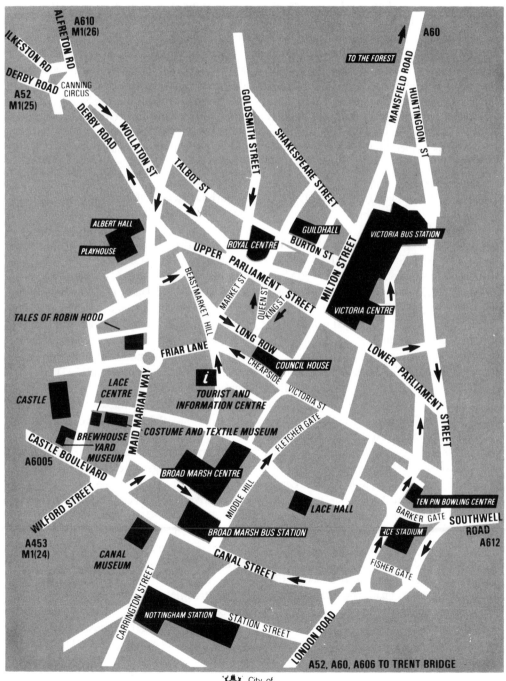

City of
Nottingham

Designed by the City of Nottingham Tourism and P.R. Office

tury SPECIALIST: Jewellery & silver GENERAL: Smalls (no furniture).

Moultons, 5 Portland Road, NG2 6DN TEL: 814354 PARKING: Easy OPEN: Tues-Sat 10-5 MIN: £2 MAX: £1,800 PERIOD: 19th-20th century SPECIALIST: Pine, fabric & curtains GENERAL: Oak & mahogany, kitchenalia, glass, silver plate OTHER INFO: 1 mile from Holme Pierpoort Hall, Vale of Belvoir, close to city centre.

ASLOCKTON (0949)

Jane Neville Gallery, Elm House, Abbey Lane, NG13 9AE TEL: 50220 FAX: 51337 ASSNS: FATG PARKING: Easy OPEN: 9-5 weekdays, phone for other times MIN: £10 MAX: £5,000 PERIOD: 20th century SPECIALIST: Sporting, wildlife & countryside pictures GENERAL: English art & limited edition prints OTHER INFO: Rural village with good inn food.

BINGHAM (0949)

E.M. Cheshire, The Manor House, Market Place TEL: 838864 ASSNS: BADA, LAPADA PARKING: Easy OPEN: Mon-Sat 10-5 MIN: £250 MAX: £10,000 PERIOD: 17th-19th century SPECIALIST: Furniture GENERAL: Early metal, treen OTHER INFO: Small town, good market place, good food shops, good inns.

ELTON (0949)

Rectory Bungalow Workshop & Studio, 1 Main Road, NG13 9LF TEL: 50878 PARKING: Easy OPEN: Saturdays 10-5 summer & 10-12, 2-3 winter-or by appt MIN: £1 MAX: £5,000 PERIOD: 17th-20th century SPECIALIST: Handpainted furniture GENERAL: Country furniture & 17th-19th century decoratives OTHER INFO: Manor Arms pub behind shop, Belvoir Castle 3 miles, Langar House Hotel & restaurant 5.

BALDERTON (0636)

Blacksmiths Forge Antiques, 74 Main Street, NG24 3NP TEL: 700008 PARKING: Own carpark MIN: £5 MAX: £800 PERIOD: 19th-20th century SPECIALIST: Pine, cast iron fireplaces GENERAL: Full range original pine furniture, satin, pottery, curios, fireplaces, tiles.

NEWARK (0636)

Castlegate Antiques Centre, 55 Castle Gate, TEL: 700076 PARKING: Easy OPEN: Mon-Sat 9-5.30 MIN: £50 MAX: £5,000 PERIOD: 17th-19th century GENERAL: Furniture, plus small stock of decorative items & paintings. Book shop, art

reference & childrens OTHER INFO: Newark Castle currently undergoing restoration, was partly demolished by Oliver Cromwell, small market town with some Tudor buildings.

D & G Antiques, 11 Kings Road, NG24 1EW TEL: 702782 PARKING: Own spaces OPEN: 9.3-5 closed Mon MIN: £30 MAX: £1,500 PERIOD: 18th-20th century GENERAL: Victorian & some period up to 1930 OTHER INFO: Excellent tourist town, castle, museum, historic buildings.

D & V Antiques, 4a Northgate, NG24 1EZ TEL: 71888 PARKING: Medium OPEN: Mon-Thurs, Sat 9.30-5 MIN: £1 MAX: £1,000 PERIOD: 19th-20th century GENERAL: Furniture, bric-a-brac, lamps OTHER INFO: Gannets cafe & Appleton Hotel (non-smoking).

Newark Antiques Centre, Regent House, Lombard Street, NG24 1XR TEL: 605504 PARKING: Own carpark OPEN: Mon-Sat 9.30-5, Suns & Bank Holidays 11-4 MIN: £25 MAX: £5,000 PERIOD: 18th-20th century SPECIALIST: Longcase clocks, textiles, jewellery GENERAL: Furniture, old pine, books, porcelain, militaria, Dutch furniture, glass, silver, commemorative china, collectables OTHER INFO: 55 units & 18 display cabinets, tearoom on site. 1 min from town centre with its historic cobbled market place, also 1 mins walk from river & the castle where King John died in 1215AD.

Newark Antiques Warehouse, Kelham Rd TEL: 74869 PARKING: Own carpark OPEN: Mon-Fri 8.30-5.30, Sat 10-4 MIN: £25 MAX: £10,000 PERIOD: 17th-20th century GENERAL: Oak, mahogany, walnut furniture & shipping goods OTHER INFO: Trade warehouse, very large stock changing daily.

Portland Antiques, 20 Portland Street, NG24 4XG TEL: 701478 PARKING: Easy OPEN: 9.30-4.30 closed Mon-Thurs MIN: £1 PERIOD: 17th-20th century GENERAL: Wide range of quality stock.

Portland Street Antiques Centre, 27-31 Portland Street, NG24 4XF TEL: 74397 PARKING: Easy OPEN: 10-5 MIN: £1 MAX: £5,000 PERIOD: 19th-20th century SPECIALIST: Militaria, coins, silver, taxidermy (DoE licence) GENERAL: Wide range of quality antiques & collectables OTHER INFO: 4 antique centres & many antique shops each showing map where others are.

Jack Spratt Antiques, Unit 5, George Street, NG24 1LU TEL: 707714 FAX: 640595 PARKING: Own

carpark OPEN: Mon-Fri 8-5.30, Sat 8-4 MIN: £10 MAX: £2,000 PERIOD: 19th-20th century SPECIALIST: Oak, fruitwood, pine furniture GENERAL: Every possible item in pine OTHER INFO: Largest pine warehouse in the Midlands.
Wade-Smith & Read, 1-3 Castlegate TEL: 73792 PARKING: Medium OPEN: Mon-Wed, Fri, Sat 9-5 & by appt MIN: £200 MAX: £12,000 PERIOD: 17th-20th century SPECIALIST: Early oak & walnut GENERAL: English furniture 17th & 18th century OTHER INFO: Huge church, 2 museums, fine town hall by John Carr of York, 1770. Millgate House Hotel (Georgian small & traditional).

SOUTHWELL (0636)
Strouds of Southwell Antiques, 3-7 Church Street, NG25 0HG TEL: 815001 FAX: 813064 PARKING: Easy OPEN: Mon-Sat 10-5 MIN: £10 MAX: £50,000 PERIOD: 17th-19th century SPECIALIST: Period furniture, pewter, farmhouse tables GENERAL: Longcase clocks, paintings etc OTHER INFO: Opposite the amazing Minster, a huge early cathedral in this tiny market town.

OLLERTON (0623)
Hamlyn Lodge, Station Road, NG22 9BN TEL: 823600 PARKING: Own carpark OPEN: Tues-Sat 10-5, Sun 12-4 & bank hols MIN: £30 MAX: £4,000 PERIOD: 18th-20th century SPECIALIST: Furniture only GENERAL: Mixed original & restored condition. All restorations & cabinet-making inhouse house OTHER INFO: Housed in converted 18th century farmhouse within conservation area, working watermill and a teashop.

MANSFIELD (0623)
The Bookshelf, 7a Albert Street, NG18 1EA TEL: 648231 PARKING: Medium OPEN: Mon, Tues, Thurs-Sat 9.30-5, Wed 10-2 MIN: £1 PERIOD: 17th-20th century GENERAL: All from Archeology to Zeus OTHER INFO: Mansfield Museum & Art Gallery.

CHESTERFIELD (0246)
Anthony D. Goodlad, 26 Fairfield Road, Brockwell TEL: 204004 PARKING: Easy OPEN: By appt 10-5 MIN: £1 MAX: £300 PERIOD: some 19th but mainly 20th century SPECIALIST: Militaria chiefly World War I & II.
Ian Morris, 479 Chatsworth Road, S40 3AD TEL: 235120 PARKING: Easy OPEN: Mon-Fri 9-5, Sat 12-5 MIN: £1 MAX: £2,000 PERIOD: 18th-20th century GENERAL: Furniture, paintings, smalls,

Shipping items OTHER INFO: Chesterfield Parish Church (crooked spire), 8 miles to Chatsworth and to Hardwick Hall, 10 miles Haddon Hall, 5 miles Bolsover Castle, Peak District Ntl Park 4 miles.
Tilleys Vintage Magazine Shop, 29-31 South Street North, New Whittington, S43 2AA TEL: 454270 PARKING: Easy OPEN: Tues-Sat normally 10-6, but pls phone first MIN: £1 MAX: £1,200+ PERIOD: 19th but mainly 20th century SPECIALIST: Magazines GENERAL: Comics, annuals, postcards, cigarette cards, prints, programmes, books (inc vintage paperbacks), ephemera, tins and all types of printed material.
Brian Yates Antiques & Restorations, 420 Chatsworth Road, S40 3BQ TEL: 220395 PARKING: Own carpark OPEN: Mon-Sat 9.30-5.30 & by appt MIN: £50 MAX: £5,000 PERIOD: 17th-18th century SPECIALIST: Oak & country furniture plus accessories GENERAL: Longcase clocks, brass, copper, oils & watercolours OTHER INFO: Largest open air market in country, crooked spire, home of George Stephenson.

BARLOW (0742)
Hackney House Antiques, Hackney Lane, S18 5TG TEL: 890248 PARKING: Own carpark OPEN: Tues-Sun 9-6 MIN: £25 (prints) MAX: £1,500 (clocks) PERIOD: 19th-20th century GENERAL: General antiques OTHER INFO: Tearoom & restaurant on site. Local B&Bs & holiday cottages.

DRONFIELD (0246)
Bardwell Antiques, 51 Chesterfield Road, S18 6XA TEL: 412183 FAX: 412183 PARKING: Easy OPEN: Mon-Sat 9.30-5 MIN: £1 MAX: £2,000 PERIOD: 19th-20th century GENERAL: All types of furniture, pottery OTHER INFO: Small tourist town with good facilities.

KILLAMARSH (0742)
Hauenplan's Architectural Emporium, The Old Station, Station Road, S31 8EN TEL: 489972, home (0246) 433315 PARKING: Own carpark OPEN: Tues-Sat 10-4 MIN: £5 MAX: £25,000 PERIOD: 18th-20th century SPECIALIST: Architectural fittings, decorative & garden items OTHER INFO: Many pieces have appeared in films and TV.

ROTHERHAM (0709)
Roger Appleyard Ltd., Fitzwilliam Road, Eastwood Trading Estate, S65 1SL TEL: 377770 FAX: 829395 ASSNS: LAPADA PARKING: Own carpark OPEN: Mon-Fri 8-5 MIN: £5 MAX: £4,000

Nottinghamshire and South Yorkshire

PERIOD: 18th-20th century GENERAL: Furniture OTHER INFO: 10,000 sq ft warehouse.

John Shaw Antiques Ltd, 103 Lawmarsh Hill, S62 6DL TEL: 522340 PARKING: own carpark OPEN: Mon-Sat 9-5 MIN: £10 MAX: £10,000 PERIOD: 18th-20th century GENERAL From a glass fish to a stuffed fish.

Philip Turner Antiques, 94a Broad Street, Parkgate TEL: 5246240 PARKING: Easy OPEN: 9-5.30 & anytime by appt MIN: £50 MAX: £1,000 PERIOD: 19th-20th century SPECIALIST: Quality oak furniture c 1900 GENERAL: Selected furniture particularly suitable for German, Japanese & American markets.

HOYLAND (0226)

Charisma Antiques, St Paul's Former Methodist Church, Market Street, S74 9QR TEL: 747599 PARKING: Easy OPEN: Mon-Sat 10-5 MIN: £5 MAX: £2,500 GENERAL: General antiques OTHER INFO: 1809 Methodist chapel with 3 floors of stock.

OUGHTIBRIDGE (0742)

Julie Goddard Antiques, 7-9 Langsett Road South, S30 3GY TEL: 862261 PARKING: Own carpark OPEN: Tues 10-1, Mon, Thurs-Sat 10-4.30 MIN: £1 MAX: £2,500 PERIOD: 18th-early 20th century SPECIALIST: 19th century furniture GENERAL: Moorcroft & mixed pottery OTHER INFO: Very scenic, hilly Pennine village close to M1 (J36) & Holmfirth.

SHEFFIELD (0742)

A & C Antiques, 239 Abbeydale Road, S7 9FJ TEL: 589161 PARKING: Easy OPEN: Mon-Sat 10.30-5 MIN: £5 MAX: £ 2,000 PERIOD: 19th-20th century SPECIALIST: Jewellery & quality smalls OTHER INFO: Chatsworth House, Derbyshire, Abbeydale Ind. Hamlet, Peak district.

Anita's Holme Antiques, 144 Holme Lane, S6 4JW TEL: 336698 PARKING: Easy OPEN: 9-5 MIN: £3 MAX: £250 PERIOD: 20th century SPECIALIST: China & plates GENERAL: Cross section OTHER INFO: New supertram will terminate here. Near parks & museums.

Dronfield Antiques, 375 Abbeydale Road, S7 1FS TEL: 550172 FAX: 556024 PARKING: Easy OPEN: Mon-Wed, Fri, Sat 10.30-5 MIN: £1 MAX: £2,000 PERIOD: 19th-20th century GENERAL: Interesting bric-a-brac, Victorian, Edwardian & 1920's plus shipping furniture (also held at large warehouse).

Fulwood Antiques & Basement Gallery, 7 Brookland Avenue, S10 4GA TEL: 307387, 301346 PARKING: Easy OPEN: Wed, Fri 10-5, Sat 10-1 MIN: £1 general, £50 paintings, MAX: £1,500 general, £5,000 paintings PERIOD: 18th century to 1935 SPECIALIST: Watercolour & oils GENERAL: General antiques.

Fun Antiques, 72 Abbeydale Road, S7 1FD TEL: 553424 FAX: 588599 PARKING: Easy OPEN: By appt only MIN: £10 MAX: £1,000 PERIOD: 19th-20th century SPECIALIST: Early toys, advertising items, black art, fairground arcade machines, dolls & teddy bears, sporting items, Disney - general decorative eccentricities. OTHER INFO: Many local museums, large shopping mall, lots of junk shops & cheap B&B's.

D.J. Green Antiques, 334 Abbeydale Road, S7 1FN TEL: 5500881 FAX: 550881 ASSNS: LAPADA PARKING: Easy OPEN: Mon-Sat 9.30-5 MIN: £20 MAX: £5,000 PERIOD: 18th-20th century SPECIALIST: Mainly furniture GENERAL: Silver + plate, glass, pictures etc.

Hibbert Brothers Ltd, 117 Norfolk Street, S1 2JE TEL: 722038 ASSNS: FATG PARKING: Easy OPEN: Mon-Sat 9-5.30 MIN: £20 MAX: £30,000 PERIOD: 19th-20th century SPECIALIST: Paintings of the area GENERAL: Fine original oil paintings & watercolours OTHER INFO: Next to Town Hall Crucilla & Lyceum theatres & new Nova Hotel all within 50 yds.

Paraphernalia, 66-68 Abbeydale Road TEL: 550203 PARKING: Easy OPEN: 9.30-5 MIN: £1 MAX: £600 PERIOD: 19th-20th century SPECIALIST: Brass & iron beds, lighting, kitchenalia, china, etc.

Sheffield Pine Centre, 356-358 South Road, Walkley, S6 3TE. TEL: 336103, 587458 PARKING: Easy OPEN: Mon-Sat 9-5.30 MIN: £5 MAX: £1,000 PERIOD: 18th-20th century SPECIALIST: Stripped pine GENERAL: Victorian, Edwardian furniture OTHER INFO: Workshop at Lowfield Cutlery Forge, Guernsey Road, Heeley, S2 4HG.

Tilleys Vintage Magazine Shops, 281 Shoreham Street, S1 4SS TEL: 752442 PARKING: Own carpark OPEN: Mon-Sat 9-5 & by appt MIN: £1 MAX: £1,000+ PERIOD: 19th but mainly 20th century SPECIALIST: Magazines, comics, newspapers GENERAL: Postcards, posters, annuals, cigarette cards, prints, programmes, books (inc vintage paperbacks), ephemera OTHER INFO: BBC Radio Sheffield regularly do live programmes from shop.

Turn of the Century Antiques, 48-50 Barber Road, Crookesmoor, S10 1ED TEL: 670947 PARKING: Easy OPEN: 10-6 approx MIN: £10 MAX: £10,000 PERIOD: 17th-19th century SPECIALIST: 18th century longcase clocks, all clock restoration/repair GENERAL: Furniture, oils & watercolours.

BAKEWELL (0629)

Bakewell Antiques & Collectors Centre, King Street, DE45 1DZ TEL: 812496 FAX: 814531 PARKING: Own small carpark OPEN: Mon-Sat 10-5, Sun 11-5 MIN: £1 MAX: £5,000 PERIOD: 18th-20th century GENERAL: 15+ dealers. Quality furniture, ceramics, clocks, barometers, books, prints, pictures, silver, decorative items OTHER INFO: Good refreshments on site.

Beedham Antiques Ltd, Holme Hall, DE45 1GE TEL: 813285 PARKING: Own carpark OPEN: By appt MIN: £500 MAX: £30,000 PERIOD: 16th-17th century SPECIALIST: English & Continental oak & other furniture & related objects.

Chappell's Antiques & Fine Art, King Street, DE45 1DZ TEL: 812496 FAX: 814531 ASSNS: BADA, LAPADA, CINOA PARKING: Own carpark OPEN: Mon-Sat 9.30-5.30 MIN: £20 MAX: £15,000 PERIOD: 18th-19th century SPECIALIST: Blue John & Derby porcelain GENERAL: Fine period English furniture, porcelain, clocks, barometers, metals, treen.

Michael Goldstone, Avenel Court, DE45 1DZ TEL: 812487 ASSNS: BADA, CINOA PARKING: Own carpark OPEN: Mon-Sat 9-6 MIN: £25 MAX: £20,000 PERIOD: 17th-18th century SPECIALIST: Early oak & country furniture OTHER INFO: Early market town with weekly market since 1326.

Martin & Dorothy Harper, King Street, DE45 1DZ TEL: 814757 ASSNS: LAPADA PARKING: Easy OPEN: Mon-Wed, Fri, Sat 10-5.30, MIN: £5 MAX: £5,000 PERIOD: 18th-19th century GENERAL: Furniture & general antiques.

Alan Hill Books, 3 Buxton Road, TEL: 814841 ASSNS: PBFA PARKING: Difficult OPEN: Mon-Sat 10-5 MAX: £500 PERIOD: 17th-20th century SPECIALIST: Topographical books & maps GENERAL: Antiquarian & secondhand books, maps & prints.

Water Lane Antiques, Water Lane, DE45 1EW TEL: 814161 PARKING: Easy OPEN: Mon-Sat 9.30-5.30 MIN: £50 MAX: £8,000 PERIOD: 18th-19th century SPECIALIST: Ashford marble & Blue John GENERAL: Furniture & decorative items.

ASHBOURNE (0335)

Yvonne Adams, 47 Church Street TEL: 346466 PARKING: Easy OPEN: Tues & Weds AM MIN: £30 MAX: £2,000 PERIOD: 17th-19th century SPECIALIST: Oak and country furniture and general antiques.

Pamela Elsom - Antiques, 5 Church Street, DE6 1AE TEL: 343468 ASSNS: LAPADA PARKING: Easy OPEN: Mon 2-5, Tues, Thurs-Sat 10-5 MAX: £5,000 PERIOD: 17th-19th century GENERAL: Antique furniture, general antiques, secondhand books OTHER INFO: Gateway to the very scenic Peak District National Park (5 miles).

Manion Antiques, 23 Church Street, DE6 1AE TEL: 343207 PARKING: Easy OPEN: Thurs-Sat 10-5 & by appt MIN: £20 MAX: £2,000 PERIOD: 18th-19th century GENERAL: Wide selection of quality antiques.

Out Of Time, 21 Church Street TEL: 342096 PARKING: Easy OPEN: Mon, Tues, Thurs-Sat 10-5.15 MIN: £5 MAX: £800 PERIOD: 18th-20th century GENERAL: General antiques.

Rose Antiques, 37 Church Street TEL: 3433822 PARKING: Easy OPEN: 10-5 SPECIALIST: General antiques.

Spurrier-Smith Antiques, 28, 39-41 Church Street TEL: 343669 ASSNS: LAPADA PARKING: Own carpark OPEN: Mon, Tues, Thurs-Sat 10-5.30 MIN: £2 MAX: £15,000 PERIOD: 17th-20th century SPECIALIST: English furniture & fine art GENERAL: General antiques OTHER INFO: Comfortable B&B furnished in antiques.

Kenneth Upchurch, 30b Church Street TEL: Derby (0332) 754499 PARKING: Medium OPEN: 11.15-5 MIN: £10 MAX: £1,500 PERIOD: 19th century SPECIALIST: Victorian oils GENERAL: Oils & watercolours, some 18th-19th century pottery & porcelain OTHER INFO: Dovedale 5 miles.

YEAVELEY (0335)

Gravelly Bank Pine Antiques, TEL: 330237 PARKING: Own carpark OPEN: Seven days a week 9-7 MIN: £10 MAX: £650 PERIOD: 19th-20th century SPECIALIST: Antique pine furniture GENERAL: General furniture, kitchens, bedrooms.

DRAGON ANTIQUES

1 Tamworth Street,
Duffield, Derbyshire
Telephone: 0332 842332

J. A. Palfree

Antique and Decorative Furnishings
Clocks – Poreclain – Staffordshire
Figures – Antiquarian Books

DUFFIELD (0332)
Dragon Antiques, 1 Tamworth Street, TEL: 842332 ASSNS: GMC PARKING: Easy OPEN: Mon-Sat 9.30-5.30 MIN: £5 MAX: £5,000 PERIOD: 18th-20th century SPECIALIST: Longcase, bracket & mantel clocks GENERAL: General antiques.

BELPER (0773)
Belper Antiques Centre, 2 Queen Street, DE56 1NR TEL: 823002 PARKING: Free 100 yds OPEN: Mon-Sat 10.30-5.30, Sun 12.30-6 MIN: £1 MAX: £2,000 PERIOD: 18th-20th century GENERAL: Extensive range of quality antiques.

Sweetings Antiques, 1 & 1a The Butts, DE56 1HX TEL: 825930 PARKING: Easy OPEN: Mon-Sat 9.30-5.30 MIN: £1 MAX: £3,000 PERIOD: 19th-20th century SPECIALIST: Old stripped pine, hand stripped satin walnut GENERAL: Furniture and general antiques OTHER INFO: Heart of Amber Valley, Alton Towers, Haddon Hall, Factory Shops.

HEANOR 0773)
Bygones, 23c Derby Road TEL: 768513 PARKING: Easy OPEN: 10-5 closed Mon & Wed MIN:£1 MAX: £550 PERIOD: 19th-20th century SPECIALIST: Langleyware GENERAL: General antiques OTHER INFO: Art gallery on 2 floors. Picture framing service.

RIDDINGS (0773)
South Street Trading Co, 31-32 South Street, DE55 4EJ TEL: 541527 FAX: 541527 PARKING: Medium OPEN: Mon-Sat 9-5.30, Sat 9.30-12 MIN: £5 MAX: £12,000 PERIOD: 20th century SPECIALIST: Hand built steam fired models GENERAL: Collectables OTHER INFO: Midland Railway Centre, Crich Tramway Museum.

DERBY (0332)
Abbey House Antiques, 115 Woods Lane, DE3 3UE TEL: 31426 FAX: 31426 PARKING: Easy OPEN: By appt only (resident) PERIOD: 18th-20th century SPECIALIST: Antique dolls, teddies & all things juvenile GENERAL: Bespoke pine furniture. Full furniture restoration service OTHER INFO: Crown Derby Museum. Good facilities.

Tanglewood, 142 Ashbourne Road TEL: 46005 PARKING: Medium OPEN: Thurs-Sat 10-5 MIN: £10 MAX: £1,800 PERIOD: 18th-19th century SPECIALIST: Country pine from British Isles & Eire GENERAL: Furniture.

Lincolnshire

The Lincolnshire Wolds. By courtesy of Lincolnshire County Council

The tour of Lincolnshire passes through drained fens and some of the richest agricultural land in the country, much of it reclaimed from the sea. Most of the county is flat, even the Lincolnshire Wolds, running parallel to the sea, only rise to 550 feet at their highest point. There have been settlements here since the Stone Age. The Romans built their roads and forts. Later, in the 9th and 10th centuries, much of the county was settled by Danes. The Black Death in the 14th century left many villages depopulated and it is said that there are more than 200 lost villages in Lincolnshire.

 Following the A1 northwards we come off at the A57 and first call on the village of Askham before arriving at the historic city of Lincoln, once a Roman colony where veteran legionaries were given grants of land when they retired. Its most distinctive feature is the cathedral standing on a hill rising to 200 feet above the city. The first cathedral was built by Bishop Remigius in 1072 but it was burnt down and was rebuilt by Bishop Alexander the Magnificent in 1140 with work continuing up until the 15th century. It has a fine west front, said to symbolise Heaven's Gate, and the wonderful Angel choir has the largest eight-light window in the country. This cathedral, one of the most magnificent in England, has so many splendid things to see that the best way to appreciate it is to visit the cathedral bookshop first.

Lincolnshire

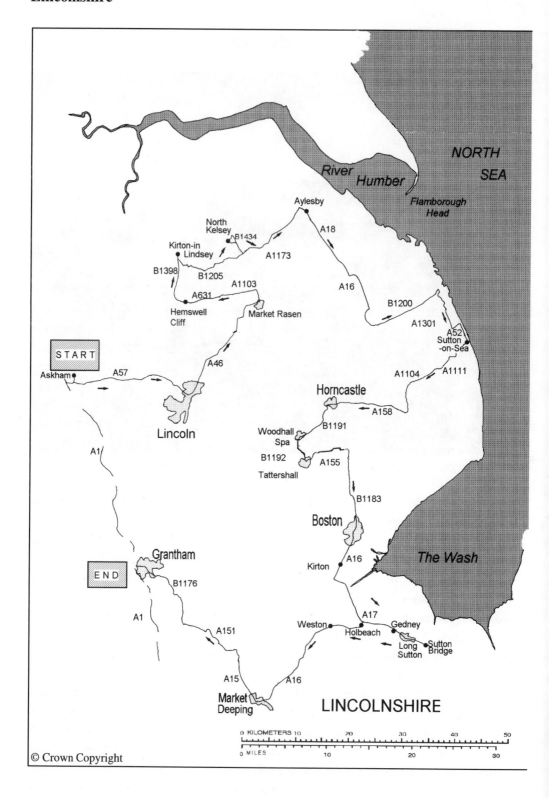

*Lincoln Cathedral. By courtesy of
Lincolnshire County Council*

The Bishop's Palace is noteworthy. By the 17th century the palace was a ruin and it was only in the late 19th century that restoration work began. Excavations have uncovered the medieval layout of the palace which dates from the 12th to 15th centuries.

Lincoln's other major landmark is its castle, built on the site of a Roman fortress. The castle was started in 1068 and houses were demolished to make room for its six acre site. Today the walls and keep still stand.

From Lincoln we follow the A46 to Market Rasen, best known nowadays for its racecourse. Many Roman remains have been found in the town and it also has a number of elegant Geogian Houses. The tour proceeds to the small villages of Hemswell Cliff, Kirton-in-Lindsey and North Kelsey before turning south and eventually arriving at Sutton-on-Sea, a quiet holiday resort set behind sea walls.

Turning inland, the next stop is Horncastle, site of a Roman fort. Although parts of the Roman wall survive, the town is mostly 19th century. Onwards now to Tattershall, where the 15th century castle is one of the finest examples of a fortified brick castle in the country. It was built on the site of 13th century castle by Ralph, Lord Cromwell who was, for a while, treasurer for the King's Exchequer. In 1911 a group of Americans bought the tower and intended to dismantle it and ship it back to the United States. This was prevented by Lord Curzon of Kedleston who bought the castle and presented it to the National Trust.

Now we travel to New Bolingbroke before arriving in Boston. In 1630, about ten years after the Pilgrim Fathers had left for the New World, a group of Puritans set sail from Boston for America and there founded the town of Boston, Massachusetts. The church of St Botolph's contains a memorial to John Cotton, the leader and minister of this band of Puritan settlers, as well as to the five Lincolnshire men who became governors of the state of Massachusetts. The church also has elaborately carved 14th century misericords, a chancel with a fine medieval painted ceiling, a 272 foot high tower from the top of which, on a clear day, you can see Lincoln about 20 miles away.

The Guildhall, now used as a museum and dating from the 15th century, contains the original cells occupied by the Pilgrim Fathers in 1607 after their first unsuccesful attempt to escape to Holland in search of religious freedom.

In the 13th century Boston was a thriving port but by the 16th century it was in decline because of the

Maud Foster Mill, Boston.
By courtesy of Lincolnshire County Council

silting of the River Witham. However the drainage of the fens and improvements to the river channel such as the opening of the Grand sluice in the 18th century brought great improvements so that by the 19th century the docks were, and continue to be, busy and profitable.

Continuing south, the route passes through the village of Kirton and then the market town of Holbeach, one of the bulb-growing centres of Lincolnshire.

Detouring eastward, we next visit the pretty market town of Long Sutton which has a perpendicular church with a detached 162 feet high timber and lead spire considered one of the finest in the country. The next stop, Sutton Bridge, is where legend has it King John lost his treasure in nearby Cross Keys Wash

Retracing the route, we now call on the old town of Market Deeping, on the River Welland and situated on the edge of the Fens. This was once a town of some importance in the area although it has declined and now there is no longer a market held here. A point of interest is the rectory built in the 13th century which is the oldest rectory still used for its original purpose. The town possesses several fine, historic houses and a good restored perpendicular church with a rood-loft doorway.

The last stop is in Grantham on the River Witham, birthplace of Sir Isaac Newton and Margaret Thatcher. The town has a long history. It has benefited through the centuries from being on the Great North Road and has one of the oldest inns in the country, The Angel and Royal in the High Street. Reputedly King John held court here in 1213 and Richard III signed the Duke of Buckingham's death warrant in 1483. Another inn, the Beehive, has a real beehive for its sign. Seven miles south of the town stands Woolsthorpe Manor, birthplace of Sir Isaac Newton and where it is said the apple fell from the tree and hit him on the head leading to him formulate the theory of gravity. There is also the National Trust property of Belton House 3 miles north east of Grantham on the A607 to Lincoln. This is a late 17th century house with a plasterwork ceiling by Edward Goudge, carvings of the Grinling Gibbons school, portraits, furniture, tapestries and memorabilia of the Duke of Windsor.

Another stately home, again seven miles from the town but this time off the A607 towards Nottingham, is Belvoir Castle, (pronounced Beever) seat of the Dukes of Rutland. There was once a Norman castle on the site but the present building, magnificent as it is, dates from 1816. From here the visitor gets a splendid view over the Vale of Belvoir. The castle contains many art treasures and interesting militaria and there is a fine Statue Garden with 17th century sculptures.

ANTIQUE DEALERS
ASKHAM (0777)
Sally Mitchell Fine Arts, Thornlea, Askham, NG22 0RN TEL: 83234 ASSNS: FATG PARKING: Own carpark OPEN: By appt MIN: £20 MAX: £5,000 PERIOD: 19th-20th century SPECIALIST: 500+ sporting & country paintings & prints OTHER Lincoln 20 miles, Southwell Cathedral 15 miles, Doncaster racecourse 20, Sherwood Forest 7.

LINCOLN (0522)
C. & K.E. Dring Antiques, 111 High Street, LN5 7PY TEL: 540733 PARKING: Medium OPEN: 10-5 MIN: £5 MAX: £2,000 PERIOD: 18th-20th century SPECIALIST: Inlaid furniture GENERAL: Toys, prints, clocks & shipping etc OTHER INFO: Cathedral, Castle, Roman remains, City Museum, Museum of Lincolnshire Life. Good facilities.

Dorrian Lambert Antiques, 64-65 Steep Hill TEL: 545916 PARKING: Easy OPEN: Mon, Tues, Thurs-Sat 10.30-5 MIN: £10 MAX: £5,000 PERIOD: 18th-20th century SPECIALIST: Antique jewellery, collectables, small furniture unusual items, pottery, metalwork OTHER INFO: Shop is opposite Jews House (one of the oldest buildings in Europe).

Mansions, 5 Eastgate, LN2 1QA TEL: 513631 PARKING: Easy OPEN: Mon-Sat 10-5 MIN: £10 MAX: £500 PERIOD: 18th-20th century SPECIALIST: Period lighting GENERAL: Beaded & decorative items, fabrics, small furniture.

Mansions, Cobb Hall, St Pauls Lane, LN1 3AL TEL: 513631 PARKING: Easy OPEN: Mon-Sat 10-5 MIN: £10 MAX: £500 PERIOD: 18th-20th century SPECIALIST: Period lighting GENERAL: Beaded & decorative items, fabrics, small furniture, papier maché.

Richard Pullen Jewellers, 28 The Strait, LN2 1JD TEL: 537170 ASSNS: NAG PARKING: Easy OPEN: Mon, Tues, Thurs-Sat 10-4.30 MIN: £20 MAX: £3,000 PERIOD: 19th-20th century SPECIALIST: Antique silver & jewellery.

J. & R. Ratcliffe, 46 Steep Hill, LN2 1LU TEL: 537438 PARKING: Easy OPEN: 10-5 MIN: £5 MAX: £5,000 PERIOD: 17th-19th century SPECIALIST: Old English & Continental furniture GENERAL: General antiques.

Rowletts of Lincoln, 338 High Street, LN5 7DQ TEL: 524139 PARKING: Easy OPEN: 9-5 MIN: £1 MAX: £4,000 PERIOD: 19th-20th century SPECIALIST: Late Victorian/Edwardian jewellery.

MARKET RASEN (0673)
Carole's Corner, 11 Market Place, LN8 3HT TEL: 844625 PARKING: Easy OPEN: 10-4 PERIOD: Mainly 20th century GENERAL: 3 rooms full of all sorts-not all antiques but nice to see.

Harwood Tate, Church Mill, Caistor Road, LN8 3HX TEL: 843579 PARKING: Own carpark OPEN: Mon-Fri 9-5.30, Sat 10-1 MIN: £25 MAX: £5,000 PERIOD: 18th-19th century GENERAL: Oak, mahogany, rosewood furniture, clocks, paintings, prints, textiles, ornamentals.

HEMSWELL CLIFF (0427)
Guardroom Antique Centre, The Guardroom, Old RAF Hemswell (nr Caenby Corner), DN21 5TU TEL: 668312 FAX: 668312 PARKING: Own carpark OPEN: Seven days 10-5 MIN: £1 MAX: £5,000 PERIOD: 19th-20th century SPECIALIST: Continental furniture GENERAL: Old & new pine, shipping goods, smalls, collectables, almost anything pre 1950 OTHER INFO: 35 unitholders, further 300+ units within 400 yds.

Hemswell Antiques Centres, Caenby Corner Estate, DN21 5TJ TEL: 668389 PARKING: Own carpark OPEN: Seven days 10-5 MIN: £1 MAX: £20,000 PERIOD: 18th-20th century SPECIALIST: Period, pine & shipping furniture GENERAL: Longcase clocks, barometers, jewellery, prints, books, silver, pictures, ceramics & collectables OTHER INFO: 300 dealers in UK's largest antique centre, own licensed restaurant & coffee shop, accommodation arranged. Lincoln 10 miles.

KIRTON-IN-LINDSEY (0652)
Keith Van Hefflin, 12 High Street TEL: 648044 ASSN: Gemmological Assn.(own research lab & museum contacts) PARKING: Own carpark OPEN:

10-5 MIN: £1 MAX: £5,000 PERIOD: 17th-20th century SPECIALIST: Jewellery, curios, gold watches GENERAL: Antique coins, porcelain & paintings OTHER INFO: Original working windmill, gliding club. Private guide/courier (Mr. Williams of Redbourne Cottage) available to & from hotels/airports & general transport.

NORTH KELSEY (0652)

Sykes Antiques, Station Yard TEL: 678036 PARKING: Own carpark OPEN: Seven days 9-5.30 or by appt MIN: £10 MAX: £1,000 PERIOD: 19th century GENERAL: 10,000 sq ft of top quality pine.

AYLESBY (0472)

Robin Fowler Period Clocks, Washingdales, DN37 7LH TEL: 751335 ASSNS: BHI, GMC PARKING: Own carpark OPEN: By appt MIN: £200 MAX: £10,000 PERIOD: 17th-19th century SPECIALIST: Clocks & barometers.

SUTTON-ON-SEA (0507)

Knicks Knacks Antiques, 41 High Street, LN12 2EY TEL: 441916 PARKING: Medium OPEN: Tues-Sun 10-1, 2-5 MIN: £1 MAX: £500 PERIOD: 19th-20th century SPECIALIST: Brass, iron beds, lighting, fireplaces, Deco GENERAL: 8 rooms of bric-a-brac, linen, cast iron, brass, copper, bygones OTHER INFO: We have a museum of Victorian shops & the inside of typical Victorian house.

HORNCASTLE (0507)

Clare Boam, 22 North Street, LN9 5DX TEL: 522381 PARKING: Easy OPEN: Mon-Sat 9-5, Sun 2-4.30 MIN: £1 MAX: £1,000 PERIOD: 19th-20th century GENERAL: Bric-a-brac, general furniture OTHER INFO: Admiral Rodney Hotel.

Lincolnshire Antiques Centre, 26 Bridge Street, LN9 5HZ TEL: 527794 FAX: 526670 PARKING: Own carpark OPEN: Mon-Sat 9-5 MIN: £1 MAX: £5,000+ PERIOD: 17th-20th century GENERAL: Furniture, jewellery, silver, collectables OTHER INFO: 30+ dealers under one roof and country giftware shop. Close to all amenities.

Seaview Antiques, 47a East Street TEL: 523287 PARKING: Medium OPEN: Mon-Sat 9-5 but trade anytime MIN: £5 MAX: £5,000 PERIOD: 18th-20th century GENERAL: Furniture & smalls.

Laurence Shaw Antiques, 77 East Street, LN9 7AA TEL: 527638 PARKING: Own carpark OPEN: 8.30-5 MIN: £10 MAX: £10,000 PERIOD: 17th-19th century SPECIALIST: Books GENERAL: Wide range of quality antiques, 20th

century books OTHER INFO: Next to Tourist Info and famous Magpies restaurant.

WOODHALL SPA (0526)

Underwoodhall Antiques, Broadway Centre TEL: 353815 PARKING: Easy OPEN: 10-5 MIN: £1 MAX: £500 PERIOD: 19th-20th century SPECIALIST: Postcards, Worcester, Royal Doulton GENERAL: General antiques OTHER INFO: Tearoom attached, association with RAF Dambusters 617 Squadron. Golf course.

TATTERSHALL (0526)

Wayside Antiques, Market Place, LN4 4LQ TEL: 342436 PARKING: Easy OPEN: Mon-Sat 10-5 but anytime by appt MIN: £2 MAX: £2,000 PERIOD: 18th-20th century GENERAL: Furniture, clocks etc OTHER INFO: Near Tattershall Castle.

BOSTON (0205)

Mary Holland Antiques, 7a Red Lion Street, PE21 0PH TEL: 363791, home 353840 PARKING: Easy OPEN: Tues-Wed, Fri-Sat 10-5 & by appt MIN: £1 MAX: £1,000 PERIOD: 19th-20th century GENERAL: General antiques OTHER INFO: 4 antique shops behind us. Tourist Centre. The Boston Stump, White Hart Hotel, Shod Friars Hall, The Docks. Wormgate, Guildhall, library. Weds & Sat. market day. (Wed. also auction). Next door stocks dolls houses & furniture, gold & china etc

Portobello Row, 93-95 High Street TEL: 368692 PARKING: Own carpark OPEN: Tues-Wed, Fri-Sat 10-4, Mon & Thurs 10-2.45 MIN: £1 PERIOD: 19th-20th century SPECIALIST: Blue & white china, postcards, 40-60's clothing, lamps, postcards GENERAL: General antiques OTHER INFO: Market days Wed & Sat. White Hart & New England hotels, lots of connections with Pilgrim Fathers.

KIRTON (0205)

Kirton Antiques, 3 High Street, PE20 1DR TEL: 722595, 722134 FAX: 722895 ASSNS: LAPADA PARKING: Own carpark OPEN: Mon-Fri 8.30-5, Sat 8.30-12, but anytime by appt MIN: £1 MAX: £10,000 PERIOD: 17th-20th century SPECIALIST: Chests of drawers GENERAL: General antiques OTHER INFO: Guildhall Museum, Boston, incorporating cells where Pilgrim Fathers were kept prior to sailing for Boston, Mass.

GEDNEY (0406)

Paul Johnston, Chapel Gate, PE12 0DB TEL: 362414 ASSNS: BADA PARKING: Easy OPEN: 10-6. Specialist dealer in 17th-18th century English oak furniture OTHER INFO: Gedney Church well worth visiting, excellent pub food nearby

LONG SUTTON (0406)

J.W. Talton, 15-19 Market Street, PE12 9DD TEL: 362147 PARKING: Easy OPEN: 9-5 except Weds 9-12 MIN: £15 MAX: £1,000 PERIOD: 19th-20th century GENERAL: Small furniture, silver + plate, porcelain.

SUTTON BRIDGE (0406)

The Antique Shop, 100 Bridge Road, PE12 9SA TEL: 350535 PARKING: Easy OPEN: 9-5.30 MIN: £5 MAX: £4,000 PERIOD: 19th century SPECIALIST: Oil lamps, tables & chairs, sideboards GENERAL: China, brass.

Bridge Antiques, 32 Bridge Road, PE12 9UA TEL: 350704 PARKING: Own carpark OPEN: Mon-Fri 8-5 or by appt MIN: £25+ PERIOD: 20th century SPECIALIST: Jacobean style, barleytwist, pineapple, linen fold GENERAL: 250 pieces selected 1920's oak & walnut furniture.

Old Barn Antiques Warehouse, 220 New Road, PE12 9QE TEL: 350435 PARKING: Own carpark

OPEN: Mon-Sat 9-5.30 MIN: £5 PERIOD: 19th-20th century SPECIALIST: Pine GENERAL: Oak, mahogany, walnut shipping goods, unstripped pine.

HOLBEACH (0406)

P.J. Cassidy (Books), 1 Boston Road, PE12 7LR TEL: 426322 FAX: 426322 PARKING: Easy OPEN: Mon-Sat 10-6 MIN: £1 MAX: £150+ PERIOD: 17th-20th century SPECIALIST: Antique maps, prints & books OTHER INFO: Small market town, with 3 good hotels.

WESTON ST MARYS (0406)

Dean's Antiques, The Walnuts TEL: 370429 PARKING: Own carpark OPEN: 10-4 MIN: £1 MAX: £200 PERIOD: 19th-20th century SPECIALIST: Farm & country bygones GENERAL: Pine & general furniture, bric-a-brac, brass, copper, old tools OTHER INFO: Display of old farm tools, kitchen & dairy bygones.

MARKET DEEPING (0778)

Portland House Antiques, 23 Church Street, PE6 8AN TEL: 347129 PARKING: Easy OPEN: Mon-Sat 10-4.30 MIN: £100 MAX: £8,500 PERIOD: 18th-20th century GENERAL: Furniture, decorative arts OTHER INFO: George Hotel, Stamford.

GRANTHAM (0476)

The Attic, 84 Westgate, NG31 6LE TEL: 64990 PARKING: Easy OPEN: 8.30-6 MIN: £1 MAX: £1,500 PERIOD: 19th-20th century GENERAL: General antiques.

Grantham Clocks, 30 Lodge Way, NG31 8DD TEL: 61784 ASSNS: BHI PARKING: Easy OPEN: Anytime by appt MIN: £20 MAX: £4,000 PERIOD: 18th-20th century SPECIALIST: Antique clocks GENERAL: Full range of clocks only, restoration guaranteed OTHER INFO: Grantham is birthplace of Isaac Newton & Margaret Thatcher.

Grantham Furniture Emporium, 4-6 Wharf Road TEL: 62967 PARKING: Own carpark OPEN: Tues, Thurs-Sat 10-5, Sun 11-5 MIN: £1 MAX: £3,000 PERIOD: 19th-20th century GENERAL: 3,000 sq ft of Victorian, Edwardian, 20's & shipping furniture OTHER INFO: Australian owners. Good town facilties. Belton Woods Country Club.

Notions, 2a Market Place TEL: 63603 PARKING: Easy OPEN: 10-5 MIN: £1 MAX: £500 GENERAL: Furniture & decorative items from Victorian to 1960's.

Humberside and Yorkshire

This tour ranges through charming Yorkshire villages, seaside resorts and market towns. It also visits the Humberside port of Hull and then the city of York, steeped in two thousand years of history.

The route starts by leaving the M62 motorway at Junction 37 and taking the A614 for Market Weighton's (pronounced Weeton) once the home of William Bradley, the Market Weighton Giant. At 7ft 9ins he is reputed to be the tallest Englishman ever. He died in 1820 and is buried in the local churchyard where a plaque may be seen. Another plaque with his footprint drawn on it marks his home, Bradley House on the corner of York Road. His chair may be seen in the Londesborough Arms Hotel in the High Street.

We now proceed via South Cave to Hull. Standing on the mouth of the River Humber, Hull is officially called Kingston-upon-Hull. Its prosperity has been based on the fishing industry, now in decline. There is much of interest in the town. Blaydes House, in the High Street, is a mid Georgian merchant's house with a fine staircase and panelled rooms. Wilberforce House, also in the High Street, was the birthplace of William Wilberforce who fought for the abolition of slavery; it now houses a museum to commemorate his struggle. One of the oldest secular buildings in the town is the Old Grammar School, built in the late 16th century. This contains a museum showing the town's history. Standing about seven miles north east of the town is Burton Constable, a magnificent Elizabethan house built about 1570. It contains a fine collection of furniture, pictures, works of art and 18th century scientific instruments.

Travelling north, next is Beverley, now in Humberside but once the capital of the East Riding of Yorkshire. The Minster with its twin towers dominates the town. Started in the 13th century, it is reputed to be one of the finest Gothic buildings in Europe. The decorated style of ecclesiastical architecture is demonstrated to good effect in the Percy tomb, particularly in its canopy. Other notable points are the east window with its original glass, the 17th century woodcarving on the choir stalls and the Saxon *fridstol* or sanctuary chair beside the altar which is where, it is thought, an official sat to hear pleas for sanctuary.

Other interesting and historic buildings exist. North Bar is the only remaining 15th century gateway of the five that once allowed access through the town walls. Another church of particular interest, St Mary's, was the Minster's chapel of ease and was also Norman in origin although it has been altered and enlarged over the centuries. The Guildhall, in Register Square, has an outstanding example of stucco work in its ceiling showing the all-seeing figure of Justice. The Guildhall was bought by the council in 1500 for use as a town hall and it now contains the Mayor's Parlour and the Tourist Information Office.

Heading east for the coast we come to Hornsea which has a good sandy bathing

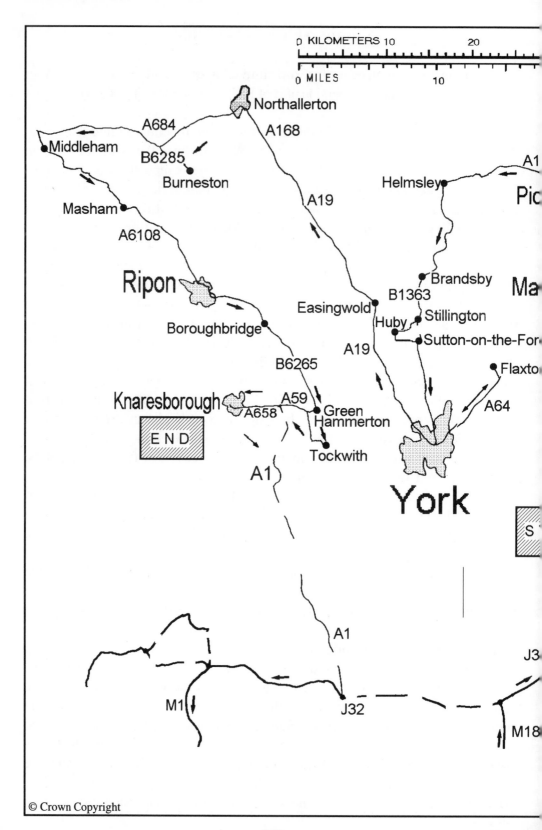

© Crown Copyright

beach and, in the older part, pretty cottages with pantiled roofs. The town stands by Hornsea Mere, the largest lake in Humberside, and a sanctuary for birds.

The next stop, the seaside resort of Bridlington, also has good sandy beaches and a harbour for trawlers. The old part of the town lies about a mile inland and was originally built around an Augustinian priory which now serves as the parish church. Set on the cliffs overlooking Bridlington Bay stands Sewerby Hall built between 1714 and 1720. Its 50 acres of gardens include an old English walled garden, a small zoo and an aviary. There is also a museum dedicated to the aviator, Amy Johnson. Another great house, Burton Agnes Hall, lies six miles to the south west of Bridlington. This is an outstanding example of Elizabethan architecture. It contains collections of antique furniture, porcelain and the largest collection in the north of French Impressionist and Modern paintings including Renoir, Pissaro, Corot, Utrillo, Gauguin, Augustus John, etc.

At nearby Flamborough Head the chalk wolds meet the sea in a series of dramatic cliffs which have been eroded into intricate shapes. An octagonal lighthouse stands on top of the Head. In the local church there is a 15th century rood screen.

We now move inland via the village of Kilham to Driffield (properly called

Heavily eroded cliffs near Flamborough Head

Great Driffield), a busy market town. Its most prominent feature is the 110 foot high tower of the 15th century church. Sledmere House stands eight miles north west of the town. Originally built in the mid 18th century the house was burnt down in 1911. However, during the First World War it was reconstructed and restored and contains much of its original furniture and pictures.

The next call is on Malton, the site of a Roman fort. The town began to prosper when the River Derwent, upon which it stands, was made navigable in the 18th century. Six miles to the west of the town stands the magnificent mansion, Castle Howard. A castle in name only, this palatial building was designed by Vanbrugh and built between 1699 and 1726. It is set in beautiful parkland and contains many impressive rooms and fine collections of pictures, statuary, costume and furniture.

Following the tour we pass through the charming villages of Snainton and Thornton le Dale to reach Pickering. Standing on the edge of the North Yorkshire Moors there has been a settlement at Pickering since before the Norman Conquest. Its castle was probably first built in the 12th century. Situated in good hunting country, during the Middles Ages the castle was frequently host to the reigning monarchs of the day. It saw action in various raids by the Scots and rebellions by local lords. By the 16th century, though, the castle was in decay. At that time some repair work was done but the castle was largely uninhabited with only the Mill Tower being used as a prison and the chapel as a courthouse. It is only since 1926, after two centuries of neglect, that repair and restoration work have been done.

Along the A170 we come to Helmsley, a pretty stone-built town standing just three miles from the ruins of the magnificent Rievaulx Abbey. Sited in a beautiful steep wooded valley by the River Rye, the Cistercian abbey was founded in 1131. For a century the abbey prospered and became very wealthy. However, the extensive building works imposed a heavy burden and by the 13th century the abbey was deep in debt. At its height, it had 140 monks and 500 lay brothers but by the time of the Dissolution it had declined to only 22 monks.

We now turn southwards along the B1363 through the villages of Brandsby, Stillington where Laurence Sterne was vicar and Sutton-on-the-Forest to arrive in York. This city, rich in history, can only be covered briefly here. All visitors to the city should go to the Tourist Information Centre and also to the exhibition, the York Story in the Heritage Centre in Castlegate, which tells the story of York.

Initially, York was founded as the Roman city of *Eboracum*. It was established as a fort and military headquarters to keep down potential rebellions and to guard against raids by the northern tribes. The city continued in importance after the Romans left. It retains much of its medieval walls and too many historic buildings to mention them all individually.

No visit to the city would be complete without a visit to York Minster, the largest medieval cathedral in Britain. The magnificence of Durham Cathedral and the great Yorkshire Cistercian abbeys spurred on the authorities here to build an even greater cathedral in York. Construction of the present building started in the 13th century and took about 250 years to complete. The cathedral has so many wonderful things to see. Amongst these are the glorious windows with their original glass. Indeed the cathedral has the largest collection of medieval glass in Britain. One of the reasons for this is that the Minster was spared during the Civil War. The citizens of York surrendered to Sir Thomas Fairfax, leading the Parliamentary army, on condition that none of their churches, including the Minster, would be damaged.

Another fascinating feature of York is the Shambles, an area of narrow cobbled streets dating from the 18th century and earlier with their original buildings. Another point of interest is Fairfax House in Castlegate. It is described as a classic masterpiece of 18th century architecture and is reputed to be one of the finest townhouses in England. It contains a superb collection of 18th century furniture

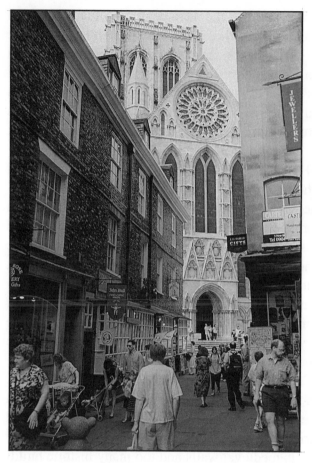

York Minster and the Shambles

and clocks collected by Noel Terry, the former owner.

There are numerous museums in York, including the National Railway Museum in Leeman Road, York Castle Museum detailing social history, the Yorkshire Museum which contains collections of Roman, Anglo-Saxon and Viking artefacts and the Yorkshire Museum of Farming at Murton which is set in an eight acre country park.

After York, we make a detour to the village of Flaxton before taking the A19 through the small town of Easingwold to Northallerton and then on to Burneston and Middleham. This town was closely associated with Richard III. The ruined castle, which was once his home, was started in the latter part of the 12th century. The castle became part of the estate of the Earl of Warwick. When he was killed in the Battle of Barnet in 1471 it passed to the Crown and was given to Richard of Gloucester, later Richard III. After Richard's defeat at the Battle of Bosworth it again passed to the Crown and was neglected until it fell into ruins. The stump of a cross in the town's market square is thought to represent Richard III's heraldic boar.

Turning south again we come to Masham, on the River Ure, famous for a very strong beer, Threakston's Old Peculiar, brewed here. Masham is a pretty town with a large market square. At the corner of the square stands an impressive church which includes a tower with an octagon topped by a spire.

Next the route reaches Ripon standing on the meeting of the Rivers Cover, Skell and Ure. Its cathedral is the most outstanding feature of this thriving market town which confers upon it the status of city. Ripon Cathedral was built over many centuries and within its structure is an illustration of the evolution and change that took place in ecclesiastical architecture. The crypt was built in 670AD by St Wilfrid to protect the bones of saints. His church, built above the crypt, was destroyed by marauding Danes but it was rebuilt by the Archbishops of York who used it when visiting this part of their diocese. Because a succession of Archbishops were responsible for the rebuilding the mixture of architectural styles occurred. The chapter house dates from about the 12th century and is typical of the Norman style. The Early-English style may be seen in the simple beauty of the west front. In contrast, the east windows are a breath-taking example of the Decorated style from approximately the 14th century. The Perpendicular style, unique to English stonemasons, may be seen in the reconstructed medieval nave. After the Reformation, the Archbishops of York no longer held such importance and Ripon's church lost its prime purpose. It continued to serve as the parish church even though it was too large for a town the size of Ripon. However, by 1836 it was designated as the cathedral for this part of Yorkshire as the area's population had grown considerably and a separate diocese was deemed necessary. Restoration work and upgrading of the interior was carried out and included an Arts and Craft movement pulpit made from bronze and marble and the fine reredos behind the high altar.

A 90 feet high obelisk surmounted by a weather vane in the shape of a wakeman's horn stands in Ripon market square. In medieval times the wakeman was responsible for sounding the horn each night to summon the Town Watch to their duty. Although the office of Wakeman was replaced by the Mayor in 1617 the Hornblower still sounds the horn from each corner of the market square at 9pm every evening. The house of the last Wakeman and the first Mayor of Ripon may be seen at the corner of the square.

There are a number of interesting places to visit near Ripon. Amongst these are the ruins of Fountains Abbey, now awarded World Heritage status. These still beautiful ruins are all that remain of one of the richest Cistercian abbeys in England. Three miles south of Ripon off the A61 there is a fine example of a moated manor house, Markenfield Hall. Then four miles south east of the town stands Newby Hall, a lovely Adam style house.

Now continuing down the B6265 we arrive in Boroughbridge, once on a major coaching road, it has the large

The Wakeman's House, Ripon

353

inns typical of coaching towns. Now, though, the main trunk route bypasses it and it is a quiet pleasant place to visit. On the River Ure, its bridge was once a crossing place betweem the former West and North Ridings of Yorkshire. Outside the town stands the Devil's Arrows, three 20 feet high monoliths dating from the Bronze Age.

Pausing in the villages of Green Hammerton and Tockwith we now arrive at our final stop, Knaresborough. Sited on a steep gorge cut by the River Nidd, terraces of houses rise up the sides and cobbled lanes run down to the river. There are also the remains of a castle originally started by Serlo de Burg who received the land from William the Conqueror. Richard II was imprisoned here for a time and one of the knights who killed Thomas à Becket, Sir Hugh de Morville, stayed here. Another local attraction is the Dropping Well whose water has such a high mineral content that objects dropped into it petrify. Legend has it that the prophetess, Mother Shipton, was born in a nearby cave.

The grandest of Gothic Revival houses stands four and a half miles west of Knaresborough. Allerton Park's Great Hall and Dining Room are reputed to be amongst the finest carved wood rooms in England.

Having reached the end of this tour we follow the A1 to its junction with the M62 to return south.

ANTIQUE DEALERS
MARKET WEIGHTON (043)
Houghton Hall Antiques, Cliffe-Northcave Road (1 mile), YO4 3RE TEL: 873234 PARKING: Own carpark OPEN: Seven days 8.30-4.30 MIN: £5 MAX: £6,000 PERIOD: 17th-20th century SPECIALIST: Furniture GENERAL: General antiques OTHER INFO: Londesborough Arms Hotel/restaurant, George Hotel Beverley.
SOUTH CAVE (0430)
The Old Copper Shop & Posthouse Antiques, 69 & 75 Market Place TEL: 423988 PARKING: Easy OPEN: Mon, Wed-Sat 9.30-4.30 MIN: £5 MAX: £1,000 PERIOD: 19th-20th century GENERAL: General antiques.

Penny Farthing Antiques, 60 Market Place TEL: 422958 PARKING: Easy OPEN: Mon-Sat 9.30-5 MIN: £5 MAX: £3,000 PERIOD: 18th-20th century SPECIALIST: Brass & iron bedsteads GENERAL: General antiques.
HULL (0482)
Grannies Parlour & Grannies Treasures Antique Centre, 33 Anlaby Road, HUI 2PG TEL: 228258 PARKING: Medium OPEN: Mon-Sat 11-5 MIN: £1 MAX: £500 PERIOD: 19th-20th century SPECIALIST: Advertising items, dolls, teddies, kitchenalia GENERAL: All collectables & antiques OTHER INFO: Town centre 10 mins.

David K. Hakeney Antiques, 64 George Street, HU1 3AB TEL: 228190, (0860) 507774 FAX: 228190 ASSNS: LAPADA PARKING: Medium OPEN: Mon-Fri 10-5, Sat 10-1 MIN: £10 MAX: £5,000 PERIOD: 18th-20th century GENERAL: General antiques.

David K.Hakeney Antiques Trade Warehouse, 400 Wincolmlee TEL: 228190, (0860) 507774 FAX: 228190 ASSNS: LAPADA PARKING: Medium OPEN: Mon-Fri 10-5, Sat 10-1 MIN: £10 MAX: £5,000 PERIOD: 18th-20th century GENERAL: General antiques.

Imperial Antiques, 397 Hessle Road, HU3 4EH TEL: 27439 PARKING: Easy OPEN: 9-6 MIN: £50 MAX: £500 PERIOD: 18th-19th century SPECIALIST: Antique & old stripped pine GENERAL: Bespoke reproduction pine OTHER INFO: Sunnybank Hotel.
BEVERLEY (0482)
James Starkey Fine Art, 49 Highgate, HU17 0ON TEL: 881179 FAX: 861644 PARKING: Easy OPEN: Mon-Fri 10-5, Sat 10-1 MIN: £20 MAX: £20,000 PERIOD: 17th-20th century SPECIALIST: Paintings GENERAL: Few small antiques OTHER INFO: The Gothic Beverley Arms Hotel in shadow of Beverley Minster.
HORNSEA (0964)
Padgetts Ltd, 19 Hull Road, HU18 1RL TEL: 534086 ASSNS: PCCGB PARKING: Own carpark OPEN: By appt MIN: £5 MAX: £5,000 PERIOD: 18th-20th century SPECIALIST: Cameras, longcase clocks GENERAL: Photographic & scientific equipment, all types of clocks OTHER INFO: Hornsea Pottery (open), Merlstead Hotel recommended.
BRIDLINGTON (0262)
Priory Antiques, 47-49 High Street, Yo16 4PR TEL: 601365 PARKING: Easy OPEN: Tues, Wed, Fri 10-5 MIN: £5 MAX: £4,500 PERIOD: 18th-19th century SPECIALIST: Fine Georgian & Victorian furniture GENERAL: Metalware, clocks & barometers OTHER INFO: Best fish 'n' chips for miles.
FLAMBOROUGH (0262)
Lesley Berry Antiques, The Manor House, YO15 1PD TEL: 850943 PARKING: Own carpark OPEN: 9.30-6 MIN: £2 MAX: £1,500 PERIOD: 17th-19th century GENERAL: General antiques OTHER INFO: Member Wolsey Lodges. Accommodation available.
KILHAM (0262)
Old Ropery Antiques, East Street, YO25 0SG TEL: 420233 PARKING: Easy OPEN: Tues-Fri 9-5 MIN: £100 MAX: £6,000 PERIOD: 17th-19th century SPECIALIST: Clocks GENERAL: Some furniture & scientific instruments. Always a good selection of barometers.
DRIFFIELD (0377)
Antique Pine & Furniture Shop, Smith & Smith Designs, 58a Middle Street North, YO25 7SU TEL: 256321 PARKING: Easy OPEN: Mon-Sat 9.30-5 MIN: £25 MAX: £2,000 PERIOD: 18th-20th century SPECIALIST: Pine & country furniture GENERAL: Antique & reproduction + bespoke furniture OTHER INFO: Bell Hotel

The Crested China Company, Station Road, YO25 7PY TEL: 257042, 255002 PARKING: Own carpark OPEN: By appt or take a chance MIN: £1 MAX: £400 mostly PERIOD: Mainly

1880-1930 SPECIALIST: Goss & crested china OTHER INFO: Bell Hotel, superb facilities.
MALTON (0653)
Matthew Maw, 18 Castlegate TEL: 694638 PARKING: Easy OPEN: Mon-Sat 9-5 MIN: £10 MAX: £1,000 PERIOD: 19th-20th century GENERAL: Traditional furniture, low priced shipping goods (no smalls) OTHER INFO: 30 mins from where the TV series, Heartbeat is filmed.
SNAINTON (0723)
Cottage Antiques, 19 High Street, YO13 9AE TEL: 859577 PARKING: Medium OPEN: Mon-Fri 8.30-5, Sat 8.30-12 MIN: £1 MAX: £3,000 PERIOD: 19th century SPECIALIST: Longcase clocks GENERAL: General antiques OTHER INFO: Hand made furniture & antique shops in village, good facilities.
THORNTON DALE (0751)
Stable Antiques, 4 Pickering Road TEL: 74435 for appts & info PARKING: medium OPEN: From 2pm & by appt, closed Mons MIN: £3 MAX: £600 PERIOD: 19th-20th century SPECIALIST: 19th century porcelain, silver GENERAL: General antiques OTHER INFO: Spacious attractive welcoming shop.
PICKERING (0751)
Antiques & Things, Southgate TEL: 76142 PARKING: Own carpark OPEN: 10-5, closed Weds PERIOD: 19th-20th century GENERAL: Mixture, pottery, smalls, furniture etc OTHER INFO: Excellent holdiay centre.
C.H. Reynolds Antiques, 122 Eastgate, YO18 7DW TEL: 72785 PARKING: Easy OPEN: Seven days 9.30-5.30 MIN: £5+ PERIOD: 18th-20th century GENERAL: General antiques OTHER INFO: Close to moors & N.Yorks rail.
HELMSLEY (0439)
Rievaulx Books, 18 High Street, YO6 5AG TEL: 70912 PARKING: Easy OPEN: Mon-Sat 10.30-5, Sun 2-5 MIN: £1 MAX: £200 PERIOD: 19th-20th century SPECIALIST: Art, architecture & 20th century wood engravings GENERAL: Secondhand & antiquarian books.
Westway Pine, Westway Cottage, Ashdale Road, YO6 5DE TEL: 70172 PARKING: Easy OPEN: Mon-Sat 9-5.30 & by appt MIN: £10+ MAX: £2,000 PERIOD: 18th-20th century SPECIALIST: Pine furniture (restored) OTHER INFO: We offer en-suite B&B's.

York Street Antiques, 7 Church Street, YO6 5AD TEL: 70833 ASSNS: LAPADA PARKING: Own carpark OPEN: Fri, Sat 10-4, also summer Tues & Thurs MIN: £5 MAX: £5,000 PERIOD: 17th-19th century SPECIALIST: Metalware, particularly brass & copper GENERAL: General antiques.
BRANDSBY (0347)
L.L. Ward & Son, Bar House, YO6 4RQ TEL: 888651 ASSNS: GMC PARKING: Own carpark OPEN: 9-6 PERIOD: 18th-19th century SPECIALIST: Antique stripped pine OTHER INFO: Based in the Howardian Hills.
STILLINGTON (0347)
Pond Cottage Antiques, Brandsby Road TEL: 810796 FAX: 810796 PARKING: Own carpark OPEN: 9-7 MIN: £1 MAX: £900 PERIOD: 19th-20th century SPECIALIST: Pine & kitchen antiques GENERAL: Antique & reproduction pine, kitchenalia, dairy items.
SUTTON-ON-THE-FOREST (0904)
O'Flynns Antiquarian Books, Naffis Farm, York Road, YO6 1ER TEL: 641404 FAX: 611872 PARKING: Medium OPEN: 9-6 MIN: £1 MAX: £1,500 PERIOD: 17th-20th century SPECIALIST: Antiquarian & secondhand books GENERAL: Antique maps & prints.
HUBY (0423)
Haworth Antiques, Harrogate Road, LS17 0EF TEL: 734293, (0831) 692263 ASSNS: BWCMG PARKING: Own carpark OPEN: 10-5 & by appt MIN: £100 MAX: £4,000 PERIOD: 18th-20th century SPECIALIST: Antique clock & clocks restoration OTHER INFO: 6 SW Harrogate.
YORK (0904)
Barbara Cattle, 45 Stonegate, YO1 2AW TEL: 623862 ASSNS: BADA OPEN: 9-5.30 PERIOD: 18th-20th century SPECIALIST: Period & antique silver & jewellery.
Barker Court Antiques, 44 Gillygate, YO3 7EQ TEL: 622611 PARKING: Easy OPEN: 10.30-5.30 MIN: £5 MAX: £100 PERIOD: 19th-20th century GENERAL: Antiques and collectables OTHER INFO: Minster Art Gallery. Personally recommended eats: Gillygate Wholefood Bakery, Mamma Mia, Waggon & Horses.
Bobbins Wool Crafts Antiques, 31-33 Goodramgate, YO1 2LS TEL: 653597 PARKING: Medium OPEN: Mon -Sat 10-5.30 MIN: £2

MAX: £1,000 PERIOD: 19th-20th century SPECIALIST: Oil lamps GENERAL: Antiques & collectables.

Danby Antiques, 61 Heworth Road, YO3 0AA TEL: 415280 PARKING: Own carpark OPEN: By appt MIN: £3 MAX: £750 PERIOD: 19th-20th century SPECIALIST: Writing accessories (fountain pens & unusual collectables). Fountain pen repairs OTHER INFO: 15 mins walk to town centre.

Holgate Antiques, 52 Holgate Road, YO2 4AB TEL: 630005 PARKING: Easy OPEN: Mon-Sat 10-5 MIN: £5 MAX: £2,000 PERIOD: 19th-20th century SPECIALIST: Pine GENERAL: Bric-a-brac, mahogany furniture OTHER INFO: Holmewood House Hotel.

Robert Morrison & Son, Trentholme House, 131 The Mount, YO2 2DA TEL: 655394 ASSNS: BADA PARKING: Own carpark OPEN: Mon-Fri 9-5, Sat 9-1 MIN: £100 MAX: £33,000 PERIOD: 18th-19th century GENERAL: Georgian & Victorian furniture.

Newgate Antiques Centre, 141 Newgate, YO1 2LA TEL: 679844 ASSNS: NAG PARKING: Medium OPEN: Mon-Thurs 9-5,Fri, Sat 9-5.30 MIN: £2 MAX: £3,000 PERIOD: 18th-20th century SPECIALIST: Antique jewellery, silver, general antiques & collectables.

Ken Spelman, 70 Micklegate, YO1 1LF TEL: 624414 FAX: 626276 ASSNS: ABA, PBFA PARKING: Easy OPEN: Mon-Sat 9-5.30 MIN: £1 MAX: £15,000 PERIOD: 17th-20th century SPECIALIST: Fine arts, English Literature (18th century) GENERAL: 40,000 books on all subjects, catalogues issued worldwide OTHER INFO: Open coal fire, 19th century shelving.

Thacker's, 42 Fossgate TEL: 633077 PARKING: Medium OPEN: 10-5 MIN: £5 MAX: £5,000 PERIOD: 17th-20th century SPECIALIST: Silver, furniture, glass, porcelain OTHER INFO: Next door to one of the oldest buildings in England, Merchant Adventurers Hall.

York Antiques Centre, 2 Lendal, YO1 2AA TEL: 641445 PARKING: Medium OPEN: MIN: £5 MAX: £5,000 PERIOD: 18th-20th century SPECIALIST: Silver, porcelain, militaria, toys GENERAL: Across the board antiques & collectables OTHER INFO: Greek restaurant in building.

FLAXTON (0904)
Elm Tree Antiques, YO6 7RJ TEL: 468462 PARKING: Own carpark OPEN: Mon-Sat 9-5, Sun 10-5 MIN: £5 MAX: £10,000 PERIOD: 18th-20th century SPECIALIST: Dining furniture GENERAL: Antiques & furniture.

EASINGWOLD (0347)
42 Antiques, Long Street TEL: 821078 PARKING: Easy OPEN: Mon-Sat 9-6 PERIOD: 18th-20th century GENERAL: This 'n' that, good antiques when possible OTHER INFO: The fun shop, everything sold on the minimum profit.

Old Flames, 30 Long Street TEL: 821188 PARKING: Easy OPEN: Mon-Sat 10-5 MIN: £60 MAX: £2,000 PERIOD: 18th-19th century SPECIALIST: Original cast iron fireplaces GENERAL: Architectural antiques, lighting.

NORTHALLERTON (0609)
Antique & Art, 7 Central Arcade, DL7 8PY TEL: 772051 PARKING: Easy OPEN: Mon-Wed, Fri, Sat 10-4 MIN: £5 MAX: £2,500 PERIOD: 19th-20th century GENERAL: Mainly small items, silver, EPNS, china, furniture.

Collectors Corner, 145-146 High Street TEL: 777623 PARKING: Easy OPEN: Mon-Sat 10-12.30, 1.30-4 MIN: £2 MAX: £200 PERIOD: 18th-20th century SPECIALIST: Clothes, books, postcards GENERAL: Abundance of mixed smalls OTHER INFO: Market days Wed & Sat.

BURNESTON (0677)
W. Greenwood Fine Art, The Gallery, Oakdene, DL8 2JE TEL: 424830, 423217 PARKING: Own carpark OPEN: By appt MIN: £100 MAX: £5,000 PERIOD: 18th-20th century SPECIALIST: Oils & watercolours of Yorkshire GENERAL: Paintings & frames.

MIDDLEHAM (0969)

White Boar Antiques & Books, Kirkgate, DL8 4PF TEL: 23901 PARKING: Easy OPEN: 10-5.30 MAX: £1,000 PERIOD: 19th-20th century SPECIALIST: Books GENERAL: Small china, porcelain OTHER INFO: Good facilities

MASHAM (0765)

Aura Antiques, 1-3 Silver Street, HG4 4DX TEL: 689315 PARKING: Own carpark OPEN: Mon-Sat 9.30-5 MIN: £10 MAX: £5,000 PERIOD: 18th-19th century SPECIALIST: Period mahogany especially dining furniture GENERAL: Antiques & furniture OTHER INFO: Next to Black Sheep (top restaurant).

RIPON (0765)

Balmain Antiques, 13 High Skellgate TEL: 601294 PARKING: Own carpark PERIOD: 18th-19th century GENERAL: General antiques.

Sigma Antiques & Fine Art, Water Skellgate TEL: 603163 FAX: 690933 PARKING: Medium OPEN: Mon-Sat 10.30-5 & by appt MIN: £2 MAX: £50,000 PERIOD: 17th-20th century GENERAL: Huge stock, furniture, decorative items, bronze, porcelain, jewellery, paintings, silver, objets d'art etc OTHER INFO: Occasional antiquities. Fountain Abbey, Studley Royal, Newby Hall, Harewood House

BOROUGHBRIDGE (0423)

Jeffrey Bates, Bridge Street, YO5 9LA TEL: 324258 FAX: 324258 PARKING: Own carpark OPEN: Mon-Wed, Fri, Sat 10.30-5 MIN: £5 MAX: £2,500 PERIOD: 18th-19th century SPECIALIST: Walking sticks, snuff boxes, small silver GENERAL: Mainly small items, some furniture, many pictures, prints.

Country Antiques, 38 High Street, YO5 9AW TEL: 340300 PARKING: Easy OPEN: Mon-Sat 10-4 PERIOD: 18th-19th century SPECIALIST: Silver of all periods GENERAL: Small furniture, treen, metalware.

Galloway Antiques, High Street, YO5 9AW TEL: 324602 ASSNS: LAPADA PARKING: Easy OPEN: Mon-Sat 9.15-5.15, Sun 11-4 MIN: £30 MAX: £10,000 PERIOD: 17th-20th century GENERAL: Furniture, paintings, antiques, decorative items.

Anthony Graham Antiques, Aberuge, Bridge Street, YO5 9LA TEL: 323952 PARKING: Own carpark OPEN: Mon-Wed, Fri, Sat 9.30-5 MIN: £5 MAX: £2,000 PERIOD: 18th-19th century GENERAL: Smalls, furniture, decorative items.

St James House Antiques, 7 St James House TEL: 322508 PARKING: Own carpark OPEN: Mon-Wed, Fri, Sat 9-5.30 MIN: £5 MAX: £5,000 PERIOD: 18th-19th century GENERAL: General antiques. Restoration.

R.S. Wilson & Sons, 4 Hall Square, YO5 9AN TEL: 322417 ASSNS: BADA PARKING: Easy OPEN: Mon-Sat 9-5.30 but Thurs closed pm PERIOD: 17th-19th century GENERAL: Furniture & accessories.

GREEN HAMMERTON (0423)

The Main Pine Company, Grangewood, The Green, YO5 8DB TEL: 330451 FAX: 331278 PARKING: Own carpark OPEN: Mon-Sat 9-5, Sun 11-4 MIN: £1 MAX: £5,000 PERIOD: 18th-20th century SPECIALIST: Antique pine.

TOCKWITH (0423)

Raymond Tomlinson (Antiques) Ltd, Moorside, YO5 8QG TEL: 358833 FAX: 358188 ASSNS: LAPADA PARKING: Own carpark OPEN: Mon-Fri 8-5 (trade only) MIN: £5 MAX: £5,000 PERIOD: 18th-20th century SPECIALIST: Oriental ceramics GENERAL: 48,000 sq ft warehouse of antique furniture. OTHER INFO: Phone for map & directions. Full export & packing service. Large restoration company.

KNARESBOROUGH (0423)

Robert Aagard Ltd, Frogmire House, Stockwell Road, HG5 0JP TEL: 864805 FAX: 869356 PARKING: Own carpark OPEN: 9.30-5 PERIOD: 18th-20th century SPECIALIST: Antique fire surrounds, chimneypieces GENERAL: Fireplaces, interiors, accessories, restoration.

Charles Shaw Antiques, The Old Vicarage, 2 Station Road (off A59), HG5 9AA TEL: 867715 PARKING: Own carpark OPEN: 8-6 MIN: £10 MAX: £ 7,000 PERIOD: 17th-20th century SPECIALIST: Taxidermy & country items GENERAL: Old books & pictures, large & small antiques OTHER INFO: Next to railway station.

John Thompson Antiques, Swadforth House, Gracious Street, HG5 8DT TEL: 864698 ASSNS: LAPADA PARKING: Own carpark OPEN: 9-5.30 closed Thurs MIN: £100 MAX: £30,000 PERIOD: 18th-19th century SPECIALIST: Clocks & musical boxes GENERAL: Furniture, decorative items.

West Yorkshire

Leeds City Skyline. By courtesy of City of Leeds Promotions & Tourism

This comparatively short tour takes in the industrialised Leeds/Bradford conurbation as well the delightful towns and villages of rural West Yorkshire.

The first stop, after leaving the motorway, is in Bawtry, a market town on the Great North Road. The Crown Inn is a relic of that great coaching route. There are also 18th century almshouses and an animal pound once used for strays.

The route continues to Doncaster, a busy industrial town. There was a settlement here as early as Roman times. The Mansion House is of particular interest being one of only three in the country that were built as residences of the mayor. Started in 1745, it is a fine Georgian building. Inside there is a ballroom with an ornamental ceiling and Adam style marble fireplaces.

Moving on, Leeds is an important industrial and commercial centre still retaining a number of historical buildings. Amongst these, St Peter's Church has an Anglo-Saxon cross, St John's Church has a wealth of 17th century woodwork, the grammar school was founded in 1552 and there are numerous Victorian buildings that reflect the city's 19th century prosperity. Five miles east of Leeds stands Temple Newsam, so named because the estate originally belonged to the Knights Templar. The 17th century house was the birthplace of Lord Darnley and a centre for the plotting surrounding Mary Queen of Scots. The house contains fine collections of furniture, silver, ceramics and pictures.

Another wonderful country house, Harewood House, can be found 8 miles north of Leeds. Built in the 18th century and designed by John Carr and Robert Adams, it is still the home of the Lascelles family. It contains superb ceilings, plaster-work and Chippendale furniture as well as collections of English and Italian paintings and Sevres and Chinese porcelain.

The university city of Bradford, next on the tour, has for long been associated with the wool industry. It has also been a cathedral city since 1920 when its parish church was upgraded to a cathedral. Nearby Mirfield contains Roe Head where the Brontës went to school

The following stop is Huddersfield. This was the old woollen centre for the West Riding of Yorkshire and has built its prosperity on cloth. The Tolson Museum illustrates the growth and development of the town and its relationship to the cloth industry. The museum is housed in Ravensknowle Hall, an Italianate man-sion built in the mid 19th century by a local textile manufacturer.

The route turns north west to Sowerby Bridge where there are several 17th century houses, and then to Halifax. Although well known as an industrial textile town and headquarters of the country's biggest building society, this town also has features of historic interest. Its perpendicular church dates from 1490 and inside there is a life-size figure known as Old Tristram who is holding an alms box. The town hall was designed by Sir Charles Barry who also designed the Houses of Parliament. Piece Hall, in Thomas Street, was built in 1779 as a cloth-market. Shibden Hall stands close to the town on the A58 and is an early 15th century half-timbered house furnished with articles from the 17th and 18th cen-turies.

We detour to visit Walsden before taking the A6033 to Bingley, situated on the Leeds and Liverpool Canal and the original home of Airedale terriers, first bred here for hunting otters. Our next stop, Keighley (pronounced Keethley), stands on the junction of the Rivers Aire and Worth. Four miles west of the town there is possibly the most famous tourist attraction in Yorkshire: the Brontë Parsonage and Museum. This Georgian parsonage was the home of the Brontës and is fur-nished in the period of the family with many of their relics including furniture, clothes, manuscripts and drawings.

Continuing north westwards we reach Skipton, an important market town on the Airedale Moors and standing at the farthest point north of the Leeds and Liverpool Canal. The town's real growth began at the end of the 18th century although there was a settlement here much earlier as shown by the castle and the church. Skipton Castle was started in the 11th century and is one of the most complete and best preserved medieval castles in the country. The castle came into the hands of the Clifford family in 1309 and they have made many alterations and additions to it over the centuries. More reminders of the Cliffords are found in the town's perpendicular church in the form of monuments to the family.

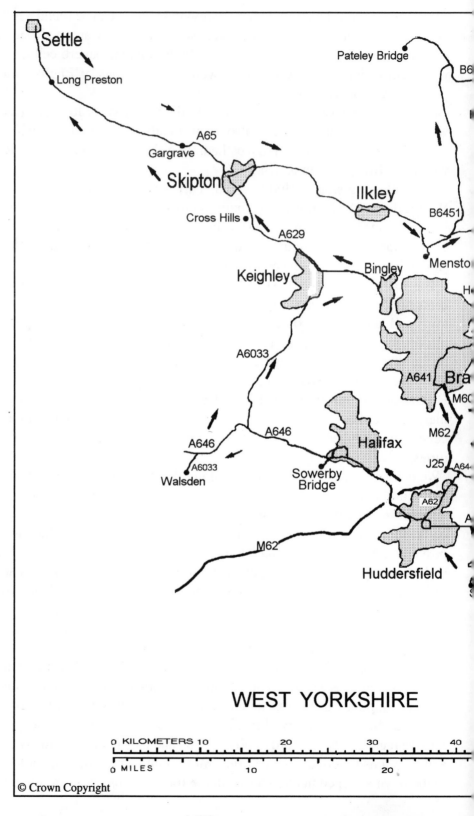

WEST YORKSHIRE

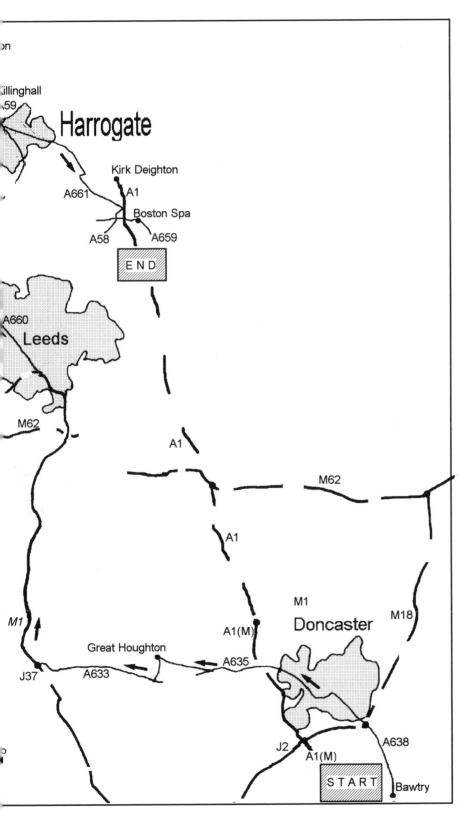

*Kirkstall Abbey, Leeds. By courtesy
of City of Leeds Promotion & Tourism*

We now detour along the A65 to visit Gargrave, then Long Preston, with the remains of a Roman fort next to the church and finally, on this detour, Settle, a small market town set beneath limestone cliffs in Ribblesdale on the main road from Yorkshire to Cumbria. It gives the impression of a solidly Georgian town but look into the courts and alleys and earlier houses may be seen. Of particular interest is the 17th century building known as The Folly with its elaborate front.

Retracing our route along the A65 we continue to Ilkley which started life as a Roman fort standing at 750 feet above sea level on Ilkley Moor; possibly not a choice posting in Roman times. Now, however, it is an elegant town with late Victorian buildings. Its growth was due to its establishment as a spa town and it became the favoured resort for Bradford wool magnates in the 19th century. A small 16th century manor house in Castle Yard displays items of local history from Roman times to the 19th century.

After first visiting Menston we head north to Pateley Bridge, a very attractive town that give the impression, in summer, of being full of flowers from the hanging baskets and window boxes that decorate the houses. A museum displaying aspects of 19th century Dales life is housed in the town's former workhouse.

We continue, via Markington and Killinghall, to the elegant town of Harrogate, a relative upstart of a town that owes its existence to the 18th century fashion for spa water. The original spring was discovered in the then Knaresborough Forest in 1571 by a local man. He had the area around it paved and it was named Tewit Well. It was at the end of the 18th century that the town started to grow although the town centre was mostly constructed in the 19th century. The site of the original spring is still marked by a domed building in The Stray, the common that runs around the southern side of Harrogate. The Royal Pump Room Museum, an octagonal building from 1842, stands over a sulphur spring and also houses the local museum.

From Harrogate the tour goes to Kirk Deighton and then the final destination, the Georgian town of Boston Spa on the River Wharfe.

ANTIQUE DEALERS
BAWTRY (0302)
Swan Antiques, 2 Swan Street, DN10 6JQ TEL: 710301 PARKING: Easy OPEN: Seven days 10-5 MIN: £1 MAX: £5,000 PERIOD: 18th-20th century SPECIALIST: Early porcelain & pottery GENERAL: General antiques.

Treasure House (Bawtry) Ltd, Swan Street TEL: 710621 PARKING: Easy OPEN: 10-5 MIN: £1 MAX: £3,000 PERIOD: 19th-20th century GENERAL: General antiques OTHER INFO: We are an antiques centre with 13 dealers.

Timothy D. Wilson, Grove House, Wharf Street, DN10 6HZ. TEL: 710040 ASSNS: BADA, CINOA PARKING: Own OPEN: Mon-Sat 9-5 or by appt MIN: £50 MAX: £20,000 PERIOD: 17th-18th century SPECIALIST: Fine old English oak furniture & Windsor chairs GENERAL: Country furniture and general antiques OTHER INFO: An 18th century crossroads for the coaching trade & surrounding villages are birthplaces of The Pilgrim Fathers.

DONCASTER (0302)
Keith Stones Grandfather Clocks, 5 Ellers Drive, Bessacar, DN4 7DL TEL: 535258 PARKING: Easy OPEN: By appt MIN: £600 MAX: £2,500 PERIOD: 18th-19th century SPECIALIST: Longcase clocks, painted dials OTHER INFO: ° mile from racecourse & Dome Leisure Centre.

GREAT HOUGHTON (0226)
Farmhouse Antiques, 7 High Street TEL: 754057 PARKING: Easy OPEN: Mon/Thurs 1-5, Sat 10-12, 1-5 MIN: £1 MAX: £2,500 PERIOD: 19th-20th century SPECIALIST: Susie Cooper & Art Deco ceramics GENERAL: Victorian & later furniture, Victoriana, glass OTHER INFO: 15 mins Nostell Priory.

LEEDS (0532)
The Antique Exchange, 400 Kirkstall Road, LS4 2JX TEL: 743513 PARKING: Easy OPEN: Mon, Thur-Sat 10.30-3 MIN: £199 MAX: £3,000 PERIOD: 19th-20th century SPECIALIST: Satin walnut & ash bedroom furniture.

Geary Antiques, 114 Richardshaw Lane, Pudsey, LS28 6BN TEL: 564122 PARKING: Own carpark OPEN: Mon, Tues, Thurs-Sat 10-5.30 MAX: £5,000 SPECIALIST: Georgian, Victorian, Edwardian furniture, upholstery fabrics. Restoration

Windsor House Antiques Ltd, 18-20 Benson Street, LS7 1BL TEL: 444666 FAX: 426394 ASSNS: LAPADA PARKING: Own carpark OPEN: Mon-Fri 8-5 & by appt MIN: £50 MAX: £100,000 PERIOD: 18th-20th century SPECIALIST: European bronzes, works or art, Orientalist paintings GENERAL: Enormous stocks 18th-19th century furniture & objects OTHER INFO: B&B's & hotels organised for prospective clients.

Year Dot, 15 Market Street Arcade, LS1 6DH TEL: 460860 PARKING: Difficult OPEN: 9.30-5 MIN: £1 MAX: £1,250 PERIOD: 18th-20th century GENERAL: Jewellery, pottery, small furniture.

HORSFORTH (0532)
Bill Thirkill Antiques, Springfield Cottage, 107 West End Lane, LS18 5ES TEL: 589160 PARKING: Own carpark OPEN: 8.30 onwards MIN: £15 MAX: £2,200 PERIOD: 18th-19th century SPECIALIST: Porcelain, pottery GENERAL: Furniture, metalware, musical.

BRADFORD (0274)
Langleys Ltd, 59 Godwin Street, BD1 2SH TEL: 722280 ASSNS: NAG PARKING: Difficult OPEN: Mon, Tues, Thurs-Sat 9-5 MIN: £200 MAX: £8,000 PERIOD: 18th-20th century SPECIALIST: Early/mid Victorian, Art Deco GENERAL: Fine early diamond & gem sets, jewellery to present day.

MIRFIELD (0924)
Lawn & Lace, 5 Knowl Road TEL: 491083 PARKING: Own carpark OPEN: Wed-Sat 9.30-5.30 PERIOD: 19th-20th century SPECIALIST: Lace, textiles, dolls GENERAL: Small furniture, ceramics OTHER INFO: Some older textiles.

SHEPLEY (0484)
D.W. Dyson Antique Weapons, Woodlea, HD8 8ES TEL: 607331 FAX: 604114 ASSNS: GMC, Arms & Armour Society, Reg. firearms dealer,

OMRS PARKING: Own carpark OPEN: Anytime by appt MIN: £100 MAX: £000's PERIOD: 17th-20th century SPECIALIST: Antique arms & armour of all kinds, restoration, miniature guns and intricate presentation pieces made. British Gallantry medals always in stock.

HUDDERSFIELD (0484)

Beau Monde Antiques, 343a Bradford Road, Fartown, HD2 2QF TEL: 427565 PARKING: Easy OPEN: Mon-Sat 9.30-6, Wed AM only MIN: £1 MAX: £500 PERIOD: 19th-20th century GENERAL: Mixed.

Peter Berry Antiques, 119 Wakefield Road, Moldgreen, HD5 9AN TEL: 544229 PARKING: Easy OPEN: Mon-Sat 10-5.30 MIN: £20 MAX: £5,000 PERIOD: 18th-19th century SPECIALIST: Period furniture & its finest quality restoration GENERAL: Complementary china, pottery, pictures OTHER INFO: Highest level restoration for clocks, ceramics, prints maps etc.

Fillans Antiques, 2 Market Walk TEL: 531609 FAX: 432688 ASSNS: NAG, Gemological Assn of GB PARKING: Medium OPEN: 9.30-5 PERIOD: 19th-20th century SPECIALIST: Fine Victorian, Edwardian jewellery GENERAL: Secondhand & antique jewellery, silver.

SOWERBY BRIDGE (0422)

Memory Lane, 69 Wakefield Road TEL: 833223 FAX: 883324 PARKING: Easy OPEN: Mon-Sat 10-5 MIN: £1 PERIOD: 19th-20th century SPECIALIST: Pine, oak, dolls, teddies, toys GENERAL: Every & anything OTHER INFO: Calderdale is just one big tourist area.

Talking Point Antiques, 66 West Street TEL: 834126 PARKING: Easy OPEN: Thurs-Sat 10.30-5.30 & by appt MIN: £1 PERIOD: 19th-20th century SPECIALIST: Windup gramophones, 78's & related items GENERAL: English pottery & porcelain (with restoration available), decorative items, curios OTHER INFO: Pennine market town with canal marina & scenery.

HALIFAX (0422)

Ken Balme Antiques, 10-12 Keighley Road, Ovenden, HX2 8AL TEL: 344193 PARKING: Medium OPEN: Mon-Tues, Thurs-Sat 9.30-5 MIN: £1 MAX: £300 PERIOD: 18th-19th century SPECIALIST: Commemorative ware, Victorian glass, candlesticks.

Simon Haley, 89 Northgate TEL: 360434 PARK-

ING: Easy OPEN: 10.30-5 MIN: £5 MAX: £2,000 SPECIALIST: Toys GENERAL: General antiques.

Halifax Antique Centre, Queens Road, (nr King Cross A58) TEL: 366657 PARKING: Own carpark OPEN: Tues-Sat 10-5 PERIOD: 19th-20th century SPECIALIST: Art deco, costume, mechanical music, jewellery etc.

Muir Hewitt Art Deco Originals, Halifax Antiques Centre, Queens Road, TEL: 366657 & 202744 PARKING: Own carpark OPEN: 10.30-5 SPECIALIST: Art Deco pottery including Susie Cooper, Clarice Cliff, Charlotte Rhead, furniture lighting & mirrors.

WALSDEN (0706)

Cottage Antiques Ltd, 788 Rochdale Road, OL14 7UA TEL: 813612 PARKING: Own carpark OPEN: Tues-Fri 12-4.30, Sat, Sun 10-5 MIN: £1 MAX: £1,500 PERIOD: 18th-20th century GENERAL: British & Continental country furniture (mainly pine), kitchenalia.

BINGLEY (0274)

Bingley Antiques Centre, Keighley Road TEL: 567316 PARKING: Own carpark OPEN: Mon, Wed-Fri 9.30-5, Tues 10-5, Sat 9-5, Sun 2-5 MIN: £1 MAX: £5,000 PERIOD: 17th-20th century GENERAL: Quality antiques mainly £150 up to £1,500 OTHER INFO: Also nearby warehouse of shipping goods.

KEIGHLEY (0535)

Keighley Antiques, 153 East Parade, BD21 5HX TEL: 663439 PARKING: Medium OPEN: 10-5 MIN: £5 MAX: £1,000 PERIOD: 18th-20th century SPECIALIST: Antique jewellery GENERAL: Bric-a-brac, china etc.

CROSS HILLS (0535)

Heathcote Antiques, 1 Aire Street Junction, BD20 7RT TEL: 635250 PARKING: Own carpark OPEN: 10-5.30 MIN: £5 MAX: £5,000 PERIOD: 19th-20th century SPECIALIST: Old unrestored pine GENERAL: Clocks, wide variety of smalls, porcelain, pottery, (especially Blue & White), small furniture OTHER INFO: Good tourist area, gateway to the Yorkshire Dales.

SKIPTON (0756)

Adamson Armoury, 70 Otley Street, BD23 1ET TEL: 791355 PARKING: Medium OPEN: Mon-Sat 9.30-4.30 MIN: £20 MAX: £1,000 PERIOD: 17th-20th century SPECIALIST: Antique edge weapons GENERAL: Antique weapons.

Corn Mill Antiques, High Corn Mill, Chapel Hill, BD23 1NL TEL: 792440 PARKING: Own carpark OPEN: Mon, Thurs-Sat 10-4 MIN: £10 MAX: £5,000 PERIOD: 19th-20th century GENERAL: Quality furniture, porcelain, clocks etc OTHER INFO: Next to good coffee house in interesting market town amidst Yorkshire Dales. Near castle.

GARGRAVE (0756)

Harry Blackburn Antiques, 9 East Street, BD23 3RS TEL: 749796 PARKING: Easy OPEN: 10-5 PERIOD: 19th-20th century GENERAL: Most items at times, no furniture or jewellery OTHER INFO: B&B's etc plentiful.

Bernard Dickinson, The Estate Yard, West Street TEL: 748257 PARKING: Own carpark OPEN: 9-5.30 PERIOD: 17th-18th century SPECIALIST: English oak & walnut GENERAL: Furniture.

Gargrave Gallery, 48 High Street, BD23 3RB TEL: 749641 PARKING: Easy OPEN: Appt advisable MIN: £3 MAX: £3,000 PERIOD: 18th-20th century SPECIALIST: Clocks, barometers GENERAL: General antiques.

R.N. Myers, Endsleigh House, High Street, BD23

3LX TEL: 749587 ASSNS: BADA PARKING: Easy OPEN: 9-5.30 & by appt PERIOD: 17th-early 19th century SPECIALIST: 18th century furniture & porcelain GENERAL: Porcelain, pottery, metalware, pictures, prints.

LONG PRESTON (0729)
Gary K. Blissett, Summerfield, 3 Station Road, BD23 4NH TEL: 840384 PARKING: Easy OPEN: By appt MIN: £50 MAX: £3,000 PERIOD: 19th-20th century GENERAL: Paintings & watercolours.

SETTLE (0729)
The Antique Shop, Market Square TEL: 822460 PARKING: Easy OPEN: 9-5 closed Weds MIN: £40 MAX: £7,000 PERIOD: 18th-19th century SPECIALIST: Dining room furniture GENERAL: Country furniture OTHER INFO: The Riddings, country guest house.

Nan Books, Roundabout, 41 Duke Street, BD24 9AJ TEL: 823324 PARKING: Easy OPEN: Tues, Fri, Sat 11-12.30, 2-5.30 MIN: £1 MAX: £500 PERIOD: 18th-19th century SPECIALIST: Glass, ceramics OTHER INFO: Tourist centre for Yorkshire Dales, Settle-Carlisle railway.

Folly Antiques, The Folly, Chapel Street PARKING: Easy OPEN: Mon-Sat 10-5.30 MIN: £10 MAX: £5,500 PERIOD: 17th-18th century GENERAL: General antiques OTHER INFO: In part of 17th century manor house near main square.

Roy Precious, King William House, High Street, BD24 9EX TEL: 823946 PARKING: Easy OPEN: 10-5.30 closed Weds MIN: £20 MAX: £6,000 PERIOD: 17th-18th century SPECIALIST: Oak & country furniture, portraits GENERAL: Some pottery, treen & pewter OTHER INFO: Blue Goose, Falcon Manor, Royal Oak.

Well Cottage Antiques, High Street, BD24 9EX TEL: 823593 PARKING: Easy OPEN: Tues, Thurs-Sat 10-5.30 MIN: £1 MAX: £350 PERIOD: 19th-20th century SPECIALIST: Framed cigarette cards, cricket pictures GENERAL: China, pine, collectables OTHER INFO: Picturesque market town with market Tues, ° day Weds.

ILKLEY (0943)
Burrow & Rapier, 37 The Grove, LS29 0QN TEL: 817631 PARKING: Easy OPEN: Mon-Sat 10-5.30 MIN: £5 MAX: £8,000 PERIOD: 19th century GENERAL: Fine furniture, antiques, reproduction items OTHER INFO: Opposite Monkmaris restaurant, French, German spoken.

MENSTON (0943)
Park Antiques, 2 Northview, Main Street, LS29 6JW TEL: 872392 PARKING: Easy OPEN: Seven days 10-6.30 MIN: £400 MAX: £5,000 PERIOD: 19th century SPECIALIST: Quality rosewood, walnut & mahogany. Soft furnishings, clocks OTHER INFO: Harry Ramsden's world famous fish'n'chips ° mile, Emmerdale Farm's Woolpack Inn 1° miles.

PATELEY BRIDGE (0423)
Cat in the Window Antiques, 22 High Street, HG3 5JU TEL: 711343 PARKING: Easy OPEN: Tues, Thurs-Sat 2-5 & by appt MIN: £1 MAX: £350 PERIOD: 19th-20th century SPECIALIST: Linens, metals GENERAL: Small furniture, collectables, baubles, bangles & beads. Pictures, ceramics, glass + lots more OTHER INFO: Pretty town, wonderful scenery, lots of flowers in spring & summer, Magical pre-Christmas.

Brian Loomes, Calf Haugh Farmhouse, HG3 5HW TEL: 711163 PARKING: Own carpark OPEN: 711163 MIN: £300 MAX: £10,000 PERIOD: 17th-19th century SPECIALIST: British clocks only (large stock), Author of many clock reference books OTHER INFO: Very picturesque area, good walking country known as Little Switzerland.

BIRSTWITH (0423)
John Pearson Antique Clock Restoration, Church Cottage, HG3 2NG TEL: 770828 ASSNS: BHI PARKING: Own carpark OPEN: Anytime by appt MIN: £1,000 PERIOD: 17th-19th century SPECIALIST: English longcase clocks GENERAL: Carriage, wall, bracket & French clocks OTHER INFO: Complete restoration for every single part, internationally recognised.

MARKINGTON (0765)
Daleside Antiques, Hinks Hall Lane, HG3 3NU TEL: 677888 FAX: 677886 PARKING: Own carpark OPEN: Mon-Fri 7.30-5.30 & by appt MIN: £10 MAX: £4,000 PERIOD: 17th-18th century SPECIALIST: Old & period pine and mahogany display cabinets.

KILLINGHALL (0423)
Norwood House Antiques, 38 Ripon Road, HG3 2DH TEL: 506468 PARKING: Easy OPEN: 10-4 MIN: £50 MAX: £10,000 PERIOD: 18th-19th century SPECIALIST: English & Continental furniture GENERAL: General antiques OTHER

INFO: 2 miles from Harrogate on edge of Yorkshire Dales.

HARROGATE (0423)

Bloomers Antique Costume & Textiles, 41 Cheltenham Crescent, HG1 1DN TEL: 569389 PARKING: Medium OPEN: Mon, Tues, Thurs-Sat 11-5 MIN: £1 MAX: £1,500 PERIOD: 18th-20th century SPECIALIST: Antique lace & fans GENERAL: All textiles inc shawls, quilts, linens, costume & accessories, beadwork, embroideries OTHER INFO: Famous spa with conference & hotel facilities, museum, 3 antique markets, good fashion outlets.

Derbyshire Antiques Ltd, 27 Montpellier Parade, HG1 2TG TEL: 503115 PARKING: Easy OPEN: Mon-Sat 10-5.30 MIN: £50 MAX: £20,000 PERIOD: 17th-18th century SPECIALIST: Oak, walnut GENERAL: Decorative items.

Dragon Antiques, 10 Dragon Road, HG1 5DF TEL: 562037 PARKING: Very easy OPEN: Mon-Sat 11-6 & by appt (resident) MIN: £5 MAX: £1,750 PERIOD: 19th-20th century GENERAL: Glass, china, pottery, cameras. Postcards (25p-£35) OTHER INFO: Art Deco cabinets, modern postcards.

The Ginnel Antique Centre, Corn Exchange Buildings, The Ginnel, HG1 2RB TEL: 508857 PARKING: Easy OPEN: Mon-Sat 9.30-5.30 MIN: £5 MAX: £10,000 PERIOD: 18th-20th century SPECIALIST: 50 dealers incl furniture, porcelain, paintings, silver, jewellery, metalware, books. Roman & Chinese antiquities, glass, marine items, clocks OTHER INFO: Largest antiques centre outside London with dateline quality & excellent decor & dining facilities.

Michael Green Traditional Interiors, Library House, Regent Parade TEL: 560452 PARKING: Easy OPEN: Mon-Fri 9-5.30, Sat 9-4 MIN: £3 MAX: £2,500 PERIOD: 18th-20th century SPECIALIST: Pine furniture GENERAL: Old kitchen treasures, Victorian doors, collectables, kitchenalia. Restoration OTHER INFO: Delightful position overlooking Christchurch Stray.

Haworth Antiques, 26 Cold Bath Road, HG2 0NA TEL: 521401 ASSNS: BCWMG PARKING: Own carpark OPEN: Mon-Sat 10-5 & by appt MIN: £50 MAX: £4,000 PERIOD: 18th-20th century SPECIALIST: Antique clocks, clock restoration GENERAL: Useful furniture

OTHER INFO: We back on to Crown Hotel up the hill. Excellent restaurants.

London House Oriental Rugs & Carpets, 9 Montpellier Parade, HG1 2TJ TEL: 567167 PARKING: Easy OPEN: Mon-Sat 9.30-5.30 MIN: £20 MAX: £8,000 PERIOD: 19th-20th century SPECIALIST: 200 individual carpets (12-25 ft) GENERAL: 4,000 decorative individual Oriental carpets & rugs.

Charles Lumb & Sons Ltd, 2 Montpellier Gardens, HG1 2TF TEL: 503776 FAX: 530074 ASSNS: BADA PARKING: Easy OPEN: Mon-Sat 9-1, 2-6 MIN: £50 MAX: £25,000 PERIOD: 18th-19th century SPECIALIST: Welsh furniture & decorative accessories OTHER INFO: Close to Drum & Monkey restaurant.

McTague of Harrogate, 17-19 Cheltenham Mount, HG1 1DW TEL: 567086 ASSNS: FATG PARKING: Easy OPEN: Mon-Sat 9.30-5.30 MIN: £5 MAX: £1,000 PERIOD: 18th-19th century SPECIALIST: Prints, watercolours GENERAL: Some oils.

Paraphernalia, 38a Cold Bath Road, HG1 TEL: 567968 PARKING: Easy OPEN: Weekdays 9-5 MIN: £1 MAX: £250 PERIOD: 19th-20th century SPECIALIST: Old postcards, Goss & crested china GENERAL: Commemoratives, small furniture, lots of decorative items & collectables OTHER INFO: Browsers welcome. Valley Gardens café 300 yards.

Parker Gallery, The Ginnel Antique Centre, Corn Exchange Buildings, HG1 2RB TEL: (0532) 662302 PARKING: Medium OPEN: Mon-Sat 9.30-5.30 MIN: £50 MAX: £2,000 PERIOD: 19th-20th century SPECIALIST: Yorkshire impressionists GENERAL: Oils & watercolours.

Paul M. Peters Antiques, 15 Bower Road, HG1 1BE TEL: 560118 ASSNS: LAPADA PARKING: Own carpark OPEN: Mon-Fri 10-5 MIN: £10 MAX: £5,000 PERIOD: 17th-20th century SPECIALIST: Oriental ceramics & works of art, also European ceramics, 99% to the trade.

Smith's The Rink Ltd, Dragon Road TEL: 567890 FAX: 520416 PARKING: Easy OPEN: Mon-Sat 9-5.30 MIN: £70 MAX: £60,000 PERIOD: 17th-20th century SPECIALIST: English Edwardian, English & French style Victorian furniture.

Sutcliffe Galleries, 5 Royal Parade, HG1 2SZ TEL: 562976 FAX: 528729 ASSNS: BADA, CINOA PARKING: Medium OPEN: Mon-Sat 10-1, 2-5 MIN: £1,500 MAX: £40,000 PERIOD: 19th century SPECIALIST: Fine British & European oil paintings OTHER INFO: Fashion shops, fine restaurants.

Walker Galleries Ltd, 6 Montpellier Gardens, HG1 2TF TEL: 567933 FAX: 567933 ASSNS: BADA, LAPADA PARKING: Easy OPEN: Mon-Sat 9.30-5.30 MIN: £38 MAX: £30.000 PERIOD: 19th-20th century SPECIALIST: 19th century paintings & watercolours, English & Continental OTHER INFO: Next door to excellent Drum & Monkey fish restaurant.

Christopher Warner, 15 Princes Street, HG1 1NG TEL: 503617 ASSNS: BADA PARKING: Medium OPEN: Daily 10-5 MIN: £100 MAX: £16,500 PERIOD: 17th-20th century as available SPECIALIST: 18th-19th century silver GENERAL: Quality secondhand & modern jewellery, some silver OTHER INFO: Historic castles, National Trust, excellent facilities.

Windmill Antiques, 4 Montpellier Mews, HG1 2TJ TEL: 530502 ASSNS: LAPADA PARKING: Easy OPEN: Mon-Sat 10-5.30 MIN: £20 MAX: £3,500 PERIOD: 18th-19th century SPECIALIST: Writing & jewellery boxes, Victorian rocking horses, child's chairs GENERAL: Quality furniture, copper, brass & boxes, caddies, some silver OTHER INFO: In pretty courtyard with other antique shops & restaurants closeby.

KIRK DEIGHTON (0937)

Elden Antiques, 23 Ashdale View TEL: 584770 PARKING: Own carpark OPEN: 8.30-6 MIN: £5 MAX: £1,500 PERIOD: 18th-20th century GENERAL: Furniture, china, pottery, brassware.

BOSTON SPA (0937)

London House Oriental Rugs & Carpets, 238-240 High Street TEL: 845123 PARKING: Easy OPEN: Mon-Sat 9.30-5.30 MIN: £20 MAX: £800 PERIOD: 19th-20th century SPECIALIST: 200 individual carpets 12-25 ft lengths GENERAL: 4,000 fine decorative oriental rugs OTHER INFO: Smallest spa in England, 1 min off A1.

The North West

There could not be a greater contrast between the first two areas we pass through on this tour. The Stoke-on-Trent area has an industrial landscape with typical English rural scenery nearby. However, the magnificent Peak District is just a short distance away. Although usually thought of as being in Derbyshire, the Peak District stretches into Staffordshire, Cheshire and South Yorkshire. In this region the scenery ranges from heather-covered moorlands to spectacular gorges and valleys cut by rivers through limestone cliffs. From there the tour goes on to the outskirts of Greater Manchester, then to the Wirral peninsula before doubling back to the historic city of Chester. The final part of the tour passes through charming rural market towns.

Coming off the M6 from London at Junction 15, our first call is to Trentham, before going on to the

Three Shires Head near Buxton where the counties of Staffordshire, Derbyshire and Nottinghamshire all meet.

Hartshill and Stockton Brook, areas on the edge of Stoke-on-Trent, famous as the centre of the potteries and the North Staffordshire coalfield. Stoke was also the "Five Towns", the setting in Arnold Bennett's novels. However, as the home of Wedgwood, Minton, Doulton and Spode, it is pottery and porcelain that most people associate with the town. As might be expected, there are several pottery museums. The Minton Museum in London Road, the Wedgwood Museum in Barlaston, the Sir Henry Doulton Gallery, Nile Street, Burslem, the Gladstone Pottery Museum, Uttoxeter Road, Longton, featuring a restored Victorian pottery factory, the Etruria Industrial Museum, Lower Bedford Street, Etruria, with the only surviving steam-powered potters mill.

Stoke was also important for coal mining and the great slagheaps (coal mining waste) may be seen in the town. However, they are not the eyesore that might be expected. They have been landscaped, and planted to make a park. Nearby Keele University helped the town with this, because it is very difficult to get anything

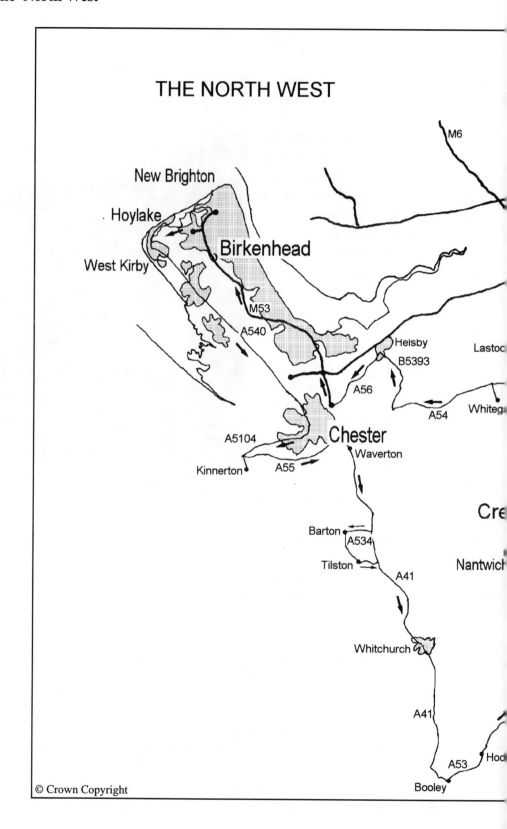

THE NORTH WEST

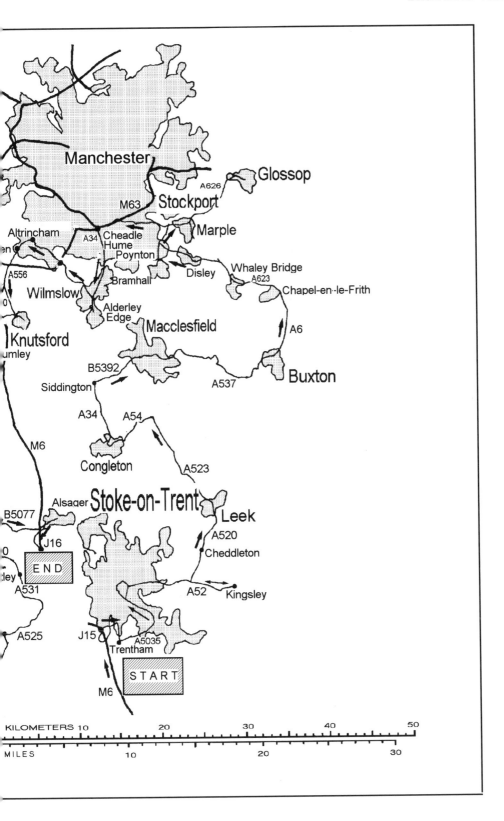

KILOMETERS 10   20   30   40   50

MILES   10   20   30

to grow on slagheaps so they served as an experimental area for the University.

The route detours through the village of Kingsley and then carries on to the next stop at Cheddleton, close to Leek, which has an interesting museum: Cheddleton Flint Mill, dating back to the 13th century. This mill has twin waterwheels and was used for grinding flint. Leek itself has been important for its silk mills. Its ancient parish church, on the site of one founded in the 11th century, has 13th century rose windows, a ducking stool and other interesting features surviving from its thousand year history including a Danish or Saxon pillar in the church-yard.

Continuing northwards we arrive in the ancient town of Congleton on the River Dane. Evidence suggests that a settlement existed here as early as the Stone Age. However, the town only grew after the Normans arrived. Four miles from the town on the A34 stands a gem of a 15th century house: Little Moreton Hall. A black and white, timber-framed building, it is said to be the most perfect example of a 15th century moated manor house still in existence.

Moving on via the village of Siddington, we arrive in Macclesfield in Cheshire. A silk manufacturing town with several 18th and 19th century mills, the story of the town's associations with silk are displayed in the Macclesfield Silk Museum and Heritage Centre in Roe Street. Paradise Mill in Old Park Lane gives demon-strations of hand-weaving and displays 26 silk hand looms. Another fascinating museum is the Jodrell Bank Science Centre and Arboretum with its 76m Lovell telescope and displays on astronomy, space and communications.

Five miles north of Macclesfield stands Adlington Hall partly built in the mid 15th century but with roots literally much older. At the heart of this typical Cheshire black and white house are two oak trees carved into pillars but with their roots still in the ground. Originally this area had been forest, some of which had been cleared to build a hunting lodge incorporating these two oaks. When the lodge was demolished this wonderful house was built around the oak pillars and they are all that remains of that original forest. The black and white features are Eliza-bethan and the South Front of the house was built in 1757. Also there is a mag-nificent organ, the largest 17th century one in England, which was once played by Handel.

We now take the A537 then the A54 to Buxton, roads singularly devoid of towns or villages. However, about six miles from Buxton stands the Cat and Fiddle, said to be the highest public house in England, and a good place to stop and look at the views. Look to the north east and see Shining Tor rising to a height of 1834 feet, to the south east is Axe Edge and the Goyt Valley.

Buxton stands at 1000 feet above sea level and is the highest town in England. It is famous for its natural mineral water and because of this, the Romans built baths here and a number of Roman roads centred on the town. The reputation of the water continued through the centuries. Mary, Queen of Scots came here,

The Pavilion Gardens, Buxton, in winter. By courtesy of Donald C. Crawford

while a prisoner, to cure her rheumatism. In the late 18th century the Duke of Devonshire built The Crescent, a copy of Bath's Royal Crescent, in an effort to turn Buxton into a spa town to rival Bath.

The town has a charming small opera house, the centre of the prestigious Buxton International Festival of Music and the Arts in July each year. Also worth mentioning are the Pavilion Gardens which are 23 acres of gardens with pleasant walks. Buxton Museum and Art Gallery in Terrace Road displays the geology, archeology and history of the area. There is also a good open market in Higher Buxton.

Poole's Cavern, on the southern edge of Buxton, has some remarkable limestone formations, many of them given names. There is evidence that the cave was inhabited by Stone Age man and that the Romans used it as a temple. Poole is said to have been a medieval outlaw who used the cavern as his hide-out.

From Buxton we continue onwards to Chapel-en-le-Frith, Whaley Bridge and the small town of Disley which sits astride the main A6 road. Just half a mile to the west of the town stands Lyme Park, an Elizabethan house with later additions and alterations. The original building dated from 1465 but nothing of that survives. Another house was built on the site in the 16th century. It is set in extensive grounds with herds of red and fallow deer roaming free.

Our next stop, Poynton, a suburb of Stockport on the Macclesfield Canal, was formerly an important mining area with sixty working pits at the beginning of this century. We carry on to Marple, junction of the the Rivers Goyt and Etherow, and the Peak Forest and the Macclesfield Canal, and then to the industrial town of Glossop whose prosperity came from cotton and woollen mills. Three-quarters of mile north west of the town there is the Roman fort of Melandra Castle, the remains of which cover about two acres.

The next stop is Stockport, on the River Mersey. After this we carry on to Cheadle, a suburb of Stockport, followed by Wilmslow, close to an interesting mill owned by the National Trust. Quarry Bank Mill, $1^1/_2$ miles north of Wilmslow on the B5166, is an award winning museum of the cotton industry which has the largest working waterwheel in England. It also recreates the Apprentice House of the 1830s, where pauper children working in the mill lived.

Alderley Edge, our next stop, is a market town and takes its name from sandstone cliffs a mile away. Although the town's buildings are mostly 19th century it reputedly has the oldest timber framed house in Cheshire, Chorley Old Hall. There is also a most unusual watermill at Nether Alderley, $1^1/_2$ miles from the town on the A34. Because the stream upon which this 16th century mill stands was too small to provide enough power, a dam was built to make a small reservoir to remedy the situation; three more reservoirs were constructed later.

The tour continues to the ancient borough of Altrincham, granted its charter in 1290, although there is nothing left to see of that distant past. The National Trust property of Dunham Massey stands 3 miles to the south west of the town on the A56. This is a fine 18th century house with a good collection of Huguenot silver, furniture and family portraits set in a lovely garden and deer park.

Nearby Bowdon is a very pretty village with its church mentioned in the Domesday Book. Now on to Knutsford, the "Cranford" of Elizabeth Gaskell's novel. The town has a number of the famous Cheshire black and white houses, a coaching inn, The Royal George, a Victorian Gothic town hall and Georgian houses. Knutsford is also famous for its Mayday celebrations, said to be the most impressive in England. A fine Palladian mansion, Tabley House, stands two miles west of the town on the A5033. It is particularly known for its fine collection of English paintings.

Another mansion, Tatton Park, stands outside the town. The present building was started in the late 18th century and the owners furnished it in lavish style, all of which can be seen today. The grounds are lovely, too. Landscaped by Humphrey Repton, they incorporate Tatton and Melchett meres and include an Italian terrace garden and a Japanese garden complete with Shinto temple.

From Knutsford we turn westward to a number of small villages: Plumley, Lastock Graham, Davenham, Whitegate and Helsby before taking the M53 onto the Wirral Peninsula to reach Birkenhead. Originally a small village built around a 12th century priory, Birkenhead began to grow when the Laird shipbuilding yards were opened in 1824 and the docks in 1847. Neighbouring Hoylake, a settlement in pre-Roman times, became a major port until its sheltered harbour silted up. Now it is a pleasant holiday resort with sandy beaches and safe bathing. Our last stop on the Wirral is West Kirby, also on the coast and offering bathing beaches and golf.

Heading back inland along the A540 we next arrive in Chester. This is the only city in England to have preserved all of its city walls. The Romans established a fort here and it was home to a Roman legion for the entire 300 years of the Roman occupation of Britain. A good place to go for more information on Chester in Roman times is the Grosvenor Museum which, amongst other things, has a very fine collection of antiquities.

Amongst the city's other museums are the Chester Heritage Centre in Bridge Street Row, the early 14th century Water Tower and the 13th to 14th century King Charles Tower from where Charles I watched the defeat of his army at Rowton Moor in September 1645. Both towers are on the City Walls.

Chester has prospered through the centuries. First it was a successful port, but this ended in the 15th century when the River Dee silted up. However, the

Two tiered shopping galleries, Chester

commercial life of Chester was so strong by this time that the town continued to thrive.

The medieval two tier shopping galleries are the most well known of Chester's many attractions. Another major landmark is the cathedral, dating from the 12th century. It was built of sandstone and, by the 19th century, was crumbling badly.

It was extensively restored, by among other architects, Sir George Gilbert Scott. They had to replace the flying buttresses, windows, vaulted wooden ceilings, choir stalls and the organ.

Chester is an extremely picturesque city, loved by almost everybody who visits it. To really appreciate the city and see more of its memorable sights than are mentioned here, it is essential to visit the Tourist Information Centre in the Town Hall.

From Chester we move on to the the small villages of Lower Kinnerton, Waverton, Barton and Tilston, then to Whitchurch in Shropshire. This small town has a number of interesting features. The church, rebuilt in 1713, includes a fine 15th century Talbot tomb and an 18th century organ case. From Whitchurch the tour passes through the villages of Booley, Hodnet, Woore and Betley before arriving in Nantwich, known from Roman times until the mid 19th century for salt production. The town has suffered badly in wars over the centuries. It resisted the Normans and consequently suffered considerable damage, it was attacked repeatedly by the Welsh and was also caught up in the Civil War when the town was besieged by Royalists and had to be relieved by Parliamentary troops under the command of Sir Thomas Fairfax and Sir William Brereton. As if this was not enough, the town also had two devastating fires in 1438 and 1583. In spite of all this it still has a fine 14th century church, impressive enough, both inside and out, to be called "the cathedral of south Cheshire". Another building that survived the last fire is the timber framed Sweetbriar Hall, built in the mid 15th century. In the High Street there are some lovely Elizabethan buildings overhanging the street which were built after the 16th century fire.

Nearby Dorfold Hall, one mile west on the A534, is a Jacobean country house started in 1616 with later additions and alterations. It has particularly fine plaster ceilings using a Tudor rose, fleur-de-lys and thistle in the decoration to celebrate the joining of England, Scotland and Wales under James I in March 1603.

Leaving Nantwich we arrive in nearby Crewe, strongly associated with railways. The first line to arrive in Crewe was the Warrington to Birmingham one in 1837. Before the arrival of the railways Crewe was primarily an agricultural town but it became important for the manufacture of railway engines and the railways became the town's principal employer.

Our final stop on this tour is the mainly agricultural town of Alsager, named for the most important local family. From here it is only a couple of miles along the B5078 to Junction 16 of the M6 motorway and the return journey to London.

ANTIQUE DEALERS
TRENTHAM (0782)
England's Museum of Print, The Courtyard, Trentham Gardens, Stone Road, ST4 8AX TEL: 657341 FAX: 644536 PARKING: Own carpark OPEN: 11-5 MIN: £8 MAX: £3,000 SPECIAL-IST: 19th-20th century etchings & lithos.

STOKE-ON-TRENT (0782)
Ann's Antiques, 26 Leek Road, Stockton Brook TEL: 503991 PARKING: Easy OPEN: Mon-Wed, Fri-Sat 10-5 MAX: £1,000 PERIOD: 19th-20th century GENERAL: Furniture & general antiques.

Castle Antiques, 113 Victoria Street, Hartshill, ST4 6EU TEL: 625168 PARKING: Easy OPEN: Mon-Wed, Fri, Sat 10.30-3.30 PERIOD: 18th-20th century GENERAL: Victorian & Edwardian furniture.

KINGSLEY (0538)
Country Cottage Interiors, Newall Farmhouse, Hazles Cross Road, ST10 2AY TEL:754762 PARK-ING: Own carpark OPEN: 8.30-5 MIN: £1 MAX: £800 PERIOD: 18th-19th century GENERAL: Stripped & unstripped period English pine & kitchenalia OTHER INFO: Beautiful area. Small (4-5) self-catering cottage on premises.

CHEDDLETON (0538)
Jewel Antiques, Whitegates, 63 Basford Bridge Lane TEL: 360744 PARKING: Own carpark Easy OPEN: By appt MIN: £50 MAX: £5,000 PERIOD: 18th-20th century SPECIALIST: Oil lamps, jewellery, paintings GENERAL: Small furniture.

LEEK (0538)
Anvil Antiques Ltd., Mills Cross Street, ST13 6BL TEL: 371657 FAX: 385118 PARKING: Own carpark OPEN: Mon-Sat 9-6 PERIOD: 18th-19th century SPECIALIST: Architectural items GENERAL: Antique & reproduction pine a speciality, both for home & export markets.

Sylvia Chapman Antiques, 4 St Edward Street, ST13 5DS TEL: 399116 PARKING: Easy opposite OPEN: Mon-Wed, Fri-Sat 12-5.30 MIN: £25 MAX: £500 PERIOD: 19th & early 20th century SPECIALIST: Pottery, Victorian cranberry glass GENERAL: General antiques.

Compton Mill Antique Centre, Compton, ST13 5NJ TEL: 373396 FAX: 399092 PARKING: Own carpark OPEN: Mon-Sat 9-6, Sun 1-5.30 MIN: £1 MAX: £2,000 PERIOD: 19th century SPECIAL-IST: Antique & reproduction pine GENERAL: 40,000 sq ft shipping furniture, oak, mahogany, pine etc, bric-a-brac OTHER INFO: Own restaurant, container packing service, hotels arranged, car to & from Manchester Airport.

England's Gallery, Ball Haye House, 1 Ball Haye Terrace, ST13 6AP TEL: 373451 International Arts Guild PARKING: Easy OPEN: Tues-Sat 10-5 MIN: £95 PERIOD: 19th-20th century GENERAL: Victorian oils & watercolours OTHER INFO: Bespoke Welsh dressers, a decorator's joy.

Gemini Trading, Limes Mill, Abbotts Road, ST13 6EY TEL: 387834 FAX: 399819 PARKING: Easy OPEN: Mon-Fri 9-5 or by appt MIN: £5 MAX: £900 PERIOD: 19th-20th century SPECIALIST: Pine furniture GENERAL: Kitchenalia & decoratives OTHER INFO: Good pub meals opposite.

Roger Haynes Antique Finder, 31 Compton, ST13 5NJ TEL: 385161 FAX: 385161 PARKING: Easy OPEN: Mon-Fri 9.30-6 but appt a must as 99% is export trade PERIOD: 19th-20th century SPECIAL-IST: Pine furniture (no reproduction whatsoever) GENERAL: Great stock of decorative accessories.

Johnsons, Park Works, Park Road, ST13 8SA TEL: 386745 FAX: 384862 PARKING: Easy OPEN: Mon-Sat 9-6 & by appt MIN: £5 MAX: £2,000 PERIOD: 18th-19th century SPECIALIST: Period pine furniture GENERAL: Antique pine, decorative smalls, bespoke reproduction pine furniture.

Leek Antiques Centre, 4-6 Brook Street, ST13 5JE TEL: 398475 PARKING: Easy OPEN: 10-5 MIN: £1 MAX: £2,000 PERIOD: 19th-20th century SPECIALIST: (12 dealers) furniture, pottery, porcelain, pine, gallery.

Odeon Antiques, 76-78 St Edward Street, ST13 5DL TEL: 387188 FAX: 398208 PARKING: Easy OPEN: Mon-Sat 10-5 MIN: £5 MAX: £2,000 PERIOD: 19th-20th century SPECIALIST: Lighting GENERAL: Pine, collectables.

Old & New, 59 St Edward Street, ST13 5DN TEL: 384174 PARKING: Easy OPEN: 9-6 MIN: £25 MAX: £650 PERIOD: 20th century SPECIALIST: Edwardian, Art Deco.

CONGLETON (0260)
The Antique Shop, 2 Cross Street TEL: 298909 PARKING: Easy OPEN: Mon, Tues, Thurs-Sat 10-4.30 MIN: £5 MAX: £500 PERIOD: 19th-20th century SPECIALIST: Large quantity of pottery & stripped furniture OTHER INFO: 5 antique shops here & bric-a-brac markets on Tues and Fri.

Little's Collectables, 8-10 Little Street, CW12 1AR

TEL: 299098 PARKING: Easy OPEN: 9.30-5.30 MIN: £1 MAX: £800 PERIOD: 18th-19th century GENERAL: Victorian furniture, pictures, china, glass, Wedgwood, Doulton. Collectables up to present day OTHER INFO: Shop is 1610 all with original beams. Winebar/bistro next door. Lion & Swan, 17th century hotel above.

Pine Too, 8-10 Rood Hill, CW12 1LG TEL: 279228 FAX: 279228 PARKING: Easy OPEN: Mon-Sat 9.30-5.30 MIN: £2 MAX: £1,000 PERIOD: 19th-20th century SPECIALIST: Pine, genuine old & reproduction GENERAL: Bespoke production.

SIDDINGTON (0625)

Gordon L. Bagshaw, The Old Smithy, Capesthorne Estate Yard, SK11 9JX TEL: 860909 FAX: 860909 ASSNS: Northern Ceramics Assn PARKING: Own carpark OPEN: Mon-Sat by appt MIN: £5 MAX: £2,000 PERIOD: 18th-19th century SPECIALIST: Full or museum restoration of pottery, porcelain & clock dials & cases etc GENERAL: Small furniture, ceramics, pictures, clocks etc OTHER INFO: 10 year fully qualified lecturer in antiques & antique restoration (presently at 3 colleges). Capesthorne Hall, other workshops, good facilities

MACCLESFIELD (0625)

Paula Bolton Antiques, 83-85 Chestergate, SK11 6DG TEL: 433033 FAX: 430033 PARKING: Own carpark OPEN: Mon-Sat 9.30-5.30 MIN: £5 MAX: £5,000 PERIOD: 19th century GENERAL: General antiques & collectables.

Philip Brooks, 6 West Bank Road off Prestbury Road, Upton, SK10 3BT TEL: 426275 PARKING: Easy OPEN: By appt only MIN: £50 MAX: £1,000 PERIOD: 19th-20th century SPECIALIST: Oils & watercolours, British & foreign impressionists.

Cheshire Antiques, 88-90 Chestergate TEL: 423268 PARKING: Easy OPEN: 11-5 not Weds MIN: £50 MAX: £4-5,000 PERIOD: 17th-20th century GENERAL: Early oak, Georgian, Victorian mahogany tables, chairs, longcase clocks & barometers OTHER INFO: Prestbury Village, olde worlde & very pretty.

Robert Copperfield, English Homes Antiques, 5-7 Chester Road, SK11 8DG TEL: 511233 PARKING: Medium OPEN: Mon-Sat 10-5 PERIOD: 17th-20th century SPECIALIST: English & Continental furniture OTHER INFO: The oldest established antiques business in Macclesfield.

D.J. Massey & Son, 47 Chestergate TEL: 616133

PARKING: Easy OPEN: Mon-Sat 9-5.30 MIN: £20 MAX: £6,000 PERIOD: 20th century SPECIALIST: Secondhand wristwatches & jewellery.

BUXTON (0298)

Antiques Warehouse, 25 Lightwood Road, SK17 7BJ TEL: 72967, home 871932 FAX: 871932 PARKING: Own carpark OPEN: Mon-Sat 10-4.30 & by appt MIN: £5 MAX: £2,000 PERIOD: 17th-20th century SPECIALIST: Plenty of 19th century mahogany & unrestored brass & iron beds GENERAL: Furniture, some smalls & pictures, ideal for EEC, Australian and USA markets OTHER INFO: Buxton is famous for its well-dressing.

Aquarius Antiques, 3a Church Street, SK17 6HD TEL: 72209 PARKING: Medium OPEN: 9.30-5.30 closed Mon, Wed MIN: £1 MAX: £800 PERIOD: 19th-20th century GENERAL: Mainly Victorian, Edwardian & Art Deco furniture, some ceramics.

G & J Claessens Antiques, George Street, SK17 6AT TEL: 72198 ASSNS: LAPADA PARKING: Medium OPEN: Mon-Fri 10-5, Sat 10-2 MIN: £500 MAX: £10,000 PERIOD: 18th-19th century GENERAL: Victorian, Edwardian, clocks, marbles, bronzes, pictures, French furniture, decorative items.

A & A Needham, West End Galleries, 8 Cavendish Circus, SK17 6AT TEL: 24546 PARKING: Medium OPEN: Mon-Fri 9.30-5, Sat 9.30-1.30 PERIOD: 19th-20th century SPECIALIST: Bronzes GENERAL: Antique, works of art, furniture, clocks.

What Now Antiques, Cavendish Arcade, The Crescent, SK17 6BQ TEL: 27178 PARKING: Easy OPEN: Mon-Sat 10.30-5, Sun 2-5 MIN: £1 MAX: £1,250 PERIOD: 19th-20th century SPECIALIST: Moorcroft pottery, watercolours, lamps, lighting GENERAL: Furniture & decorative items 1850-1950, & general antiques OTHER INFO: Shop in converted thermal bath in historic crescent. 5 other antique shops 100 yds.

CHAPEL-EN-LE-FRITH (0298)

The Clock House, 48 Manchester Road, SK12 6SR TEL: 815174 FAX: 815174 ASSNS: BHI, AWCCC (USA) PARKING: Easy OPEN: Seven days even bank hols 10-6 MIN: £10 MAX: £3,500 PERIOD: 17th-19th century SPECIALIST: Vintage wrist watches, jewellery GENERAL: Clocks, barometers. Repairs OTHER INFO: Producer of Teach Yourself video on clock repairs & dial restoration.

WHALEY BRIDGE (0663)

Nimbus Antiques, 14 Chapel Road, SK12 7DD

TEL: 734248 PARKING: Own carpark OPEN: Mon-Sat 9-6, Sun 2-6 MIN: £100 MAX: £4,000 PERIOD: 18th-19th century SPECIALIST: Furniture & clocks GENERAL: Wide furniture range, all restored & renovated on site.

BRAMHALL (061)
David H. Dickinson Antiques & Fine Art, P.O.Box 29, SK7 2EJ TEL: 440 0688 ASSNS: LAPADA PARKING: Own carpark OPEN: Strictly by appt only MIN: £500 MAX: £50,000 PERIOD: 18th-19th century SPECIALIST: Extraordinary works of art & decoration GENERAL: For interior decorator trade OTHER INFO: Near Manchester Airport

DISLEY (0663)
Mill Farm Antiques, 50 Market Street, SK12 2DT TEL: 764045 PARKING: Easy OPEN: Seven days 9-6 MIN: £75 MAX: £5,000 PERIOD: 18th-20th century SPECIALIST: Pianos, clocks, mechanical music GENERAL: Shipping furniture & general antiques.

MARPLE BRIDGE (061)
The Mulberry Bush, 20 Town Street, SK6 5AA TEL: 427 8825 PARKING: Easy OPEN: 9-5 MIN: £10 MAX: £5,000 PERIOD: 18th-20th century GENERAL: Quality mix of furniture, smalls, collectables OTHER INFO: On riverside street in refurbished village. Our famous flight of canal locks.

POYNTON (0625)
Harper Fine Paintings, Overdale, Woodford Road, SK12 1ED TEL: 879105 PARKING: Own carpark OPEN: 10-9 MIN: £100 MAX: £40,000 PERIOD: 18th-20th century SPECIALIST: Victorian oils and early Victorian watercolours OTHER INFO: Mottram Hall Hotel, Shrigley Hall (country hotel).
Recollections, 1st floor, 77 Park Lane, SK12 1RD TEL: 859373 PARKING: Easy OPEN: Mon, Tues, Thurs-Sat 10-5 MIN: £1 MAX: £200 PERIOD: 19th-20th century SPECIALIST: Old costume jewellery & accessories. Antique linen & lace, glass GENERAL: Popular collectables.

STOCKPORT (061)
E.R. Antiques Centre, 122 Wellington Street (off Wellington Road), SK1 1YH TEL: 429 6646, home 480 5598 PARKING: Medium OPEN: Mon-Sat 12-5.30, Weds pm only MIN: £1 MAX: £250+ PERIOD: 19th-20th century SPECIALIST: Pressed & cut coloured glass, Victorian collectables GENERAL: Aladdin's cave of small gift items: jewellery, costume, real curios 1870-1930's, silver

+ plate, lots of Blue & White OTHER INFO: 6 dealers. We adore cats & stock Winstanleys. Owner is a clairvoyant & psychometrist.
Halcyon Antiques, 435 Buxton Road, Great Moor, SK2 7HE TEL: 483 5038 PARKING: Easy OPEN: Mon-Sat 10-5 MIN: £1 MAX: £2,000 PERIOD: 18th-20th century GENERAL: Porcelain, glass, silver, furniture, jewellery, linen.
Howarth Antiques, 147 Wellington Road North, Heaton Norris TEL: 443 1096 FAX: 443 1096 PARKING: Easy OPEN: Mon-Sat 10-5, Sun 11.30-5 MIN: £20 MAX: £2,000 PERIOD: 18th-20th century SPECIALIST: Chaise longues GENERAL: From bric-a-brac to dining suites.
Imperial Antiques, 295 Buxton Road, Great Moor, SK2 7NR TEL: 483 3322 FAX: 483 3322 ASSNS: LAPADA PARKING: Easy OPEN: 9.30-5 MIN: £10 MAX: £5,000 PERIOD: 18th-20th century SPECIALIST: Oriental and Persian carpets GENERAL: Silver + plate ware.
Limited Editions, 35 King Street East, SK1 1XJ TEL: 480 1239 PARKING: Own carpark OPEN: Mon-Wed, Fri-Sat 9.45-6 MIN: £5 MAX: £20,000 PERIOD: 19th century SPECIALIST: 50+ chairs & tables GENERAL: 18th-20th century furniture & upholstery, various smalls OTHER INFO: Etrop Grange hotel near airport (much of furniture supplied by us, half-tester beds etc).
Page Antiques, 424 Buxton Road, Great Moor TEL: 483 9202 PARKING: Own carpark OPEN: 10-5.30 MIN: £1 MAX: £3,000 PERIOD: 18th-20th century SPECIALIST: Furniture GENERAL: Silver, china, metalware, etc.

GLOSSOP (0457)
Derbyshire Clocks, 104 High Street West, SK13 8BB TEL: 862677 PARKING: Easy OPEN: 9-5

closed Tues MIN: £300 MAX: £5,000 PERIOD: 18th-19th century SPECIALIST: Antique clocks GENERAL: English longcase, wall, bracket & Vienna wall clocks.

Old Cross Gallery Antiques, 16 Henry Street, (Norfolk Square), SK13 8BW TEL: 854052 PARKING: Medium OPEN: Wed-Sat 9-5 MIN: £1 MAX: £1,000 PERIOD: 19th-20th century GENERAL: Country furniture & objets d'art, watercolours.

CHEADLE HULME (061)

Allan's Antiques, 10 Ravenoak Road, SK8 7DL TEL: 485 3132 PARKING: Medium OPEN: Mon, Tues, Thurs-Sat 10-1, 2-5 MIN: £1 MAX: £5,000 PERIOD: 18-20th century SPECIALIST: Silver esp. cutlery GENERAL: Furniture, smalls OTHER INFO: Near one of UK's finest half timbered buildings, Millington Hall, 17th century restaurant.

Malcom Frazer Antiques, 19 Brooklyn Crescent, SK8 1DV TEL: 428 3781 PARKING: Own carpark OPEN: By appt MIN: £100 MAX: £10,000 PERIOD: 18th-19th century SPECIALIST: Marine art & antiques GENERAL: Ships furniture & military chests OTHER INFO: Close to Stockport & Manchester.

WILMSLOW (0625)

Peter Bosson, 10b Swan Street, SK9 1HE TEL: 525250, 527857 ASSNS: Antiquarian Horological Assn PARKING: Medium OPEN: Tues, Thurs-Sat 10-12.45, 2.15-5 MIN: £10 MAX: £5,000 PERIOD: 18th-20th century SPECIALIST: Barographs GENERAL: Clocks, barometers, scientific instruments OTHER INFO: Styal Mill (NT), Stanneylands Hotel, The Bank café/winebar (50 yards), 3 miles Manchester airport.

ALDERLEY EDGE (0625)

Alderley Antiques, 17 London Road, SK9 7JT TEL: 583468 ASSNS: LAPADA PARKING: Easy OPEN: Mon, Tues, Thurs-Sat 10-1, 2-5, Wed 10-1 MIN: £100 MAX: £15,000 PERIOD: 18th-19th century SPECIALIST: Georgian furniture GENERAL: Furniture, clocks, paintings, silver, objets d'art OTHER INFO: Area of natural beauty.

Anthony Baker Antiques, 14 London Road, SK9 7JS TEL: 582674 ASSNS: LAPADA PARKING: Easy OPEN: Tues-Sat 10-5.30 MIN: £5 MAX: £3,000 PERIOD: 18th-19th century. GENERAL: Furniture, collectables.

Brook Lane Antiques, 67 Brook Lane, SK9 7RW TEL: 584896 PARKING: Own carpark OPEN: Mon-Sat 9-5 MIN: £3 MAX: £3,000 PERIOD: 19th-20th century GENERAL: Furniture, beds, bric-a-brac OTHER INFO: 30 mins to ancient City of Chester, 15 mins to old village of Knutsford with 4-5 other antiques shops & good antiques centre.

Sara Frances Antiques, 2 West Street, SK9 7EG TEL: 585549 FAX: 586015 PARKING: Easy OPEN: Tues-Sat 10-5.30 MIN: £50 MAX: £4,000 SPECIALIST: 17th, 18th century oak & country furniture GENERAL: 19th century decoratives & soft furnishings OTHER INFO: No.15 Winebar, The Edge Hotel, Tatton Hall (Knutsford).

ALTRINCHAM (061

Altrincham Antiques, 15-23 Tipping Street, WA14 2EY (and at 39 Hale Road) TEL: 941 3554, (0836) 316366 FAX: 941 3554 PARKING: Own carpark OPEN: Mon-Fri 10-7, Sat-Sun 10-6 MIN: £5 MAX: £5,000 PERIOD: 19th-20th century SPECIALIST: 10 rooms of the old & unusual OTHER INFO: Stage props from famous films (James Bond etc).

Cottage Antiques, Rose Cottage, Hasty Lane, Hales Barn, Ringway TEL: 980 7961 PARKING: Own carpark OPEN: Mon-Sat 9-6 & by appt MIN: £5 MAX: £10,000 PERIOD: 17th-20th century GENERAL: General antiques OTHER INFO: 5 mins Manchester Airport, 1 min from M56, J6 & 5 major hotels. Yatton Park House & Gardens, Dunham Park House & Gardens, Warry Bank Mill.

Halo Antiques, 97 Hale Road, WA15 9HL TEL: 941 1800 FAX: 929 9565 PARKING: Own carpark OPEN: Tues-Sat 10-5 trade only MIN: £10 MAX: £1,000 PERIOD: 19th-20th century SPECIALIST: Old pine OTHER INFO: 5 mins Manchester Airport on A538, collection possible.

Squires Antiques, 25 Regent Road, WA14 1RX TEL: 928 0749 PARKING: Own carpark OPEN: Tues, Thurs-Sat 10-5 MIN: £10 PERIOD: 19th-20th century SPECIALIST: Small silver & decorative items, gifts GENERAL: General antiques OTHER INFO: Very busy Cheshire market town.

BOWDON (061)

Eureka Antiques, 79 Church Brow, WA14 2SF TEL: 926 9722 PARKING: Medium OPEN: Tues, Thurs-Sat 10-5 MIN: £5 MAX: £8,000 PERIOD: 19th century SPECIALIST: Agate jewellery, Tartanware, 19th century furniture GENERAL: Coloured glass OTHER INFO: Good facilities.

KNUTSFORD (0565)

David Bedale, 5-7 Minshull Street, WA16 6HG

TEL: 653621 PARKING: Medium OPEN: Mon-Sat 9.30-1, 2-5.30 MIN: £100 MAX: £15,000 PERIOD: 17-19th century GENERAL: 18th-19th century furniture & unusual decorative items OTHER INFO: Tatton Park, La Belle Epoque restaurant, Cottons Hotel

Cranford Galleries, 10 King Street, WA16 6DL TEL: 633646 ASSNS: FATG PARKING: Medium OPEN: Mon, Tues, Thurs-Sat 11-1, 2.30-5 MIN: £50+ MAX: £3,850+ PERIOD: 18th-19th century GENERAL: General antiques, picture framing.

Glynn Interiors, 92 King Street TEL: 634418 PARKING: Easy OPEN: Mon, Tues, Thurs-Sat 10-5 MIN: £50 MAX: £3,000 PERIOD: 19th century SPECIALIST: Upholstery GENERAL: Inlaid furniture, decorative items OTHER INFO: Penny Farthing Museum, Courtyard Coffee House at rear.

Knutsford Antique Centre, 16 King Street TEL: 755334 PARKING: Easy OPEN: Mon, Tues, Thurs-Sat 10-5, Sun 11-4 MIN: £5 MAX: £2,000 PERIOD: 18th-20th century GENERAL: Very varied stock of antiques & collectables OTHER INFO: 5 dealers in this interesting centre in fashionable village.

PLUMLEY (0565)

Coppelia Antiques, Holford Lodge, Plumley Moor Road, WA16 9RS TEL: 722197 FAX: 722744 PARKING: Own carpark OPEN: By appt MIN: £100 MAX: £50,000 PERIOD: 17th-18th century SPECIALIST: Longcase clocks GENERAL: Quality Georgian furniture & clocks.

LOSTOCK GRAHAM (0606)

Lostock Antiques, 210 Manchester Road, CW9 7NN TEL: 45523 PARKING: Easy OPEN: Tues-Sat 10.30-5.30, Sun 1-5 MIN: £1 MAX: £1,500 PERIOD: 19th century SPECIALIST: Our own brand of furniture polishes, lots of French mirrors, beds, etc GENERAL: Books, bric-a-brac, kitchenalia, painted furniture. Full restoration.

DAVENHAM (0606)

Forest Books of Cheshire, at Magpie Antiques, 2-4 Church Street, CW9 8NA PARKING: Easy OPEN: Tues, Thurs, Sat 11-5, Fri & some Mons 2-5 not bank hols MIN: £1 MAX: £250+ PERIOD: 19th-20th century SPECIALIST: Wildlife, gardening, fishing & other English life, Cheshire & N.Wales, some prints & pictures.

Magpie Antiques, 2-4 Church Street, CW9 8NA PARKING: Easy OPEN: Tues, Thurs, Sat 11-5, Mon, Fri 2-5 MIN: £1 MAX: £250 PERIOD: 19th-20th century SPECIALIST: Country style items GENERAL: Pictures, smalls, some furniture etc OTHER INFO: Small conservation area, coaching inn, Northwich Salt Museum & salt-mining area.

WHITEGATE (0606)

The Antiques Shop, Cinder Hill, CW8 2BH TEL: 882215 PARKING: Own carpark OPEN: Tues-Wed, Fri-Sat 10-5, Mon 2-5 MIN: £10 MAX: £2,000 PERIOD: 18th-20th century GENERAL: General antiques OTHER INFO: Self-contained holiday bungalow in grounds.

HELSBY (0928)

Sweetbriar Gallery, 106 Robin Hood Lane TEL: 723851 FAX: 723851 ASSNS: Paperweight Collectors Assn PARKING: Own carpark OPEN: By appt MIN: £2 MAX: £2,500 PERIOD: 19th-20th century SPECIALIST: Paperweights (international dealer), perfume bottles, etchings, some other pictures, particulary wild life specialist artists: Tunnicliffe & Frank Brangwyn.

BIRKENHEAD (051)

Bodhouse Antiques, 379 Newchester Road TEL: 644 9494 FAX: 644 9494 PARKING: Own carpark OPEN: Mon-Fri 9-5 & by appt MIN £:10 MAX: £5,000 PERIOD: 19th century GENERAL: General antiques OTHER INFO: Fluent Italian, good knowledge other European languages. Packaging & courier service.

NEW BRIGHTON (051)

Arbiter, 10 Atherton Street TEL: L45 2NY PARKING: Easy OPEN: Tues-Fri 11-5, Sat 1-5 MIN: £10 MAX: £1,000+ PERIOD: 3000 BC- 1950's SPECIALIST: Oriental & ethnic, Arts and Crafts movement including good Art Deco, named items and small antiquities OTHER INFO: President China Trade Society.

HOYLAKE (051)

The Clock Shop, The Quadrant, L47 2EE TEL: 632 1888 ASSNS: BHI, BWCMG PARKING: Easy OPEN: Mon-Fri 9-5, Sat 10-2 MIN: £20 MAX: £4,000 PERIOD: 18th-20th century SPECIALIST: Clocks & barometers GENERAL: Jewellery OTHER INFO: 5 mins Royal Liverpool Golf.

Market Antiques, 80 Market Street, L47 3BB TEL: 632 4059 FAX: 632 4059 PARKING: Easy OPEN: Thurs, Fri 10-1, 2.15-5, Sat 10-5 MIN: £1 MAX: £2,000 PERIOD: 17th-20th century SPECIALIST: Furniture GENERAL: Small range of furnishings OTHER INFO: Good sunsets.

The 6th Annual

CHESTER ANTIQUES SHOW

County Grandstand, Chester Racecourse

16 - 19 FEBRUARY 1995

Just outside the City Walls,
on the SW corner of this delightful City

50 stands and 8 room-settings on 3 floors

Exhibitors from
all over Britain

Adm: £4 inc Catalogue
(car park extra)

Penman Antiques Fairs

Enq: 0444 482514

WEST KIRBY (051)
Helen Horswill Antique & Decorative Arts, 62 Grange Road, L48 4EG TEL: 625 2803/8660 PARKING: Easy OPEN: Mon-Sat 10-1, 2.30-5 or by appt MIN: £5 MAX: £5,000 PERIOD: 17th-20th century GENERAL: Country furniture & artifacts, Victorian & Edwardian upholstered sofas & chairs OTHER INFO: Good cafés & bistros etc.
Victoria Cottage Antiques, 6 Village Road, L48 3JW TEL: 625 7517 PARKING: Easy OPEN: Mon, Tues, Thurs-Sat 10-5 MIN: £9 MAX: £450 PERIOD: 18th-19th century SPECIALIST: Staffordshire figures GENERAL: Victorian coloured glass & wine glasses. 18th century engravings, pottery, porcelain OTHER INFO: Opposite Moby Dick pub, 5 mins from seafront.
CHESTER (0244)
Adam Antiques, 65 Watergate Row, CH1 2LE TEL: 319421 ASSNS: LAPADA PARKING: Medium OPEN: 10-5 MIN: £10 MAX: £5,000 PERIOD: 18th-20th century GENERAL: Decorative & traditional furniture, clocks, objets d'art.
Aldersley Hall, 47 Northgate Street TEL: 324885

PARKING: Own carpark OPEN: Mon-Sat 8.30-5.30 MIN: £5 MAX: £300 PERIOD: 20th century SPECIALIST: Art Deco, ceramics, nurseryware GENERAL: Dolls, teddies, kiddies furniture OTHER INFO: Special B&B rates.
Angela Antiques, 32 Christleton Road, CH3 5UG TEL: 351562 PARKING: Easy OPEN: 10-5 MIN: £2 MAX: £400 PERIOD: 19th-20th century GENERAL: Collectables, pine, lace, linen, decorative items OTHER INFO: By superb riverside B&B's-River Peace, The Moorings.
The Antique Shop, 40 Watergate Street, CH1 2LA TEL: 315286 PARKING: Medium OPEN: Mon-Sat 10-5.30 MIN: £25 MAX: £1,500 PERIOD: 18th-20th century SPECIALIST: Metalware, Doulton, Blue & White, pot lids, Maling, Moorcroft, prints & maps.
Avalon Stamp & Postcard Shop, 1 City Walls/Rufus Court, Northgate Street, CH1 2JG TEL: 318406 PARKING: Difficult OPEN: 9.30-5.30 MIN: £1 PERIOD: 19th-20th century SPECIALIST: Stamps, postcards.
Barn Antiques, 25 Christleton Road, Boughton TEL: 344928 PARKING: Easy OPEN: Mon-Sat 9-5 MIN: £10 MAX: £500 PERIOD: 19th-20th century GENERAL: Shipping & medium priced antiques.
Baron Fine Art, 68 Watergate Street, CH1 2LA TEL: 342520 ASSNS: LAPADA, FATG PARKING: Medium OPEN: Mon-Sat 9.45-5.30 MIN: £20 MAX: £24,000 PERIOD: 19th-20th century GENERAL: Mid 19th century - contemporary watercolours & oils OTHER INFO: Also good centre for touring N.Wales, Liverpool etc
Chester Furniture Cave, The Old Chapel, Christleton Road, Boughton TEL: 314798 PARKING: Easy OPEN: Mon-Sat 9.30-5 MIN: £50 MAX: £5,000 PERIOD: 18th-20th century GENERAL: Good quality shipping & antique furniture.
Farmhouse Antiques, 23 Christleton Road, Boughton TEL: 322478 PARKING: Medium OPEN: Mon-Sat 9-5 MIN: 1p MAX: £5,850 PERIOD: 19th-20th century SPECIALIST: Early 19th century longcase clocks GENERAL: Country type stock, kitchenalia, Blue & White china, book sets, old golf clubs, mechanical music.
Jamandic Ltd, 22 Bridge Street Row, CH1 1NN TEL: 312822 FAX: 349756 ASSNS: Fellow Interior Designer & Decorators Association (IDDA)

PARKING: Easy OPEN: Mon-Fri 9-5.30, Sat 10-1 MIN: £300 MAX: £20,000 PERIOD: 18th-20th century SPECIALIST: Decorative furniture and accessories.

Kayes (M.Kaye Ltd), 9 St Michaels Row, CH1 1EF TEL: 327149 FAX: 318404 ASSNS: NAG PARKING: Easy OPEN: 9-5.15 MIN: £10 MAX: £15,000 SPECIALIST: Mid 17th-early 19th century silver. Rings & jewellery 1870-1930.

Lowe & Sons, 11 Bridge Street Row, CH1 1PD TEL: 325850 FAX: 345536 ASSNS: NAG, CMJ PARKING: Medium OPEN: Mon-Sat 9.15-5.15 PERIOD: 18th-20th century SPECIALIST: Silver & jewellery OTHER INFO: An old Victorian shop with gallery. The company was established in 1770 & has been in these premises since 1804.

Made of Honour, 11 City Walls (next to the Eastgate Clock, wall level) TEL: 314208 PARKING: Medium OPEN: Mon-Sat 9.30-5.30 MIN: £2 MAX: £2,000 PERIOD: 19th-20th century SPECIALIST: English pottery & porcelain, Staffordshire figures, woodwork, beadworks OTHER INFO: Eric Jones, owner, lecturer & broadcaster on antiques.

Melody's Antique Galleries, 30-32 City Road TEL: 341818, 328968 FAX: 341818 ASSNS: LAPADA PARKING: Easy OPEN: Mon-Sat 10-5.30 MIN: £1 MAX: £10,000 PERIOD: 18th-20th century SPECIALIST: Furniture, pine, jewellery, porcelain GENERAL: 10,000 sq ft of mixed furniture OTHER INFO: Our store, the biggest antiques gallery in Cheshire, is a shopping mall with 10 quality shops & its own pub, Harker's Bar.

Richard Nicholson of Chester, 25 Watergate Street, CH1 2LB TEL: 326818 FAX: 336138 PARKING: Medium OPEN: Mon-Sat 10-1, 2.15-5 MIN: £1 MAX: £3,000 PERIOD: 17th-20th century GENERAL: Antiquarian maps & prints OTHER INFO: Map catalogue subscription service.

Richmond Galleries, Ground floor, Watergate Buildings, New Crane Street, CH1 4JE TEL: 317602 PARKING: Easy OPEN: Mon-Sat 9.45-5.15 MIN: £20 MAX: £1,000 PERIOD: 18th-20th century SPECIALIST: Antique pine, Spanish, French, country furniture & decorative items.

Stothert Antiquarian Books, 4 Nicholas Street, CH1 2NX TEL: 340756 OPEN: Mon-Sat 9.30-1, 2-5.30 PERIOD: 18th-20th century.

Watergate Antiques, 56 Watergate Street, CH1 2LD TEL: 344516 FAX: 320520 PARKING: Own carpark OPEN: Mon-Sat 9.30-5 MIN: £20 MAX: £12,000 PERIOD: 18th-19th century SPECIALIST: Silver & silver plate, ceramics GENERAL: Glass, militaria.

LOWER KINNERTON (0244)

Brian Edwards Antique Exports, Gell Farm TEL: 660240 FAX: 661324 PARKING: Own carpark OPEN: Anytime gladly by prior appt (resident) MIN: £5 MAX: £5,000 PERIOD: 17th-20th century GENERAL: 15,000 sq ft warehouse of antique & shipping goods.

WAVERTON (0244)

J. Alan Hulme, 52 Mount Way, Waverton, CH3 7QF TEL: 336472 ASSNS: IMCOS PARKING: Easy OPEN: 9-8 by prior appt MIN: £1 MAX: £350 PERIOD: 17th-20th century SPECIALIST: UK county maps, engravings of topographical views, fashion, flowers, humour, birds, sporting, Vanity Fair

BARTON (0829)

Derek Rayment Antiques, Orchard House, SY14 7HT TEL: 270429 ASSNS: BADA, LAPADA PARKING: Own carpark OPEN: Anytime by appt

MIN: £60 MAX: £10,000+ PERIOD: 18th-19th century SPECIALIST: Only barometers.

TILSTON (0829)

Well House Antiques, The Well House, SY14 7DP TEL: 250332 PARKING: Own carpark OPEN: Wed-Sat 9.30-4.30 & by appt MIN: £5 MAX: £1,000+ PERIOD: 18th-20th century GENERAL: General antiques OTHER INFO: Victorian parlour & garden on show

WHITCHURCH (0948)

Dodington Antiques, 15 Dodington, SY13 1EA TEL: 663399 PARKING: Own carpark OPEN: Usually anytime by appt (resident) MIN: £25 MAX: £7,000 PERIOD: 18th-19th century SPECIALIST: Country oak & mahogany furniture OTHER INFO: Also at The Old Music Hall (2 doors away).

BOOLEY (0939)

Marcus Moore Antiques & Restorations, Booley House, SY4 4LY TEL: 200333 PARKING: Own carpark OPEN: Anytime by appt MIN: £5 MAX: £5,000 PERIOD: 17th-18th century SPECIALIST: Georgian mahogany, oak & pine.

HODNET (0630)

Hodnet Antiques, 13a, 19a Shrewsbury Street TEL: 638591 PARKING: Own carpark OPEN: Tues, Fri 11-3 & by appt MIN: £1 MAX: £1,000 SPECIALIST: Furniture GENERAL: General antiques.

BETLEY (0270)

Betley Court Gallery, Main Road, CW3 9BH TEL: 820652 FAX 820122 PARKING: Own carpark OPEN: Anytime (resident) MIN: £20 MAX: £2,500 PERIOD: 18th-20th century SPECIALIST: Doulton Lambeth, Wedgwood GENERAL: Oils, watercolours, ceramics, furniture.

NANTWICH (0270)

Rex Boyer Antiques, Townwell House, 52 Welsh Row, CW5 5EJ TEL: 625953 ASSNS: LAPADA PARKING: Own carpark OPEN: Normal (resident) MIN: £50 MAX: £12,000 PERIOD: 18th-19th century SPECIALIST: English furniture.

Chapel Antiques, 47 Hospital Street, CW5 5RL TEL: 629508 PARKING: Easy OPEN: 9.30-5.30 closed Mon & Wed pm MIN: £5 MAX: £3,500 PERIOD: 17th-19th century GENERAL: General antiques. Furniture repairs & restorations

Roderick Gibson, 70-72 Hospital Street, CW5 5RP TEL: 625301 FAX: 629603 ASSNS: LAPADA PARKING: Easy OPEN: Mon-Sat 9-5 MIN: £3 MAX: £3,000 PERIOD: 18th-19th century

GENERAL: Quality antiques, decorative items, collectables, garden statuary.

Lions & Unicorns Commemoratives, Kiltearn House, 33 Hospital Street, CW5 5RL TEL: 628892 FAX: 626646 ASSNS: Commemorative Collectors Club (CCC) PARKING: Own carpark OPEN: Anytime by appt MIN: £1 MAX: £350 PERIOD: 19th-20th century SPECIALIST: Commemoratives of the Royals & the famous in all mediums, china, glass, textiles, tin & paper GENERAL: General antiques OTHER INFO: Lamb Hotel, Crown Hotel-very old black & white timber.

Love Lane Antiques, Love Lane TEL: 626239 PARKING: Easy OPEN: Mon, Tues, Thurs-Sat 10-5 GENERAL: General antiques & collectables.

Nantwich Art Deco & Decorative Arts, 87 Welsh Row, CW5 5ET TEL: 624876 PARKING: Easy OPEN: Mon, Thurs-Sat 10-5 MIN: £1 MAX: £300 PERIOD: 20th century SPECIALIST: Art Deco, ceramics. 1930's pottery, cabinets, mirrors OTHER INFO: Stapeley Water Gardens on outskirts (A51). Bridgemere Garden World 8 miles (A51).

Richardson Antiques, 89 Hospital Street, CW5 5RU TEL: 625963 PARKING: Easy OPEN: Mon-Sat 9.30-5.30 MIN: £1 MAX: £5,000 PERIOD: 18th-19th century GENERAL: General antiques.

Wyche House Antiques, The Old Surgery, 50 Welsh Row TEL: 627179 ASSNS: LAPADA PARKING: Easy MIN: £15 MAX: £10.000 PERIOD: 18th-20th century SPECIALIST: Cranberry Glass GENERAL: 17th-19th century furniture, 18th & 19th century china. Good selection of silver items.

CREWE (0270)

Steven Blackhurst, 102 Edleston Road TEL: 258617, 665991 PARKING: Difficult OPEN: 9.30-5 MIN: £10 MAX: £600 PERIOD: 19th-20th century GENERAL: Stripped pine, some reproduction pine, dried flowers etc OTHER INFO: Good chiropodist near, useful for hikers!

ALSAGER (0270)

Forest Books of Cheshire, The Bookshop Upstairs, 14b Lawton Road, ST7 2AF TEL: 882618 PARKING: Easy OPEN: Tues, Sat 11-5.30, Thurs, Fri 11-7, closed bank hols & fortnight in Feb and Aug MIN: £1 MAX: £900 PERIOD: 19th-20th century SPECIALIST: British wildlife, agriculture, gardening, birds, fishing, drama GENERAL: Wide but emphasis on history & other higher educations OTHER INFO: Some print & paper emphemera.

Lancashire and Merseyside

This tour of Lancashire and Merseyside encompasses the cradle of the Industrial Revolution and visits the towns and cities that grew and prospered in the 19th century. Today, unfortunately, some of these are in decline as they have lost their main industries and are now struggling to find new paths to prosperity.

Manchester is one of the great English cities. It still retains some of it magnificent Victorian commercial and industrial buildings built at the height of its prosperity as the primary centre in Lancashire for coal and cotton. Its great expansion occurred during the 18th and 19th centuries with the Industrial Revolution. This was further encouraged by the opening of the Manchester Ship Canal in 1894 connecting the city to Liverpool.

The Industrial Revolution might have brought wealth to the few but it increased the poverty and misery of

Blackpool Tower. By courtesy of Blackpool Borough Council

the masses living in filthy slums and working in appalling conditions. By 1819 calls for Parliamentary reform had increased considerably. At that time only the landed classes were represented in Parliament and the growing industrial cities like Manchester had no representation at all. Parliament would do nothing to help the desperate working classes so, in the eyes of many, it was thought Parliament should be changed. Agitation and demonstrations grew, Habeas Corpus was suspended and seditious meetings were banned. This caused a fresh wave of demonstrations throughout the country.

All this discontent and unrest culminated, on the 16th August 1819, with the Peterloo Massacre. On that date a crowd of some 80,000 people gathered on St Peter's Fields in Manchester to hear a Radical speaker. The crowd was peaceful and contained many women and children. On seeing the size of the crowd the magistrates panicked and read the Riot Art and then ordered the yeomanry to arrest the speaker. They, in their turn, also panicked and charged the crowd with

Lancashire and Mersey side

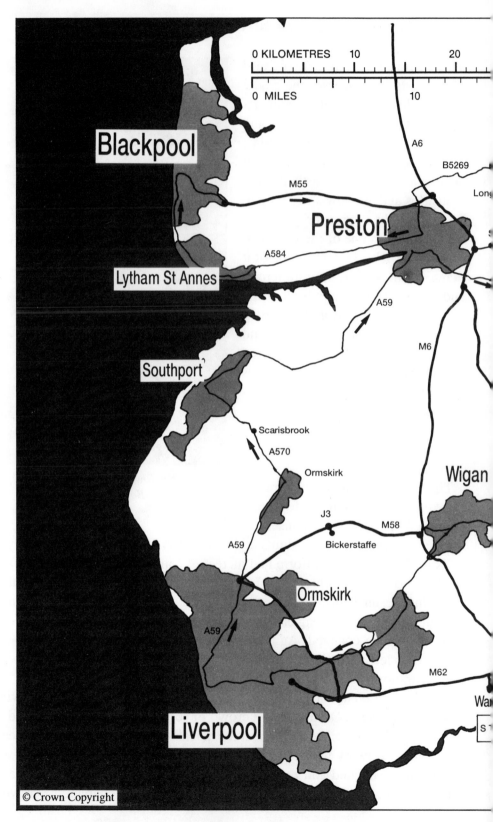

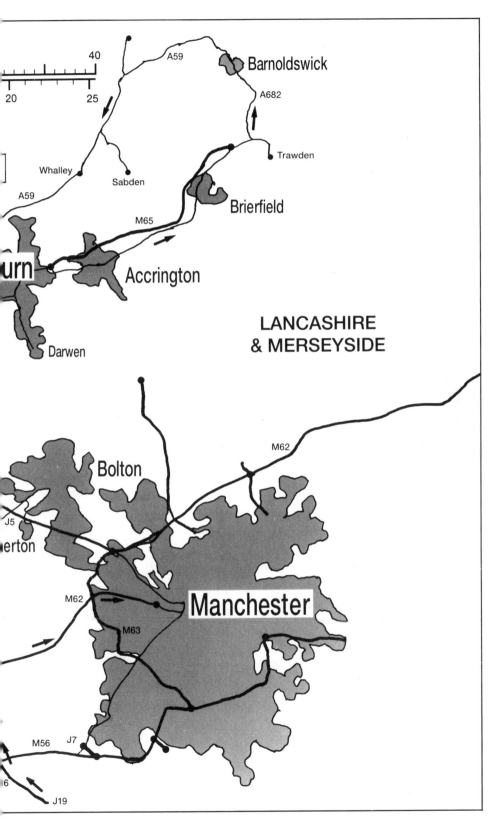

sabres which resulted in eleven people killed and hundreds injured. The name Peterloo was given as an ironic reference to the Battle of Waterloo four years earlier.

During the 19th century, Manchester's prosperity continued unchecked. The great Gothic town hall, covering nearly two acres and completed in 1877, stands as a monument to the Victorian industrialists. The city was badly damaged during the Second World War but other great Victorian buildings survive. The City Art Gallery, in Mosley Street, was designed by Sir Charles Barry, who also designed the Houses of Parliament. Originally the building was the headquarters of the Royal Manchester Institution for the Promotion of Literature, Science and the Arts. Now it contains an extremely fine and important collection of pictures including works by Turner, Gainsborough, Stubbs, Boucher, etc. It also has a good collection of Pre-Raphaelite and Victorian paintings. There are many other fine museums and galleries in Manchester. An unusual one is the Greater Manchester Police Museum in Newton Street. This is set in a Victorian police station and features a reconstructed 1920s Charge Office, cells and collections of uniforms and other exhibits.

Manchester is also a city of culture. Its major theatre, in the Royal Exchange, puts on many plays just before they go to the West End of London. The Free Trade Hall, extensively damaged by bombing in the Second World War but now rebuilt, is the home of the world famous Hallé Orchestra. The city also had the first free library in Europe, the Chetham Library opened in 1656 and was funded by a bequest from Humphrey Chetham. The John Rylands Library, also originally funded by a local family, has an amazing collection of medieval books including a Gutenburg Bible, books printed by William Caxton and manuscripts dating back to 3000BC. It also has a superb collection of jewelled medieval bindings. Manchester's third great library, the Central Library, is reputed to have one of the largest collections of books in the country.

The city's Victorian splendour can blind the visitor to its older attractions. Manchester Cathedral dates from the 15th century and was built for a college of priests to pray for for souls of benefactors. The church was restored and enlarged when it became a cathedral in 1847 but much of the older fabric survives in spite of a damage caused by a landmine during the Second World War. The choir stalls are particularly fine examples of 16th century woodcarving. The medieval shopping streets of The Shambles were also destroyed by bombing but the 14th century Wellington Inn has survived and now stands incongruously surrounded by modern shops.

Leaving Manchester we proceed northwest to Atherton, an industrial town whose economy was based on coal and cotton, and then to Bolton. For many years, Bolton meant cotton; it was one of the great Lancashire centres for fine weaving and spinning of cotton. Two important inventions of the Industrial Revolution were made by residents of the town: the spinning mule by Samuel Crompton and the water frame by Arkwright. These helped to revolutionised the cotton industry.

Two miles north east of the town centre stands Hall i' th' Wood, the 15th century home of Samuel Crompton which now contains some of his relics. The house is very picturesque and interesting in its own right. It was built in 1483 in the post and plaster style, an extension was added in 1591 and another in 1648. Samuel Crompton was living here in the last quarter of the 18th century.

One and a half miles from the town centre stands another very old and interesting house, Smithills Hall. This is one of the oldest manor houses in Lancashire and a house has stood on this site since the 14th century. The Great Hall has an open timber roof and is the oldest part of the building which has been added to and improved over the centuries giving it a most attractive, if haphazard, appearance.

Back in the town, the Old Man and Scythe inn dates from the 13th century and it was here, in October 1641, that the Earl of Derby was put for the night by Cromwell before he was beheaded next day in the market place in retaliation for a Royalist massacre.

Our next stop, Wigan, was an important coal-mining town but it dates back to Roman times. The town was made famous by George Orwell's book, *The Road to Wigan Pier*. The pier in question was a wharf on the Leeds to Liverpool canal and is now the site of a living museum dedicated to showing local life at the turn of the century.

Turning westwards along the M58, we come off at Junction 3 to visit Bickerstaffe before entering the city of Liverpool. Started as a small settlement on the north bank of the Mersey in the 1st century AD, it had grown into a busy fishing port by the 12th century when it was granted a charter by King John. However, it was the city's trade with the Indies and the Americas in the 17th and 18th centuries which brought real prosperity. Initially the trade was in sugar and slaves but, with the coming of steam ships, the port expanded further until, at its height, Liverpool had seven miles of docks and was the terminus for Cunard and White Star liners.

The city's best known landmark is the Royal Liver Building on the banks of the Mersey. It has two cathedrals, one Anglican completed in 1978 and the other Roman Catholic finished in 1967. Another building of interest is St George's Hall, described as the finest example of the Greco-Roman style in Europe, which was built in 1854. Liverpool Town Hall, completed in 1754, was designed by John Wood who also designed many of the elegant buildings of Bath.

As might be expected, there are many interesting museums and galleries. The Walker Art Gallery is said to be one of the finest in Europe with collections of European art from the 14th century to the present day and includes work by Rubens, Rembrandt, Poussin, Monet, Seurat and Degas. The Museum of Labour

Lancashire and Mersey side

History is housed in the former Sessions House and is devoted to the last 150 years of working class life on Merseyside. Then there is the award-winning Merseyside Maritime Museum on Albert Dock with floating exhibits and working displays. This museum tells the story of Liverpool from small hamlet to major international port.

The city also has a number of historic houses. In the city centre Bluecoat Chambers is a fine Queen Anne building with a cobbled quadrangle. Next there is Croxteth Hall and Rare Breeds Centre five miles north east of the city centre and set in a 500 acre country park with a superb collection of animals. Perhaps the best known of Liverpool's ancient buildings is Speke Hall near the city's airport. This is an Elizabethan half-timbered house built around a courtyard. Its attractions include the Great Hall, priest holes, Jacobean plasterwork and extensive gardens and woodlands.

Moving inland, the route reaches Ormskirk which received its charter as a market town in 1286 although very few ancient buildings survive. It does have some Georgian houses in Burscough Street including the fine Knowles House built in the 1770s. The local church of St Peter and St Paul is unusual in having both a tower and a spire side by side. The tower is 15th century while the spire was built about a hundred years later. There is a 12th century window in the chancel and four 15th century effigies.

The route goes to the coast again to Southport, an attractive seaside resort, known for its golf and beautiful public gardens, before reaching Preston, on the River Ribble. This town has a long, honourable history. In 1179 it was the first town in Lancashire to receive a borough charter and in 1328 it received the right to hold a trade fair every twenty years. In 1815 it was the first town outside London to have gas-lit streets and its by-pass, built in 1958, was the first stretch of motorway in Britain. It became an important centre for cotton spinning and engineering during the 19th century as well as the centre for the county council. The Harris Museum and Art Gallery is housed in a magnificent Greek Revival building, completed in 1893. It contains a good collection of British paintings as well as displays of ceramics, glass and costume.

Five miles east of Preston, on the A675, stands Hoghton Tower. A 16th century fortified hilltop mansion, this is where James I knighted a joint of beef, hence sirloin. The house contains collections of Chinese teapots, dolls houses and documents relating to the house.

Blackburn, our next stop, has been a textiles centre since Flemish weavers settled here in the 14th century. However, it was the Leeds Liverpool Canal that brought about its 19th century prosperity demonstrated by its fine Cotton Exchange from 1865. The Lewis Textile Museum illustrates the history of cotton much of which is associated with the city. Blackburn became a cathedral city in 1926 and its fine Gothic revival style parish church, St Mary's, was upgraded to a cathedral.

Adjoining Darwen is situated in a narrow valley cut by the river for which the town is named. The original settlement started on the east bank of the River Darwen but the town's growth in the 19th century took place along the A666 road, then a turnpike. Originally, cotton was the prime industry but gradually the mills were turned over to making paper. A mile south of the town centre, on the A666, stands the India Mill Chimney. Unmissable because it rises to a height of 300 feet, it was built in 1867 in the style of an Italian belltower. Outside India Mill a 450 horse power cross compound steam engine from 1905 is displayed.

Further east, Accrington, standing on the crossing point of two turnpikes, was just a small village until the 19th century. Again it was the opening of the Leeds Liverpool Canal in 1801 and the the coming of the railway in 1847 that brought about the town's industrial growth. Its prosperity was based upon weaving, brick-making and engineering. Although the church of St James dates from 1763 the remainder of the important public buildings are solidly Victorian. The town's Haworth Art Gallery is reputed to have the finest collection of Tiffany glass in the world.

We carry on eastwards through Brierfield and Trawden, then turn north for Barnoldswick. This town, now in Lancashire, was in Yorkshire until the boundary changes of 1974. Until the 1930s the town's prosperity was based upon cotton weaving but then Rolls Royce set up a factory to manufacture engines. St Mary-le-Gill, the perpendicular parish church, is of medieval origin and contains Jacobean pews and a three decker pulpit.

Detouring on to country roads we visit the hamlet of Harrop Fold and then the quiet and attractive village of Bolton-by-Bowland which has a perpendicular church built in the mid 15th century with an extremely fine tower. We detour again to the village of Sabden before rejoining the A59 for Whalley. A very attractive town of ancient origin, it stands on the River Calder and its bridge still retains some medieval masonry. One feature of the town is the Cistercian abbey established in the 13th century. Now all that remains are some walls and a gateway in the grounds of the abbot's house which was rebuilt after the Dissolution and used as a residence by a local family. Nearby stands the church of St Mary which is even older than the abbey and must stand on the site of a pre-Norman church demonstrated by the three earlier crosses in the churchyard. Of more recent origins, the viaduct that looms over the town is an impressive feat of engineering. More than 600 yards long and opened in 1850, this viaduct was constructed across the wide valley of the Calder as part of the Blackburn to Clitheroe railway.

The route now takes the A584 to the coastal town of Lytham St Anne's which offers a complete contrast to its brash neighbour, Blackpool. The town is the result of an amalgamation between Lytham, mentioned in the Domesday book, and St Anne's. The intention of joining the two places was to stop Blackpool swallowing both villages. The town, laid out as a garden city in the late 18th and

Part of Blackpool's Golden Mile. By courtesy of Blackpool Borough Council

early 19th centuries, offers few concessions to holiday makers. Visitors to Lytham St Anne's come for the peace and quiet, pleasant walks and, famously, golf at the Royal Lytham St Anne's Golf Club, one of the venues for the British Open Championships.

Blackpool, next, is synonymous with English holiday making. Its name conjures up pictures of it famous tower, pier and illuminations. Its career as a holiday resort started in the 18th century but it was the coming of the railways to the town in 1846 that really began its meteoric rise to become the most famous of English seaside towns. Traditionally Lancashire factories and mills shut down for a week in the summer and it was their workers that brought prosperity to the town as they descended on it determined to enjoy themselves. Everything in Blackpool is geared for fun: the renowned Tower Ballroom, the seven miles of bathing beaches, the Golden Mile, the crazy golf courses, amusement arcades, theatres, three piers, the Pleasure Beach, water slides, etc.

Moving back inland along the M55 we come to our final stop, in Longridge, standing between the valleys of the Rivers Ribble and Hodder. This was the site of extensive quarries providing the fine sandstone used in many 19th century Lancashire buildings. On Higher Road there is a group of twenty cottages called Club Row, built between 1794 and 1804, which are interesting because they are said to be the oldest houses in Lancashire to be built by the members of a building society.

ANTIQUE DEALERS
WARRINGTON (0925)
A. Baker & Sons, 10 Cairo Street, WA1 1ED TEL: 33706 FAX: 33706 ASSNS: NAG PARKING: Medium OPEN: 9.30-4.50 MIN: £10 MAX: £10,000 SPECIALIST: 18th-19th century vinaigrettes GENERAL: 19th-20th silver & jewellery OTHER INFO: 86 years in same family. Royal Garden Hotel, Lord Daresbury Hotel.

The Rocking Chair Antiques, Unit 3, St Peters Way TEL: 52409 FAX: 52409 PARKING: Easy OPEN: 9-5 GENERAL: Shipping items 1900-1930.

Victoriana Antiques, 85a Walton Road, Stockton Heath TEL: 263263, 261035 PARKING: Own carpark OPEN: Tues-Wed, Fri-Sat 1-5 & by appt MIN: £5 MAX: £1,500+ PERIOD: 18th-20th century SPECIALIST: Antique metals (fireside furniture, decorative items). 1900-1930 lighting GENERAL: Smaller items of furniture 1800-1930 OTHER INFO: Birthplace of Lewis Carroll.

MANCHESTER (061)
A.S. Antique Galleries, 26 Broad Street, Pendleton, Salford, M6 5BY TEL: 737 5938 FAX: 737 6626 PARKING: Easy OPEN: Normal MIN: £50 MAX: £10,000 PERIOD: 19th-20th century SPECIALIST: Enormous stock Art Nouveau, Arts & Crafts, Art Deco, bronzes, ivories, glass, furniture, silver etc GENERAL: Victorian & earlier furniture, lighting, metalware OTHER INFO: 5 mins drive from city centre.

Browzers Bookshop, 14 Warwick Street, Prestwich, M25 7HN TEL: 798 0626 ASSNS: PBFA PARKING: Easy OPEN: Tues, Thurs-Sat 10-5 MIN: £1 MAX: £450 PERIOD: 19th-20th century SPECIALIST: Antique engravings, some maps GENERAL: Books on antiques & collecting.

Bulldog Antiques, 393 Bury New Road, Prestwich, M25 8UB TEL: 798 9277, home 7907153 PARKING: Easy OPEN: Mon-Sat 10.30-5.30 MIN: £25 MAX: £10,000 PERIOD: 18th-20th century SPECIALIST: Furniture, clocks GENERAL: General antiques OTHER INFO: Local period tavern-B&B 15th century with good food.

Henry Donn Gallery, 138-142 Bury New Road, Whitefield TEL: 766 8819 ASSNS: FATG PARKING: Own carpark OPEN: Mon-Sat 9.30-5.15 MIN: £40 MAX: £10,000 PERIOD: 20th century SPECIALIST: L.S. Lowrey & Northern artists GENERAL: Original oils, watercolours, limited editions, sculpture OTHER INFO: M62 jt 17, Whitefield was one time home of Clive of India.

Failsworth Mill Antiques, Ashton Road West, Failsworth, M35 0ER TEL: 684 7440 PARKING: Own carpark OPEN: Mon-Fri 9-5 MIN: £5 MAX: £10,000 PERIOD: 18th-20th century GENERAL: Former cotton mill now with 50,000 sq ft antique & French furniture, architectural antiques.

Forest Books of Cheshire, The Ginnel Gallery, 18-22 Lloyd Street, M2 5WA TEL: 834 0747 (books), 833 9037 (Ginnel Gallery) PARKING: Medium OPEN: Tues-Sat 10.530, closed bank hols MIN: £1 MAX: £1,000 PERIOD: 17th-20th century SPECIALIST: Collecting, drama. art history, local interests, drama, attractive literature GENERAL: Prints, pictures, postcards OTHER INFO: Next to Town Hall & Granada Studios.

Garson & Co Ltd, 47 Houldsworth Street, Piccadilly, M1 2ES TEL: 236 9393 FAX: 236 4211 PARKING:Own carpark OPEN: Mon-Fri 8-5 MIN: £20 MAX: £50,000 PERIOD: 17th-20th century SPECIALIST: Carved gold French mirrors, tables GENERAL: Blackgammon, bronzes, paintings, prints, watercolours, limited editions, telescopes, private chapel altars, books etc OTHER INFO: Clients' comments: 'Another world, mindboggling, too much to see in one trip'

The Ginnel Gallery Antique Centre, Basement, 18-22 Lloyd Street, M2 5WA TEL: 833 9037 PARKING: Easy OPEN: Tues-Sat 10-5.30 MIN: £3 MAX: £3,000 PERIOD: 17th-20th century SPECIALIST: Art Deco, antiquarian books, 1950's & 60's GENERAL: Furniture, pottery, glass, books OTHER INFO: Large city site with restaurant.

Manchester Antique Company, 95 Lapwing Lane, West Didsbury TEL: 434 7752 PARKING: Own carpark OPEN: Mon-Sat 9.30-5 MIN: £20 MAX: £35,000 PERIOD 17th-20th century SPECIALIST: Continental furniture, Dutch marqetry GENERAL: 35,000 sq ft of shipping goods to period furniture etc. Vast stock of walnut OTHER INFO: 5 mins city centre, lawn tennis club opposite.

Marks Antiques, 16 Waterloo Street, Oldham TEL: 624 5975 FAX: 624 5975 PARKING: Easy OPEN: Mon-Sat 9.30-5 MIN: £5 MAX: £1,000 PERIOD: 17th-20th century SPECIALIST: Jewellery GENERAL: Silver, pottery OTHER INFO: Also Marks Pawnbrokers.

Village Antiquities, 416 Bury New Road, Prestwich

TEL: 773 3612 PARKING: Easy OPEN: Mon-Sat 10-5 but Wed 10-1 MIN: £5 MAX: £2,500 PERIOD: 18th-20th century GENERAL: Furniture & general antiques OTHER INFO: Browsers very welcome.

ATHERTON (0942)

Victoria's, 144-145 Bolton Road TEL: 882311 PARKING: Easy OPEN: Mon-Sat 10-5.30 MIN: £2 MAX: £2,000 PERIOD: 19th century SPECIALIST: Pine & furniture GENERAL: Cornucopia.

BOLTON (0204)

Bolton Antiques Centre, Central Street, BL1 2AB TEL: 362694 PARKING: Easy OPEN: Mon-Sat 10-5, Sun 11-4.30 PERIOD: 19th century GENERAL: Antiques, collectables, jewellery.

G. Oakes & Son, 160-162 Blackburn Road, BL1 8DR TEL: 26587 PARKING: Easy OPEN: Mon-Sat 9-5 MIN: £5 MAX: £1,500 PERIOD: 19th-20th century SPECIALIST: Shipping goods GENERAL: Antiques, Victorian, quality 20th century furniture OTHER INFO: On good trade run.

Park Galleries Antiques & Fine Art, BL1 4SJ TEL: 29827, (061) 7645853 PARKING: Easy (at side) OPEN: Thurs-Sat 11-5 & anytime by appt MIN: £5 MAX: £3,500 PERIOD: 17th-early 20th century SPECIALIST: Antique & period furniture GENERAL: Porcelain, metalware, miniatures, decoratives, 19th century oils.

Tiffany Antiques, Bolton Antique Centre, Central Street, BL1 2AB TEL: 362694, home (0270) 257425 PARKING: Easy OPEN: Seven days 9.30-5 MIN: £3 MAX: £300 PERIOD: 19th-20th century GENERAL: Collectables, ceramics, glass OTHER INFO: La Curio café in antique centre.

EDENFIELD (0706)

The Antique Shop, 17 Market Street, BL0 0JA TEL: 823107, 822351 PARKING: Easy OPEN: Mon-Sat 10-4 MIN: £5 MAX: £5,000 PERIOD: 18th-20th century GENERAL: General antiques items OTHER INFO: Close to M66-J1. Local steam train, theatre, trout farm, 10pin bowling.

WIGAN (0942)

Colin de Rouffignac, 57 Wigan Lane, WN1 2LF TEL: 37927 ASSNS: BNTA PARKING: Easy OPEN: Mon, Tues, Thurs-Sat 10-5 MIN: £5 MAX: £10,000 PERIOD: 18th-20th century SPECIALIST: Paintings GENERAL: Jewellery, furniture.

Whatnot Antiques, 90 Wigan Lane, WN1 2LF TEL: 491880 PARKING: Easy OPEN: Mon, Tues,

Thurs-Sat 10-5 MIN: £1 MAX: £2,000 PERIOD: 17th-20th century GENERAL: Good range of general antiques OTHER INFO: A visit to Wigan Pier a must.

BICKERSTAFFE (0695)

E.W. Webster Antiques, Wash Farm, L39 0HG TEL: 24326 PARKING: Own carpark OPEN: Anytime by appt PERIOD: 1700-1830 GENERAL: Georgian furniture, needlework, decorative items.

LIVERPOOL (051)

Architectural Antiques, 60 St Johns Road, Waterloo, L22 9GQ TEL: 949 0819 PARKING: Easy OPEN: Mon-Sat 10-5 MIN: £50 MAX: £3,000 PERIOD: 18th-19th century SPECIALIST: Antique fireplaces GENERAL: Stripped pine, panel, doors, rolltop baths, Belfast sinks OTHER INFO: 5 mins seafront. Everchanging stock.

Edwards, 45a Whitechapel, L1 6DT TEL: 236 2909 PARKING: Medium OPEN: Mon-Fri 10-4 MAX: £500 PERIOD: 19th-20th century SPECIALIST: Secondhand or antique jewellery or silver only OTHER INFO: In city centre.

Lyver & Boydell Galleries, 15 Castle Street, L2 4SX TEL: 236 3256 ASSNS: LAPADA, FATG PARKING: Medium OPEN: Mon-Sat 10.30-5.30 MIN: £5 MAX: £10,000 PERIOD: 18th-20th century SPECIALIST: Victorian and earlier oils & watercolours GENERAL: Antique maps & prints OTHER INFO: Conservation area in city centre. Close to famous Albert Dock.

Magg's Antiques Ltd, 26-28 Fleet Street, L1 4AR TEL: 708 0221 FAX: 708 0221 PARKING: Medium OPEN: Mon-Fri 9-5 MIN: £20 MAX: £2,000 PERIOD: 17th-19th century SPECIALIST: Chests of drawers GENERAL: Victorian & Edwardian furniture, 1920's Shipping goods.

Ryanwood Antiques, 102 Seel Street, L1 4BT TEL: 709 7776 PARKING: Easy OPEN: Mon-Sat 9.30-5 MIN: £5 MAX: £15,000 PERIOD: 18th-20th century GENERAL: Good selection furniture, glass, china, silver + plate, pictures OTHER INFO: Close to tourist attractions, art galleries etc.

ORMSKIRK (0695)

Alan Grice Antiques. 106 Aughton Street, L39 3BS TEL: 572007 PARKING: Own carpark OPEN: Mon-Sat 10-6 MIN: £80 MAX: £3,500 PERIOD: 17th-20th century SPECIALIST: English furniture.

SCARISBRICK (0704)

Carr Cross Gallery, Southport Road TEL: 880638

PARKING: Easy OPEN: Mon-Sat 10-5 MIN: £50 MAX: £2,000 PERIOD: 18th-19th century SPECIALIST: Fireplaces, architectural antiques.

SOUTHPORT (0704)

C.K. Broadhurst & Co Ltd, 5-7 Market Street, PR8 1HD TEL: 532064, 534110 FAX: 542009 ASSNS: ABA, PBFA PARKING: Easy OPEN: Mon-Sat 9-5.30 MIN: £1 MAX: £5,000+ PERIOD: 18th-20th century SPECIALIST: Art, architecture, modern firsts, topography, private press. GENERAL: All subjects.

Decor Galleries, 52 Lord Street, PR8 1QB TEL: 535734 PARKING: Easy OPEN: Mon-Sat 9.30-5 MIN: £150 MAX: £4,000 PERIOD: 19th-20th century SPECIALIST: Furniture, lamps GENERAL: 19th century antiques, decorative fittings, fabrics.

PRESTON (0772)

The Antique Centre, 56 Garstang Road, PR1 1NA TEL: 882078 PARKING: Easy OPEN: Mon-Sat 9.30-5.30, Sun 10.30-5.30 MIN: £100 MAX: £15,000+ PERIOD: 18th-20th century GENERAL: 30 dealers with wide range of antiques & collectables.

Peter Guy's Period Interiors, 26-30 New Hall Lane, PR1 4DU TEL: 703771 FAX: 703771 ASSNS: LAPADA PARKING: Own carpark OPEN: Mon-Sat 9.30-5.30 MIN: £10 MAX: £10,000 PERIOD: 18th-20th century SPECIAL-IST: Georgian case furniture GENERAL: French & English furniture & accessories.

K.C. Antiques, The Antique Centre, 56 Garstang Road, PR1 1NA TEL: 882078 PARKING: Easy OPEN: Mon-Sat 9-5.30, Sun 10.30-5.30 PERIOD: 18th-19th century GENERAL: Quality mahogany, pine & oak.

Orchard Antiques, 447 Blackpool Road, Lane Ends, Ashton TEL: 769749 PARKING: Easy OPEN: Tues-Sat 10-5.30 MIN: £5 MAX: £350 PERIOD: 18th-20th century SPECIALIST: Deco, old porcelain, small furniture, linen GENERAL: Wide range of quality antiques & curios.

Swag, 24-26 Leyland Road, Penwortham, PR1 9XS TEL: 744970 PARKING: Medium OPEN: Mon-Sat 10-6 MIN: £1 MAX: £2,500 PERIOD: 19th-20th century SPECIALIST: Antique dolls GENERAL: General antiques.

Ray Wade Antiques, 113 New Hall Lane, PR1 5SB TEL: 792950, home 700815 PARKING: Easy OPEN: Mon, Tues, Thurs-Fri 10-5.30, Sat 11-4

approx MIN: £10 PERIOD: 18th-19th century SPECIALIST: Decorative antiques of all types GENERAL: General antiques OTHER INFO: Restoration available for furniture ceramics & paintings. Valuations for probate etc.

LYTHAM ST ANNES (0253)

The Snuff Box, 5 Market Buildings, Hastings Place, FY8 4ES TEL: 738656 PARKING: Easy OPEN: Mon, Tues, Thurs-Sat 10-5 MIN: £1 MAX: £1,000 PERIOD: 19th-20th century SPECIALIST: Silver + plate, jewellery, watches GENERAL: Range of smalls OTHER INFO: Opposite County Hotel, we speak German.

BLACKPOOL (0253)

R & L Coins, 521 Lytham Road, FY4 1RJ TEL: 343081 FAX: 408058 ASSNS: BNTA PARKING: Own carpark OPEN: Mon-Fri 10-4 PERIOD: 17th-20th century SPECIALIST: Coins, jewellery GENERAL: Manufacture & wholesale of diamond rings OTHER INFO: Roman times to date. Phone/mail orders OK.

BLACKBURN (0254)

R.C. Lynch Antiques, 726 Preston Old Road, Feniscowles TEL: 209943 PARKING: Own carpark OPEN: Mon-Sat 9.30-5 MIN: £1 MAX: £2,000+ PERIOD: 17th-20th century SPECIALIST: Fireplaces, pictures, violins, cellos GENERAL: Musical instruments, fireplaces, furniture, pottery OTHER INFO: Closeby Houghton Tower (open) where King knighted the Sirloin of beef.

DARWEN (0254)

K.C. Antiques, 538 Bolton Road TEL: 772252 PARKING: Easy OPEN: Mon-Sat 9-5, Sun 1-4 PERIOD: 18th-19th century GENERAL: Quality mahogany, pine, oak.

ACCRINGTON (0254)

Coin & Jewellery Shop, 129a Blackburn Road, BB5 0AA TEL: 384757 PARKING: Medium OPEN: Mon, Tues, Thurs-Sat 9.30-5 PERIOD: 19th-20th century SPECIALIST: Coins & medals GENERAL: Badges, tins, smalls, jewellery.

BRIERFIELD (0282)

J.H. Blakey & Sons, Burnley Road TEL: 602493 FAX: 617550 PARKING: Easy OPEN: Mon-Fri 8-12.30, 1.30-5.30, Sat 8-12 PERIOD: 18th-20th century GENERAL: Good range of furniture, pictures, metalware & collectables.

TRAWDEN (0282)

The Old Rock, Keighley Road TEL: 869478 FAX:

865193 PARKING: Own carpark OPEN: Mon-Fri 9-5, Sat, Sun 10-4 MIN: £3 MAX: £2,500 PERIOD: 18th-20th century SPECIALIST: Antique stained glass GENERAL: Furniture OTHER INFO: Brontë's Haworth 9 miles, Penelope Keith's beloved Wycollar 1 mile.

BARNOLDSWICK (0282)
Roy W. Bunn, 34-36 Church Street TEL: 813703 ASSNS: LAPADA PARKING: Easy OPEN: By appt only MIN: £50 MAX: £1,000 PERIOD: 19th century SPECIALIST: Staffordshire figures.

BOLTON-BY-BOWLAND (0200)
Marian Howard Farmhouse Antiques, Corner Shop, 23 Main Street TEL: 447294, 446244 PARKING: Easy OPEN: Sat, Sun, Bank hols only 12-4.30 & by appt PERIOD: 19th-20th century SPECIALIST: Large stock patchwork, white lace & table linen GENERAL: Small Victoriana & jewellery OTHER INFO: We are often described as an Aladdin's Cave. Ribble Valley tourist area with farmhouse B&B's, country pubs, set in lovely lanes.

HARROP FOLD HAMLET (0200)
Harrop Fold Clocks, TEL: 447665 PARKING: Own carpark OPEN: By appt only MIN: £1,500 MAX: £8,000 PERIOD: 18th century SPECIALIST: Longcase clocks GENERAL: English wall clocks OTHER INFO: 2 self catering holiday cottages all year (brochure).

SABDEN (0282)
Pendle Antiques Centre Ltd, Union Mill, Wait Street, BB6 9ED TEL: 776311 FAX: 778643 PARKING: Own carpark OPEN: Seven days 10-5 MIN: £1 MAX: £10,000 PERIOD: 19th-20th century SPECIALIST: Furniture GENERAL: Georgian to 1930's furniture, pine, painted furniture, bric-a-brac OTHER INFO: Refreshments.

WHALLEY (0254)
Edmund Davies & Son Antiques, 32 King Street, BB6 9SL TEL: 823764 PARKING: Easy OPEN: Mon-Sat 10-5.30 MIN: £2 MAX: £5,000 PERIOD: 17th-19th century SPECIALIST: Longcase clocks GENERAL: 17th-18th century oak & country furniture, especialy rush seated chairs OTHER INFO: Trade warehouse, 15th century Abbey.

SAMLESBURY (0254)
Samlesbury Hall Ltd, Preston New Road, PR5 0UP TEL: 812010 PARKING: Own carpark OPEN: 11.30-4 GENERAL: From bric-a-brac & collectables to expensive antiques OTHER INFO: We are a 14th century black & white timbered Manor House, (Entrance £2 to Hall itself).

LONGRIDGE (0772)
Charnley Fine Arts, Charnley House, Preston Road TEL: 782800 FAX: 785068 PARKING: Own carpark OPEN: Anytime by appt MIN: £100 MAX: £10,000 PERIOD: 17th-20th century SPECIALIST: Victorian watercolours GENERAL: Paintings OTHER INFO: Near M6 juncs 31 & 32, B&B in Georgian Farmhouse.

Kitchenalia, The Old Bakery, 36 Inglewhite Road, PR3 3JS TEL: 785411 PARKING: Easy OPEN: Mon, Tues, Thur-Sat 10-5 MIN: £1 MAX: £1,000 PERIOD: 19th-20th century SPECIALIST: Kitchen collectables GENERAL: Pine country furniture, butchers blocks, Victorian pine pews & lots of 'what's that for' items OTHER INFO: In beautiful Ribble Valley near Trough of Bowland. Many good pubs etc.

The Lake District

The Lake District, Cumbria, with its magnificent lakes, towering mountains and windswept fells, is one of the most dramatically beautiful areas in England. Now a National Park covering about 900 square miles, the region contains some of the highest mountains in England.

Our first stop, however, is in Lancashire just outstide of the Lake District. Standing on the River Lune, the county town of Lancaster has been in existence since at least Roman times. The Roman fortress of *Longoricum* stood on the site of the present castle and traces of the fosse may still be seen on the north side of the hill. The castle was started in 1094, later John of Gaunt, the Earl of Lancaster and father of Henry IV, enlarged it and then further additions were made in Elizabethan times.

The River Lune is tidal at this point and much of Lancaster's medieval prosperity came because of its role as a port. This continued throughout the centuries and by the 18th century Lancaster was the fourth busiest slave-trading port in England. The Custom House on St George's Quay dates from this period and now houses the Maritime Museum. Another museum may be found at 15 Castle Hill which is an artisan's house furnished in the style of 1820. In Castle Street stands the Judges Lodgings which, built in the 1620s, is the oldest house in the town. It got its name from the fact that between 1826 and

Windermere

1975 it was used by visiting judges who came for the assizes three times a year. Lancaster also has a Roman Catholic cathedral and a university.

The tour, via Middleham and then Yealand Conyers, now moves into the Lake District and to our next stop, Kendal. The economy of this ancient market town was originally based upon wool but now it is the administrative centre for the Lake District National Park and a popular tourist destination. There are a number of notable buildings. Kendal Castle was the birthplace of Catherine Parr, the last wife of Henry VIII. The impressive Georgian house, Abbot Hall, stands near the parish church. This house contains collections of portraits by George Romney and Daniel Gardner as well as Lake District landscapes. There is also a collection of furniture by Gillows of Lancaster. The adjacent Museum of Lakeland Life and Industry features displays of everything from hip baths to sheep dips.

The route now turns north west to Windermere which, surprisingly, does not stand on the lake of the same name but about a mile away. Our next stop is situated on Lake Windermere. Bowness-on-Windermere is an old settlement that expanded with the coming of the railways. Dotted around the encircling hills are the mansions built by 19th century Lancastrian industrialists. The town is now a centre for the tourism and has good facilities for water sports as well as boat trips around the lake.

Continuing along the A591, the route reaches Rydall Water and Grasmere, one of the best known of lakeland villages because of its association with William Wordsworth. His home, Dove Cottage, is a popular tourist attraction here. The poet is buried in the churchyard as are members of his family and also Hartley Coleridge.

Just off the A593, near to Ambleside, there is a very popular drive. It is Wrynose Pass which continues into Hardknott Pass. This road is only suitable for drivers (and passengers) with nerves of steel and cars in good mechanical order. Much of the road is single track with gradients of 1 in 3 in places. It is unsuitable for use in winter conditions as the numerous road signs will warn you. However, the views are breathtakingly beautiful right through both passes. Situated in Hardknott Pass, commanding the road, is the Roman fort once called *Mediobogdum* and now marked on maps as Hardknott Castle. From here the views are spectacular. The highest peaks of the Lake District can be seen as can the sea at Ravenglass. The fort, built in the 2nd century AD, covers some three acres and considerable remains are visible. It was not manned by imperial legions but by auxiliaries recruited from the Roman province of Dalmatia in former Yu-

Warning signs at the beginning of Hardknott Pass

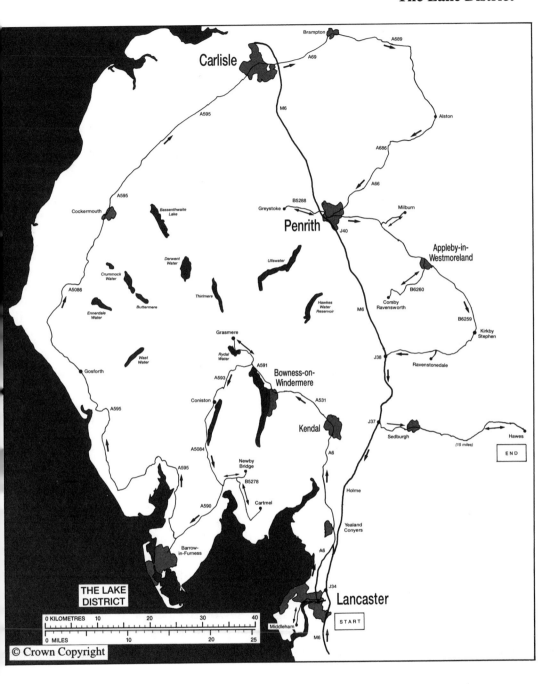

© Crown Copyright

Lake Bassenthwaite seen from the B5292

goslavia. As little has changed in nearly two thousand years, it can be seen that this must have been a desperately lonely and uncomfortable posting especially for Southern Europeans.

Back on the tour, the next stop, Coniston, is situated at the north west edge of Coniston Water. Its original industries were mining and quarrying but now it receives most of its income from tourism. Overlooked by Coniston Old Man which rises to 2635 feet, it is ideally located for walkers exploring the surrounding peaks. Sir Donald Campbell was killed on Coniston Water when he attempted to beat his own world water speed record in 1967. Although his body was never found there is a memorial to him in the village.

We continue south via the pretty village of Newby Bridge to Cartmel, a pleasant old town which was the site of an important priory. Much of the building was destroyed during the Dissolution but the church still stands and is used as the parish church.

Our next stop is Barrow-in-Furness which has developed over the last 100 years from a small village to a major town. Its growth started with the Industrial Revolution and the coming of railways in 1846. It became a centre for engineering and shipbuilding; the Polaris submarine was built here. One and a half miles to the north of the town stands the impressive ruins of Furness Abbey. Built from the local sandstone in the 12th century, by the time of the Dissolution of the Monasteries in 1537 this abbey was one of the wealthiest in the country. Its wealth may still be judged by the size and beauty of the extensive ruins.

The tour now runs parallel to the coast along the A595 until it reaches Gosforth. Its most notable feature is a collection of Anglo-Saxon and Norse crosses in the churchyard of St Mary's. One of these is 14 feet high and carved from red sandstone. On it are depicted figures from Norse mythology and Christianity.

Continuing along the A595 we next reach Cockermouth, birthplace of William Wordsworth and Fletcher Christian who led the mutiny on the Bounty. Standing on the Rivers Cocker and Derwent, it has a castle, the earliest parts of which date from the mid 13th and 14th centuries with 18th and 19th century additions.

We then move on to Carlisle which first achieved importance as the Roman headquarters for the area. As a border town it suffered centuries of hostilities with the Scots. After the Norman Conquest William had to take an army north to subdue the area and import English peasants to colonise the region. In 1092 William II started work on Carlisle Castle sited on a bluff above the River Eden. Over the centuries the castle survived many battles and sieges and, on occasion, was taken by the Scots and then retaken by the English. It was not until the 16th century that relations between the Scots and English improved enough for constant battles and skirmishes to cease. In 1568 it was used for two months as a prison for Mary, Queen of Scots. In 1596 it again came under attack when Lord Scott of Buccleugh attempted to rescue a follower imprisoned here for raiding cattle. During the Civil War the castle changed hands frequently. First it held out for the King and was taken by Parliament and then retaken by Royalists. However, after the Roundhead victory at Preston the castle was finally taken by Parliamentary troops.

The last real action seen here was during the Jacobite Rebellion of 1745 when Bonnie Prince Charlie led a Scottish army to try to regain the throne. He got as far as Derby from where he was forced to retreat to Carlisle by the Duke of Cumberland. Prince Charles left about 400 Highland soldiers to defend the castle but the Duke of Cumberland triumphed. Carlisle Castle was then used as a prison for Scots captured after the Battle of Culloden prior to their execution.

The city also has a fine cathedral built in the local sandstone. Founded by Henry I about 1120, it became a cathedral in 1133. It suffered considerably in the Scottish raids and was eventually finished in the late 14th century. During the Civil War Parliamentary forces destroyed part of the nave which has never been replaced and leaves it as one of the smallest cathedrals in England. It has a splendid medieval glass east window and fine 15th century choir stalls.

Following the A69 we come to Brampton, a small market town granted its Charter in 1252. It has few ancient buildings because it was the target for raids by the Scots and suffered greatly as a result. The Tourist Information Centre is housed in the octagonal Moot Hall built in 1817. Nearby the town stands Naworth Castle, a border fortress built in 1335 which later passed into the hands of the powerful

Howard family. To the north of Brampton can be seen some of the few surviving Cumbrian sections of Hadrian's Wall.

We next call at Alston, reputed to be England's highest market town at 919 feet above sea level. This small town grew up as a result of lead mining in neighbouring hills which has been carried out since Roman times. Now on to Penrith, a prosperous market town which has suffered attacks by the Scots over the centuries. Beacon Hill, rising over the town, was the site of many warning fires. Penrith Castle was built in the late 14th century to provide protection from the Scots. Richard of Gloucester, later to become Richard III, was its keeper when he held the title Lord Warden of the Western Marches. It later passed to the Earl of Warwick, nicknamed Kingmaker, and his badge, a bear and ragged staff, may be seen on the north west corner of the tower of St Andrew's Church.

The route detours westward to visit Greystoke with its large church dating from the middle of the 13th century and closely associated with the Barons of Greystoke Castle over the centuries. It contains some fine medieval glass, miserichords and carved stalls.

Our next two stops, Crosby Ravenscroft and Milburn, are on country roads off the A66. We then follow the B6259 to Kirkby Stephen which stands at 600 feet above the Eden Valley. Its 13th century church has a number of carved stones that pre-date the Norman Conquest including one with the Danish devil, Loki, carved upon it.

Turning eastward we reach Ravenstonedale. Its church of St Oswald was built in the middle of the 18th century on the site of a much earlier one, some of which has survived. From the earlier church comes a most unusual pulpit with three levels. At the lowest level sat the clerk, on the second the vicar took the service and the sermon was preached from the topmost level.

The route now takes the M6 southward for just a few miles to Junction 37 before taking the A684 to Sedbergh. Although Sedbergh has officially been in Cumbria since the boundary changes of 1974, it still remains part of the Yorkshire Dales National Park. It is an ideal centre for walkers exploring the beautiful countryside surrounding it. The town contains some buildings of note. Amongst these is Sedbergh School founded in 1525. The restored church of St. Andrew was originally Norman and contains a number of interesting monuments.

We continue eastward along the A684 to our final stop at the village of Hawes in North Yorkshire. Here the Upper Dales Folk Museum has displays on life in the Dales including peat cutting, hand knitting and cheese making.

ANTIQUE DEALERS
LANCASTER (0524)
G.B. Antiques Ltd, The Antique Centre, Lancaster Leisure Park, Old Hornsea Pottery, Wyresdale Road, LA1 3LA TEL: 844734 FAX: 844735 PARKING: Own carpark OPEN: Seven days 10-5 MIN: £5 MAX: £6,000 PERIOD: 19th-20th century GENERAL: 100+ dealers & 30,000 sq ft of pine, mahogany, pine, oak furniture, linen, Art Deco, glass, porcelain, dolls & teddies OTHER INFO: Café on site.

Vicary Antiques, 18a Brock Street TEL: 843322 PARKING: Medium OPEN: Mon, Tues, Thurs-Sat 10-5 MIN: £1 MAX: £1,000+ PERIOD: 19th-20th century SPECIALIST: Paintings 1880-1950, Arts & Crafts, furniture, metalware, etchings, art pottery GENERAL: Books, fabrics.

MIDDLETON VILLAGE (0524)
G & G Exports, 'Golly Goulding', 25 Middleton Road TEL: 851565 FAX: 851565 PARKING: Own carpark OPEN: Seven days 9.30-5.30 but anytime by appt MIN: £30 MAX: £1,000 PERIOD: 20th century SPECIALIST: Shipping furniture GENERAL: 20,000 sq ft of oak, walnut, mahogany & some pine.

YEALAND CONYERS (0524)
M. & I. Finch Antiques/Hector Finch Lighting, 15-17 Yealand Road, LA5 9SG TEL: 732212 PARKING: Own carpark OPEN: Mon-Sat 10-6 MIN: £50 MAX: £7,000 PERIOD: 18th-20th century SPECIALIST: Lighting GENERAL: Period furniture, some prints & smalls OTHER INFO: Pretty village with Grade II houses, Leighton House, (open summer), home of Gillow family. New Inn.

HOLME (0524)
JBW Antiques, Duke Street, TEL: 781377, PARKING: Own carpark OPEN: Mon-Fri 9-5, Sat 9-4 MIN: £5 MAX: £500 PERIOD: 18th-20th century SPECIALIST: Continental porcelain GENERAL: General antiques OTHER INFO: Next to MG Centre, classic car complex. 20 mins south of Bowness.

KENDAL (0539)
Below Stairs, 78 Highgate TEL: 741278 PARKING: Medium OPEN: Mon-Sat 10-4 MIN: £5 MAX: £500 PERIOD: 19th-20th century GENERAL: Metalware, china, glass.

The Silver Thimble, 39 Allhallows Lane TEL: 731456 PARKING: Medium OPEN: Mon-Sat 10-4 MIN: £1 MAX: £2,500 PERIOD: 19th-20th century GENERAL: General antiques OTHER INFO: Abbey Hall Gallery (award winning museum). several good antique shops.

BOWNESS-ON-WINDERMERE (0539)
Unicorn Antiques, 1 Longlands, Lake Road, LA23 3LN TEL: 488747 PARKING: Medium OPEN: Seven days 10.30-5.30 MIN: £1 MAX: £2,000 PERIOD: 19th-20th century SPECIALIST: Old bottles & salt glaze jars c.1900 GENERAL: General antiques OTHER INFO: Heart of Lake District, Beatrix Potter House & Exhibition.

Utopia Antiques Ltd, Lake Road, LA23 2JG TEL: 488464 PARKING: Own carpark OPEN: Mon-Sat 10.30-5.30 MIN: £10 MAX: £5,000 PERIOD: 19th-20th century SPECIALIST: Antique pine furniture GENERAL: Pine & decorative accessories, aromatic products.

White Elephant Antiques, 66 Quarry Rigg TEL: 446962 PARKING: Own carpark OPEN: Seven days 9.30-5.30 MIN: £1 MAX: £1,000 PERIOD: 18th-20th century SPECIALIST: Copper, brass GENERAL: Bric-a-brac, furniture OTHER INFO: Totaly unskilled owner who sells the odd treasure for buttons and doesn't even know it.

WINDERMERE (0539)
Birdcage Antiques, College Road, LA23 1BX TEL: 445063 PARKING: Own carpark OPEN: Wed, Fri, Sat 10-5 MIN: £50 MAX: £1,000 PERIOD: 19th-early 20th century SPECIALIST: Oil, gas, electric lighting GENERAL: Antiques & collectables.

GRASMERE (0539)
Aladdins Cave Antiques, Langdale Road, LA22 9QZ TEL: 435774 PARKING: Easy OPEN: Seven days 10-5 MIN: £1 MAX: £3,000 PERIOD: 19th-20th century GENERAL: Brass, copper, coloured glass, treen, Lake District books & prints, furniture OTHER INFO: Dove Cottage (Wordsworth), Lake & boating, famous hotel: Michael's Nook, Beatrix Potter's house 12 miles.

Andrew & Kay Saalmans, The Stables, College Street, LA22 9SW TEL: 435453 PARKING: Easy OPEN: 10-6 MIN: £1 MAX: £250 PERIOD: 19th-20th century GENERAL: Brass & copperware, silver + plate, books, prints.

CONISTON (0539)
The Old Man Antiques, Yewdale Road, LA21 8DU TEL: 441389 PARKING: Easy OPEN: Seven days 9.30-4.30 Easter-November 5th MIN: £2

MAX: £500 PERIOD: 19th-20th century SPECIALIST: Barometers as available GENERAL: Silver, glass, clocks, smalls OTHER INFO: The only antiques shop in Coniston, where Sir Donald Campbell sank with Bluebird attempting water speed record. At foot of famous mountain mined for copper & slate since the Stone Age.

NEWBY BRIDGE (0539)

Shire Antiques, The Post House, High Newton, Newton-in-Cartmel, LA11 6JQ TEL: 531431 PARKING: Own carpark OPEN: Wed-Mon 9-5 MIN: £100 MAX: £15,000 PERIOD: 17th-18th century SPECIALIST: Early oak furniture GENERAL: Some early brass & metalware OTHER INFO: Probably most beautiful county in UK, fabulous hotels, soft, gentle weather.

Town Head Antiques, LA12 8NP TEL: 531321 FAX: 530019 ASSNS: LAPADA PARKING: Own carpark OPEN: 9-1, 2-5 MIN: £5 MAX: £10,000 PERIOD: 18th-19th century GENERAL: General antiques OTHER INFO: In wing of large country house on the shores of Lake Windemere.

CARTMEL (0539)

Anthemion, LA11 6QD TEL: 536295 ASSNS: BADA, LAPADA PARKING: Easy OPEN: Seven days 10-5 , closed only 5 days a year (race days or bank hols) MIN: £50 MAX: £30,000 PERIOD: 17th century-1830 SPECIALIST: English period furniture with associated decorative items.

Peter Bain Smith Bookseller, Old Market Square, LA11 6QB TEL: 536369 PARKING: Easy OPEN: Seven days 11-5.30 Summer, Wed-Sun 1.30-4.30 Winter MIN: £1 MAX: £300 PERIOD: 19th-20th century SPECIALIST: Local topography, English classics, childrens' GENERAL: Most subject, wide selection OTHER INFO: 4 pubs.

Norman Kerr Antiquarian Booksellers, Gatehouse Bookshop & Priory Barn, LA11 6PX TEL: 536247 ASSNS: ABA, PBFA OPEN: By appt only please PERIOD: 17th-20th century GENERAL: Antiquarian & other quality books OTHER INFO: Unspoilt village on southern fringe of Lake district dominated by its 12 century Priory Church. Good Food Guide hotels.

BARROW-IN-FURNESS (0229)

Henry Vincent, 239 Rawlinson Street, LA13 0AD TEL: 823432 PARKING: Medium OPEN: Mon-Wed, Fri, Sat 10-4 MIN: £1+ MAX: £150 PERIOD: 19th-20th century GENERAL: General antiques.

GOSFORTH (0946)

Archie Miles Bookshop, Beck Place, CA20 1AT TEL: 725792 PARKING: Easy OPEN: Tues-Sat 10-5.30 & by appt MIN: £1 MAX: £1,500 PERIOD: 17th-20th century SPECIALIST: English Literature, illustrated books, topography GENERAL: Most subjects OTHER INFO: In Lake District National Park, Ravenglass & Eskdale Railway, Muncaster Castle, Gardens & Owl Centre, Wastwater, working watermill all within 6 miles.

COCKERMOUTH (0900)

Cockermouth Antiques, 5 Station Street, CA13 9QW TEL: 826746 PARKING: Easy OPEN: Mon-Sat 10-5 MIN: £1 MAX: £2,000 PERIOD: 17th-20th century GENERAL: General antiques.

Holmes Antiques, 1 Market Square, CA13 9NH TEL: 826114 PARKING: Easy OPEN: Mon-Wed, Fri, Sat 10-5 MIN: £1 MAX: £5,000 PERIOD: 18th-20th century SPECIALIST: Paintings GENERAL: General antiques OTHER INFO: Wordsworth House (birthplace of William Wordsworth), Toy,

JANE POLLOCK ANTIQUES
4 Castlegate, Penrith, Cumbria CA11 7HZ
Telephone: 0768 67211

Open: 9.30am–5pm, closed Wednesday

We have the largest selection of nineteenth and twentieth century silver in the North West. We specialise in cutlery from complete canteens to individual knives and forks. We also stock pottery, porcelain, collectors items, wooden boxes and some small furniture.

mining & printing museums.

Market Antiques, 2 Main Street TEL: Mon-Sat 10-5 PARKING: Easy OPEN: Mon-sat 10-5 MIN: £5 PERIOD: 19th-20th century GENERAL: Widest possible range OTHER INFO: Birthplace of William Wordsworth & Fletcher Christian.

CARLISLE (0228)

J.W. Clements, 19 Fisher Street, CA3 8RF TEL: 25565 ASSNS: Cumbrian ADA PARKING: Difficult OPEN: Mon-Wed, Fri, Sat 9.30-5 MIN: £20 MAX: £5,000 PERIOD: 19th-20th century SPECIALIST: Jewellery GENERAL: Silver, ceramics OTHER INFO: Cathedral, Castle, Tulle House Museum.

Second Sight Antiques, 4a Mary Street, CA2 6JZ TEL: 359229, 591525 ASSNS: FSB PARKING: Easy OPEN: Mon-Wed, Fri, Sat 10-5 MIN: £1 MAX: £3,000 PERIOD: 17th-20th century GENERAL: General antiques OTHER INFO: New reclaimed pine furniture. Hotel opposite.

Souvenir Antiques, 4 Kinmont Arcade, Treasury Court, Fisher Street TEL: 40281 PARKING: Medium OPEN: Mon-Sat 10-5 MIN: £1 MAX: £500 PERIOD: 19th-20th SPECIALIST: Antique maps of Cumbria GENERAL: Ceramics & good variety of collectables including Roman coins OTHER INFO: In quiet courtyard off pedestrianised precinct in historic city.

BRAMPTON (0228)

Mary Fell Antiques, (Collectors Corner), 32-34 Main Street, CA8 1RS TEL: 22224 PARKING: Own carpark OPEN: Mon-Sat 11-5 MIN: £10 MAX: £2,000 PERIOD: 18th-20th century SPECIALIST: Fine porcelain GENERAL: General antiques OTHER INFO: Interesting collectables. Small market town close to Roman Wall. Lanercost

Priory, Haworth Castle (home of Earl of Carlisle).

ALSTON (0434)

Just Glass, Brownside Coach House, CA9 3BP TEL: 381263 PARKING: Own carpark OPEN: Mon, Wed-Sat 10-6 but Oct-Easter by appt only for glass MIN: £10 MAX: £300 PERIOD: 18th century to 1920 SPECIALIST: North east pressed glass GENERAL: Georgian, Victorian pressed glass OTHER INFO: We are also Egon Ronay recommemded small tearoom (since 1978) with superb full service.

PENRITH (0768)

Antiques of Penrith, 4 Corney Square, CA11 7PX TEL: 62801 PARKING: Easy OPEN: Mon-Sat 10-12, 1.30-5 MIN: £1 MAX: £thousands PERIOD: 18th-20th century GENERAL: Huge variety & extensive stock of furniture, brass, copper, china, Staffordshire, pewter, glass, silver + plate.

Joseph James, Corney Square, CA11 7PX TEL: 62065 PARKING: Medium OPEN: Mon, Tues, Thurs-Sat 9-5.30 MIN: £2 MAX: £1,500 PERIOD: 18th-20th century GENERAL: Furniture, porcelain, glass

Penrith Coin & Stamp Centre/Gray Jewellers, 37 King Street TEL: 64185 PARKING: Easy OPEN: Mon-Sat 9-5.30 but closed Weds in winter MIN: £5 MAX: £5,000 PERIOD: 18th-19th century SPECIALIST: Coins from Roman up to date GENERAL: Antique gold & silver jewellery.

Jane Pollock Antiques, 4 Castlegate, CA11 7HZ TEL: 67211 PARKING: Easy OPEN: Mon, Tues, Thurs-Sat 9.30-5 MIN: £5 MAX: £5,000 PERIOD: 18th-20th century SPECIALIST: Silver GENERAL: Pottery, porcelain, wooden boxes, collectables OTHER INFO: Hornby Hall country house accommodation (tel: 891114).

The Lake District

GREYSTOKE (0768)

Roadside Antiques, Watsons Farm, Greystoke Gill, CA11 0UQ TEL: 483279 PARKING: Own carpark OPEN: Seven days 10-6 MIN: £1 MAX: £1,500 PERIOD: 19th-20th century SPECIALIST: Victorian Staffordshire figures GENERAL: Quality Victorian & Edwardian antiques, furniture, jewellery OTHER INFO: Beckstones Art Gallery (quality modern original paintings), Herdwick Inn.

MILBURN (0768)

Netherley Cottage Antiques, CA10 1TN TEL: 361403 PARKING: Own carpark OPEN: Thursdays 9-5.30 but almost anytime by appt MIN: £1 MAX: £120 PERIOD: 18th-20th century SPECIALIST: Kitchenalia GENERAL: Treen, unusual country pieces, some watercolours, books & prints OTHER INFO: Facing attractive village green, welcome to walk around garden.

CROSBY RAVENSWORTH (0931)

Jennywell Hall Antiques, CA10 3JP TEL: 715288 PARKING: Own carpark OPEN: Most times but phonecall advisable (resident) MIN: £10 MAX: £2,000 PERIOD: 18th-19th century GENERAL: Oak & mahogany furniture, pictures, glass, ceramics, decorative items OTHER INFO: 4 self-catering holiday cottages associated with us.

KIRKBY STEPHEN (0768)

Haughey Antiques, 28-30 Market Street, CA17 4QW TEL: 371302 ASSNS: LAPADA PARKING: Own carpark OPEN: Mon-Sat 10-5 PERIOD: 17th-19th century GENERAL: Furniture, clocks, garden statuary.

David Hill Antiques, 36 Market Square TEL: 371598 PARKING: Easy OPEN: Mon-Sat 9.30-4 MIN: £1 MAX: £950 PERIOD: 19th-20th century SPECIALIST: Ironware, clocks GENERAL: Bric-a-brac.

Mortlake Antiques, 32-34 Market Street, CA17 4QW TEL: 371666 PARKING: Easy OPEN: 10-5 MIN: £2 MAX: £1,500 PERIOD: 18th-20th century SPECIALIST: Original Victorian pine furniture GENERAL: General antiques OTHER INFO: Oustandingly beautiful area - we hire out mountain bikes with routes & guides.

RAVENSTONEDALE (0539)

The Book House, CA17 4NQ TEL: 623634 PARKING: Easy OPEN: Mon, Wed-Sat 9-5 MIN: £1 MAX: £1,000 PERIOD: 19th-20th century SPECIALIST: Industrial history, railways, gardening, old girls GENERAL: Secondhand & antiquarian books only OTHER INFO: Good centre for Northern Dales & Eden Valley. We offer comfortable B&B.

SEDBERGH (0539)

R.F.G. Hullett & Son, 6 Finkle Street, LA10 5BZ TEL: 620298 FAX: 621396 ASSNS: ABA PARKING: Easy OPEN: Mon-Sat 10-12, 1.15-5 MIN: £10 MAX: £10,000 PERIOD: Incunabala to modern firsts SPECIALIST: Fine antiquarian books & general antiquarian books: topography, natural history, fine arts

Stable Antiques, 15 Back Lane, LA10 5AQ TEL: 620251 PARKING: Easy OPEN: Mon-Sat 9-5.30 & by appt MIN: £1 MAX: £1,000 PERIOD: 17th-20th century SPECIALIST: Metal & treen GENERAL: China, glass, prints, silver, small furniture OTHER INFO: B&B above shop, wonderful walks in Yorkshire Dales.

HAWES (0969)

Sturmans Antiques, Main Street, DL8 3QW TEL: 667742 PARKING: Medium OPEN: Seven days 10-5.30 MIN: £1 MAX: £5,000 PERIOD: 18th-20th century SPECIALIST: Quality Victorian & Edwardian furniture GENERAL: Oils & watercolours, porcelain, glassware, metalware. Good selection longcase & wall clocks & other quality furniture OTHER INFO: Highest market town in Yorkshire in heart of Herriot Country with beautiful scenery.

The Far North East

Whitby Abbey

This tour visits the North Yorkshire moors and wild countryside of Northumbria as well as the heartland of Britain's once great ship-building industry on the Rivers Tyne and Tees. The moors are a product of man. Bronze Age man cleared the forests for agriculture leaving behind barrows and stone cairns. Medieval monks in the great Yorkshire abbeys also cut down trees to clear areas for sheep and for making charcoal. Without trees the soil became acid and was swept away by wind and water leaving only enough nutrients for heather, grass and bracken. In Northumbria the hand of man can also be seen in the Border Forest, the largest man-made forest in Europe and planted by the Forestry Commission. However, this is wild country with the rugged Cheviot Hills in the west and and rocky cliffs on the east coast facing the cold North Sea. The Romans built their wall south of this county and over the centuries the region was the scene of many battles and skirmishes between the English and Scots.

Leaving the A1 we start our tour in the village of Sleights before coming to Whitby, Situated on the mouth of the River Esk. It is a popular holiday resort as it has a picturesque harbour, good safe beaches and is close to the North Yorkshire National Park. Bram Stoker, creator of Dracula, and Captain Cook were past residents of the town. Captain Cook's house may be seen in Grape Lane. Forming a distinctive landmark on the cliffs above the town are the ruins of a 13th century abbey.

Moving on, the route reaches Darlington. This was originally an Anglo-Saxon settlement whose first prosperity was founded on wool then later linen and carpet

Whitby Harbour

making. As these declined it became a centre for the manufacture of locomotives, railway wagons and bridge building. The town's Railway Centre and Museum has many exhibits of interest for the railway enthusiast including Stephenson's Locomotion.

First stopping in the village of Manfield, we carry on westward to Barnard Castle, named for its castle which overlooks the River Tees from a clifftop. The castle dates from the late 11th to early 12th century and was for centuries subject to ownership disputes. Over the window of one of its buildings there is a carving of a wild boar, probably dating from the period when it was occupied by Richard, Duke of Gloucester, later Richard III. It contains a magnificent hall built by the Bishop of Durham at the end of the 13th century.

The town of Barnard Castle has many features worth seeing as well. There is a covered market cross which is so big that it served as the town hall during the 18th century. It was at one of the town's many inns, the King's Head, that Charles Dickens reputedly wrote *Nicholas Nickleby*. Also of interest is the 16th century Blagraves House. The town has the spectacular Bowes Museum set in 20 acres of gardens and strongly reminiscent of a French chateau. It contains collections of paintings, furniture, tapestries, porcelain, glass, jewellery, sculpture and metalwork.

Five miles east of the town, along the A688, stands Raby Castle, one of the largest 14th century castles in Britain and built by the Nevill family. The castle saw action in the Civil War when it was taken in a surprise attack by Royalist troops. Now it contains a fine collection of English, Dutch and Flemish pictures and good period furniture. There is also an exhibition of horse-drawn carriages and fire engines.

Moving north along the A68, we first visit West Auckland and then Consett, famous for its ironworks which, at their height, produced more than a million tons of steel a year.

The route now makes a detour along the A695 to visit Hexham, a pretty town well placed for exploring Hadrian's Wall and other Roman remains in the area.

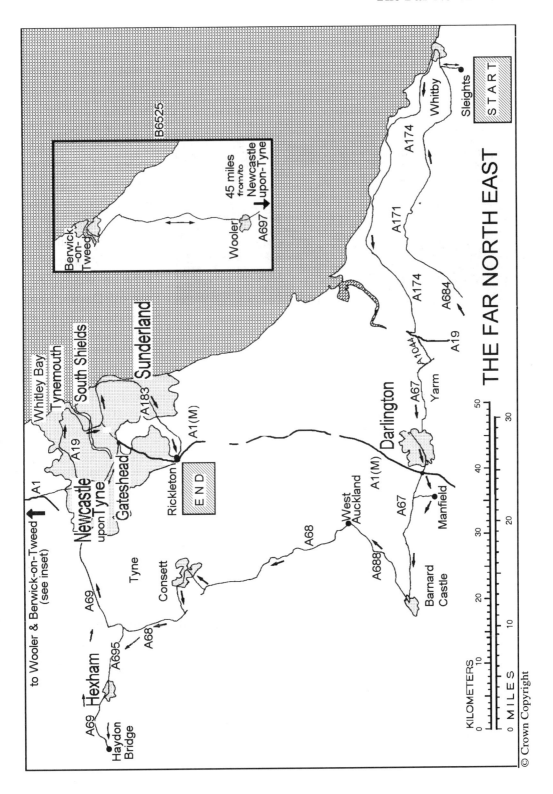

THE FAR NORTH EAST

© Crown Copyright

Bowes Museum, Barnard Castle

The town has a very large church which was once a great abbey. Dating from about 1200 it contains many features of interest including a Saxon crypt. There are numerous old and interesting buildings in the town including the old prison dating from 1330 and now housing the Tourist Information Offices and the 15th century Moot Hall.

About four miles north of Hexham on the A6079 Chesters Fort may be found. This was a Roman fortification built as part of Hadrian's Wall. Characteristically, the Romans did not bend their wall to go round the River Tyne here, instead they built a bridge over it and the fort was to defend the bridge. The excavated site is well maintained in one of the most beautiful valleys in the area. Amongst the excavations may be seen the bathhouse and an underground strongroom where the legion's pay and standards were kept. On the site there is also a museum displaying Roman finds from several of the sites in Northumberland.

We continue to Haydon Bridge before returning eastwards to Newcastle-upon-Tyne. This city was an important ship building centre as well as a noted area for coal mining, locomotives and armaments. Newcastle is an ancient town established by the Romans because of its convenience for Hadrian's Wall. It is also the cathedral city for the area. The cathedral's most notable feature is its tower, built between 1450 and 1475. The pinnacled flying buttresses holding up a small spire give the building a touch of flamboyance and examples of the decorated style may be seen in the canopy over the font and on some of the windows.

Also of interest is the castle. Constructed on the site of a Roman camp, the present building was started by Robert, eldest son of William the Conqueror. Improvements were made over the centuries and the castle saw action in the border wars. Indeed it changed hands on occasion and was held by King David of Scotland for a number of years.

Our next stop is much further north and is the town of Wooler, situated on the River Till and the north east edge of the Cheviot Hills. There is a mound of a Norman castle here but most of the houses date from the late 19th century as the town suffered a disastrous fire in 1862. From here it is only a few miles to Berwick-on-Tweed, England's most northerly town. As might be imagined from its situation, Berwick has been the scene of much fighting in the border wars. It changed hands thirteen times until it finally surrendered to the English in 1482. Of particular note are the town walls which were replaced in the Elizabethan period. Built to withstand gunpowder, they are up to ten feet thick in places. Berwick has a wealth of historical buildings including 18th century houses and one of the few churches to have been built during Oliver Cromwell's Commonwealth.

Berwick Barracks, in the town centre, contains an interesting museum which chronicles the history of the King's Own Scottish Borderers. The early 18th century Barracks, designed to house 36 officers and 600 men, were built in three blocks around a square. On the fourth side stands a beautifully decorated gatehouse.

Now we return south to Tynemouth sited on the River Tyne. The ruins of Tynemouth Castle and Priory stand on a headland in a good defensive position. The priory was established in the 11th century on the site of an earlier monastery. During the border wars with the Scots a fortified gatehouse was added to the building which persuaded Henry VIII to turn the priory into a royal castle after the Dissolution of the Monasteries.

Next stop is Gateshead, on the Tyne, which has been closely associated with ship building and repairing. It has five bridges connecting the town to Newcastle. The most recently built, the Tyne Bridge, crosses the river with a single span of 531 feet. At its highest point it is 200 feet above the river.

Continuing south, South Shields was the site of the Roman fort of Arbeia, built to defend the eastern end of Hadrian's Wall.

The last stop is Sunderland, on the River Wear and another ship building centre. About four miles west of the town stands Hylton Castle which probably dates from 1400. We now follow the A1(M) for the homeward journey.

ANTIQUE DEALERS

SLEIGHTS (0947)

Coach House Antiques, 75 Coach Road, YO22 5BT TEL: 810313 PARKING: Easy OPEN: 10-5 summer MIN: £1 MAX: £750 PERIOD: 18th-20th century SPECIALIST: Oak & country furniture GENERAL: Unusual & decorative items.

WHITBY (0947)

The Bazaar, Skinner Street, YO21 3AH TEL: 602281 PARKING: Easy OPEN: Mon-Sat 10-5.30 MIN: £1 MAX: £450 PERIOD: 18th-20th century GENERAL: General antiques OTHER INFO: Whitby, historic architecture. Well worth visiting.

Caedmon House, 14 Station Square TEL: 602120, 603930 PARKING: Medium OPEN: 10-5 MIN: £2 MAX: £2,500 PERIOD: 19th-20th century SPECIALIST: Dresden china, old dolls, small furniture, toys GENERAL: House clearances, Victorian crystoleums & lustres, Sunderland pottery, Moorcroft old & new OTHER INFO: Bramstoker wrote Dracula here, best museum in the North, Heartbeat country, Captain James Cook's Trail. Shop is called after Caedmon, the first English poet who lived in Whitby Abbey at time of Lady Hilda. At the synod here date for Easter was set for Christians worldwide. (Wow! What Disney would give for all this history).

The Mount Antiques, Khyber Pass, YO21 3HD TEL: 604516 PARKING: Own carpark OPEN: 10.15-4.30 MIN: £10 MAX: £2,500 PERIOD: 18th-19th century GENERAL: General antiques.

DARLINGTON (0325)

Robin Finnegan Jewellers, 83 Skinnergate, DL3 7LX TEL: 489820 FAX: 357674 ASSNS: NAG, Gemmological Assn of GB PARKING: Medium OPEN: Mon-Sat 10-5.30 MIN: £1 MAX: £20,000 PERIOD: 17th-20th century SPECIALIST: Jewellery, coins, medals, collectors items GENERAL: New, secondhand & antique jewellery, smalls OTHER INFO: Friendly family firm sometimes close to insanity that lets chipmunks in the shop, so nobody too serious please.

Nichol & Hill, 20-22 Grange Road, DL1 5NG TEL: 375431, 936584 FAX: 382863 PARKING: Medium OPEN: Mon-Fri 8.30-5, Sat 10-5 MIN: £100 MAX: £3,000 PERIOD: 19th-early 20th century SPECIALIST: Furniture GENERAL: Complete restoration & upholstery service OTHER INFO: Scene of BBC TV's series *Harry*.

Alan Ramsey Antiques, 10 Dudley Road, Yarm Road Industrial Estate, DL1 4GG TEL: 361679, (0642) 711311 PARKING: Own carpark OPEN: Tues, Thurs, Fri 10-3 PERIOD: 19th-20th century GENERAL: 2,000 sq ft antique furniture OTHER INFO: Trade only.

MANFIELD (0325)

D.D. White Antiques, Lucy Cross Cottage, DL2 2RJ TEL: 374303 PARKING: Own carpark OPEN: By appt MIN: £40 MAX: £2,000 PERIOD: 18th-20th century SPECIALIST: Georgian, Victorian, Edwardian furniture GENERAL: Shipping furniture OTHER INFO: Headlam Hall Hotel, Black Bull fish restaurant, B&B's.

BARNARD CASTLE (0833)

Stephanie Grant Art & Antiques, The Ancient Manor House, 38-40 The Bank TEL: 37437 PARKING: Easy OPEN: Mon-Sat 10-5 other dealers, Stephanie Grant by appt MIN: £1 MAX: £5,000 PERIOD: 17th-20th century SPECIALIST: Paintings, antique pine & oak furniture GENERAL: Smalls, rugs, pottery, silver etc OTHER INFO: Properties said to have belonged to stewards to Henry VII & James I.

Town House Antiques, 7 Newgate TEL: 37021 PARKING: Easy OPEN: Wed, Fri, Sat 11-5 MIN: £10 MAX: £1,500 PERIOD: 18th-20th century SPECIALIST: Furniture & decorative items GENERAL: Georgian, Victorian, Edwardian furniture OTHER INFO: 12th century castle ruins, High Force (highest waterfall in England).

WEST AUCKLAND (0388)

Eden House Antiques, 10 Staindrop Road, DL14 9JX TEL: 833013 ASSNS: GMC PARKING: Own carpark OPEN: Mon-Sat 10-6.30 MIN: £1 PERIOD: 18th-20th century SPECIALIST: Clocks GENERAL: General antiques & quality English reproduction furniture OTHER INFO: Home of Mary Ann Cotton, famous multiple murderess & football's World Cup winners 1909, 1911. 13th century Manor House Hotel.

CONSETT (0207)

Harry Raine, Kelvinside House, Villa Real, DH8 6BL TEL: 503935 PARKING: Easy OPEN: Anytime by appt MIN: £200 MAX: £4-6,000 PERIOD: 18th-19th century GENERAL: Furniture.

HEXHAM (0434)

Arthur Boaden Antiques, 29-30 Market Place, NE46 3PB TEL: 603187 ASSNS: LAPADA PARK-

ING: Medium OPEN: Mon-Sat 9-12.30, 1.20-5 MIN: £1 MAX: £5,000 PERIOD: 19th-20th century GENERAL: Antique, secondhand & reproduction furniture, general antiques OTHER INFO: Heart of Roman Wall country.

J.A. & T. Hedley, 3 St Mary's Chare TEL: 602317 PARKING: Easy OPEN: Mon-Sat 9-5 MIN: £1 MAX: £3,000 PERIOD: 18th-20th century GENERAL: Furniture, porcelain, glass & sundries OTHER INFO: Furniture restorers.

The Violin Shop, 27 Hencotes, NE46 2EQ TEL: 607897 PARKING: Medium OPEN: Mon-Sat 10-5 MIN: £5 MAX: £15,000 PERIOD: 18th-20th century SPECIALIST: Stringed instruments GENERAL: Occasionally other instruments OTHER INFO: Restorations. Instruments made.

HAYDON BRIDGE (0434)

Haydon Bridge Antiques, 3 Shaftoe Street, NE47 6JX TEL: 684461 PARKING: Easy OPEN: Tues, Wed, Fri, Sat 11-5.30 & by appt MIN: £2 MAX: £2,000 PERIOD: 19th-20th century GENERAL: Furniture, paintings, china, bric-a-brac, furnishing pieces OTHER INFO: Next to wonderful restaurant/B&B furnished with antiques.

NEWCASTLE-ON-TYNE (091)

Causey Antiques, Causey Street, Gosforth TEL: 2859062 PARKING: Medium OPEN: Thurs-Sat 10-4 MIN: £1 MAX: £400 PERIOD: 19th-20th century GENERAL: China, furniture, medals, toys, glass, clocks, gold & silver OTHER INFO: Gosforth Park Hotel & Racecourse.

Dean Art Gallery, 42 Dean Street, NE1 1PG TEL: 2321208 PARKING: Medium OPEN: Mon-Fri 10-5, Sat 10-1 MIN: £300 MAX: £5,000 PERIOD: 19th-20th century SPECIALIST: Period local artists GENERAL: Oils & watercolours & some rare prints OTHER INFO: River Tyne & Quayside, Surtees & Vermont hotels very near.

H & S Collectables, 149 Salters Road, Gosforth, NE3 2UT TEL: 2846626, home 2863498 PARKING: Easy OPEN: Mon-sat 10-5 MIN: £5 MAX: £900 PERIOD: 19th-20th century SPECIALIST: Tyneside Malingware 1890-1963 GENERAL: Antiques & Victoriana, clocks, small furniture, silver, decorative items, collectables OTHER INFO: Valuations. Off Gosforth High Street.

Geoffrey Hugall Antiques, 19 Clayton Road, Jesmond, NE2 4RS TEL: 2818408 PARKING: Easy OPEN: Mon-Fri 10-5, Sat 10-4 PERIOD: 18th-19th century GENERAL: Quality general antiques OTHER INFO: Other antique shops nearby.

Intercoin, 99 Clayton Streeet, NE1 5PZ TEL: 2322064 PARKING: Easy OPEN: Mon-Sat 9-5 PERIOD: 18th-19th century SPECIALIST: Coins, medals, banknotes, silver items OTHER INFO: Free identification & valuations.

MacDonald Fine Art, 2 Ashburton Road, Gosforth, NE3 4XN TEL: 2856188 PARKING: Easy OPEN: Mon-Sat 10-5 PERIOD: 19th-20th century SPECIALIST: Watercolours & oils.

TYNEMOUTH VILLAGE (091)

Maggie Mays, 49 Norton Park Terrace (opposite Gunner Inn, Preston Road) TEL: 257076, (0850) 907049 PARKING: Medium OPEN: Mon, Tues, Thurs-Sat 10.30-5.30 MIN: £5 MAX: £2,000 PERIOD: 19th-20th century SPECIALIST: Local artist & Northumbria 1850-1940 GENERAL: Antiques & small furniture, Art Deco, brass fenders, lamps, rugs, pine, beds etc.

Renaissance Antiques, 11 Front Street, NE30 4HG TEL: 2595555 PARKING: Easy OPEN: Mon, Tues, Sat 10.30-12.30, 2-3.45 MIN: £5 MAX: £1,000 PERIOD: 19th-20th century GENERAL: Furniture, bric-a-brac.

Ian Sharp Antiques, 23 Front Street, NE30 4DX TEL: 2960656 ASSNS: LAPADA PARKING: Easy OPEN: Mon-sat 10-5.30 & by appt MIN: £50 MAX: £5,000 PERIOD: 18th-19th century SPECIALIST: Northeastern pottery, local artists' oils & watercolours GENERAL: Georgian, Victorian, Edwardian furniture, pottery, porcelain, decorative items OTHER INFO: Pretty 17th-18th century village dominated by The Priory & Castle burial place of Northumberland kings & saints.

David R. Strain Antiques, 66 Front Street TEL: 2592459 ASNS: LAPADA PARKING: Easy OPEN: Mon-Fri 9.30-5, Sat 9.30-1 MIN: £5 MAX: £6,000 PERIOD: 18th-19th century SPECIALIST: Furniture GENERAL: China, glass, weapons, books, silver & jewellery OTHER INFO: Valuations.

WHITLEY BAY (091)

The Bric-a-Brac Shop, 195 Park View, NE26 3RD TEL: 2526141 PARKING: Medium OPEN: Mon-Sat 10-1, 3-5 MIN: £1 MAX: £4,000 PERIOD: 19th-20th century GENERAL: Furniture, china, silver, curios, bric-a-brac OTHER INFO: Good seaside resort. Ideal touring centre for Northumbria.

WOOLER (0668)

Millers Antiques, 1-5 Church Street, NE71 6BZ TEL: 81500, 7281 PARKING: Easy OPEN: By appt MIN: £50 MAX: £10,000 PERIOD: 17th-20th century GENERAL: 30,000 sq ft Georgian, Regency, Victorian furniture.

BERWICK-ON-TWEED (0289)

Treasure Chest, 43 Bridge Street TEL: 307736 PARKING: Easy OPEN: Mon-Wed, Fri, Sat 10.30-3 MIN: £1 MAX: £400 PERIOD: 19th-20th century GENERAL: Wide range, small furniture OTHER INFO: Award winning restaurant next door.

SOUTH SHIELDS (091)

The Curiosity Shop, 16 Frederick Street, NE33 5EA TEL: 4565560 ASSNS: FSB PARKING: Easy OPEN: Mon, Tues, Thurs-Sat 9-5 MIN: £5 MAX: £5,000 PERIOD: 19th-20th century GENERAL: Furniture & antiques OTHER INFO: Best range of Indian restaurants in UK.

SUNDERLAND (091)

Peter Smith Antiques, 12-14 Borough Road, SR1 1EP TEL: 5673537 FAX: 5142286 ASSNS: LAPADA PARKING: Easy OPEN: Mon-Fri 9.30-4.30, Sat 9.30-12 MIN: £5 MAX: £10,000 PERIOD: 18th-20th century GENERAL: Furniture, clocks, bric-a-brac OTHER INFO: Good beaches, illuminations, Metro Centre.

GATESHEAD (091)

N. Jewett, 639-643 Durham Road, Lowfell, NE9 5HA TEL: 4877636 PARKING: Easy OPEN: Mon-Sat 10-5 MIN: £350 PERIOD: 18th-20th century SPECIALIST: Furniture GENERAL: Variety also fine reproductions OTHER INFO:

Sovereign Antiques, 35 The Boulevard, Antique Village, Metro Centre, NE11 9YN TEL: 4609604 PARKING: Easy (Metrocentre) OPEN: Mon-Sat 10-8, Thurs till 9pm MIN: £5 MAX: £8,000 PERIOD: 18th-20th century SPECIALIST: Jewellery, diamonds, silver, maps & prints OTHER INFO: The Metro Centre has just everything and needs a full day.

RICKLETON (091)

Harold J. Carr Antiques , Field House, NE38 9HQ TEL: 3886442 FAX: 3886442 ASSNS: LAPADA PARKING: Difficult OPEN: Trade only PERIOD: 19th-20th century GENERAL: Export furniture, shipping oak, walnut & mahogany.

Index of Towns

Index of Specialist Dealers

422

424